Human Motion Analysis

Human Motion Analysis

Current Applications and Future Directions

Edited by

Gerald F. Harris
Marquette University
Medical College of Wisconsin
Shriners Hospital for Crippled Children

Peter A. Smith
Shriners Hospital for Crippled Children
Rush-Presbyterian-St. Luke's Medical Center

TECHNICAL
ACTIVITIES

IEEE
PRESS

A Volume in the TAB-IEEE Press Book Series—Design and Applications
Willis J. Tompkins, *Editor in Chief*, TAB-IEEE Press Book Series
T. J. Tarn, *Editor*, Design and Applications
IEEE Engineering in Medicine and Biology Society, *Sponsor*

The Institute of Electrical
and Electronics Engineers, Inc., New York

This book may be purchased at a discount from the publisher when ordered
in bulk quantities. For more information contact:

IEEE PRESS Marketing
Attn: Special Sales
P.O. Box 1331
445 Hoes Lane
Piscataway, NJ 08855-1331
Fax: (908) 981-9334

©1996 by the Institute of Electrical and Electronics Engineers, Inc.
345 East 47th Street, New York, NY 10017-2394

Printed in the United States of America

10 9 8 7 6 5 4 3 2 1

ISBN 0-7803-1111-6
IEEE Order Number: PC4648

Library of Congress Cataloging-in-Publication Data

Human motion analysis : current applications and future directions /
   edited by Gerald F. Harris, Peter A. Smith.
        p.   cm. — (TAB-IEEE Press book series ; design and
   applications)
        Based on the Shriners Workshop on Human Motion Analysis, San
Diego, Calif., held at the 15th Annual International Conference of
the IEEE Engineering in Medicine and Biology Society.
      Includes index.
      ISBN 0-7803-1111-6 (alk. paper)
      1. Gait in humans—Congresses.   2. Human locomotion—Congresses.
3. Movement disorders—Diagnosis—Congresses.   I. Harris, Gerald F.
II. Smith, Peter A., (date).   III. IEEE Engineering in Medicine
and Biology Society. Conference (15th : 1993 : San Diego, Calif.)
IV. Shriners Workshop on Human Motion Analysis (1993 : San Diego,
Calif.) V. Series.
      [DNLM: 1. Movement—physiology—congresses.   2. Muscles—
physiology—congresses.   WE 103 H9166 1996]
QP310.W3H84   1996
612.7'6—dc20
DNLM/DLC
for Library of Congress   95-41085
                                                                    CIP

This book is dedicated to
Marilyn, Heather, Jeremy, and Amanda
and
the Smith Family

Contents

List of Contributors

Ziad O. Abu-Faraj, Ph.D.

Post-Doctoral Research Fellow
Department of Biomedical Engineering
Marquette University
Milwaukee, Wisconsin

Post-Doctoral Research Fellow
Department of Biomedical Engineering
Shriners Hospital for Crippled Children
Chicago, Illinois

Faruk S. Abuzzahab, Jr., Ph.D.

Research Associate
Department of Biomedical Engineering
Marquette University
Milwaukee, Wisconsin

Research Associate
Shriners Hospital for Crippled Children
Chicago, Illinois

Michael D. Aiona, M.D.

Assistant Chief of Staff
Shriners Hospital for Crippled Children
Portland, Oregon

Assistant Clinical Professor
Department of Surgery
Oregon Health Sciences University
Portland, Oregon

Thomas P. Andriacchi, Ph.D.

Associate Chairman for Research, and
    Section Director for the Section
    of Biomechanics
Department of Orthopedic Surgery
Rush-Presbyterian-St. Luke's
    Medical Center
Chicago, Illinois

Randal R. Betz, M.D.

Assistant Chief of Staff, and
    Medical Director of SCI Unit
Shriners Hospital for Crippled Children
Philadelphia, Pennsylvania

Associate Professor
Department of Orthopaedic Surgery
Temple University Hospital and School
    of Medicine
Philadelphia, Pennsylvania

Gary D. Brooking, M.S.

Research Fellow
Department of Electrical Engineering
University of Virginia
Charlottesville, Virginia

An-Hsiung Chang, M.D.

Foot Fellow
Department of Orthopaedic Surgery
Medical College of Wisconsin
Milwaukee, Wisconsin

Roy B. Davis, III, Ph.D., P.E.

Director
Gait Analysis Laboratory
Department of Orthopaedics
Connecticut Children's Medical Center
Hartford, Connecticut

Associate Professor
Department of Orthopaedic Surgery
University of Connecticut School
    of Medicine
Farmington, Connecticut

Scott L. Delp, Ph.D.

Assistant Professor
Departments of Biomedical Engineering,
    and Physical Medicine
    and Rehabilitation
Northwestern University
Chicago, Illinois

Senior Research Scientist
Sensory Motor Performance Program
Rehabilitation Institute of Chicago
Chicago, Illinois

Peter A. DeLuca, M.D.

Medical Director
Gait Analysis Laboratory
Department of Orthopaedics
Connecticut Children's Medical Center
Hartford, Connecticut

Associate Professor
Department of Orthopaedic Surgery
University of Connecticut School
    of Medicine
Farmington, Connecticut

Janice J. Eng, Ph.D., P.T.

Post Doctoral Fellow
Department of Kinesiology
Simon Fraser University
Burnaby, British Columbia, Canada

Gerald F. Harris, Ph.D., P.E.

Professor
Department of Biomedical Engineering
College of Engineering
Marquette University
Milwaukee, Wisconsin

Director of Research
Department of Orthopaedic Surgery
Medical College of Wisconsin
Milwaukee, Wisconsin

Director
Gait Analysis Laboratory
Shriners Hospital for Crippled Children
Chicago, Illinois

Milad Ishac, M.Sc.

Research Assistant
Department of Kinesiology
University of Waterloo
Waterloo, Ontario, Canada

Jeffrey E. Johnson, M.D.

Associate Professor
Division of Foot and Ankle Surgery
Department of Orthopaedic Surgery
Medical College of Wisconsin
Milwaukee, Wisconsin

Kathy A. Johnson, Ph.D.
Research Scientist
Laboratory for Knowledge-Based
    Medical Systems
The Ohio State University
Columbus, Ohio

Kenton R. Kaufman, Ph.D.
Director of Orthopedic Research
Motion Analysis Laboratory
Children's Hospital, San Diego
San Diego, California

Adjunct Associate Professor
Department of Orthopedic Surgery
University of California, San Diego
La Jolla, California

Steven M. Kidder, M.S.
Research Fellow
Department of Orthopaedic Surgery
Medical College of Wisconsin
Milwaukee, Wisconsin

Research Fellow
Department of Biomedical Engineering
Marquette University
Milwaukee, Wisconsin

Rudi Kobetic, M.S.
Biomedical Engineer
Department of Research
Veterans Administration Medical Center
Cleveland, Ohio

Ken N. Kuo, M.D.
Professor of Orthopedics
Department of Orthopedic Surgery
Rush Medical College
Chicago, Illinois

Attending Orthopaedic Surgeon
Shriners Hospital for Crippled Children
Chicago, Illinois

Larry W. Lamoreux, Ph.D.
Biomechanical Engineer
Orthopaedic Biomechanics Laboratory
Shriners Hospital for Crippled Children
San Francisco, California

Adjunct Associate Professor
Department of Orthopaedic Surgery
University of California, San Francisco
San Francisco, California

Richard P. Mikosz, Ph.D.
Assistant Professor
Department of Orthopaedic Surgery
Rush-Presbyterian-St. Luke's
    Medical Center
Chicago, Illinois

Joseph Nery, B.S.
Gait Analysis Laboratory Engineer
Department of Orthopaedic Surgery
Medical College of Wisconsin
Milwaukee, Wisconsin

Tom F. Novacheck, M.D.
Director
Motion Analysis Laboratory
Gillette Children's Hospital
St. Paul, Minnesota

Assistant Professor of Orthopaedic Surgery
Orthopaedic Surgery Department
University of Minnesota
Minneapolis, Minnesota

Kenneth S. Olree, M.S.
Engineer
Motion Analysis Laboratory
St. Louis Children's Hospital
St. Louis, Missouri

Sylvia Õunpuu, M.Sc.
Kinesiologist
Gait Analysis Laboratory
Department of Orthopaedics
Connecticut Children's Medical Center
Hartford, Connecticut

Instructor
Department of Orthopaedic Surgery
University of Connecticut School
    of Medicine
Farmington, Connecticut

Jacquelin Perry, M.D.

Chief, Pathokinesiology/Polio Service
Pathokinesiology Service
Rancho Los Amigos Medical Center
Downey, California

Professor of Orthopaedics, and
    Professor of Biokinesiology
    and Physical Therapy
Departments of Orthopaedics, and
    Biokinesiology and Physical Therapy
University of Southern California
Los Angeles, California

Michael J. Shereff, M.D.

Associate Professor, and
    Director of Foot and Ankle Division
Department of Orthopaedic Surgery
Milwaukee, Wisconsin

Sheldon R. Simon, M.D.

Judson Wilson Professor, and
    Chief of Orthopaedics
Department of Orthopaedic Surgery
The Ohio State University
Columbus, Ohio

Jack W. Smith, M.D., Ph.D.

Associate Professor
Laboratory for Knowledge-Based
    Medical Systems
The Ohio State University
Columbus, Ohio

Peter A. Smith, M.D.

Attending Orthopaedic Surgeon
Shriners Hospital for Crippled Children
Chicago, Illinois

Assistant Professor
Department of Orthopedic Surgery
Rush-Presbyterian-St. Luke's
    Medical Center
Chicago, Illinois

Philip J. Smith, Ph.D.

Professor
Cognitive Systems Engineering
    Laboratory
The Ohio State University
Columbus, Ohio

David H. Sutherland, M.D.

Medical Director
Motion Analysis Laboratory
Childen's Hospital
San Diego, California

Professor
Department of Orthopaedics
University of California, San Diego
La Jolla, California

Ronald J. Triolo, Ph.D.

Assistant Professor
Departments of Orthopaedics
    and Biomedical Engineering
Case Western Reserve University
Cleveland, Ohio

Director of Research
Health Hill Hospital for Children
Cleveland, Ohio

Christopher L. Vaughan, Ph.D.

Adjunct Professor
Department of Biomedical Engineering
University of Cape Town
Cape Town, South Africa

Chief Biomedical Engineer
Department of Biomedical Engineering
Groote Schuur Hospital
Cape Town, South Africa

Jacqueline J. Wertsch, M.D.

Professor and Research Director
Department of Physical Medicine
    and Rehabilitation
Medical College of Wisconsin
Milwaukee, Wisconsin

Director
EMG Fellowship Program
Department of Physical Medicine
    and Rehabilitation
Zablocki Veterans Administration
    Medical Center
Milwaukee, Wisconsin

David A. Winter, Ph.D., P. Eng.
Distinguished Professor Emeritus
Department of Kinesiology
University of Waterloo
Waterloo, Ontario, Canada

George Wynarsky, Ph.D.
Adjunct Lecturer
Department of Materials Science
and Engineering
University of Michigan
Ann Arbor, Michigan

Gerald F. Harris
Peter A. Smith

Preface

The field of human motion analysis has developed into a major component of orthopaedic medicine. It is used for presurgical planning, postsurgical follow-up, evaluation of various surgical and nonsurgical interventions, and for numerous research investigations. This text began with a one-day workshop on human motion analysis sponsored by Shriners Hospitals for Crippled Children. The workshop was conducted on October 27, 1993, at the Fifteenth Annual International Conference of the IEEE Engineering in Medicine and Biology Society (EMB-S). The workshop included national and international researchers from engineering, orthopaedics, academic, medical-industrial, and clinical disciplines. It focused on scientific and technical advances, with emphasis on applications, limitations, and problems to be solved. Through the support of the Shriners Hospitals, the EMB-S, and collaboration of the keynote speakers, this work was planned for publication.

The text is designed to address current applications and future directions in human motion analysis. It has been written to convey basic as well as advanced concepts to engineers (Part 1) and clinicians (Part 2).

Part 1 of the text presents current and emerging concepts in motion analysis technology. Challenges and innovative strategies in mathematical modeling, instrumentation, and control theory are discussed. Computer modeling advances with applications in movement disability analysis and surgical correction are summarized. A full system is described for foot and ankle motion analysis, including details on instrumentation, calibration, validation, and biomechanical modeling requirements.

Part 2 of the text addresses the important aspects of clinical data interpretation and decision making with numerous examples. Special focus is given to the use of gait analysis for presurgical planning and postsurgical follow-up. The unique roles of dynamic electromyography (EMG), kinematics, and kinetic data in clinical applications are described. Chapters are included on selective dorsal rhizotomy, functional electrical stimulation, recently developed methods for analysis of segmental adult foot and ankle motion, and kinetic characteristics of the pediatric planovalgus foot. Finally, emerging clinical horizons in intelligent multimedia applications are presented.

The pediatric experience with human motion analysis over the past 30 years demonstrates how engineering and clinical synergy has improved medical treatment. In the management of children with cerebral palsy, surgeons now perform several necessary operations under the same anesthesia, thus greatly reducing cost, pain, and inconvenience. Clinical and research applications in human motion analysis have resulted in the development of new operations with detailed outcome follow-up. As a result, children are receiving fewer and better surgeries. All contributors to this text have graciously agreed to return royalties to the Shriners Hospitals for Crippled Children.

Gerald F. Harris
Peter A. Smith

Acknowledgments

It is with grateful appreciation that we thank all those who have helped make this book possible. In particular, we would like to express our gratitude to the Shriners Hospitals for Crippled Children, not only for the financial support of the workshop, from which this work resulted, but even more for the kindness and philanthropy extended freely to children throughout the world. We want especially to thank Dr. Newton C. McCollough and Dr. Elwood W. Speckmann at the International Shrine Headquarters for their continued help, encouragement, and support. Their vision has advanced the application of pediatric gait analysis throughout the Shrine system for improved preoperative assessment and postoperative follow-up of children with cerebral palsy and other neuromuscular disorders. The Shrine serves as a beacon of inspiration for us and many others who have contributed to this work.

A special thanks is extended to the Engineering in Medicine and Biology Society (EMB-S) of the Institute of Electrical and Electronics Engineers (IEEE) for supporting the day-long "Shriners Workshop on Human Motion Analysis" at the 15th Annual International Conference in San Diego, California (October 27, 1993). The Society Conference and Program Chairs, Andy Szeto and Raj Rangayan, offered the administrative and facilities support needed to conduct the workshop.

The text consists of two parts, one technical and one clinical. We would like to extend our sincere thanks to all the workshop keynote speakers and chapter authors, engineers, physicians, and health care professionals who have contributed to the book's synergism.

Profound gratitude is also extended to the 40 chapter reviewers, who provided independent critiques and constructive feedback to our authors.

Dudley Kay and the staff at IEEE Press were most gracious and accommodating in helping us prepare the text. They coordinated yet another set of text reviews as part of a recently adopted IEEE Technical Activities Board (TAB) initiative. Finally, we'd like to thank Susan K. Tatiner and Denise Gannon for all the editorial help.

A very special thanks is extended to our editorial assistant, Kathy Reiners, for her unending pursuit of excellence in keeping this project on schedule and in helping with manuscript preparation.

Sahar Hassani provided much help in preparing the book and deserves our thanks.

Dr. Ziad O. Abu-Faraj was invaluable in bringing the book to fruition. Our many thanks go for his long hours of meticulous work.

Last of all, we'd like to thank the graduate and undergraduate students in the Biomedical Engineering Department at Marquette University who helped us improve the workshop presentation with their ideas and suggestions.

Chapter 1

Gerald F. Harris
Jacqueline J. Wertsch

Human Motion Analysis

*Historical Perspective
and Introduction*

1.1. HISTORICAL OVERVIEW OF HUMAN MOTION ANALYSIS

Human motion analysis is frequently used today for both clinical and research applications. The art and science of motion analysis has expanded beyond basic descriptions of ambulatory patterns to include front-line clinical roles in rehabilitation, surgery, prosthetics, orthotics, ergonomics, and athletics. The combination of a careful clinical assessment and motion analysis can be a powerful tool for the clinician or researcher.

Human motion has been observed since antiquity. Body positioning was important to the practice of *Cong Fou*, which was a series of ritualistic postures and motions used by Taoist priests in 1000 B.C. [1]. The relationship between motion and muscle was appreciated by the ancient Greeks and described by Hipprocrates in his book *On Articulations* [1]. In ancient Rome, Galen created a classification of movement in which exercises were described according to the part of the body used, activity level, duration, and frequency [1]. Interest in the role of movement and exercise in health continued over the centuries, but a new era began in 1836 with work by the W. Weber and E. Weber brothers that introduced the scientific investigation of the mechanics of human gait. They measured and reported on stance and swing phase, trunk movements, step duration, and step length [2]. In 1881 V. Vierordt contributed to the development of kinematics by studying footprint patterns with colored fluid projections. This allowed analysis of body part movement in space during gait [2]. In the 1880s E. Marey introduced the use of photographic techniques using light stripes attached to body parts [2]. About the same time, E. Muybridge began to use cameras triggered sequentially to record motion during gait [3]. In 1895 W. Braune and O. Fischer added mathematical techniques to allow calculation of velocities, accelerations, and forces during gait [2]. In 1932 the di-

1

rect measurement of ground reactive forces became possible with the pneuomographic methods developed by R. Schwartz and W. Veth [2]. Over the next several decades, enormous advances in instrumentation and imaging technology allowed the development of the modern motion analysis laboratory, which has now become a vital clinical and research tool.

Gait analysis has played a key role in the advancement of surgical treatment of children with cerebral palsy from the days of isolated procedures to the current comprehensive multilevel approaches [4]. Gait analysis also has proved useful in the study of neuromuscular disorders [5–7], the evaluation of prosthetic joint replacement [8–14], and the study of athletic injuries [15,16], amputees [17–20], orthotics [21–23], and assistive devices [24]. Although simple observational analysis of gait characteristics by a trained observer is clinically useful, recent advances in bioengineering technology now allow precise analysis of many specific gait characteristics such as joint angles, angular velocities, and angular accelerations (kinematic analysis); ground reaction forces; joint forces, moments, and powers (kinetic analysis); electromyographic activity; and energy consumption.

1.2. EARLY METHODS OF MOTION ANALYSIS

Observational gait analysis has always been a useful clinical tool. It is best done by systematically concentrating first on one body part and then another, with a consistent approach proving most helpful [25,26]. A major limitation of observational gait analysis is difficulty in observing multiple events at multiple body segments concurrently [27,28]. What appears observationally to be equinus at the beginning of stance might instead be a neutral ankle combined with a flexed knee. Events happening faster than 1/12 of a second (83 ms) cannot be perceived by the human eye [29]. This limitation can be overcome through videotape frame-by-frame or slow motion replay [30,31]. Observation in only one plane, however, can lead to misinterpretation. For example, if observed only in the coronal plane, femoral internal rotation with knee flexion may be misinterpreted as knee valgus. Electrogoniometers also can be used to measure two-dimensional (2-D) or three-dimensional (3-D) joint motion [32,33]. Although electrogoniometric (EGM) systems are difficult to apply, measure only relative joint angles, and can encumber a small subject [29], they are relatively inexpensive and easy to operate, and they provide immediate data.

1.3. ADVANCES IN TECHNOLOGY

In the past decade, automated tracking systems for motion analysis have demonstrated increasing clinical acceptance. Passive reflective or actively illuminated markers are automatically tracked with these multicamera systems. The marker configuration is coupled to a biomechanical or mathematical model [15,30,34]. This allows calculation of angular and linear position, velocity, and acceleration of the body segments with respect to either a fixed laboratory coordinate system or with reference to another body segment. A rigid body in space must be represented by at least three markers [35–37]. Once the markers are identified in 3-D space, their collective position is used to describe the body segment motion characteristics. Classically, Euler angles are used to provide this 3-D representation

[33,36,38]. Other methods for describing 3-D motion include direction cosines [39], helical axes [40,41], and the method of Grood and Suntay [38].

Body segment motion combined with force data gathered from a force plate or force dynamometer can be used to calculate the internal joint moments causing motion. At each joint a state of equilibrium exists between the internal muscular forces and external loads [27,30,42,43]. The internal joint forces and moments are generated by muscles, ligaments, and bony structures. At each joint these internal joint forces are balanced by external ground reactive forces, body segment mass, and mass distribution (mass moment) effects. It needs to be appreciated, however, that muscular co-contraction is not revealed in the calculated joint moments [30]. Moment analysis can be useful in preoperative assessment and can provide insight into subtle functional musculoskeletal adaptations. For example, preoperative knee adductor moments have been suggested as predictors of surgical results from high tibial osteotomy [44]. Moment analysis has shown increased flexion moments at the hip and knee in the anterior-cruciate-ligament-deficient patient [45]. The relationship between joint moments and dynamic deformities in cerebral palsy have been described [46] and can be useful for clinical decision making [27].

For the past 40 years we have been able to measure ground reaction forces with instrumented plates, using strain gage or piezoelectric transducers (Advanced Mechanical Technology, Inc., Kistler) [47]. Today information from force plates can be automatically synchronized with motion data, allowing calculation of joint moments. Processing of the output data can provide ground reaction force vector components: vertical load, shear loads, torque about the vertical axis, and body center of pressure location. The vertical load pattern in normal individuals walking at a fixed normal cadence forms an M-shaped curve with peak magnitudes typically at about 110 percent body weight [30,48]. Changes in cadence affect the magnitude and duration of the vertical load curve and the slope of the M-curve reflective of the rate of limb loading [49–52]. Ground reaction forces can also be measured with pressure-sensitive insole systems (Electrodynograph, EMED, F-Scan) [53]. Force plates generally provide data on barefoot, isolated steps, while insole systems allow analysis of ongoing step-to-step variations in normal walking [54–56].

Although vacuum tube amplifiers allowed detection of electromyographic signals as early as the 1920s, electromyography did not gain clinical acceptance until Inman's work on the shoulder region in 1944 [57]. Currently, dynamic or kinesiologic electromyography (EMG) is used to gain information about the timing and relative intensity of muscle activity. Both cable and radiotelemetry systems are available for recording EMG signals. Although cable systems are reliable and less expensive than telemetry, they can encumber the subject. Radio telemetry frees the subject from an umbilicus but is vulnerable to electromagnetic interference and can require frequent technical service. New combined cable telemetry, which sends multiple signals on a single cable, is now available and offers the advantages of both systems.

Both fine wire and surface electrodes have been used for gait EMG analysis. Signals picked up from adjacent muscles (muscle cross talk) can be seen, especially with surface electrodes [58]. The raw EMG signal can be analyzed or processed. The most common methods of EMG signal processing are full-wave rectification, linear envelope or moving average, and integration of the full-wave rectified EMG. The linear envelope is created by filtering a full-wave rectified signal with a low-pass filter. The linear envelope is useful to assess on/off activity, but clonus bursts of muscle activity may not be seen [59]. Use of the term *integrated EMG* for the linear envelope is discouraged to avoid confusion with mathematical integration of the signal [30].

There can be constant change throughout the gait cycle in multiple factors known to affect the relationship between the EMG signal and the force generated. These factors include the joint angle, the muscle fiber length, and the type of contraction (isometric, eccentric, concentric). Other variables known to influence the recorded EMG signal include magnitude of tension, velocity of shortening, velocity of lengthening, rate of tension buildup, fatigue, and reflex activity [30]. It should be appreciated that although gait EMG can give information on when a muscle is active and can show a relative increase in activity, dynamic EMG does not tell us about the strength of the muscle, whether the muscle is under voluntary control, or whether the contraction is isometric, concentric, or eccentric [59,60–65].

1.4. INTRODUCTION TO THE TEXT

1.4.1. Part I: Current Technological Concepts and Emerging Horizons

Part I of the text presents current concepts and emerging horizons in human motion analysis technology. Methods commonly used for data capture and analysis are described with a view toward the engineer or technical user. Because kinetics are gaining increasing acceptance in clinical application, 3-D moments and powers are presented along with several clinical examples. Technical challenges in descriptive gait analysis are presented and include soft tissue motion and distal extremity motion analysis. New strategies for application of gait information for muscle control in locomotion are also described. Computer modeling advances with applications in movement disability analysis and surgical correction are summarized. A system for 3-D foot and ankle motion analysis is described and includes details on the instrumentation, calibration, validation, and biomechanical modeling requirements. Methods for the mathematical description of in vivo joint kinematics using current imaging techniques are presented, and future trends in human motion analysis are discussed. Summary descriptions of the Part I chapter contents are provided in the remainder of this section.

Roy Davis (Chapter 2) offers a tutorial review of current methods and future directions in clinical gait analysis. He discusses details of marker placement and body segment orientation, body-fixed coordinate systems, technical and anatomical coordinate systems, and calibration approaches. A specific clinical example is provided to illustrate the kinematic and kinetic data reduction process and to illustrate how to determine joint moments of force. A knee alignment fixture is described, and a detailed description of marker placement with the Newington gait analysis system (Newington, Connecticut) is offered. Technical challenges for accurate computation are defined as including joint center locations (especially the hip), segment mass and mass distribution properties, and first and second derivatives. Caution is urged to avoid overinterpretation of joint kinetic patterns. Current controversies in data collection and processing are discussed. A methodological comparison of 2-D and 3-D clinical gait analysis systems is offered, including clinical illustrations. A discussion of the future of gait analysis focuses on realistic requirements for surgical simulation. More immediate enhancements might include pattern recognition, graphical visualization, forward simulation modeling, and coupled dynamic analysis. The importance of system calibration and standardization of display conventions and terminology is stressed.

Larry Lamoreux (Chapter 3) discusses the effects of movement of skin-mounted reference markers relative to the underlying skeleton, including methods for measurement and correction. Examples are provided from studies of pelvic and lower limb motion during walking. Skin motion errors are usually noted to translate into joint angle errors and give rise to translation errors of the imbedded coordinate system. Although the patterns can be interpreted confidently, caution is suggested when interpreting moment curve zero crossings (transition between flexor and extensor moments). To minimize skin motion errors, the author suggests that marker mass be reduced and markers be placed near the segment ends. Encircling elastic bands are recommended when projecting wands are necessary to measure axial rotation. It is noted that measurable systematic skin motion errors can be compensated biomechanically and mathematically, and that random skin motion error occasionally can be reduced by filtering or by using rigid body constraints with multiple marker arrays.

A current clinical study by David Winter et al. (Chapter 4) focuses on frontal plane power profiles. In this study of nine subjects, the authors use a 16-channel biotelemetry system (14 EMG channels and 2 foot switches), two force plates, and a three-camera motion analysis system. They report that frontal plane power at the ankle shows a small absorption burst during push-off in six of the nine subjects. During the first half of stance in eight of the nine subjects, there is a small generation of frontal plane power at the knee consistent with knee abduction. Frontal plane hip power shows absorption during weight acceptance with power generation at midstance and prior to toe-off.

Richard Mikosz and Thomas Andriacchi (Chapter 5) discuss the value of kinetic data in the preoperative evaluation of the cerebral palsy child. They studied the importance of joint moments in evaluating the individual with spastic cerebral palsy and equinus deformity. Kinetic data offers insight not available from kinematic and time parameters alone. In a population of spastic cerebral palsy individuals with a clinically apparent equinus deformity of the foot, they describe two different moment patterns. The "flexion group" exhibits a moment that tends to flex the knee during stance phase ("quadriceps demand"). In contrast, the "extension group" shows a moment that tends to extend the knee ("quadriceps avoidance").

Christopher Vaughan and coauthors discuss strategies for controlling multiple muscles in human locomotion in Chapter 6. Three theoretical models providing the foundation for the work described are presented. The first model is the spinal oscillating network (SON) derived from basic research results on muscle action in the spinalized cat. The second model uses Newtonian mechanics that apply after the neural signal has activated muscle, which then begins to develop tension. The link between the neuronal control system (SON theory) and musculoskeletal effector system (Newtonian theory) is provided by the third theory of artificial neural networks (ANN). The authors present their research findings in three areas: (1) an ANN model of human gait in which EMGs are used as input to the network, (2) factor analyses of bilateral EMG signals, and (3) development of a biologically based neuron that incorporates features lacking in current ANN designs. The longer-term goal of the group is to develop and test an integrated theory of bipedal gait that combines computational models of neuronal control and musculoskeletal effector systems. The steps necessary to test their current theoretical model of human locomotion are described.

Scott Delp (Chapter 7) describes a graphics-based computer model of the lower extremity to study how various surgical procedures affect muscle function. He reports on use of the model to analyze tendon transfers, tendon lengthenings, osteotomies, and total joint replacements. Four areas in which musculoskeletal models can be useful for gaining insight are identified: (1) alteration of muscle moment arms by surgery, (2) effect of surgical alteration on muscle force-generating capability, (3) estimation of muscle lengths, and (4) visualization of interactions between kinematic and kinetic parameters. Examples are provided to illustrate the utility of the model. Limitations are described in light of current applications, and suggestions for future work are provided. It is suggested that clinical studies and computer simulations can improve both our understanding of muscle function and our capacity to provide effective treatment.

A biomechanical model for foot and ankle motion analysis in clinically oriented planes is described by Steven Kidder et al. (Chapter 8). The five-camera Vicon (Oxford, England) system of Faruk Abuzzahab et al. (Chapter 9) is used in the study to capture 3-D marker coordinate data. A four-segment rigid body model without joint constraints is used to describe motion of the tibia, hindfoot, forefoot, and hallux. Fixed axes of rotation are not assumed between body segments. This eliminates the need for additional computation while providing accurate orientation data. Three markers are placed on each of the four model segments for a total of 12 markers. In order to depict rotational motion in a meaningful clinical fashion, Euler (Cardan) angles are chosen to describe segment orientation. Radiographs are used to align the marker-based coordinates with the underlying bony anatomy of the foot. The required views are anterior-posterior, lateral, and hindfoot alignment. Kinematic data for the four foot and ankle segments are reported for five adult normals, 20 to 30 years old. The preliminary results show good correlation with cadaveric studies and stance phase studies. While variability between subjects might be due to differences in anatomic foot structure, good single-subject repeatability is noted. Plans for further model improvement and error reduction are provided.

Instrumentation, calibration, and validation of a novel foot and ankle motion analysis system are described by Abuzzahab et al. (Chapter 9). The system is designed to track the tibia, hindfoot, forefoot, and hallux during stance and swing phases of gait. A five-camera, video-based Vicon (Oxford, England), system is employed to acquire data from 12 reflective skin markers (16-mm diameter). The system is tuned to capture motion data within a capture volume measuring 2.4 m × 0.5 m × 0.6 m, which is adequate for a normal adult stride. Residual errors of 2.0 mm or 0.083 percent of the capture volume length dimension are reported. Resolution of the system varies between 0.13 and 1.33 mm depending upon the axis of reference and position within the capture volume. Static accuracy in all cases exceeds 98.3 percent. Dynamic calibration of the system yielded resolution values between 0.1 and 0.6 mm and accuracies in excess of 99 percent. A spectral analysis of marker position during static tests was also performed, showing correlation to the sampling characteristics of video data acquisition. Typical system output is provided for a subject tested with a target marker placed over the medial malleolus. Results are similar to those reported with other systems that use comparably placed ankle markers. Marker dropout was limited to 10 frames of data (167 ms) and was chiefly due to contralateral limb obstruction. The system was successfully used to track foot and ankle motion during both stance and swing phases of normal adult gait.

George Wynarsky and Gerald Harris (Chapter 10) present a general method to define in vivo bone and joint kinematics. The method is noninvasive, considers all six degrees of freedom, and provides an accurate mathematical description of joint motion. It is based on current imaging techniques and rigid-body kinematics. The method was originally developed in order to illustrate and investigate coronal plane motion of the subtalar joint. Digitized imaging scans are used to determine geometric property values for each bony segment. Spatial location is determined by rigid-body translations of the centers of mass of the segments. Segment orientations are determined by a set of three invariant principal axes fixed in each bony segment. Positions of one bone relative to another are described in terms of principal-axis direction cosines, standard Euler angles, clinical-plane angles (sagittal, coronal, and transverse plane rotations), and helical (screw) axis parameters. Each method offers an alternative mathematical description of joint motion. Results from the subtalar joint study demonstrate that the joint does not act as a simple hinge about a fixed oblique axis of rotation. This is best illustrated by the changing orientation of the helical axis direction cosines as the joint moves from maximum inversion to maximum eversion. The accuracy demonstrated in the digitizing process, solid model generation, and geometric property calculations is sufficient to show the viability of these methods to define in vivo joint motion. The chapter examines the advantages and characteristics of each mathematical method, current limitations, and potential clinical applications.

In the final chapter of Part I, Kenton Kaufman and David Sutherland (Chapter 11) discuss future trends in human motion analysis. They note that increasing emphasis is placed on outcome assessment by today's health care community. Accurate methods are needed to quantify the numerous variables that define outcome. The objective metrics provided through gait analysis techniques are described as central to measurement of a patient's progress. According to the authors, the future of gait analysis will depend upon progress and change brought about through health care reform, analytical techniques, and interpretation techniques of gait studies. Because an important feature of a reformed health care system will be an emphasis on disease prevention and outcome assessment, they state that it will become increasingly important to realize the role of gait analysis in eliminating unnecessary surgery and maximizing the surgical effect with multilevel recommendations. The authors note that advances in computer technology, biomechanical models, gait classification techniques, and telecommunications will shape the future. They predict that gait analysis in the future must be able to identify critical tests, interpret data more rapidly, and predict and quantify the outcome.

1.4.2. Part II: Clinical Applications: Methods and Practice

Part II of the text presents a series of human motion analysis examples with a focus toward the clinician, therapist, and surgeon. Basic and important considerations in data interpretation and clinical decision making are described with numerous clinical examples. The use of gait analysis for presurgical planning and postsurgical follow-up of children with cerebral palsy is emphasized. The unique and important role of dynamic EMG in gait analysis is described, including clinical examples. Methods for utilizing joint kinetic data are presented as they apply to interpretation and clinical decision making for gait abnormalities resulting from neuromuscular disorders. Detailed clinical research studies of selective dorsal rhizotomy and functional neuromuscular stimulation are included both to reinforce the basic principles of data interpretation and to illustrate current trends in gait analysis application. The development of motion analysis methods to investigate the adult foot and ankle and pediatric planovalgus foot is also described, as are methods for evaluating plantar pressure alterations with the use of metatarsal and scaphoid pads. The final chapter of Part II discusses applications of intelligent multimedia technology in human motion analysis, with suggestions for clinical application and training.

Kaufman and Sutherland (Chapter 12) stress the usefulness of 3-D motion analysis in preoperative planning and postoperative assessment of patients with disorders of the musculoskeletal system. To better understand the gait patterns in patients with lower lumbar and sacral spinal defects, they use tibial nerve blocks to produce plantar flexor paralysis. The findings show that the magnitude of the second vertical force peak is reduced with a decrease in single limb support duration. In an ongoing study of oxygen consumption with knee brace usage, the authors hypothesize that there will be less energy expenditure if the knee unlocks automatically during swing. In the prosthetic user, it is shown that knee friction affects the excursion of the prosthetic shank without affecting the period. Human motion analysis is cited as useful in studying the development of normal walking in children, in distinguishing physiologic genu varum from Blount's disease, in managing rectus femoris spasticity in cerebral palsy, and in formulating a multilevel operative and treatment plan for the extensively involved cerebral palsy child.

Tom Novacheck (Chapter 13) reviews the role of gait analysis in the surgical decision-making process in children with cerebral palsy. He discusses the gait deviations that occur with femoral anteversion, including internal hip rotation and internal foot progression angle. Correction is suggested if external rotation is insufficient to maintain a normal foot progression angle, the hip is subluxated, or the anteversion is greater than 45 degrees. An external foot progression angle is seen in external tibial torsion. Surgical intervention can include a femoral derotation, hamstring lengthening, and possibly a rectus transfer. External foot progression angle is also seen in pes valgus. Anterior tilt of the pelvis with a reduction in hip extension during terminal stance is seen with psoas contracture and/or spasticity. Kinetics show an increased hip extensor moment and delayed crossover of the hip flexion/extension moment. Gait characteristics and surgical procedures are also discussed for adductor, hamstring, rectus femoris, and equinus contracture/spasticity.

Jacquelin Perry (Chapter 14) discusses the role of dynamic EMG in gait analysis. EMG provides a description of the electrical signals generated during muscle activation. Dynamic EMG during gait can give information not provided by motion analysis. This is illustrated by a study of the Solid Ankle Cushioned Heel (SACH) foot in below-knee (BK) amputees in which motion analysis and power calculations implied a savings in energy expenditure, but in fact energy cost measurement showed the opposite. Dynamic EMG identified the source of extra energy expenditure as increased muscle action (intensity and duration) of the quadriceps and hip extensors. Dynamic EMG is used to assist in surgical planning by defining muscle firing patterns and to help identify synergies, postural reflexes, and contractures. Applications of dynamic EMG for evaluation of patients with spastic paralysis, stiff knee gait, varus foot, and postpolio syndrome are also discussed. Technical considerations including noise filtering, cross talk, bandwidth, electrode variables, signal analysis methods, and muscle effort versus force are reviewed.

Silvia Õunpuu (Chapter 15) illustrates how joint kinetics (moments and powers) can be used to better understand the mechanics of gait and brace wear. The floor reaction orthosis (FRO) has been prescribed for patients with significant lower extremity weakness resulting in a crouched position during stance. Joint kinetics show that a properly functioning FRO reduces the knee extensor moment demand during stance. Management of the myelomeningocele patient can require consideration of both surgical and orthotic options. Kinetic motion analysis provides insight into excessive internal joint moment generation that poses a potential risk to the knee. A study of the posterior leaf spring (PLS) orthosis was conducted to examine its effect upon power generation at the ankle in children with cerebral palsy. Compared to barefoot walking, use of a PLS results in a decrease in push-off power at the ankle, a decrease in total energy generation, and an increase in total power absorption. Studies on preoperative and postoperative joint kinetic data are presented to explore the potential role of kinetics in preoperative planning.

Michael Aiona (Chapter 16) describes the use of motion analysis for the evaluation of dorsal segmental rhizotomy. The history of selective dorsal rhizotomy (SDR) is reviewed. W. Peacock is credited with popularizing this procedure and utilizing the principles of rootlet selection in cauda equina surgery. The surgical procedure is described, and literature on the use of gait analysis in SDR is reviewed. A prospective study of gait in 24 ambulatory spastic diplegic patients revealed significant increases in stride length without any change in cadence or significant improvement in speed. Following rhizotomy, other abnormal gait patterns were revealed. Future studies on energy consumption are needed to determine if the resultant gait changes provide increased efficiency.

Ronald Triolo et al. discuss technical and clinical challenges of standing and walking with functional neuromuscular stimulation (FNS*) in Chapter 17. FNS has been applied to those with complete and incomplete spinal cord lesions, stroke, head trauma, and other neuromuscular disfunction such as cerebral palsy and myelomeningocele. It has also been used to assist with bowel or bladder function and respiration. The authors summarize their clinical experiences at the Shriners Hospital in applying FNS to children, teenagers, and young adults paralyzed by spinal cord injuries in order to provide standing, walking, and other lower extremity function. They also summarize their technical experiences in synthesizing ambulatory motions at the Department of Veterans Affairs Medical Center. Although walking with FNS is impractical for long distances, the authors note that stepping short distances within the vicinity of a wheelchair, ascending or descending a curb, or sidestepping at a counter are activities that might complement quiet standing and increase an individual's independence. Human motion analysis is cited as an important tool for identifying and rectifying deviations observed in FNS–generated gait.

Jeffrey Johnson et al. (Chapter 18) report on 3-D motion analysis of the adult foot and ankle. A four-segment biomechanical model was used in conjunction with 12 anatomic reflective markers. The authors utilized a five-camera motion analysis system with a single force plate. Averaged results from clinical trials with five normal healthy volunteers provided 3-D kinematics of the tibia, hindfoot, forefoot, and hallux segments. Results were reported during both stance and swing phases. For each subject the motion curve offset was determined from radiographs of the foot and ankle. Overall, there was considerable variance in the offsets, but the patterns of the motion data were quite consistent.

Peter Smith et al. (Chapter 19) present a biomechanical evaluation of the planovalgus foot in cerebral palsy. The chapter details the use of gait and plantar pressure analysis

---

*The term *FNS* refers to the activation and coordination of paralyzed muscles via the excitation of intact peripheral nerves with small electrical currents to produce useful, purposeful movements.

to investigate planovalgus foot deformity following subtalar stabilization. Planovalgus deformity is characterized by valgus of the hindfoot and a pronated posture of the midfoot with a flattened longitudinal arch. It is also commonly associated with hallux valgus at the metatarsal phalangeal joint. Difficulties arising because of the deformity include poor stance phase stability, shoe wear problems, and impaired push-off power during walking. Surgical treatment in the group studied consisted of a subtalar arthrodesis using a screw coursing from the subtalar neck into the calcaneus. All subjects underwent 3-D kinematic and kinetic gait analysis as well as plantar pressure evaluation using a portable, microprocessor-based insole system. Postoperative results from the gait and plantar pressure studies show slight improvements in sagittal plane ankle power with dramatic lateral shifts in foot pressure distribution.

Ziad Abu-Faraj et al. (Chapter 20) report on quantitative studies of plantar load redistribution caused by metatarsal pads and by scaphoid pads. Pressures were recorded from 10 normal adult subjects in each study from eight discrete plantar locations. A portable, microprocessor-based data acquisition system was used to acquire data during multiple 400-step trials. With metatarsal pad use, significant increases in peak pressures, contact durations, and pressure-time integrals were noted at the metatarsal shaft region. With scaphoid pad use, significant increases in all three metrics (peak pressure, pressure-time integral, load duration) were seen at the medial longitudinal arch area. The redistribution of plantar pressures in both studies tended to relate not only to the pad dimensions, but also to anatomic foot configuration, foot size, and pad location.

Sheldon Simon et al. (Chapter 21) report on the use of artificial intelligence and an expert system in motion analysis. The aims of their applications of intelligent multimedia technology are to decrease report-generation time, provide help with interpretation, and offer expert consultation. Artificial intelligence (AI) methods are suggested to help with identifying abnormalities and causes, and determining explanations of causes. Interactive communication between analyst and user is also suggested. Two modules have been developed in the project. One is a knowledge-based system for qualitative analysis of walking disorders (QUAWDS) that is used to aid in report generation and in providing explanations. QUAWDS is designed to interpret the gait of neuromuscular patients. It employs AI and utilizes an expert system. The other module is a gait analysis interpretation tool (GAIT), which is a multimedia instruction system for tutoring. The multimedia database includes text, voice, graphics, video, and animation. GAIT provides video, stick figure animation, graphics, and text as well as voice annotation and a structured data display based on relevance. The current media of choice is CD-ROM. GAIT utilizes actual clinical data to tutor the student, which requires that the student deal with actual situations such as missing data or marker placement errors. The training system is suggested for physical therapists, physicians, fellows, residents, and students.

References

[1] Basmajian JV. *Therapeutic Exercise*. 3rd ed. Baltimore, Md: Williams and Wilkins Publishing Co., 1978:1,3,5.

[2] Steindler A. *Kinesiology of the Human Body*. Springfield, Ill: 1970, Charles C Thomas Publisher, 1970:631,632.

[3] Muybridge E. *The Human Figure in Motion*. New York, NY: Dover; Reprinted in 1955 from original volume published in 1887.

[4] DeLuca PA. Gait analysis in the treatment of the ambulatory child with cerebral palsy. *Clin Orthop* 1991;264:65-75.

[5] Sutherland DH. Gait analysis in neuromuscular disease. San Diego Children's Hospital instructional course 1990:333–341.

[6] Olney SJ, Griffin MP, Monga TN, McBride ID. Work and power in gait of stroke patients. *Arch Phys Med Rehabil* 1991;72:309–314.

[7] Wagenaar RC, Beek WJ. Hemiplegic gait: A kinematic analysis using walking speed as a basis. *J Biomech* 1992;25:1007–1015.

[8] Collopy MC, Murray MP, Gardner GM, Di Ulio RA, Gore DR. Kinesiologic measurements of functional performance before and after geometric total knee replacement. *Clin Orthop* 1977;126:196.

[9] Rittman N, Kettelkamp DB, Pryor P, Schwartzkopf GL, Hillberry B. Analysis of patterns of knee motion walking for four types of total knee implants. *Clin Orthop* 1981;155:111.

[10] Murray MP, Gore DR, Laney WH, Gardner GM, Mollinger LA. Kinesiologic measurements of functional performance before and after double compartment Marmor knee arthoplasty. *Clin Orthop* 1983;173:191.

[11] Olsson E. Gait analysis in hip and knee surgery. *Scan J Rehab Med* 1986;15s:5–53.

[12] Berman AT, Zarro VJ, Bosacco SJ, Israelite C. Quantitative gait analysis after unilateral or bilateral total knee replacement. *J Bone Joint Surg Am* 1987;69:1340–1345.

[13] Berman AT, Zarro VJ, Bosacco SJ, Israelite C. Quantitative gait analysis after unilateral or bilateral total hip replacement. *Arch Phys Med Rehabil* 1991;72:190–194.

[14] Wykman A, Olsson E. Walking ability after total hip replacement. *J Bone Joint Surg Br* 1992; 74:53–56.

[15] Andriacchi TP, Mikosz RP. Musculoskeletal dynamics, locomotion and clinical applications. In: Mow VC, Hayes WC eds. *Basic orthopaedic biomechanics*. New York, NY:Raven Press;1991:51–92.

[16] Jacobs R, Schenau GJ. Intermuscular coordination in a sprint push-off. *J Biomech* 1992;25(9):953–965.

[17] Waters RL, Perry J, Antonelli D, Hislop H. Energy cost of walking of amputees: The influence of level of amputation. *J Bone Joint Surg Am* 1976;58:42–46.

[18] Skinner HB, Effeney DJ. Gait analysis in amputees. *Am J Phys Med Rehabil* 1985;64:82–89.

[19] Gitter A, Czerniecki JM, DeGroot DM: Biomechanical analysis of the influence of prosthetic feet on below-knee amputee walking. *Am J Phys Med Rehabil* 1991; 70:142–148.

[20] Colborne GR, Neumann S, Longmuir PE, Berbrayer D. Analysis of mechanical and metabolic factors in the gait of congenital below-knee amputees: A comparison of SACH and Seattle feet. *Am J Phys Med Rehabil* 1992;71:272–278.

[21] Lehmann JF, Condon SM, de Lateur BJ, Price R: Gait abnormalities in peroneal nerve paralysis and their correction by orthoses: A biomechanical study. *Arch Phys Med Rehabil* 1986;67:380–386.

[22] Lehmann JF, Condon SM, Price R, de Lateur BJ. Gait abnormalities in hemiplegia: Their correction by an ankle-foot orthoses. *Arch Phys Med Rehabil* 1987;68:673–771.

[23] Brodke DS, Skinner SR, Lamoreux LW, Johanson ME, St. Helen R, Moran SA, Ashley RK. Effects of ankle-foot orthoses on the gait of children. *J Ped Orthop* 1989; 9:702–708.

[24] Logan L, Byers-Hinkley K, Ciccone CD. Anterior versus posterio walkers: a gait analysis study. *Dev Med Child Neurol* 1990;32:1044–1048.

[25] Perry J. *Gait Analysis Systems in Gait Analysis: Normal and Pathological Function.* Thorofare, NJ: Slack Inc;1992:353–411.

[26] Winter D. Concerning the scientific basis for the diagnosis of pathological gaits and for rehabilitation protocols. *J Phys Ther* 1985;37:245–252.

[27] Gage JR. *Gait Analysis in Cerebral Palsy.* New York, NY: MacKeith Press, Blackwell Scientific Publications Ltd;1991:61–100, 101–117, 153.

[28] Saleh M, Murdoch G. In defence of gait analysis. *J Bone Joint Surg Br* 1985; 67:237–241.

[29] Gage JR, Õunpuu S. Gait analysis in clinical practice. Seminars in Orthopedics 1989; 4(2):72–87.

[30] Winter DA. *Biomechanics and Motor Control of Human Movement.* 2nd ed. New York, NY: John Wiley & Sons Inc; 1990:21, 45–47, 77, 85–90, 127, 191–212.

[31] Krebs DE, Edelstein JE, Fishman S. Reliability of observational kinematic gait analysis. *Phys Ther* 1985:65,1027–1033.

[32] Lamoreux LA. Kinematic measurements in the study of human walking. *Bull Prosthetic Res* 1971;3:10–15.

[33] Chao EYS. Justification of triaxial goniometer for the measurement of joint rotation. *J Biomech* 1980;13:989–1006.

[34] Vaughan CL, Nashman JH, Murr MS. What is the normal function of tibialis posterior in human gait? In: Sussman MD. *The diplegic child.* Rosemont, Ill: American Academy of Orthopaedic Surgeons;1992:397–409.

[35] Antonsson EJ. A three-dimensional kinematic acquisition and intersegment dynamic analysis system for human motion. Cambridge, Mass: Massachusetts Institute of Technology, 1982:PhD thesis, vol 1.

[36] Ramakrishnan HK, Kadaba MP. On the estimation of joint kinematics during gait. *J Biomech* 1991;24(10):969–977.

[37] Meirovich L. *Methods of Analytical Dynamics.* New York, NY: McGraw-Hill; 1970:123–124.

[38] Grood ES, Suntay WJ. A joint coordinate system for the clinical description of three-dimensional motions: Applications to the knee. *J Biomech Eng* 1983;105:136–144.

[39] Shames IH. *Engineering Mechanics.* 2nd ed. Englewood Cliffs, NJ: Prentice-Hall; 1967:21.

[40] Woltring HJ, Huiskes R, DeLange A. Finite centroid and helical axis estimation from noisy landmark measurement in the study of human joint kinematics. *J Biomech* 1985;18:379–389.

[41] Shiavi R, Limbird T, Frazer M, Stivers K, Strauss A, Abramovitz J. Helical motion of the knee: Kinematics of uninjured and injured knees during walking and pivoting. *J Biomech* 1987;20:653–665.

[42] Seireg A, Arvikar RJ. The prediction of muscular load sharing and joint forces in the lower extremities during walking. *J Biomech* 1975;3:51–61.

[43] Vaughan CL, Davis BL, O'Connor J. *Dynamics of Human Gait*. Champaign, Ill: Human Kinetics;1992:15–43.

[44] Prodromos CC, Andriacchi TP, Galante JO. A relationship between gait and clinical changes following high tibial osteotomy. *J Bone Joint Surg Am* 1985;67:1188–1194.

[45] Andriacchi TP, Kramer GM, Landon GC. The biomechanics of running and knee injuries. In: Finerman G ed. American Academy of Orthopedic Surgeons, Symposium on Sport Medicine, The knee. St. Louis, Mo:CV Mosby;1985:23–32.

[46] Lai K, Kuo KN, Andriacchi TP. Relationship between dynamic deformities and joint moments in cerebral palsy. *J Ped Orthop* 1988;8:690–695.

[47] Elftman H. Force plate studies. In Klopsteg PE, Wilson PD eds. *Human Limbs and Their Substitutes*. New York, NY: Hafner; 1968:451–454.

[48] Sutherland DH, Olshen RA, Biden EN, Wyatt MP. *The Development of Mature Walking*. Philadelphia, Pa: JB Lippincott Co; 1988:176–177

[49] Crowinshield RD, Brand RA, Johnston RC. The effects of walking velocity and age on hip kinematics and kinetics. *Clin Orthop* 1978;132:140–144.

[50] Mann RA, Hagy J. Biomechanics of walking, running, and sprinting. *Am J Sports Med* 1980;8(5):345–350.

[51] Skinner SR, Barnes LA, Perry J, Parker J. The relationship of gait velocity to the rate of lower extremity loading and unloading. *Trans Orthop Res Soc* 1980;5:273.

[52] Soames RW, Richardson RPS. Stride length and cadence: Their influence on ground reaction forces during gait. In: Winter DA, Norman RW, Wells RP, Hayes KC, Patla AE eds. *Biomechanics IX-A*. Champaign, Ill; Human Kinetics Publishers;1978; 406–410.

[53] Wertsch JJ, Webster JG, Tompkins WJ. A portable insole plantar pressure measurement system. *J Rehabil Res Dev* 1992;29(1):13–18.

[54] Zhu H, Wertsch JJ, Harris GF, Alba HM, Price MB. Sensate and insensate in-shoe plantar pressures. *Arch Phys Med Rehabil* 1993;74(12):1362–1368.

[55] Zhu H, Wertsch JJ, Harris GF, Loftsgaarden JD, Price MB: Foot pressure distribution during walking and shuffling. *Arch Phys Med Rehabil* 1991;72(6):390–397.

[56] Zhu H, Wertsch JJ, Harris GF, Price MB, Alba HM. Pressure distribution beneath sensate and insensate feet. *Proc IEEE Eng Med Bio Soc* 1989;11:822–823.

[57] Inman VT, Saunders JB, Abbott LC. Observations of function of the shoulder joint. *J Bone Joint Surg Am* 1944;26:1–30.

[58] Koh TJ, Grabiner MD. Cross talk in surface electromyograms of human hamstring muscles. *J Orthop Res* 1992;10:701–709.

[59] Gage JR. EMG fundamentals and interpretation. In: Clinical decision making in gait analysis. St. Paul, Minn: Gillette Children's Hospital (course syllabus) April 1992: 45–50.

[60] Inman VT, Ralston HJ, Saunders JB, Feinstein B, Wright EW. Relation of human electromyogram to muscular tension. *Electroencephalogr Clin Neurophysiol* 1952;4:187.

[61] Bigland B, Lippold OCJ. The relation between force, velocity, and integrated electrical activity in human muscles. *J Physiol Br* 1954;123:214.

[62] Close JR, Nickel ED, Todd FN. Motor-unit action-potential counts: Their significance in isometric and isotonic contractions. *J Bone Joint Surg Am* 1960;42:1207.

[63] Bouisset S. EMG and muscle force in normal motor activities. In: Desmedt JE ed. *New Developments in Electromyography and Clinical Neurophysiology*. Basel, Switzerland: Karger; 1972:547–583.

[64] Milner-Brown HS, Stein RB. The relation between surface electromyogram and muscular force. *J Physiol Br* 1975;246:549–569.

[65] Weir JP, Wagne LL, Housch TJ. Linearity and reliability of the IEMG v torque relationship for the forearm flexors and leg extensors. *Am J Phys Med Rehabil* 1992; 71:283–287.

Part 1

Technology

*Current Concepts
and Emerging Horizons*

Roy B. Davis
Peter A. DeLuca

Chapter 2

Clinical Gait Analysis

*Current Methods
and Future Directions*

2.1. CURRENT UTILIZATION

Over the past decade, the clinical use of gait analysis has expanded in the United States. This has been the result of two significant changes: an improved understanding and interpretation of the information that the measurement systems can provide, and the development of more clinically appropriate software for the collection and reduction of data and the reporting of results. Also, over this period, hardware technology for clinical gait analysis has continued to evolve, with faster computing equipment and cameras based on solid-state electronics being two examples.

The assessment of children and adolescents with cerebral palsy (CP) constitutes the widest use of gait analysis in the clinical setting [1–4]. Typical clinical use of the gait data takes the form of case-by-case analyses with concerted efforts in understanding the biomechanical significance of particular deviations from normal patterns or values.

Clinical research in CP gait consists largely of the assessment of the preoperative to postoperative changes in gait associated with different surgical protocols. Surgical procedures that have been examined include rectus femoris transfers [5] and releases [6,7], hamstring lengthenings [8], tendoachilles lengthenings [9], gastrocnemius fascia lengthenings [10], osteotomies [11–13], and selective dorsal rhizotomies [14,15]. Other applications of clinical gait analysis include the evaluation of persons with gait impairments associated with myelomeningocele [16], stroke [17], Parkinsonism [18], postpolio sequelae [19], and amputations [20].

2.2. GAIT MEASUREMENT TECHNOLOGY

The purpose of this section is to outline briefly the several types of technology that are available for the acquisition of gait data, specifically: body segment and joint motion, ground reaction forces and pressure, and electromyographic activity. To further supplement the information provided below, the reader is referred to recent texts by M. Whittle [21] and J. Perry [2].

2.2.1. Motion Measurement

By far the most prevalent method of collecting information associated with the position of body segments and joints is through the use of external markers placed on the subject that are tracked with multicamera systems [22]. That is, markers are placed on the body segments and aligned with specific bony landmarks. The displacement of the markers, which are either passive (retroreflective) or active (light-emitting diodes), over time is simultaneously viewed and recorded by two to seven cameras. Stereometric techniques [23] are then used in a frame-by-frame analysis to combine the two-dimensional (2-D) camera images and determine the instantaneous three-dimensional (3-D) coordinates of each marker relative to a fixed laboratory coordinate system. The process that takes the 3-D marker data through to segment and joint angular position is described in some detail below.

The technology associated with this measurement approach has continued to change over the past decade. Camera hardware characteristics have improved through the application of solid-state electronics. Host computer requirements for the measurement systems have been downsized at the same time that personal computer capabilities have increased. Consequently, the computing costs associated with motion measurement systems have come down while maintaining sufficient speed for data collection and processing.

Passive marker measurement systems such as Vicon (Oxford Metrics, Ltd., Oxford, England), ExpertVision (Motion Analysis Corp., Santa Rosa, California), and Peak Performance (Peak Performance Technologies, Englewood, Colorado) use light sources placed very near each camera to generate light, which is returned from the highly reflective markers (usually small spheres). Active marker systems such as Selcon (Selspot Systems, Ltd., Southfield, Michigan) and Optotrak (Northern Digital, Inc., Waterloo, Ontario, Canada) use small light-emitting diodes (LEDs) placed directly on the subject to generate the light that is recorded by the motion cameras. The advantage of the active marker approach is that the identity (that is, the anatomical location) of each marker is known because the LEDs are sequentially pulsed by the control and data acquisition hardware. This is potentially significant because of the time saved in data reduction. The operator of the passive marker system assists the computer with marker identification. The disadvantages of this technique include the possibility for subject distraction and gait alteration because the system of cables that powers and controls the LEDs trails the subjects as they walk and the potential for "phantom marker artifact" due to reflection of LED pulses from testing surfaces such as the floor.

Readers are referred to papers by M. P. Kadaba et al. [24] and K. R. Campbell [25] that discuss their experience with the Vicon and ExpertVision systems, respectively, and to papers by T. P. Andriacchi [26] and D. Rowell and R. W. Mann [27] for more information on the Selcon system.

Other approaches to human motion measurement include cinephotography, electrogoniometry, and accelerometry. Researchers have for some time used high-speed film cameras to record human motion [28]. Cinephotography or cinefilm techniques have proved very reliable but time-consuming because each frame of data is digitized individually. Due to this labor intensity and relatively long processing time, cinefilm approaches are seldom used clinically aside from research applications.

The simplest electrogoniometer consists of a rotary potentiometer with a leg connected both to the potentiometer shaft and base for attachment to the subject. This single-axis transducer is not particularly useful because bones tend to both translate and rotate relative to each other as a joint moves. Multiaxial goniometer designs address this problem [29]. The advantage of goniometry is the real-time display of joint angle information, which is useful in some clinical applications such as biofeedback. A limiting feature of goniometry is that the devices can only measure the relative angles between two body segments and cannot provide information on the absolute orientation of a body segment in space, such as pelvic tilt, or the absolute location of a segment relative to an inertially fixed (laboratory) coordinate system—data that are required for the computation of joint kinetics. Furthermore, while goniometers can offer advantages for the rapid collection of single joint data on many subjects, the technology is cumbersome in a more typical clinical application such as the simultaneous, bilateral assessment of the hip, knee, and ankle joints.

A number of researchers have investigated the use of multiaxial accelerometers [30,31]. The transducers measure linear acceleration at the points of attachment. Multiple transducer configurations are required when joint center acceleration values are desired; for example, one triaxial transducer on the medial and lateral condyles of the thigh is required to examine the acceleration of the approximate knee center. The acceleration data can then be integrated numerically to obtain velocity and position data. Users must be careful to correct for the effects of gravity, and the results are highly dependent on the initial conditions selected for the integration process. Z. Ladin and G. Wu [32] describe an excellent application of this technology. They use a camera-based motion measurement system (Selspot) to measure displacement or position parameters and triaxial accelerometers to measure the accelerations, both of which are needed for the mechanical computation of the joint force (refer to the discussion below for a description of this computational process).

2.2.2. Ground Reaction Measurement

Force platforms are complex transducers that provide data associated with the three components of the ground reaction force, the vertical ground reaction torque, and the location of the center of pressure (that is, the point of application of the ground reaction force vector). Two technologies have been used in force plate designs: strain gauges [Advanced Mechanical Technology, Inc. (AMTI), Newton, Massachusetts, and Bertec Corp., Worthington, Ohio] and piezoelectricity (Kistler Instrument Corp., Amherst, New York). A number of investigators have used these data to better understand the mechanics of ground-subject interactions, particularly while wearing different types of shoes [33,34].

Foot pressure (or the distributed load that corresponds to the ground reaction force) measurements are accomplished through use of a flat, 2-D array of small force transducers. The size of the individual transducer cell dictates the overall resolution of the system. The advantage of this technology is that the clinical practitioner has more detailed information regarding the way that force is distributed across the plantar surface of the foot and can better identify potentially harmful loading patterns. While this technology has been used for some time in the examination of the feet of subjects with diabetes, more work is needed to complete our understanding of normal plantar pressure patterns and to establish the relationship between abnormal plantar pressure patterns and different foot pathologies [35]. Commercially available products for foot pressure measurement include EMED (Novel Electronics, Inc., Minneapolis, Minnesota), F-Scan (Tekscan, Inc., Boston, Massachusetts), and a system from AMTI. Users are advised to be careful with respect to system calibration and signal drift as well as the interpretation of the results.

2.2.3. Stride and Temporal Parameters

Parameters such as step length and walking speed can be assessed in a wide variety of ways; for example, with simple tools such as a stopwatch and tape measure, or with sophisticated arrays of photoelectric monitors. Foot switches applied to the plantar aspect of the subject's foot is one commonly used clinical technique [36]. A typical commercially available foot switch system is offered by Motion Lab Systems (Baton Rouge, Louisiana). This particular system comprises individual sensors that are applied to the bottom of the subject's foot over the bony prominences of the heel and metatarsal heads in different configurations, depending on the information desired. To determine the gait cycle events of heel contact and toe-off in normal ambulators, one might place a switch on the heel, first (or second) metatarsal head, and great toe. The application of foot switches in a clinical population is more challenging because of the greater variability of the foot-ground contact pattern. Consequently, greater care must be exercised in both data collection (e.g., switch placement) and interpretation of results [37]. Other foot switch alternatives that avoid this concern of switch placement employ either insoles that serve as one or two cell foot switches, or contact-sensitive walkways [2].

2.2.4. Dynamic Electromyography (EMG)

Through the use of surface electrodes and/or fine-wire electrodes, the voltage potentials produced by contracting muscles can be measured. These voltages (at the microvolt level) can be indicative of the timing and the intensity of the contraction. The validity and associated usefulness of these data depend on a number of variables, including the placement of the electrodes, the distance between recording electrodes, skin surface conditions, signal amplification and filtering, and the rate of data acquisition. Raw signals are commonly used to estimate the timing characteristics of the muscle activity; for example, when a muscle is active during the gait cycle. To use the data to evaluate the intensity of the contraction, the raw signal must be related to a reference signal; for example, the magnitude of the signal when the subject performs a maximum voluntary contraction. This normalization process might be difficult for patients who have limited isolated control of individual muscles, such as children with CP. Commercial EMG systems are available from Biosentry Telemetry, Inc. (Torrance, California), Motion Lab Systems (Baton Rouge, Louisiana), and B & L Engineering (Santa Fe Springs, California). The reader is referred to the text by Perry [2] for a very complete description of the collection and application of dynamic electromyography. The work by J. J. Chen and R. Shiavi [38] is representative of the massive volume of literature associated with electromyographic signal processing and analysis.

2.3. DATA REDUCTION APPROACHES

2.3.1. General Treatment

As indicated above, the prevailing approach for the collection of dynamic gait data in the clinical setting involves the placement of external markers on the surface of body segments that are aligned with particular bony landmarks, and the collection of data from multiple walking trials. The result of the data collection process is a series of *frames* of data with each frame containing the 3-D locations of the external markers at that instant in time. In this way, the 3-D path of each marker, commonly referred to as its *trajectory*, is measured for the walk. The spatial relationship between markers placed on the same body segment define the orientation, or attitude, of that body segment in space. At least three markers or reference points arranged in a noncolinear fashion on the segment are required to specify the six degrees of freedom that are associated with the position and spatial orientation of the segment. This orientation can be described through the computation of three independent absolute angles. Once the absolute orientation of each body segment is determined, then the spatial orientation of one segment relative to another may be computed. These relative angles are commonly known as *joint angles*, sometimes referred to generally as *kinematics*.

To examine this process in more detail, assume that the spatial orientation of the plane formed by the right and left anterior superior iliac spine (ASIS) and the point midway between the right and left posterior superior iliac spine (PSIS), is selected to represent the angular position of the pelvis in space; that is, pelvic tilt, obliquity, and rotation. Assume further that the 3-D locations of three markers (A, B, and C in Figure 2-1) placed over the right and left ASIS and midway between the right and left PSIS are known. The absolute orientation of the pelvis may be determined from simple vector arithmetic as follows:

- The unit vector $\hat{e}_1$ is computed from the locations of markers A and C.
- The unit vector $\hat{e}_{Py}$ is found from the locations of markers A and B.
- The unit vector $\hat{e}_{Pz}$ is calculated from the vector cross product of $\hat{e}_{Py}$ and $\hat{e}_1$.
- Finally, the unit vector $\hat{e}_{Px}$ is computed from the vector cross product of $\hat{e}_{Py}$ and $\hat{e}_{Pz}$.

In general, body-fixed coordinate systems that are based on the locations of marker positions are referred to as *technical* coordinate systems, and those that are based on the locations of bony landmark locations (as is the case for the pelvis) or joint center positions (e.g., for the thigh) are referred to as *anatomical* coordinate systems [39]. In this case, since the three external markers were placed over the reference bony landmarks, the technical coordinate system $\{\hat{e}_P\}$ coincides with the anatomical coordinate system for the pelvis. The absolute angular position of the pelvis, i.e., coordinate system $\{\hat{e}_P\}$, can now be found through the use of Euler angles [40–42]. Using Euler angles is one way to relate the rotational displacement of one coordinate system relative to another. In this case, the orientation of the pelvic coordinate system $\{\hat{e}_P\}$ is found relative to the inertially fixed laboratory coordinate system.

Carrying this examination to the thigh and hip, assume that three markers, D, E, and F, have been placed on the thigh (Figure 2-1). Employing the same vector approach that was outlined for the pelvis, one may compute a marker-based, or technical, coordinate system for the thigh. Note, however, that the desired anatomical coordinate system for the thigh (based on hip and knee joint centers) is different from the technical coordinate system. Moreover, it is improbable that the two coordinate systems are spatially oriented in the

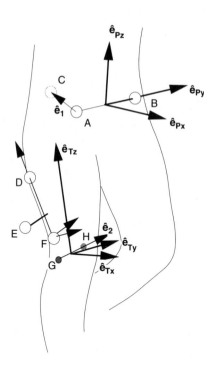

Figure 2-1. Hypothetical external marker configuration for the pelvis and thigh with the corresponding technical coordinate systems (thick vectors) and the anatomical coordinate systems (thin vectors).

same way, that is, are in alignment, because of the conic shape of the thigh. In order to establish the relationship between these two coordinate systems so that one can transform the technical coordinate system into alignment with the anatomical coordinate system, an *anatomical axes calibration* must be performed [39,43].

Particular bony landmarks on the subject's limb, for example, the medial and lateral femoral condyles, are identified by additional markers (G and H in Figure 2-1) or by an *anatomical landmark calibration stick* [44] during a standing data collection session. In one anatomical axes calibration approach, the location of these anatomical reference points relative to the thigh technical coordinate system are computed and saved (to be recalled during the frame-by-frame analysis of the motion data). A second subject calibration technique illustrates the use of these anatomical references as follows:

- The medial and lateral femoral condyle locations (G and H in Figure 2-1) are found.
- The hip center location can be estimated using anthropometric relationships based on pelvic data [45–48].
- The knee center is estimated to lie midway between the medial and lateral knee markers along unit vector $\hat{e}_2$.
- The long axis of the thigh, $\hat{e}_{Tz}$, is computed from the location of the hip and knee center.
- The unit vector $\hat{e}_{Tx}$ is calculated from the vector cross product of $\hat{e}_2$ amd $\hat{e}_{Tz}$.
- The unit vector $\hat{e}_{Ty}$ is determined from the vector cross product of $\hat{e}_{Tz}$ and $\hat{e}_{Tx}$.
- Note: Because of the actual geometry of the thigh, the long axis of the thigh $\hat{e}_{Tz}$ is not necessarily perpendicular to the approximate knee axis $\hat{e}_2$ (that is, $\hat{e}_{Ty}$ is not necessarily parallel to $\hat{e}_2$).

- The three independent angles (i.e., Euler angles) that define the orientation of the anatomical coordinate system relative to the technical coordinate system are computed and stored (to be recalled during the analysis of the motion data).

Through this subject calibration procedure, not only is the long anatomical axis of the segment approximated, but rotational offsets or marker alignment errors about the long axis are corrected for as well.

With the data from the subject calibration procedure one can use relevant anatomical references, for example, points G and H representing the location of the medial and lateral femoral condyles, which are not identified with markers during the motion trial to compute the anatomical coordinate system. Alternatively, with the subject calibration data one can align the technical coordinate system with the anatomical coordinate system through a rotational transformation using the three independent angles between the two coordinate systems. Once the anatomical coordinate system for the thigh has been found, then the three desired hip angles (flexion-extension, adduction-abduction, and internal-external rotation of the thigh relative to the pelvis) can be determined through the use of Euler angles. This process is repeated for the shank and foot to determine knee and ankle angles, respectively.

2.3.2. A Specific Clinical Example

To illustrate this kinematic data reduction process as well as the determination of the joint moments of force, the data reduction approach used in the Gait Analysis Laboratory at the Newington Children's Hospital is summarized briefly [48,49]. The laboratory currently uses a six-camera motion measurement system (Vicon) and three force platforms (AMTI). AMASS 3-D reconstruction software is used in conjunction with custom clinical output software, both of which are integrated into control software (i.e., a "shell") so as to require minimal operator interaction. While the hardware capabilities of the facility allow both bilateral (both sides simultaneously) and bidirectional (walking in both directions along a straight flat pathway) testing, the description below is limited to the right side for brevity.

The marker configuration used during the subject calibration procedure is shown in Figure 2-2. To establish an approximate knee flexion-extension axis, and to estimate the location of the knee center of rotation, either a fixture with a cluster of three markers, RK, RH, and RP, or a pair of two markers, RK and RM, is placed at the knee over the medial and lateral femoral condyles. If the knee alignment fixture is used (in cases where excessive hip adduction does not permit the use of medial knee markers), a virtual knee marker location is determined from the known geometry of the knee fixture marker cluster. The virtual knee marker location is then used along with the RK marker (on the cluster axis) to determine the approximate knee flexion-extension axis. To determine the approximate position of the ankle joint center, a pair of markers (RN and RA) is placed over the medial and lateral malleoli. The toe marker RD is placed on the dorsal aspect of the foot between the second and third metatarsal heads. In cases where the subject's feet are not plantigrade or when shoes are used, a heel marker RQ is placed on the posterior aspect of the heel so that the heel-toe marker vector is parallel to the sole of the foot. When the subject's foot is plantigrade, then a virtual heel marker location is computed directly below the ankle center at the height of the toe marker. Three markers are placed on the pelvis over the right and left ASIS and midway between the right and left PSIS. As shown, wand markers RF and

RB are securely attached to the thigh and shank as distally as possible; that is, not over large muscle masses, but with no specific anatomical alignment.

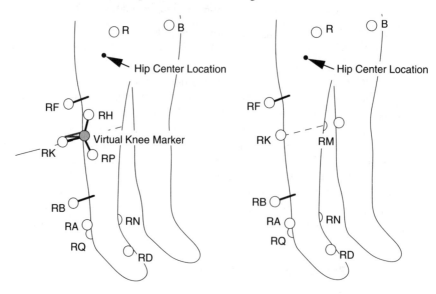

Figure 2-2. Two different options for static marker configurations used for gait analysis at the Newington Children's Hospital.

The knee and ankle joint centers are calculated to lie along the approximate knee flexion-extension axis and the RA-RN line, respectively, at a measured distance away from the lateral marker in each case. The distance is measured directly because of the asymmetries in this distance that are associated with different orthotic designs or bony deformities. The hip center location is predicted using anthropometric relationships based on pelvic data as described in R. B. Davis et al. [48]. With joint center locations estimated, long axes for the thigh and shank can be found. Then the anterior-posterior axis for each segment can be computed from the vector cross product of its long axis and the approximate knee flexion-extension axis. The medial-lateral axis for each segment is then calculated from the vector cross product of its long axis and anterior-posterior axis. This results in an orthogonal anatomical coordinate system for the thigh and shank segments. The corresponding technical coordinate system for the thigh is computed from the locations of the hip center and RF and RK markers. In a similar fashion, the RK, RB, and RA marker coordinates are used to calculate a technical coordinate system for the shank. Euler angles are employed to specify the three angles that define the spatial orientation of the anatomical coordinate system relative to the technical coordinate systems for the thigh and shank, respectively. Furthermore, the approximate ankle flexion-extension axis (defined by the RA-RN line) in terms of the shank technical coordinate system is computed and stored (to be recalled in the motion data reduction).

The foot is a particularly difficult segment to model in clinical gait analysis. The foot of a normal subject can be approximated as a rigid body with an identifiable long axis and two orthogonal transverse axes. Within the CP population, foot anatomical structure can vary significantly (e.g., varus, valgus, forefoot adductus, etc.). In children, measurement is difficult as well because small foot size in addition to deformities might limit the number and relative placement of markers on the foot. The challenge is to develop a model that works predictably well for all patients. The model shown in Figure 2-3 allows the quantification of two degrees of freedom with respect to rotation. In the static test, a heel-toe (RQ-RD) vector is used to calculate the ankle plantar/dorsiflexion angle as well as the foot rotation angle (the transverse plane rotation of the foot relative to the shank) and the foot progression angle (the transverse plane rotation of the foot relative to the laboratory fixed coordinate system). Current technological limitations do not allow the use of a heel marker during the walking trials. As an alternative, a foot (anatomical) coordinate system is calculated from the toe marker, ankle joint center, and knee joint center locations in the following way:

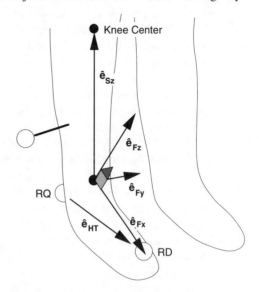

Figure 2-3. Static foot coordinate system determination used for gait analysis at the Newington Children's Hospital.

- An instantaneous flexion-extension axis for the ankle $\hat{e}_{Fy}$ is calculated from the vector cross product of the long (anatomical) axis of the shank $\hat{e}_{Sz}$, as defined by the knee and ankle center locations, and the unit vector from the ankle center to the dorsal toe marker $\hat{e}_{Fx}$. In this way, $\hat{e}_{Fy}$ is a "floating" joint axis [41] whose orientation is defined by the orientation of the longitudinal axes of the shank and foot.
- The unit vector $\hat{e}_{Fz}$ is then calculated from the vector cross product of $\hat{e}_{Fx}$ and $\hat{e}_{Fy}$.
- The heel-toe marker unit vector $\hat{e}_{HT}$ is then computed in terms of this body-fixed foot coordinate system (to be recalled for the motion data reduction).

Alignment markers RM, RN, and RQ are then removed in preparation for the motion trial. Alternatively, the knee alignment fixture and RN and RQ markers are removed, and a lateral knee marker added. Reduction of the motion data is relatively straightforward. Frame by frame, the 3-D locations of the pelvic markers allow the estimation of hip joint center location. The technical coordinate system for the thigh is then computed based on the location of hip center and thigh markers. Similarly, the shank technical coordinate system is determined based on the knee, shank wand, and ankle marker locations. The location of the ankle joint center can be calculated based on the previously stored relationship for the approximate ankle plantar-dorsiflexion axis (the RA-RN line in the static trial). The thigh and shank technical coordinate systems are then realigned (based on the static alignment angles computed in the static trial) and become the anatomical coordinate systems. The foot anatomical coordinate system is then found through the process described above and the virtual heel-toe unit vector computed.

The limb rotation algorithm is based on the determination of Euler angles with a y-x-z (or flexion-extension, adduction-abduction, and internal-external rotation) axis rotation sequence [48]. The segment and joint rotation angles that are routinely determined clinically are trunk and pelvic obliquity-tilt-rotation, hip ad/abduction-flexion/extension-rotation, knee flexion/extension, ankle plantar/dorsiflexion, and foot progression. Note that the trunk and pelvic angles are absolute angles; that is, they are referenced to the inertially fixed laboratory coordinate system. The hip, knee, and ankle angles are all relative angles; for example, the three hip angles describe the orientation of the thigh with respect to the pelvis. The foot progression angle, as described earlier, is an absolute angle, referenced to the laboratory, which indicates the position of the subject's foot with respect to the direction of forward progression. The knee ad/abduction and rotation angles are not utilized clinically because of the poor signal-to-noise ratio associated with these data [42].

It should be noted that the shank anatomical coordinate system is referenced to the approximate knee flexion-extension axis, and is therefore not influenced by (or indicative of) external tibial torsion. Specified in this way, the shank coordinate system represents the orientation of the shank at its proximal end. Clinical questions often arise regarding the movement of the foot relative to the shank in the transverse plane. This information could be provided through the determination of a distal shank coordinate system based on the orientation of the medial-lateral malleoli axis (measured during the standing data collection session). Recent research at the facility that has focused on foot dynamics has highlighted the need for a somewhat more detailed foot model. A multisegment foot model that provides information associated with heel varus-valgus and forefoot supination-pronation would be of particular interest. The work of S. M. Kidder et al. [50] and others is to be encouraged.

Paralleling the approach of B. Bresler and J. P. Frankel [51], the computation of the joint forces is a straightforward application of Newton's second law

$$\Sigma \mathbf{F} = m\mathbf{a} \qquad (2\text{-}1)$$

where $\Sigma \mathbf{F}$ = vector sum of the external forces applied to the limb segment (e.g., segment weight and ground reaction forces),
  m = segment mass, and
  $\mathbf{a}$ = linear acceleration of the center of mass of the segment.

Joint moments are then computed through the application of Euler's equations of motion [40], used widely for the description of the rotational motion of a rigid body, and written as follows:

$$\Sigma M_x = I_{xx}\alpha_x + (I_{zz} - I_{yy})\omega_z\omega_y$$
$$\Sigma M_y = I_{yy}\alpha_y + (I_{xx} - I_{zz})\omega_x\omega_z \qquad (2\text{-}2)$$
$$\Sigma M_z = I_{zz}\alpha_z + (I_{yy} - I_{xx})\omega_y\omega_x$$

where ΣM_x, ΣM_y, ΣM_z = components of the sum of the external moments applied to the limb segment (e.g., the foot),

$\alpha_x, \alpha_y, \alpha_z$ = components of the absolute angular acceleration of the body segment,

$\omega_x, \omega_y, \omega_z$ = components of the absolute angular velocity of the body segment, and

I_{xx}, I_{yy}, I_{zz} = principal mass moments of inertia of the limb segment.

The body-fixed anatomical coordinate axes are chosen such that they are approximately aligned with the principal axes of the segment and are embedded at the center of mass of the segment. Figure 2-4 illustrates the data required for this computation as well as the overall structure of the process.

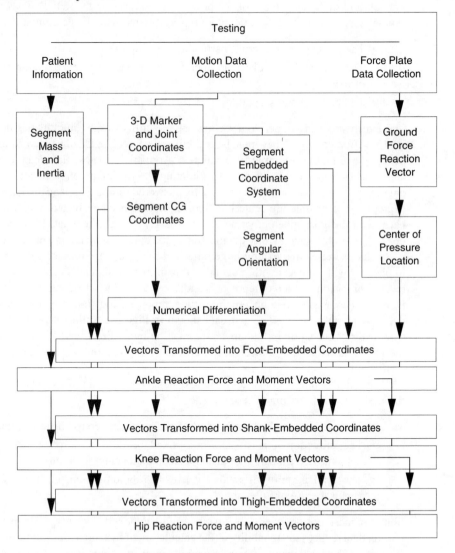

Figure 2-4. Data flow for the joint moment calculation.

Joint power can then be computed for each joint through the vector dot product of the joint angular velocity and the associated joint moment. For example, at the ankle,

$$P_{ankle} = \omega_{ankle} \cdot M_{ankle} \tag{2-3}$$

$$= \omega_{ankle|x} M_{ankle|x} + \omega_{ankle|y} M_{ankle|y} + \omega_{ankle|z} M_{ankle|z} \tag{2-4}$$

While joint power is a scalar quantity and in strictest mechanical terms one is limited to a discussion of total joint power, at the Newington laboratory, each of the three terms on the right side of Equation (2-4) are plotted individually. In this way, the joint power contributions (to the total joint power) produced in each of the joint planes can be assessed and better appreciated.

Although the amount of data associated with the calculation of joint kinetics is substantial, and the management of the process is tedious, the theoretical basis is relatively simple. The challenge of the computation is associated with the determination of:

- The joint center locations, particularly the hip [47]
- The mass and mass distribution properties of each segment (e.g., the mass moment of inertia [52])
- The first (ω) and second (a, α) derivatives [53,54]

These difficulties affect but do not eliminate the utility of the joint kinetics in the clinical interpretation process. They must be recognized, appreciated, and used to balance the tendency to overinterpret joint kinetic patterns. Arguably the most significant concern listed above deals with the uncertainty of estimating the hip joint center location. This is an ongoing problem that cannot be universally answered through statistically based predictive expressions. Dynamic hip centering algorithms have been evaluated with limited success because of the noise inherently found in the marker displacement data [55]. While A. Cappozzo [39,44] has successfully demonstrated this approach by having his subjects perform particular exercises that exhibit large ranges of motion, these protocols can be difficult to implement with subjects with movement impairment. Clinicians need to be aware of the level of precision that a plot represents and know when the data cannot be used at all; that is, when there exists great uncertainty in the hip center location (e.g., dislocated hips and pelvic bony deformity). The gait data shown in Figure 2-5 illustrates the effect of a ±1 centimeter perturbation of the hip center location in all directions. While the precision of the results is reduced as expected, the clinical interpretation value of the data is largely unaffected.

One finds a number of issues related to the collection and processing of gait data under discussion in the literature. These include:

- The use of individually placed (discrete) markers versus clusters of markers
- The estimation of quasi-static, body-fixed locations (as described above) versus the dynamic determination of instantaneous joint center locations
- The application of instantaneous axes of rotation (computed from dynamic data) versus the use of Euler angles

Some of these options were not practical until relatively recently. For example, noisy motion data reduces the reliability of the calculation of instantaneous joint centers and axes of rotation. Other debates remain largely a matter of choice because both alternatives in question have limitations. For example, discrete markers can be placed on the subject so as to maximize the distance between markers (and increase the precision of a measurement),

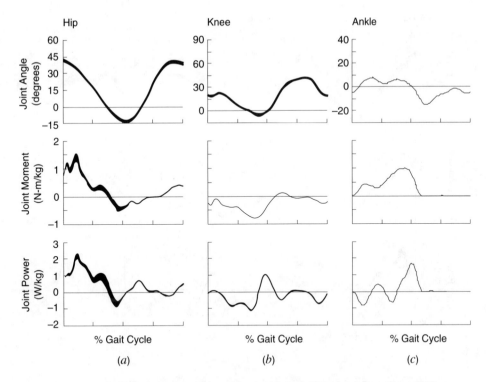

Figure 2-5. Sagittal plane kinematics and kinetics illustrating the effects of hip center location perturbation through a random ±10-mm displacement of the hip center. (*a*) Hip, (*b*) knee, and (*c*) ankle.

but the markers can move relative to each other. Rigidly connected clusters of markers are less subject to relative marker displacement, but intermarker distances are generally reduced (thereby decreasing the precision of the measurement). The effectiveness of both approaches is affected by the fact that the markers are attached to soft tissue masses that move relative to the underlying bony structure during locomotion [56]. Again, with respect to clinical interpretation, it is important that the potential for artifact be recognized and appreciated (Figure 2-6).

This brief description of the gait data reduction process provides an outline of the steps; it cannot adequately address the many details associated with the task. The reader is referred to the very complete reference text edited by N. Berme and A. Cappozzo [57] for more information on gait data acquisition and processing.

2.3.3. Two-Dimensional versus Three-Dimensional Data Collection and Reduction

All of the methods described above have been fully 3-D. In general, however, 2-D motion data reduction methods have been employed when the motion is assumed to be planar to reduce the complexity of the data collection and reduction processes. With respect to clinical gait analysis, the application of 2-D motion measurement systems rep-

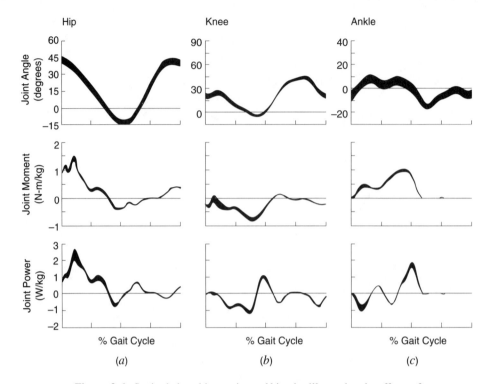

Figure 2-6. Sagittal plane kinematics and kinetics illustrating the effects of measurement and skin movement artifact through a random ±4-mm displacement of all lower extremity and pelvic markers. (*a*) Hip, (*b*) knee, and (*c*) ankle.

resents a concern. These systems are attractive to the clinical consumer because they are commonly easier to use (for example, the number of markers that can be used is limited and therefore the speed of data collection can increase) and less expensive than the more sophisticated systems. The lack of research that compares quantitatively 2-D and 3-D clinical gait analysis approaches further exacerbates the situation.

Two-dimensional gait data, typically acquired by a camera viewing the subject from one side, represents the projection of data onto a viewing plane. In this way, one cannot assess the out-of-plane motion of reference points that arise during this activity. For example, normal knee motion during gait can be considered primarily a planar movement if one views the joint motion along the flexion-extension axis of the knee. If this joint plane is not parallel to the viewing plane of the camera, then a distortion will be introduced (Figure 2-7). As the triangle representing the thigh and shank is rotated about the vertical axis, the constant knee angle appears to decrease.

R. B. Davis [58] reported on a preliminary investigation to examine the differences in 2-D and 3-D gait analysis results, specifically with respect to the computation of joint rotation angles. The 2-D approach that was used in the study was consistent with that described by D. A. Winter [59]. Normal and pathologic subjects were used for comparison. Nine subjects whose locomotion was considered normal, that is, with no history of

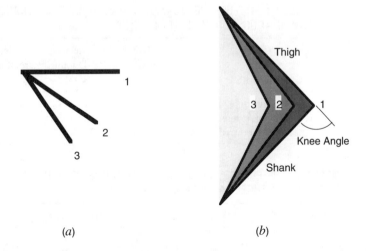

(a)   (b)

Figure 2-7. (*a*) Transverse plane view and (*b*) sagittal plane view. Out-of-plane motion artifact illustrations showing the "apparent" change in the knee angle (as viewed in the sagittal plane) as the plane is rotated about a vertical axis from point 1 to 2 to 3. Note: the true knee angle (seen in position 1) is actually unchanged as the plane is rotated from point 1 to 3.

gait-related orthopaedic difficulties, were studied. In addition, 10 subjects with varying gait impairment were selected so as to be representative of the population that is typically seen at the Newington Children's Hospital gait analysis laboratory.

For the group of normal subjects, the mean RMS difference between the 3-D joint angle and the 2-D joint angle was determined over a gait cycle for each subject's hip, knee, and ankle. These individual results were then averaged to form the group mean differences presented in Table 2-1. The mean joint angle differences are also expressed as relative percent difference values; in other words, relative to the respective joint range of motion (ROM). As might be anticipated, the hip and knee flexion/extension angles were most consistent between the two methods; that is, the smallest relative effect was realized by out-of-plane motion. The ankle plantar-dorsiflexion angle demonstrated the most sensitivity to method selection with a mean RMS difference of almost 5 degrees over a mean range of motion of approximately 27 degrees with a mean relative difference of over 18 percent. This difference is attributed to the fact that unimpaired subjects walk with an external foot progression angle of approximately 10 degrees. In the context of these preliminary findings, the large volume of literature associated with normal gait can perhaps be more objectively assessed. Clearly, 2-D ankle kinematic findings should be consumed cautiously.

Three patients were also selected to illustrate the differences that result from these two different methods (Table 2-2). As anticipated, the results illustrate the adverse effects of the out-of-plane movement of the patients on the 2-D computation. The tabulated mean relative differences are significant and highly variable; for example, ranging from 19 percent to 400 percent for ankle plantar/dorsiflexion. Figure 2-8 illustrates the difference with

TABLE 2-1 DIFFERENCE IN 3-D AND 2-D METHODS OF JOINT ANGLE COMPUTATION: NORMAL GAIT (N = 9)

	Mean RMS difference	Mean 3-D joint ROM	Mean relative % difference
Hip flexion/extension	2° ± 1°	41° ± 5°	5% ± 2%
Knee flexion/extension	3° ± 1°	58° ± 7°	5% ± 2%
Ankle plantar/dorsiflexion	5° ± 2°	27° ± 4°	18% ± 7%

TABLE 2-2 DIFFERENCE IN 3-D AND 2-D METHODS OF JOINT ANGLE COMPUTATION: THREE CASES OF IMPAIRED GAIT

Case 1: A 5-year-old male with a diagnosis of cerebral plasy, spastic diplegia

	Mean RMS difference	3-D joint ROM	Mean relative % difference
Hip flexion/extension	3° ± 5°	44°	6% ± 12%
Knee flexion/extension	2° ± 2°	44°	4% ± 5%
Ankle plantar/dorsiflexion	30° ± 12°	8°	400% ± 160%

Case 2: A 10-year-old female with a diagnosis of cerebral plasy, spastic hemiplegia

	Mean RMS difference	3-D joint ROM	Mean relative % difference
Hip flexion/extension	2° ± 3°	45°	5% ± 7%
Knee flexion/extension	8° ± 16°	44°	18% ± 36%
Ankle plantar/dorsiflexion	9° ± 6°	26°	35% ± 21%

Case 3: A 10-year-old male with a diagnosis of cerebral plasy, spastic diplegia

	Mean RMS difference	3-D joint ROM	Mean relative % difference
Hip flexion/extension	3° ± 5°	28°	10% ± 17%
Knee flexion/extension	2° ± 4°	18°	11% ± 20%
Ankle plantar/dorsiflexion	4° ± 2°	22°	19% ± 11%

respect to the joint kinetic results that a comparison of the two methods produces. While these plots represent the data for only a single patient, they do show that one can expect that the distortion associated with a 2-D method kinematics extends to the 2-D kinetic analysis as well. Through this brief comparison, one can reach the conclusion that the 2-D methods of data collection and reduction introduce significant distortions when used in patient gait evaluation.

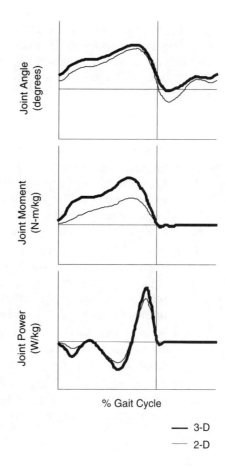

Figure 2-8. Two-dimensional versus 3-D
gait model comparison.

—— 3-D
—— 2-D

2.4. FUTURE DIRECTIONS FOR GAIT ANALYSIS

The future of clinical gait analysis can be anticipated at three different levels. The potential for innovation and change can be arguably "over the horizon," "just down the road," and "knocking at the door." The gait community has a tendency to become enthralled with exotic tools that can capture their collective imagination. These "over the horizon" developments might still be years away from practical clinical application, but practitioners look excitedly to their implementation and routine use with a "sooner" rather than "later" perspective without fully appreciating all of the technical aspects that remain to be addressed.

An excellent example of this dilemma is the simulation of gait-related surgeries. It is exciting to visualize the surgeon at a personal computer electronically manipulating the soft tissue of her or his graphical patient, and then watching as that patient ambulates across the display "postoperatively." There is a natural attractiveness to this scenario from a number of perspectives; for example, the ability to test different surgical protocols and the potential for improved outcome as well as the technical challenge of bringing together all of the required technologies. In spite of this attractiveness, the practical implementation of surgical simulation is a number of years away for several reasons. As shown in Figure 2-9, the simulation of surgery requires the effort of many investigators in a number of areas; for example:

- Significant improvement in the quality of the gait data collected clinically with a corresponding refinement of the "inverse dynamic approach" (as was described above)

- Enhancement of the forward dynamic simulation models so that they can better tolerate the relative imprecision of the clinical data (Currently, forward simulation models cannot accept the clinical results of the inverse dynamic approach, e.g., joint kinetics to produce the observed joint and segmental kinematics, termed by F. E. Zajac [60] as *inverse dynamics simulation failure.*)

- More reliable and individualized estimates of subject anthropometric values, (e.g., segment mass and mass moment of inertia) that can be obtained as part of the clinical gait analysis process without significantly increasing the expense of the process; for example, by requiring complete magnetic resonance imaging records of each segment to determine inertial properties

- A better knowledge of both normal and, particularly, abnormal muscle function; for example, the relationship between muscle force and electromyographic signal amplitude for a spastic muscle

- The quantification of surgical techniques well beyond the current standards; for example, a documentation of the biomechanical effects of lengthening a hamstring muscle by three "stripes" as opposed to two

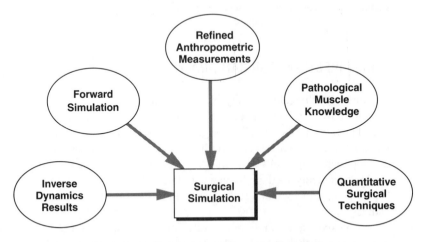

Figure 2-9. Input required for a surgical simulation.

The "just down the road" evolution of clinical gait analysis consists of efforts that are much closer to impacting current clinical gait analysis practices. It is anticipated that in the next several years, clinical gait analysis will begin to incorporate the products of work in:

- Pattern recognition techniques using approaches such as principle component analysis [61,62] or clustering analysis [63] that go well beyond the clinical efforts realized to date [64]
- Graphical visualization tools that allow the practitioner to better inspect a gait abnormality, such as those developed by S. L. Delp [65] and others
- Forward simulation modeling as described above
- Coupled dynamic analysis (e.g., D. A. Meglan [66]), to allow the consideration of how the kinematics of a particular joint are affected by the joint kinetics produced at other joints well away from the joint of interest

The most immediate needs of clinical gait analysis, that is, the future that is "knocking at our door," are associated with:

- A need for further improvement in the quality data collected; for example, careful validation of commercial products, ongoing quality control efforts in practicing laboratories, more repeatable placement of body markers, and a better understanding of the underlying gait models
- More consistent display conventions and descriptive terminology to enhance communication between clinical groups
- More definitive research that clarifies the utility of gait analysis in the clinical setting

The validity of a commercially available measurement tool cannot be assumed either at time of purchase or after an extended period of use. From a development perspective, it is not difficult to fabricate a measurement tool that produces an output that is in some way related to the input. New technologies must be rigorously tested with normal input as well as a wide array of pathologies. The gait measurement system must be tested routinely to evaluate accuracy and to confirm the required precision. With respect to motion measurement systems, examples of quality control exercises include:

- Static marker location: The comparison of camera system measures with known values
- Falling ball motion: The comparison with projectile motion theory, and computation of the gravitational constant
- Pendulum motion: The comparison with theory, for example, displacement, velocity, and acceleration
- Motorized rotating (constant velocity) platforms: The measurement of linear and angular velocities (advantageous because one is able to produce higher amplitudes than with a pendulum, but more costly and complicated)
- A small rod with two or more markers: The comparison of known and measured intermarker distance

Examples of validation tests that assess the force platforms include:

- Static weights at known platform locations
- Heavy rolling ball: Examination of force plate data, for example, center of pressure location
- Loaded "stick": a static load applied by a rod with two markers along its long axis to the force platform (The markers create a vector that should parallel the ground

reaction force vector. The tip of the rod should be coincident with the center of pressure of the force plate.)

Examples of validation exercises that test the timing and spatial relationships of the motion and force platform systems include:

- Falling ball motion
- Pendulum motion (base anchored to the force platform)
- Heavy rolling ball

The gait of normal ambulatory subjects should be periodically assessed and compared with previously collected data and results found in the literature. New facilities should test a minimum of 20 normal subjects to confirm measurement integrity before the start of routine clinical use.

Even after a system has demonstrated its validity and reliability, one must anticipate that the next patient will confound a measurement strategy or a data reduction algorithm, or the technology will fail and yet still produce a reasonably convincing result. The hip moment and power artifact shown in Figure 2-10 was produced after incidental contact between the swing limb and the stance limb. This artifact was identified before the interpretation process because the personnel involved in the data collection possessed a detailed understanding of the underlying gait models, and they remain vigilant to the potential for data corruption.

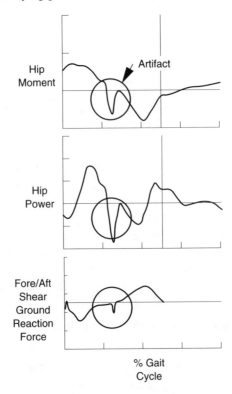

Figure 2-10. Example of joint moment artifact due to the swing limb contacting the stance limb at approximately 30% of the gait cycle.

Another aspect of clinical gait analysis that needs to be addressed in the very near future pertains to the development of more consistent display conventions and terminology. The knee moment plots shown in Figure 2-11 demonstrate this need. The same knee moment data are displayed in four different ways; as an internal moment representing the body's response to an external load, and as an external moment representing the applied external load, each with stance phase followed by swing phase, and vice versa. Clearly, the pattern associated with each set of these identical data is different. The counterproductivity of this problem is apparent when one comes to understand that qualitative pattern recognition underpins the current approach to clinical gait interpretation. Standards are essential in these areas to improve the gait knowledge base through enhanced communication between practitioners and data sharing among laboratories, as well as to more effectively communicate the test results of a particular patient to the referring physician.

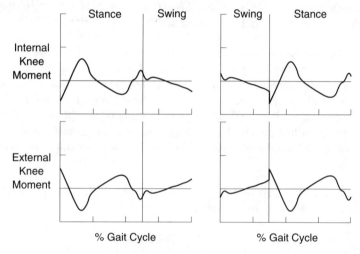

Figure 2-11. A comparison of four different display conventions for the knee moment.

The evolution of clinical gait analysis is at a crossroads. In the next five years, the clinical use of gait analysis could expand, the techniques could be refined to yield more precise information, and our knowledge of gait mechanics could rise to a new level, or clinical gait analysis might be stymied by an ambiguity of mission and definition. To succeed, we must address the immediate needs of clinical gait analysis by continuing to pay attention to the details of clinical data collection and by understanding better the gait models that we use. More definitive research to better define the utility of clinical gait analysis is needed immediately.

In looking at the current status of clinical gait analysis as well as its future, it is useful to remain mindful of perspectives developed over a decade ago. R. A. Brand and R. D. Crowninshield [67] outlined a list of requirements for the effective use of clinical gait analysis. During the past 13 years, advancements in technology and clinical protocols have produced positive results with respect to the noninvasiveness of the measurement approach and the accuracy and reproducibility of the data (although work remains to be done in this regard). Interpretation emphasis has moved beyond the sagittal plane to the coronal and transverse planes, where parameters are much more difficult to appreciate by observation alone. Certainly, the beginnings of the use of kinetic data in clinical gait interpretations (as described by Õunpuu in this text) provides information that cannot be quantified or appreciated with observational gait analysis alone. With respect to the other points made by Brand and Crowninshield, further understanding, effort, and development are needed:

- The measured parameter(s) must correlate well with the patient's functional capability.
- The measured parameters must clearly distinguish between normal and abnormal.
- The results must be communicated in a form which is readily identifiable in a physical or physiological analog.

For example, while the kinematics and kinetics associated with normal ambulators has been well documented [68], a more complete understanding of what is normal for a child with locomotive impairments is needed. Also 10 years ago, A. Cappozzo [69] offered a challenge with respect to the overall assessment of gait:

> We biomechanicians have been working hard, during the last decades, designing new instruments and experimental methodologies, applying old analytical techniques to our new problems. We have been gathering a great deal of numbers regarding the various aspects of human locomotion. Now, I think, more efforts should be devoted to speculation. We should try to identify, through generalization of single observations, the laws that govern them. ... [Biomechanical research] must overcome the stage where it supplies information about how man walks and begin to answer the relevant whys.

This statement is still absolutely relevant today as we face the immediate needs of clinical gait analysis and look to the future.

References

[1] Sutherland DH, Olshen RA, Biden EN, Wyatt MP. *The Development of Mature Walking.* London: MacKeith Press;1988.

[2] Perry J. *Gait Analysis: Normal and Pathological Function.* Thorofare, NJ: Slack, Inc.; 1992.

[3] Gage JR. *Gait Analysis in Cerebral Palsy.* London: MacKeith Press;1991.

[4] DeLuca PA. Cerebral palsy. In *The Child's Foot and Ankle*, Drennan JC ed. New York, NY: Raven Press, Ltd.;1992.

[5] Õunpuu S, Muik E, Davis RB, Gage JR, DeLuca PA. Part I: The effect of the rectus femoris transfer location on knee motion in children with cerebral palsy. *J Ped Orthop* 1993;13(3):325–330.

[6] Sutherland DH, Santi M, Abel MF. Treatment of stiff-knee gait in cerebral palsy: A comparison by gait analysis of distal rectus femoris transfer versus proximal rectus release. *J Ped Orthop* 1990;10(4):433–441.

[7] Õunpuu S, Muik E, Davis RB, Gage JR, DeLuca PA. Part II: A comparison of the distal rectus femoris transfer and release on knee motion in children with cerebral palsy. *J Ped Orthop* 1993;13(3):331–335.

[8] Thometz J, Simon S, Rosenthal R. The effect on gait of lengthening of the medial hamstrings in cerebral palsy. *J Bone Joint Surg Am* 1989;71(3):345–353.

[9] Segal LS, Thomas SE, Mazur JM, Mauterer M. Calcaneal gait in spastic diplegia after heel cord lengthening: A study with gait analysis. *J Ped Orthop* 1989;9(6):697–701.

[10] Rose SA, DeLuca PA, Davis RB, Õunpuu S, Gage JR. Kinematic and kinetic evaluation of the ankle following lengthening of the gastrocnemius fascia in children with cerebral palsy. *J Ped Orthop* 1993;13(6):727–732.

[11] Tylkowski CM, Rosenthal RK, Simon SR. Proximal femoral osteotomy in cerebral palsy. *Clin Orthop* 1980;151:183–192.

[12] Vittas D, Jansen EC, Larsen TK. Gait analysis before and after osteotomy for hallux valgus. *Foot and Ankle* 1987;8(3):134–136.

[13] Wang JW, Kuo KN, Andriacchi TP, Galante JO. The influence of walking mechanics and time on the results of proximal tibial osteotomy. *J Bone Joint Surg Am* 1990;72(6):905–909.

[14] Vaughan CL, Berman B, Peacock WJ. Gait analysis of spastic children before and after selective lumbar rhizotomy. *Dev Med Child Neurol* 1987;29(5):25.

[15] Boscarino LF, Õunpuu S, Davis RB, Gage JR, DeLuca PA. The effects of selective dorsal rhizotomy on gait in children with cerebral palsy. *J Ped Orthop* 1993;13:174–179.

[16] Thomas SE, Mazur JM, Child ME, Supan TJ. Quantitative evaluation of AFO use with myelomeningocele children. *Zeitschrift fur Kinderchirurgie (Stuttgart)* 1989;44(supp 1):38–40.

[17] Olney SJ, Monga TN, Costigan PA. Mechanical energy of walking of stroke patients. *Arch Phys Med Rehabil* 1986;67(2):92–98.

[18] Blin O, Ferrandez AM, Serratrice, G. Quantitative analysis of gait in Parkinson patients: Increased variability of stride length. *J Neurol Sci* 1990;98(1):91–97.

[19] Maynard FM. Post-polio sequelae—Differential diagnosis and management. *J Orthop* 1985;8(3):355–361.

[20] Hurley GR, McKenney R, Robinson M, Zadravec M, Pierrynowski MR. The role of the contralateral limb in below-knee amputee gait. *Prosthetics and Orthotics International* 1990;14(1):33–42.

[21] Whittle M. *Gait Analysis: An Introduction.* Oxford, England: Butterworth-Heinemann Ltd; 1991.

[22] Davis RB. Clinical gait analysis. *Proc IEEE Eng Med Bio* 1988;7(3):35–40.

[23] Woltring HJ, Huiskes R. Stereophotography. In: *Biomechanics of Human Movement: Applications in Rehabilitation, Sports and Ergonomics.* Worthington, Ohio: Bertec Corporation;1990:263–274.

[24] Kadaba MP, Wootten ME, Ramakrishnan HK, Hurwitz D, Cochran GVB. Assessment of human motion with Vicon. *Proc Biomech Symp* New York, NY: ASME;1987: 335–338.

[25] Campbell KR. ExpertVision—Data acquisition and analysis. *Proc Biomech Symp* New York, NY: ASME;1987:331–333.

[26] Andriacchi TP. Clinical applications of the Selspot system. *Proc Biomech Symp* New York, NY: ASME;1987:339–342.

[27] Rowell D, Mann RW. A benchmark with which to compare commercially available data processing methods. In: *Gangbildanlyse: Stand der Mebtechnik und Bedeutung fur die Orthopadie-Technik.* Boenick U, Nader M eds. Duderstadt, Germany: Mecke Druck und Verlag;1990:150–165.

[28] Sutherland DH, Hagy JL. Measurement of gait movements from motion picture film. *J Bone Joint Surg Am* 1972;54:787–797.

[29] Chao EY. Justification of triaxial goniometer for the measurement of joint rotation. *J Biomech* 1980;13:989–1006.

[30] Morris JR. Accelerometry in gait analysis. *Br J Surg* 1972;59(11):899.

[31] Waters RL, Morris J, Perry J. Translational motion of the head and trunk during normal walking. *J Biomech* 1973;6(2):167–172.

[32] Ladin Z, Wu G. Combining position and acceleration measurements for joint force estimation. *J Biomech* 1991;24(12):1173–1187.

[33] Cavanagh PR. A technique for averaging center of pressure paths from a force platform. *J Biomech* 1978;11(10–12):487–491.

[34] Miyazaki S, Takeuchi T, Iwakura H, Kubota T. Data processing of vertical foot forces for the clinical assessment of pathological gait. *Med Bio Eng Comp* 1983;21(6): 664–673.

[35] Cavanagh PR, Hennig EM, Rodgers MM, Sanderson DJ. The measurement of pressure distribution on the plantar surface of diabetic feet. In: Whittle M, Harris D, eds. *Biomechanical Measurement in Orthopaedic Practice.* Oxford, England: Clarendon Press;1985:159–166.

[36] Perry J, Bontrager E, Antonelli D. Footswitch definition of basic gait characteristics. In: Kenedi RM, Paul JP, Hughes J, eds. *Disability. Strathclyde Bioengineering Seminars.* London: MacMillan Press; 1979:131–135.

[37] Tyburski DJ, Davis RB, DeLuca PA. Initial contact and toe-off: A comparison of measurement technologies. In: *Proc 8th Annual East Coast Clinical Gait Laboratory Conf.* 1993:129–130.

[38] Chen JJ, Shiavi R. Temporal feature extraction and clustering analysis of electromyographic linear envelopes in gait studies. *IEEE Trans Biomed Eng* 1990;37(3):295–302.

[39] Cappozzo A. Gait analysis methodology. *Hum Mvmt Sci* 1984;3:27–50.

[40] Greenwood DT. *Principles of Dynamics.* Englewood Cliffs, NJ: Prentice-Hall, Inc.; 1965.

[41] Grood ES, Suntay WJ. A joint coordinate system for the clinical description of three-dimensional motions: Application to the knee. *J Biomech Eng* 1983;105(2):136–144.

[42] Kadaba MP, Ramakrishnan HK, Wootten ME. Measurement of lower extremity kinematics during level walking. *J Orthop Res* 1990;8(2):383–392.

[43] Berme N. Control and movement of lower limbs. In: *Biomechanics of Motion,* Morecki A, ed. New York, NY: Springer-Verlag;1980:185–217.

[44] Cappozzo A, Gazzani F. Joint kinematic assessment during physical exercise. In: *Biomechanics of Human Movement: Applications in Rehabilitation, Sports and Ergonomics,* Worthington, Ohio: Bertec Corporation; 1990:263–274.

[45] Tylkowski CM, Simon SR, Mansour JM. Internal rotation gait in spastic cerebral palsy in the hip. In: Nelson JP, ed. *Proc 10th Open Scientific Meeting of the Hip Society,* St Louis, Mo: Mosby Company; 1982:89–125.

[46] Andriacchi TP, Strickland AB. Gait analysis as a tool to assess joint kinetics. In: *Proc NATO Advanced Study Institute Biomechanics of Normal and Pathological Articulating Joints* 1983:83–102.

[47] Bell AL, Pederson DR, Brand RA. Prediction of hip joint center location from external landmarks. *Hum Mvmt Sci* 1989;8:3–16.

[48] Davis RB, Õunpuu S, Tyburski DJ, Gage JR. A gait analysis data collection and reduction technique. *Hum Mvmt Sci* 1991;10(5):575–587.

[49] Rose SA, Õunpuu S, DeLuca PA. Strategies for the assessment of pediatric gait in the clinical setting. *Phys Ther* 1991;71(12):961–980.

[50] Kidder SM, Harris GF, Johnson JE, Abuzzahab FS. A kinematic model for clinical description of foot and ankle motion. in *Proc 8th Annual East Coast Clinical Gait Laboratory Conf* 1993:111–112.

[51] Bresler B, Frankel JP. The forces and moments in the leg during level walking. *Trans ASME* 1950;72:27–36.

[52] Berme N, Cappozzo A. Subject-specific segmental inertia parameter determination— A survey of current methods. In: *Biomechanics of Human Movement: Applications in Rehabilitation, Sports and Ergonomics.* Worthington, Ohio: Bertec Corporation; 1990:179–185.

[53] Andrews BJ, Cappozzo A, Gazzani F. A quantitative method for assessment of differentiation techniques for motion analysis. In: Paul JP, Jordan MM, Ferguson-Pell MW, Andrews BJ, eds. *Computing in Medicine*, London: MacMillan Press;1981: 146–154.

[54] Lanshammar H. On practical evaluation of differentiation techniques for human gait analysis. *J Biomech* 1982;15(2):99–105.

[55] Stivers K, Tylkowski CM, Howell V. Prediction of the hip joint center location from the relative motion between the thigh and pelvis. In: *Proc 6th Annual East Coast Gait Conf*; 1990:72–74.

[56] Lafortune MA, Cavanagh PR. The measurement of normal knee joint motion during walking using intracortical pins. In: Whittle M, Harris D, eds. *Biomechanical Measurement in Orthopaedic Practice* Oxford, England: Clarendon Press;1985: 234–243.

[57] Berme N, Cappozzo A. eds. *Biomechanics of Human Movement: Applications in Rehabilitation, Sports and Ergonomics*, Worthington, Ohio: Bertec Corp:1990.

[58] Davis RB, Õunpuu S, Tyburski DJ, DeLuca PA. A comparison of two-dimensional and three-dimensional techniques for the determination of joint rotation angles. In: *Proc Int Symp on 3-D Anal of Human Mvmt* 1991:67–70.

[59] Winter DA. *Biomechanics and Motor Control of Human Movement.* New York, NY: John Wiley and Sons, Inc.; 1990.

[60] Zajac FE. Muscle coordination of movement: A perspective. *J Biomech* 1993;26(supp 1):109–124.

[61] Wooten ME, Kadaba MP, Cochran GV. Dynamic electromyography I: Numerical representation using principle component analysis. *J Orthop Res* 1990;8(2):247–258.

[62] Wooten ME, Kadaba MP, Cochran GV. Dynamic electromyography II: Normal patterns during gait. *J Orthop Res* 1990;8(2):259–265.

[63] Wong MA, Simon S, Olshen RA. Statistical analysis of gait patterns of persons with cerebral palsy. *Statistics in Medicine* 1983;2:345–354.

[64] Winters TF, Gage JR, Hicks R. Gait patterns in spastic hemiplegia in children and young adults. *J Bone Joint Surg Am* 1987;69(3):437–441.

[65] Delp SL. *Surgery Simulation: A Computer Graphics System to Analyze and Design Musculoskeletal Reconstructions of the Lower Limb*, Stanford, Calif: Stanford University, 1990: Ph.D. Dissertation.

[66] Meglan DA. Enhanced Analysis of Human Locomotion, Colombus: Ohio State University, 1991: Ph.D. Dissertation.

[67] Brand RA, Crowninshield RD. Comment on criteria for patient evaluation tools. *J Biomech* 1981;14:655.

[68] Õunpuu S, Gage JR, Davis RB. Three-dimensional lower extremity joint kinetics in normal pediatric gait. *J Ped Orthop* 1991;11:341–349.

[69] Cappozzo A. Considerations on clinical gait evaluation. *J Biomech* 1983;16:302.

Larry W. Lamoreux

Chapter 3

Coping with Soft Tissue Movement in Human Motion Analysis

3.1. INTRODUCTION

Measurements of torso and limb-segment motions are finding ever wider use in the analysis of athletic performance, in the diagnosis of motor dysfunction, and in the assessment of treatments for such dysfunction. Since the pioneering work of W. Braune and O. Fischer [1] in Germany starting in 1895, a multitude of techniques have been devised to measure motions of the human body. Some of these techniques are now embodied in well-defined products that can be purchased for routine use in athletic or rehabilitation environments. All these motion measurement systems rely upon reference markers of some kind that are attached to the body. The measurement systems typically measure reference marker motions, and from these infer the motions of the body. The accuracy of such an inference clearly depends on how accurately the reference markers move together with their respective body segments.

In most cases, what people really want to know is the motion of the skeleton. Anatomic joint motions occur between adjacent bones, and the determination of these joint motions is one of the principal goals of human motion analysis. In the interest of accurate measurements, a few daring researchers have mounted reference markers on steel pins that have been drilled into subjects' bones, but routine measurements invariably rely on markers that are mounted on the skin.

In a typical gait analysis, the lower limbs are treated as if they consisted of three rigid segments each, connected at ankles and knees and attached to a rigid pelvis at the hips [2]. Reference markers must be placed on each of these seven body segments to allow the position of each segment to be estimated, either in relation to the room or in relation to the adjacent segment. Many different combinations of reference markers, or *marker sets*, have

43

been devised to balance the desire for high measurement accuracy against the practical need for simple procedures that are feasible to use on a routine basis.

Enough markers must be attached to the subject to make it possible to define an "embedded coordinate system" in every body segment that is to be measured [3]. If three-dimensional (3-D) measurements are desired, then each body segment must have at least three reference markers that move with it. For two-dimensional (2-D) measurements, such as flexion-extension measurements in the plane of progression, only two markers are required on each segment.

In the choice of a marker set, simplicity must be given a high priority. The measurement procedure must be acceptably simple both for the person who is being measured and for the person who will process the data. Experience shows that an overly complicated procedure won't be used very much.

On the other hand, the marker set must contain enough reference markers to achieve the desired goals of measurement. As noted above, three or more markers must be attached to each body segment if it is to be tracked as a rigid body in 3-D space. In practice, that rule might require more markers than can be managed easily, either by the subject or by the measurement system. In choosing a marker set, then, compromises are almost always made to reduce the total number of markers or to prevent any two markers from coming too close to each other. For example, the same lateral knee marker might be assumed to be a marker on both the thigh and the shank, or a lateral ankle marker might be relocated a measured distance up the shank to keep it farther away from the heel marker.

Even though current measurement technologies still place limits on how many markers can be used at one time, or how close together two markers can be before they appear to merge into one, it is nevertheless true that all of the modern measurement systems have become so accurate that their limitations have ceased to be a serious threat to accuracy of human motion measurement. The greatest threat to accurate measurements is the inescapable fact that the body segments to be measured are not "rigid bodies" [4–8].

Depending on what technique is used for measurement, the reference markers that are attached to the body might be visible targets, blinking or continuously illuminated lights, retro-reflectors, magnetic coils, or coupling points for electrical output transducers. In every case, however, the critical tasks are the same: first, to attach reference markers to the skin in such a way that they move as accurately as possible with the underlying bone; and second, to define where adjacent joint centers or axes are located in relation to the reference markers. A related task is to reposition each marker as accurately as possible in the same place, relative to the underlying bone, on remeasurement of the same subject or on measurement of a different subject [5,9,10].

In view of the generally high state of development of current measurement technology, and the unalterably flexible nature of the soft tissues that cover the human skeleton, the central focus for further improvements in the accuracy of human motion measurement must be to devise marker systems that move more accurately, or more predictably, with the underlying bones.

3.2. SIGNIFICANCE OF SOFT TISSUE MOVEMENT

Movements of skin-mounted reference markers in relation to the underlying bones constitute errors. These *skin motion errors* can be insignificant, troublesome, or lethal, depending on the objective of the measurements. The significance of skin motion errors will be discussed in relation to three common measurement objectives: calculation of angular motions between adjacent body segments, calculation of moments and powers at joints, and calculation of the locations of joint axes.

3.2.1. Calculation of Joint Angles

If all that is desired is a measurement of relative angular positions between body segments, there is no theoretical requirement to know where the joint centers are. As long as each body segment has three markers mounted on it, and someone has defined the orientation of each segment's embedded coordinate system in relation to these three markers and the anatomy of the segment, then the relative angular positions between segments can be calculated. In practice, however, it might be simpler to place markers over estimated joint center locations, for two reasons. First, one marker then serves two segments and thereby reduces the total number of markers required. Second, the marker defines the presumed location of the joint axis that joins the two segments and hence can help to define the orientation of the embedded coordinate system in each segment.

Skin motion errors are manageable for most measurements of joint angles. In most cases, skin motion errors translate directly into joint angle errors. To be more precise, the skin motion errors of concern are those that give rise to relative *angular* motions between the embedded coordinate system and the corresponding underlying bones. Skin motion errors that give rise to *translation* errors of the embedded coordinate system do not degrade joint angle measurements.

Pelvis. For an estimate of the size of hip angle measurement errors due to skin motion errors on the pelvis, consider the following example. Palpation of bony prominences on a slender subject indicates that the skin over the anterior superior iliac spine (ASIS) moves cephalad about 4 mm when the hip is flexed from full extension to 90 degrees. This gives rise to a skin motion error of 4 mm if an ASIS reference marker is mounted on the skin over the ASIS. If the depth of the pelvis is assumed to be about 20 cm, and if it is assumed that the posterior pelvis marker stays stationary with respect to the underlying bone, then this ASIS skin motion error would give rise to an angular error on the order of 1.1 degrees. Such an error would show up directly as a reduction in the true hip-flexion angle, but a 1.1-degree error over a 90-degree motion, or just over 1 percent, is probably an acceptably small error if the *angle* of hip flexion is the desired measurement.

As another example, suppose that for a walking subject the total range of hip flexion is about 40 degrees for each side. Further suppose, as suggested in the example above, that there is a vertical skin motion error of the ASIS reference markers on the order of 1 mm for each 20 degrees of hip flexion. During walking, such an error would be cyclic, with the right side opposite in direction to the left side at any given time in the gait cycle. During the double support phase, one hip would be extended and the other flexed, with a total difference of about 40 degrees. The combined right ASIS and left ASIS skin motion errors should then span about 2 mm, again assuming 1 mm per 20 degrees of flexion. If it is assumed that the right and left ASIS reference markers are 24 cm apart, then the maximum hip abduction error caused by ASIS marker vertical skin motion errors should be on the order of the arctangent of 2/240, or about 0.5 degrees. The range of ab-adduction of the hip during walking is typically on the order of 10 degrees, so this constitutes an error of about 5 percent.

While the above hypothetical analyses are based on several rather gross simplifying assumptions, they nevertheless suggest that errors due to skin motion of pelvis markers are not a major source of error in measurements of hip angular position.

Errors due to changes in placement of pelvis markers, on the other hand, can be much larger. Such errors can occur whenever the markers must be replaced, either for repeat measurements of the same person or for measurements of another person. The posterior marker on the pelvis is particularly difficult to position reliably time after time, but even the ASIS markers are subject to considerable judgment. For an assumed pelvis depth of 20 cm, every centimeter change in the cephalocaudad position of the posterior or anterior pelvis markers would give rise to an error in pelvic tilt of arctan (1/20), or about 3 degrees. Considering the opportunity for differing judgments in placing the pelvis markers, errors on the order of 5 or 10 degrees in the zero position of pelvic tilt are hard to avoid.

Thigh. Skin motion errors on the thigh will affect both hip and knee angle measurements. Perhaps the simplest thigh marker set would consist of two markers, one over the greater trochanter and another over the lateral epicondyle of the femur. Because this marker set places only two markers on the thigh, it cannot be used for 3-D measurements of thigh motion. Nevertheless, it has been used frequently to measure hip and knee flexion angles for people who walk predominantly within the plane of progression; that is, without exaggerated internal or external rotation at the hip. For this simple thigh marker set, antero-posterior skin movement errors of either the trochanter marker or the knee marker would give rise to hip and knee flexion angle errors [5,7–9]. How big are these errors likely to be?

J. Perry et al. [11] have shown that a lateral marker attached to the skin over the lateral femoral condyle can move about 2 cm posteriorly during a 45-degree flexion of the knee. If a thigh length of 36 cm is assumed, this skin movement error alone could cause a hip or knee flexion error on the order of arctan (2/36), or about 3 degrees. In fact, the actual errors inherent within this marker set are probably even larger. Skin movement error of the trochanter marker is likely to add to the knee-marker error, rather than cancel it out, because flexion of the hip will cause the skin over the trochanter to be drawn anteriorly.

The skin motion error at the knee will also cause a similar angular error in relation to the long axis of the shank. Perry et al. [11] showed that the knee marker also moves posteriorly with respect to the tibia during knee flexion. The thigh angular error and the shank angular error would be additive during knee flexion, so for a knee flexion of 90 degrees, one might expect knee flexion errors on the order of −5 degrees with this marker set. They calculated maximum errors of about 7 degrees. Flexion errors of this magnitude might or might not be acceptable for routine gait analysis, depending on the circumstances. In any case, it is valuable to have some idea of how large the errors can be with such a marker set.

For 3-D measurements, three or more markers will be attached to the thigh. As will be discussed in a later section, it is relatively easy to devise marker arrangements that have small skin motion errors in the flexion-extension and ab-adduction directions. Because the thigh is so thoroughly covered with soft tissue, however, it is not at all easy to devise markers that have small skin motion errors in the axial rotation direction. At the hip, these thigh axial rotation skin motion errors translate directly into hip axial rotation errors. At the knee, their effects are less obvious, but more serious.

Modest thigh axial rotation errors of 5 or 10 degrees have only a small effect on the knee flexion angle measurement, but they have a dramatic effect on the knee axial rotation and ab-adduction measurements. H. K. Ramakrishnan and M. P. Kadaba [3] provide a thorough explanation of this difficulty. The effects of thigh axial rotation errors are so pronounced, and the errors themselves so difficult to eliminate, that knee axial rotation and abduction or adduction are often left unreported in routine gait analysis. A later section of this chapter will discuss methods for improving the accuracy of these secondary knee angle measurements.

3.2.2. Calculation of Joint Moments and Powers

As used here, the term *moment* refers to moment of force, or torque, which is the result of applying a force to a lever acting about a joint axis. Moments can be generated actively at a joint by contraction of muscles, or passively by muscle elasticity and viscosity or by ligamentous restraints. Power at a joint is equal to the joint moment times the joint angular velocity and is a measure of the rate at which work is being done at the joint.

To calculate moments at the joints of the lower limbs, four types of information must be known [6,12–17]:

1. *Position*: The location of each joint center, and the orientation of each joint axis.

2. *Acceleration*: The acceleration of each joint center.

3. *Body segment parameters*: The mass and moment of inertia of each body segment, and the location of the center of mass within each segment.

4. *Ground reaction force*: The line of action and magnitude of any ground reaction force vector.

With regard to *joint center location*, two types of errors are possible. First, the indicated joint center, that is, the joint center location calculated from measured positions of body segment markers, might move around in relation to the true axis, either in a random, jiggly fashion, or in a consistent, coherent fashion, coupled with the joint movement [7,9,11]. Second, even if the indicated location of the axis is quite stationary in relation to the underlying bone, it might be in the wrong place.

The first type of error will distort the shape of the joint moment curve; the second will tend to cause a shift of the curve up or down from the zero axis. Of the first type of error the coupled errors are more serious than the random errors. Random errors often can be reduced by filtering, while coupled errors can produce data that look consistent and reliable, but are not accurate. The second type of error is more likely to result from incorrect placement of markers, rather than from skin motion, but it nevertheless is a large threat to accuracy of joint moment calculations [10].

Compounding the difficulty of identifying the locations of joint axes is the fact that anatomic joints typically are not perfect hinges; the locations of joint axes might change as the joints move through their ranges of motion.

The question still remains: "Just how significant are these errors to the calculation of joint moments?" D. Winter [16] provides representative joint moment curves for selected normal adult subjects. He describes peak flexor:extensor moment values, in Nm/kg, of about 0.6:0.4 for the hip, 0.6:0.3 for the knee, and 1.5:0.1 for the ankle. Since the definition of a moment is a force times a lever arm, we can convert these numbers to equivalent lever arms by dividing by the conversion factor of N/kg, which is approximately 10. Then we have Nm/N and the Newtons cancel out, leaving meters. Multiplying by 100 to get centimeters, we obtain anterior:posterior lever arm lengths of approximately 6:4 for the hip, 6:3 for the knee, and 15:1 for the ankle. A. L. Bell et al. [18] and K. Stivers et al. [19] suggest that errors in locating the hip center may often be 2 cm or more. A 2-cm error in the anterior direction at the hip would change the calculated anterior:posterior lever arm ratio from 6:4 to 4:6. This would have the effect of moving the location of the zero line on the hip flexor-extensor moment curve by some 20 percent of the peak-to-peak value. The shape of the curve would remain essentially the same.

Perry's [11] measurements of lateral knee marker motion errors can be used to make similar estimates of errors at the knee. A skin marker placed over the subject's lateral femoral epicondyle moved about 2 cm posteriorly as the knee bent to 45 degrees. Suppose that M. P. Kadaba's marker set is used, in which the measurement knee axis is defined to pass through the lateral knee marker. Suppose further, for purposes of illustration, that the true knee axis passes through the lateral femoral epicondyle. Then if the lateral knee marker is placed over the lateral epicondyle while the knee is fully extended, the indicated knee axis will move ever farther posterior as the knee bends, and extensor muscle moments at the knee will be increasingly underestimated as the knee bends, changing the shape of the curve. A skin motion error of 2 cm, or .02 m, would give rise to an error of about 0.2 Nm/kg in the knee moment, which would be about 20 percent of the peak-to-peak value of knee moment for Winter's subjects walking at a freely chosen cadence. B. L. Davis [10] emphasizes the dominance of such axis location errors among the various types of errors that can degrade moment calculations.

For calculation of the inertial components of joint moments, the reference markers must define the *accelerations* of the joint centers in addition to the locations of the centers. These inertial components also depend on the estimation of body segment parameters, discussed briefly below. The inertial components tend to be minor components of the knee moment during stance phase and major components during swing phase [10].

In the presence of skin motion errors, establishing and maintaining accurate information on joint axis location is a challenging task, but calculating accurate joint center accelerations is daunting. This is the case not because the computations are difficult, but because velocity is the rate of change of position and acceleration is the rate of change of velocity. Errors that might be barely noticeable in the motion data can become quite distinct in the velocity and overwhelming in the acceleration. Figure 3-1 illustrates this point.

Figures 3-1, 3-2, and 3-3 show position, velocity, and acceleration values, respectively, calculated with and without filtering. The data arbitrarily chosen for this illustration represent vertical motion of the right ankle marker for one gait cycle from a normal adult male walking at a freely selected speed of 78 m per minute, or 130 cm per second. Data were collected with a video-based motion measurement system. Velocity values were calculated by dividing the difference between successive position values by the time interval between them; in this case, 1/60th second. Acceleration values were calculated from the velocity values by the same procedure. The smooth velocity curve was computed from the raw position data and then low-pass filtered at 6 Hz. Similarly, the smooth acceleration curve was computed from the smooth velocity data and then filtered again at 6 Hz. The choice of 6 Hz for the filter frequency in this illustration is an arbitrary one, suggested by discussions in the literature [20,21].

Figures 3-2 and 3-3 illustrate the point that some filtering of the data is necessary, when computing velocities and accelerations, in order to obtain usable data. Without removal of some of the high-frequency components, the acceleration data are essentially meaningless. The big question is, How much smoothing is correct? or, more specifically, What filter

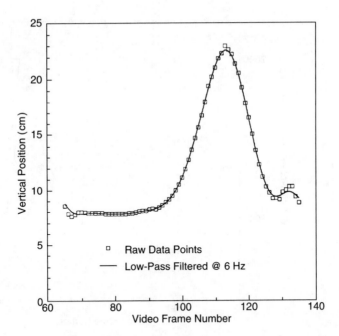

Figure 3-1. Vertical component of motion for the right lateral ankle marker on an adult male walking at a free speed of 78 m/min = 130 cm/sec.

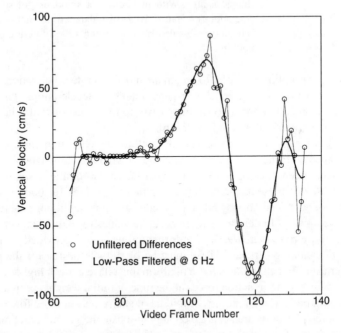

Figure 3-2. Velocity computed by simple first difference from data in Fig. 3-1. The low-pass filter is a digital implementation of Butterworth. Without filtering, the small amount of measurement noise present in the original displacement data becomes quite evident.

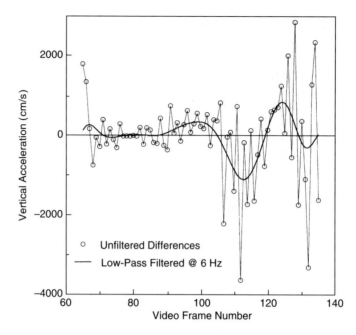

Figure 3-3. Acceleration computed by simple first difference from data in Fig.
3-2. Filtered curve is computed from filtered velocity data and then
filtered again. Without filtering or smoothing of some kind, accelerations computed from video data are essentially useless; consequently, most derivative algorithms have filtering or smoothing
built in.

frequency is optimal in order to obtain the most accurate accelerations? A lower frequency
gives smoother curves, and lower peak values of accelerations, but which frequency is
best? In general, there is no simple answer to that question, but it has received quite a bit
of attention in the literature [16,22–26].

Body segment parameters are difficult to measure on living subjects. Generally they
are estimated from the subject's height and weight in relation to published body proportions
that have been developed by dismembering and weighing a small number of cadavers
[1,27,28]. At present, the routine assignment of values for body segment parameters of
living subjects must be regarded as an educated guess, although there is continuing effort
to develop ways to determine more accurate values for individual subjects [29–34].

The *ground reaction force* information usually is provided by force platforms built
into the walking surface. These must be of suitable design for the measurements being
undertaken. For example, a force platform must have a much higher frequency response to
accurately register reaction forces at the time of initial weight acceptance, where forces are
changing rapidly, than during the middle of stance phase, when forces change slowly. The
best force platforms are accurate enough to locate the ground reaction vector within a few
millimeters. If they are properly mounted and accurately calibrated within the measurement
environment, they are not likely to be a major source of inaccuracy in computing joint
moments. If the force data are in error, however, they can seriously degrade the accuracy
of joint moment calculations [10].

It is perhaps worth noting here that force platforms are fully as accurate at measuring vibrations of their mounting foundation as they are at measuring ground reaction forces. Ideally, the foundation for a force platform should be directly supported by the ground. If force platforms are mounted on upper floors of buildings, they might not be able to provide sufficient accuracy to allow reasonably accurate computations of joint moments. For force platforms that are already installed, a simple test is to watch the output of the force platform while walking vigorously near the platform, but not on it. If no discernable output is present at the sensitivities used for gait studies, then there is no cause for concern. If the force platform has not yet been installed, vibrations of the floor at the proposed installation site can be recorded with an accelerometer that is securely clamped to the floor. The bandwidth of the accelerometer should be from DC, or at most about 1 Hz, to perhaps 50 Hz or more. Accelerometers can be calibrated in fractions of the acceleration of gravity, or g, by comparing outputs with the sensitive axis pointed straight up and straight down, a difference of $2g$. The size of error forces for any proposed force platform can be estimated by multiplying the magnitude of the observed accelerations, in g, by the *suspended weight* of the platform. If mounting on a vibrating foundation is unavoidable, it is desirable to obtain a force platform with as small a suspended mass as possible.

The computation of joint moments in small children can be degraded by center-of-pressure inaccuracies that most force-platform systems exhibit at low force levels [10]. Calculation of the location of the center of pressure becomes less precise as vertical forces become smaller, because the smallest force increment that can be resolved by the computer's analog-to-digital converter becomes a larger percentage of the total force. Accuracy should be checked in the actual force ranges that are to be used. If force data, or more likely the center-of-pressure data, are found to be unacceptably inaccurate below a certain force level, then all force data below that level should be discarded. This will result in the loss of moment and power data for small subjects during the beginning and end of stance phase.

Skin motion and marker placement errors, acceleration errors, body segment parameter estimation errors, and ground reaction force measurement errors all can degrade the calculation of joint moments. Hence it is probably inappropriate to place much meaning in the fine details of the joint moment curves. With careful data collection and processing, the overall shapes of the curves can be interpreted with some confidence, but the locations of the zero crossings, the points where the curve indicates a transition between extensor and flexor moments, should be interpreted with caution, if not outright skepticism. A consequence of the unreliable zero values is that the balance between flexor and extensor activity, as indicated by the relative areas bounded by the moment curve above and below the zero line, might be highly inaccurate.

3.2.3. Calculation of Joint Axis Locations

Joint Center Terminology. Any discussion of joint centers and joint axes relies on some rather specialized concepts and terminology. First of all, the *instantaneous center of rotation* between two objects is the point that has zero instantaneous relative velocity. In theory, such a point always exists; in practice, determining where it is with any useful accuracy might not always be possible, because the process of calculating velocities tends to emphasize any errors in the motion measurement process. This sensitivity to measurement "noise" often gives rise to a large amount of variation, or "scatter," in the computed locations of the instantaneous centers.

The *finite center of rotation*, or rotation pole, is the place where a hinge could be placed between two objects and still allow them to move from one measured relative position to another through a finite, or noninfinitesimal, angle. This hinge constraint might take them through a different path than they actually took in getting from one position to the other, but theoretically the end points can be made to match exactly. In the limit, as the finite angle becomes smaller and smaller and approaches zero, the locus of finite centers theoretically tends toward the locus of instant centers.

In practice, as the finite angle becomes smaller, errors in locating the finite center become larger. The finite center calculation can be done either mathematically or graphically, but in either case the center is located at the intersection of two lines that are defined from measured positions of reference markers on the two body segments. As the finite angle becomes smaller, these two lines become more nearly parallel, and small errors in measurement cause increasingly large errors in the location of the finite center. In the limit, as the finite angle goes to zero, the two lines become parallel and the location of the finite center is undefined.

The instant center and finite center are both 2-D concepts. The 3-D equivalents are instantaneous and finite screw axes, respectively. The respective *centers* of rotation become *axes* of rotation, and the term *screw* refers to the fact that some translation along the axis might be necessary to fully accommodate or characterize the actual relative motion. In other words, movement of a 3-D object from one position to another cannot, in general, be accomplished by a pure rotation of the object about an axis. But any movement can be accomplished by a rotation about an axis combined with a translation along the axis, in the manner of a threaded screw. As in the 2-D case, the path of the object defined by this hypothetical screw might be different from the object's actual path, but the endpoints match exactly.

Joint Center Calculations. Almost all of the human motion analysis procedures currently in use rely on somebody's educated guess about where the joint centers are located and how the joint axes are oriented. It is probably obvious to everyone that it would be better if the axis locations could be calculated from motion data, rather than "guesstimated." In theory, if three or more reference markers are placed on each of two adjacent body segments, it is possible to calculate the location of the axis of rotation between them from the measured motions of the markers. In practice, despite a great deal of research activity, there has been very limited success at computing joint center locations from measurements of skin-mounted markers [35–38]. That is because, as mentioned above, the calculation of joint axis locations is very sensitive to noise and errors in the motion data. Even when calculating the axis locations of cadaver joints or mechanical joints, the variability is surprisingly large [39,40]. Nevertheless, people keep trying to develop ways to minimize the effects of measurement noise because accurate joint moment information is not possible without accurate joint center information [10].

The joints of primary interest, at least for studies of locomotion, are the hip and the knee. The fact that the healthy hip is an almost perfect sphere makes it simpler to define than the knee. Despite this seeming simplicity, Bell et al. [18] have shown that errors in estimating hip center location on the basis of anatomic landmarks are often quite large, on the order of several centimeters. Stivers et al. [19] have proposed a method for calculating a hip center location from measured hip motions that does not rely on the computation of velocities, and therefore is claimed to be less sensitive to measurement noise.

The knee joint has received the most attention, probably because of its complexity and its vulnerability to injury [4,41–43].

3.3. MARKER SITES AND MARKER SETS

On the pelvis and lower limbs there are several places where a bone lies directly under the skin. These bony prominences are often chosen as places to attach reference markers. The pelvis, shanks, and feet are quite well endowed with bony prominences that have minimal fat and no muscles or connective tissue bands moving between the bone and the skin. The thigh is another matter. It provides essentially no useful bony prominences, and reference markers must be attached by other means, such as encircling bands.

3.3.1. Marker Sites and Marker Sets on the Pelvis

The pelvis provides bony prominences at the anterior superior iliac spines (ASIS), the iliac crests, the ischial tuberosities, and, on thin people, the posterior superior iliac spines (PSIS) and the pubis. All of these sites have been used for reference markers at one time or another, but the most common choice these days seems to be one marker on each ASIS and a third marker midway between the two PSISs. These three markers define a "pelvis plane" that is quite reliable and repeatable. Perhaps the biggest challenge is to locate consistently the posterior marker in the cephalocaudal direction, because the posterior spines are not as prominent as the anterior spines. In general, pelvis markers are not a source of great confusion or controversy.

Determining where the hip joints are located in relation to these pelvis markers is more of a challenge [18,19]. For accurate calculations of hip joint moments and powers, an accurate method for estimating or measuring the locations of the hip centers is required. When the location of the hip center is known with confidence, it can be considered a reference marker on the thigh, thereby eliminating the need for one thigh marker [3].

3.3.2. Marker Sites and Marker Sets on the Thigh

Large muscles surround the femur, and many of them are two-joint muscles that pass from the pelvis to the shank. In addition, the iliotibial band sweeps back and forth, just beneath the skin, over the greater trochanter and the lateral epicondyle of the femur. The only subcutaneous bony prominence on the femur is the medial epicondyle, and it is not in a very convenient location for placing a marker. These anatomic characteristics of the thigh make it the most challenging lower limb segment to measure.

The skin that covers the thigh stretches quite freely, much like a bundle of taut rubber bands, from the region of the iliac crests and the perineum proximally, to just below the knee distally. Consequently, the following types of error motions relative to the femur will occur: A marker placed over the greater trochanter tends to move anteriorly with hip flexion; a marker placed over the lateral epicondyle tends to move posteriorly with knee flexion; and markers placed on the anterior (posterior) surface of the thigh will tend to move distally (proximally) with hip flexion or knee flexion. In consequence of the latter, hip or knee measurements that use a simple encircling band as a thigh reference tend to underestimate hip or knee flexion angles. Bands that encircle the thigh also tend to underestimate hip axial rotation during internal or external rotation. Bands around the proximal thigh tend to rotate more like the pelvis than the femur, and even distal thigh bands rotate substantially less than the femur.

In the days before computerized motion measurement systems, data collection and processing were very tedious and time-consuming. Consequently, marker sets had to be quite simple. It was not unusual to define the thigh location by two markers only, one over the greater trochanter and one over the lateral epicondyle of the femur. This simplified marker set eliminated any possibility of measuring thigh axial rotation, but did make it possible to estimate hip and knee flexion angles with useful accuracy, as long as the subject's gait did not exhibit marked internal or external rotations of the pelvis or hips.

The existence of multicamera, computerized measurement systems has made it feasible to undertake true 3-D measurements, which require that a third marker be present on each body segment. Some marker sets have added an additional thigh reference marker mounted on a wand projecting out perpendicular to the long axis of the thigh and held in place by encircling bands. Such a marker set typically assumes that the lateral knee marker defines the location of the knee axis, while the orientation of the knee axis is defined by the direction the thigh wand marker is pointing. Other marker sets have used the hip center location as a "virtual" proximal thigh marker, in place of a "real" marker on the greater trochanter. It is noteworthy that the definition of joint axis location with such marker sets depends on the judgment, or "educated guess," of the person who applies the markers.

Still other marker sets have abandoned the trochanter and lateral knee markers altogether and mounted an array of three or more markers on the thigh. With such arrays, it is still necessary to define in some manner the location and orientation of the knee joint axis in relation to the marker array. One method that has been used is to temporarily attach medial and lateral knee markers, record the array locations and knee marker locations simultaneously, and then remove the knee markers for further data collection. With such a procedure, the defined location of the knee axis again depends on the judgment of the person who places the medial and lateral knee markers.

3.3.3. Marker Sites and Marker Sets on the Shank

The shank offers bony prominences at the tibial tubercle, the head of the fibula, the anteromedial surface of the tibia, and the medial and lateral malleoli. In addition, the most slender part of the shank, just above the ankle, provides a quite stable basis for an encircling band. Some marker sets place one of the shank reference markers on a wand that projects out to the side or front of the shank. Other marker sets have mounted marker arrays onto fitted splints that are strapped snugly against the anteromedial surface of the tibia. In systems that define a knee joint center in the process of defining a 3-D coordinate system embedded in the thigh, that knee center is also commonly used as a virtual reference marker on the shank.

3.3.4. Marker Sites and Marker Sets on the Foot

In whole-body or pelvis-and-lower-limbs gait analysis, the foot tends to be treated in a rather cavalier fashion. This uniquely human organ, with almost 30 bones and joints, is routinely treated as a rigid body. Another chapter of this book addresses the topic of measuring the internal motions of the foot, so they will not be discussed here.

For routine whole-body gait analysis, the foot offers suitable bony prominences for mounting reference markers at the following points: the distal calcaneus, the lateral calcaneus, the base or the head of the fifth metatarsal, and the dorsal surfaces of the first three metatarsals. Practical problems with foot markers arise because the markers tend to be close together, and close to the ankle marker. Many motion measurement systems have trouble distinguishing separate markers when they get too close together. Consequently, some whole-body gait marker sets have settled for only two, or even just one, marker on the foot; for example at the heel and toe or just the toe. Such compromises jeopardize or eliminate the ability to estimate the inversion/eversion component of ankle motion with meaningful accuracy, even when an ankle joint center that has been computed in the shank embedded coordinate system is treated as a virtual marker on the foot.

3.4. MINIMIZING THE EFFECTS OF SOFT TISSUE MOVEMENT

3.4.1. Marker Mass

Reference markers attached to the skin inevitably have some mass. The skin is elastic, or "springy." The accelerations of walking or other movements can stimulate these spring-mass systems to vibrate, causing an additional type of error, or noise, that further aggravates the inherent problems of skin motion. In general, larger mass means a lower frequency of vibration, and low-frequency noise is harder to filter out of the motion data than high-frequency noise. All markers should be made as light as possible, and markers that are mounted on projecting wands deserve particular attention to weight minimization.

3.4.2. Marker Placement

Several authors point out that skin motion errors vary in different anatomic locations, and emphasize that some kind of quantitative check of skin motion errors is vital [2,4,5,7–11,14,43–48]. For measurements of flexion-extension and ab-adduction angles, the long and slender character of the thighs and shanks is an advantage. This shape makes it possible to reduce the effect of soft tissue movement by attaching reference markers as close as possible to the ends of the segment. For a given error in the movement of an individual marker, errors in calculated angles will become smaller as the markers are placed farther apart. For measurements of axial rotations in these same body segments, no such advantage applies, and there is little choice but to strap projecting wands to the thigh and shank with encircling elastic bands. On the thighs, it is desirable to mount such encircling bands as far as possible distally, because the elastic skin that covers the proximal thigh tends to rotate more like the pelvis than the femur [8].

3.4.3. Marker Frames and Arrays

Pelvis. The customary three markers on the pelvis, right ASIS, left ASIS, and mid-PSIS, are intended to represent the pelvis as a rigid body. Indeed, the three markers could be connected by a frame to enforce rigidity, but such a frame would inevitably add mass and thereby aggravate skin motions at the attachment points. An alternative approach is to adjust the measured positions of the three markers slightly, during data processing, to enforce uniform spacing. Such a procedure has been reported by K. Stivers et al. [47], who claim a significant improvement in accuracy when random marker location errors are present.

Thigh. The long and slender shape of the thigh lends itself to the attachment of marker frames. A structure can be made of lightweight materials, such as thin-wall aluminum tubing or carbon fiber arrow shafts. The structure can be attached distally with an encircling band just above the knee, and proximally with a guide that allows free rotation of the frame but does not allow anteroposterior (AP) or mediolateral (ML) translation relative to the guide. This guide can be attached to the skin with adhesives, or held in place with a second encircling band placed as far proximally on the thigh as practical. Such a frame rotates with the distal end of the thigh, and is quite well constrained to follow the thigh in flexion-extension and ab-adduction movements. It can serve as a convenient mounting base for marker arrays. C. Angeloni et al. [4,9] and A. Cappozzo et al. [5] advocate the use of lightweight, large-area plates that are securely strapped to the thigh.

Shank. Lightweight marker frames can be attached to the shank even more easily than to the thigh. The long and slender shape of the shank makes for accurate attachment in flexion-extension and ab-adduction directions. Fixation in the axial rotation direction is easier on the shank than on the thigh, because there is much less soft tissue surrounding the tibia and fibula than the femur. Nevertheless, axial fixation is still a challenge, and minimal mass in marker frames and arrays is important, particularly for dynamic activities such as running or jumping. J. Ronsky and B. Nigg [45] report a custom-fitted thermoplastic splint that is held firmly against the subcutaneous, anteromedial surface of the tibia by encircling bands. They report that the low mass and relatively large area of contact of this design provide superior accuracy for activities with high shank accelerations.

Foot. As mentioned earlier, routine whole-body gait analysis usually considers the foot to be a rigid body. Because of the difficulty of tracking movements of closely spaced markers, whole-body marker sets usually limit the foot to two markers, at heel and forefoot or at lateral heel and head of fifth metatarsal or even to a single marker on the forefoot [2]. Marker arrays are seldom used because the added mass of a frame and array tends to exaggerate any skin movement errors during the high accelerations that are experienced by the foot.

3.5. CORRECTING FOR SOFT TISSUE MOVEMENT

In some special cases, it is possible to correct for skin motion errors, at least to some degree. As mentioned in passing earlier, skin motion errors that are random in nature can sometimes be effectively reduced by filtering or by imposing rigid-body constraints on multiple marker arrays. On the other hand, skin motion errors that are systematically coupled to anatomic motions can sometimes be measured and compensated for. Examples of these cases will be discussed.

3.5.1. Filtering and Smoothing

Filtering and smoothing, in the context of human motion measurements, are numerical operations conducted on time series data in order to remove the higher frequency features of the data. The term *time series* simply means a succession of repetitive measurements that have been made at uniformly spaced time intervals. For example, a typical video-based motion measurement system would make 60 measurements per second in North America and 50 per second in Europe or Japan. When the errors, or noise, in time series data is higher in frequency than the motion data of interest, then filtering or smoothing can reduce the noise without affecting the motion data very much [9,20,21,24,25,35,49].

3.5.2. Rigid-Body Constraints

A rigid-body constraint is either a mechanical frame or a mathematical adjustment that ensures a constant spacing between two or more markers that are attached to the same body segment. The intent is to force the segment to behave like a rigid body. Without such a restraint, skin motion errors will be different for different markers, causing marker spacing to change during locomotion. The use of a mechanical frame is sometimes practical, as discussed earlier, but such a frame adds mass to the markers, and thereby might reduce the frequency of marker vibration on the elastic skin, making such vibration harder to remove by filtering or smoothing. Mathematical constraints, usually based on some type of least-squared-error criterion, are receiving increasing attention in the quest for more accurate motion data [26,35,38,41,47,50].

3.5.3. Error Compensation

If a particular skin motion error is consistently the same, time after time, there is at least a possibility of finding out what the error is and correcting it [5,11,41,48]. For example, a knee-flexion electrogoniometer that is mounted between an encircling band around the distal thigh and another band around the shank will consistently underestimate knee flexion, because skin motion that accompanies knee flexion will cause the thigh band to rotate slightly in a flexion direction, relative to the femur. If another, more accurate, way to measure knee flexion can be devised, then the electrogoniometer output can be compared to this "reference" measure, and a calibration curve can be constructed. This calibration curve can then be used to correct the electrogoniometer measurements back to the corresponding reference measure. In this hypothetical case, careful use of a manual goniometer might provide such reference measurements.

For measurement of knee flexion, such an exercise is hardly worthwhile. On the one hand, the manual calibration process is tedious and probably would have to be conducted on every subject. On the other hand, a simpler solution exists in this case. As discussed earlier, it is relatively easy to build an attachment frame, incorporating both proximal and distal attachments to the thigh, that is more accurate in the flexion-extension direction than a simple encircling band.

For measurement of thigh axial rotation, however, every surface-mounted thigh marker set rotates substantially less than the femur does about the long axis of the thigh [8]. As described earlier, surface-mounted measurements underestimate thigh axial rotation by some 30 percent, even when the axial rotation fixation of markers to the skin is positioned as far as possible distally on the thigh. If the axial rotation fixation to the skin is more proximal, the error is even higher.

An even greater threat to reliable measurements of thigh axial rotation exists. This is the difficulty of consistently defining which direction is the front when placing markers on the thigh. The placement of thigh markers typically requires a judgment, or estimate, of when the thigh is facing straight ahead relative to the pelvis. This clearly is a matter of significance in defining where the zero point falls on the hip axial rotation curve. Less obviously, it also is a matter of great significance in defining not only the zero positions but also the shapes of the curves for knee axial rotation and knee varus/valgus deviation.

The thigh markers are the basis for defining the orientation of the embedded thigh coordinate system. This embedded coordinated system in turn defines the orientation of the axes for describing knee motion. If, because of thigh skin motion errors or marker placement errors, the thigh marker set and its associated knee axis location are internally or externally rotated relative to the femur, the knee flexion angles will be only slightly affected, but knee axial rotation and varus/valgus rotation will be dramatically affected. This sensitivity has been elegantly and thoroughly documented by Ramakrishnan [3]. The consequence of this sensitivity is that axial rotation and varus/valgus motion measurements at the knee are notoriously unreliable.

Fortunately, in the case of the thigh, a reliable, anatomically based calibration reference for axial rotation is readily available. This reference is provided by the shank when the knee is bent to approximately 90 degrees of flexion. Let us postulate that, in this flexed position of the knee, the tibial condyles are kept in contact with the femoral condyles by the ligamentous and muscular constraints of the knee joint. To the extent that this is true, two markers placed at proximal and distal ends of the shank will accurately, or at least repeatably, indicate the angular orientation of the femur about its long axis.

Over a range of internal and external hip rotations, this reference thigh axial position can be measured simultaneously with the axial position indicated by the skin-mounted thigh marker set. The reference measurements can then be used to calibrate the measurements derived from the thigh marker set, both in terms of amplitude sensitivity and zero position. For subsequent measurements of walking or other activities, this calibration can be applied to correct the axial rotations that are indicated by the thigh marker set. The amplitude sensitivity will be dependent on the nature of the thigh marker set. All marker sets will rotate less than the femur. The more distal the axial rotation fixation to the skin is placed, the more closely the thigh marker set will rotate with the femur. As mentioned earlier, however, even a distal attachment provides only about 70 percent of the femoral axial rotation. For such an attachment, the calibration sensitivity would be 1/0.7 or about 1.4.

Figures 3-4 and 3-5 show data from two typical internal/external rotation calibration trials. The marker set is as described by M. P. Kadaba et al. [2], with adhesive mounted markers at lateral knee and lateral ankle and laterally extending markers on sticks at midthigh and midshank. Computed joint center locations at hip and knee are used as the third markers on thigh and shank, respectively, allowing definition of embedded coordinate systems in each segment. With this marker set, the internal/external rotation orientation of the embedded coordinate systems depends on the orientation of the laterally projecting sticks. By rotating the positions of the thigh sticks internally or externally, the orientation of the embedded thigh coordinate system can be internally or externally rotated.

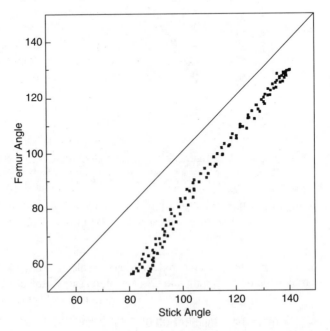

Figure 3-4. Thigh axial rotation calibration data obtained during a bent-knee trial of cyclic left hip internal and external rotation. The stick angle is computed from the skin-mounted marker set. The femur angle is hip axial rotation defined by the normal to a plane that passes through the hip, knee, and ankle centers. For this test, the thigh marker set was purposely rotated externally on the thigh. Angles are measured counterclockwise looking down, with zero straight ahead.

The calibration data are obtained with the subject standing on one leg, bending the free knee to about 90 degrees so the shank is horizontal, while the free thigh remains approximately vertical. The subject then gently internally and externally rotates the free hip while data are collected. Position data are collected for the pelvis markers, the lateral knee and ankle markers, and the thigh and shank stick markers. Figure 3-4 shows calibration data when the thigh stick was purposely mounted in an externally rotated position. Figure 3-5 depicts a separate calibration curve for internal rotation of the thigh stick. The calibration process consists of fitting a least-square line to the plotted data points, establishing a mathematical relationship between the angle measured by the marker set and the femur

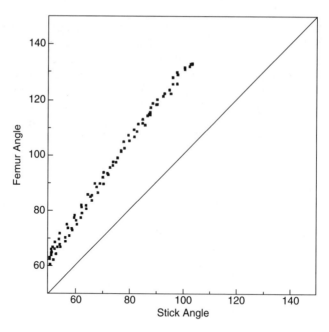

Figure 3-5. Identical test to Fig. 3-4, but with the thigh marker set intention-
ally rotated internally about 15° from the normal, directly lateral,
placement.

angle indicated by the knee and ankle markers. Table 3-1 shows the slopes and intercepts
for five trials each on both right and left legs of the same subject.

TABLE 3-1   CALIBRATION OF THIGH AXIAL ROTATIONS

Parameters of best-fit line relating thigh stick and shank centerlines for
five separate axial rotation calibrations of each leg of the same adult male
subject

Trial	Stick alignment	Slope	Intercept (radians)	Stick position at neutral (degrees)
RTC1	Neutral	1.377	0.483	4.5 internal
RTC2	Neutral	1.380	0.531	2.7 internal
TCR1	Neutral	1.367	0.619	1.8 external
TCR5	Internal rotation	1.362	0.188	16.0 internal
TCR9	External rotation	1.319	0.859	15.5 external
LTC3	Neutral	1.340	−0.530	0.2 internal
LTC4	Neutral	1.385	−0.541	0.0
TCL2	Neutral	1.397	−0.541	3.4 internal
TCL6	Internal rotation	1.388	−0.883	19.8 internal
TCL10	External rotation	1.301	−0.883	18.1 external

This calibration must be done for each leg, at each application of the markers. If a marker is moved, the calibration must be repeated. Once the calibration is established, however, the formula for the straight line can be used to adjust the rotation data by converting each measured rotation angle into the equivalent femur angle. Figures 3-6, 3-7, and 3-8, respectively, show data from three separate walking trials with the thigh stick markers first positioned correctly, then internally rotated, and finally externally rotated. In each case, both right and left legs were calibrated and then measured in a free-speed walking trial. In each of Figures 3-6, 3-7, and 3-8, the (*a*) plot shows data as collected, and the (*b*) plot shows a recomputation of all data after the hip axial rotations have been adjusted according to the calibration regression line.

Figures 3-6, 3-7, and 3-8 show the expected direct effects of thigh stick misplacement on hip axial rotations. They also show effects as predicted by Ramakrishnan [3] and Kadaba [2] on knee varus/valgus and axial rotation. It is interesting to note that they also show distinct changes in the knee flexion curves. In each case, the adjusted curves in the (*b*) parts of the figures are seen to be quite similar to one another, suggesting that the calibration and adjustment procedure is effective.

Some groups of subjects might not be capable of performing the internal/external rotation calibration maneuver. Children with spasticity, for example, have limited capability for voluntary control of motions. People with unsteady balance might have difficulty balancing on one leg. For these people, a practical axial rotation calibration of the thigh markers can still be achieved, as long as a single bent-knee measurement can be obtained. This could even be a single frame from a walking data file, provided that at some point in the gait cycle the knee bends enough to define reliably a hip-knee-ankle plane. The amplitude sensitivity that is also required to perform a calibration can be estimated on the basis of previous tests of the same marker set on similar sized people. This process might be less accurate than a full, internal/external rotation calibration, but it retains the most important part of the calibration, which is the establishment of a more accurate zero position for hip axial rotation. Furthermore, such a calibration would be based on measurements in the anatomic positions where the limb is actually being used during gait, rather than an artificially imposed calibration position.

3.6. CONCLUSIONS

Coping with skin motion errors might be described as the one remaining frontier in human motion measurement. With appropriate care, all other sources of error can be made less significant than soft tissue motion. Ingenuity will be required to progress further in the quest for greater accuracy, but continued vigilance and periodic accuracy testing are required to retain confidence in the tools that are now at our disposal. Computerized measurement systems provide a wealth of data, and it can be tempting to present calculated results even when their accuracy is unproved. It is prudent to remember, however, that inaccurate data can lead to incorrect conclusions, which in turn can give rise to inappropriate treatment. The familiar expression "Garbage in, garbage out!" is an expression of such a concern, as is the venerable quote: "It is better to know nothing than to know what ain't so!" (Josh Billings, 1818-1885).

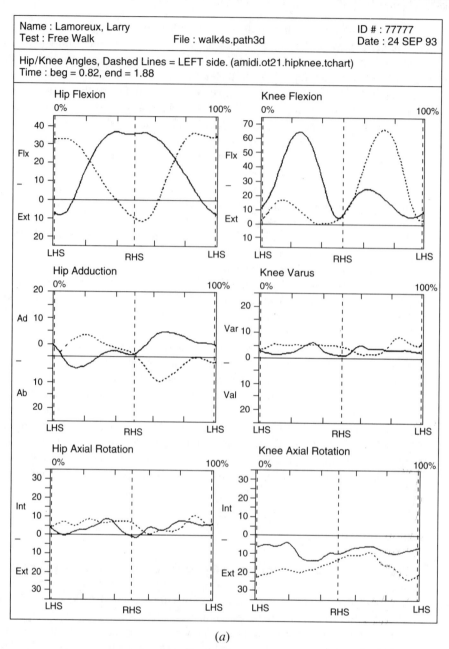

Name : Lamoreux, Larry		
Test : Free Walk	File : walk4s.path3d	ID # : 77777
		Date : 24 SEP 93

Hip/Knee Angles, Dashed Lines = LEFT side. (amidi.ot21.hipknee.tchart)
Time : beg = 0.82, end = 1.88

(*a*)

Figure 3-6. Hip and knee angular motions for both right and left legs, with thigh marker sticks oriented to point laterally. Part (*a*) shows angles computed from unaltered marker trajectories. Part (*b*) shows angles computed after the position of the thigh stick marker was adjusted on the basis of calibration data similar to that shown in Figs. 3-4 and 3-5. See the text for more details on the calibration and adjustment process. Note that the adjusted data show larger ranges of axial rotation.

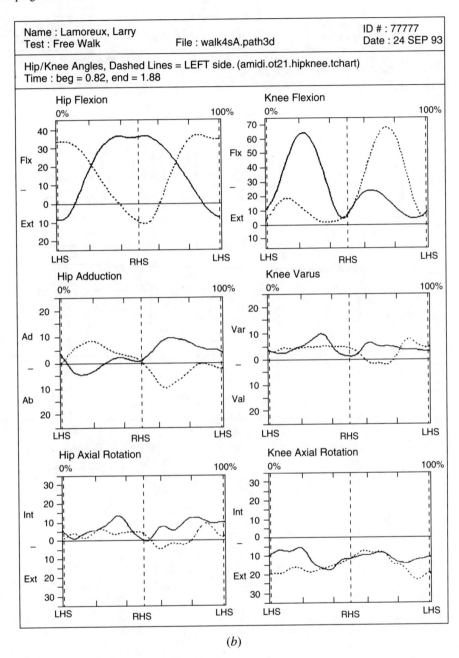

(b)

Figure 3-6. (*Continued*)

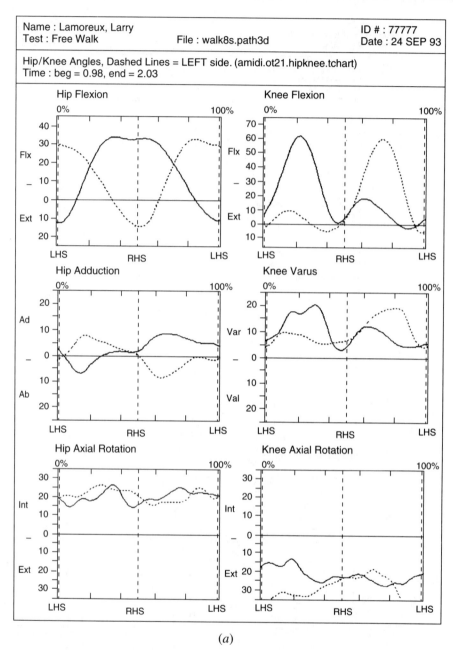

Name : Lamoreux, Larry
Test : Free Walk   File : walk8s.path3d   ID # : 77777
                                                               Date : 24 SEP 93

Hip/Knee Angles, Dashed Lines = LEFT side. (amidi.ot21.hipknee.tchart)
Time : beg = 0.98, end = 2.03

(a)

Figure 3-7. Hip and knee angular motions for right and left legs, but with thigh
marker sticks purposely rotated internally approximately 15° from
the normal lateral position. Part (a) is unaltered data; part (b) is
adjusted data, as in Fig. 3-6.

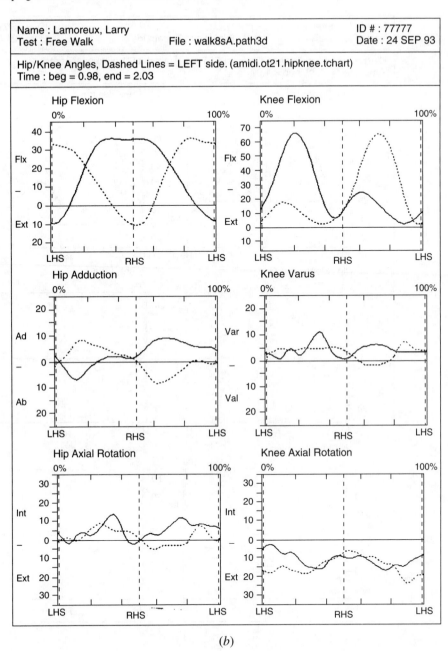

Name : Lamoreux, Larry   ID # : 77777
Test : Free Walk   File : walk8sA.path3d   Date : 24 SEP 93

Hip/Knee Angles, Dashed Lines = LEFT side. (amidi.ot21.hipknee.tchart)
Time : beg = 0.98, end = 2.03

(b)

Figure 3-7. (*Continued*)

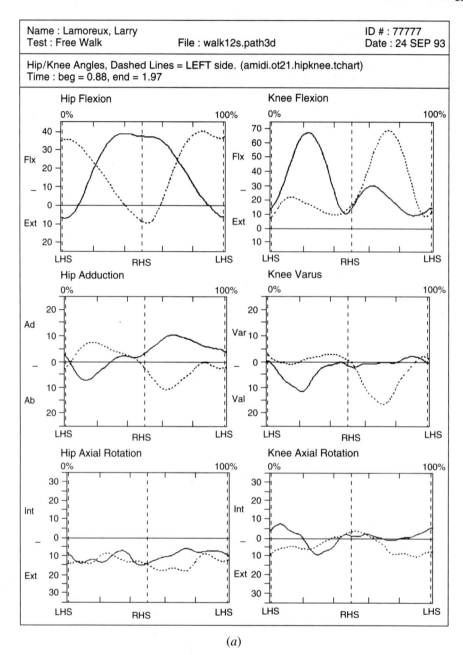

Name : Lamoreux, Larry   ID # : 77777
Test : Free Walk   File : walk12s.path3d   Date : 24 SEP 93

Hip/Knee Angles, Dashed Lines = LEFT side. (amidi.ot21.hipknee.tchart)
Time : beg = 0.88, end = 1.97

(*a*)

Figure 3-8. Hip and knee angular motions as in Figs. 3-6 and 3-7, but with thigh marker sticks purposely rotated externally approximately 15° from the normal lateral position. Note that in the unaltered data of part (*a*), the varus knee motions of Fig. 3-7 have changed to valgus motions. Both are artifacts of the misaligned embedded thigh coordinate systems. Note also that the "adjusted" curves in Figs. 3-6(*b*), 3-7(*b*), and 3-8(*b*) are all quite similar to one another.

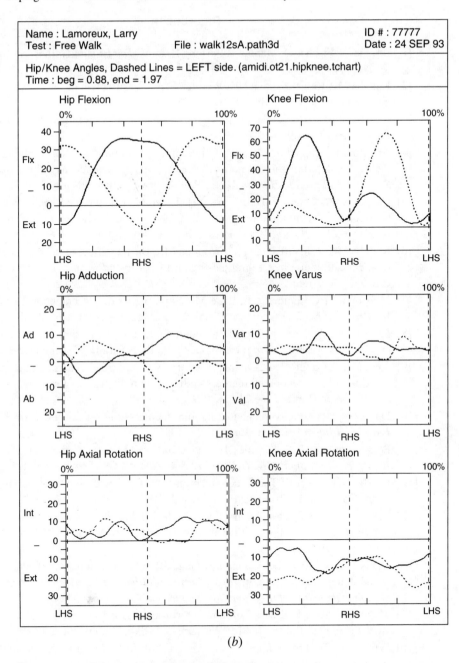

(*b*)

Figure 3-8. (*Continued*)

References

[1] Braune W, Fischer O; Maquet P, Furlong R, trans. *The Human Gait*. Berlin: Springer-Verlag; 1987.

[2] Kadaba MP, Ramakrishnan HK, Wootten ME. Measurement of lower extremity kinematics during level walking. *J Orthop Res* 1990;8:383–392.

[3] Ramakrishnan HK, Kadaba MP. On the estimation of joint kinematics during gait. *J Biomech*, 1991;24:969–977.

[4] Angeloni C, Cappello A, Catani F, Leardini A. Evaluation of soft tissue artefacts in the in vivo determination of human knee instantaneous helical axis. In: *Proc 2nd Intl Symp on 3-D Anal of Human Mvmt*; Poitier, France: June 30–July 3, 1993.

[5] Cappozzo A, Catani F, Della Croce U, Leardini A. Calibrated anatomical systems technique in 3-D motion analysis—Assessment of artefacts. In: *Proc 2nd Intl Symp on 3-D Anal of Human Mvmt*; Poitier, France: June 30–July 3, 1993.

[6] Kadaba MP, Ramakrishnan HK, Wootten ME, Burn J. Effect of uncertainties on joint moment estimation in cerebral palsy gait. In: *Proc 2nd N Amer Congr on Biomech*; Chicago, Ill: August 24–28, 1992.

[7] Lafortune MA, Lambert CE, Lake MJ. Skin marker displacement at the knee joint. In: *Proc 2nd N Amer Congr on Biomech*; Chicago, Ill: August 24–28, 1992.

[8] Lamoreux LW. Errors in thigh axial rotation measurements using skin mounted markers. In: *Proc 13th Intl Congr on Biomech*, Perth, Australia: December 9–13, 1991.

[9] Angeloni C, Cappozzo A, Catani F, Leardini A. Quantification of relative displacement of skin- and plate-mounted markers with respect to bones. In: *Proc Eighth Mtg Euro Soc Biomech*; Rome: June 21–24, 1992.

[10] Davis BL. Uncertainty in calculating joint moments during gait. In: *Proc Eighth Mtg Euro Soc Biomech*; Rome: June 21–24, 1992.

[11] Perry J, Enwemeka C, Gronley JK. The stability of knee markers during knee flexion. In: *Proc 34th Annual Mtg, Orthop Res Soc*. Atlanta, Ga: Feb 1–4, 1988.

[12] Bresler B, Frankel JP. The forces and moments in the leg during level walking. ASME Paper No. 48-A-62. *Transactions ASME*, 1950;72:27–36.

[13] Bresler B, Berry FR. Energy and power in the leg during normal level walking. Report Series II, Issue 15, Prosthetic Devices Research Project, Berkeley: University of California; 1951.

[14] Davis RB, Tyburski DJ, Õunpuu S, Gage JR. The determination of joint moments: Methodology verification. In: *Proceedings 5th Biennial Conference & Human Locomotion Symposium of the Canadian Biomechanics Society*; Ottawa, Ontario: 1988.

[15] Meglan M, Todd F. Kinetics of human locomotion. In: Rose J, Gamble J eds. *Human Walking* 2nd ed. Baltimore Md: Williams & Wilkins Publishing Co;1994.

[16] Winter D. *The Biomechanics and Motor Control of Human Gait: Normal, Elderly and Pathological* 2nd ed., Waterloo, Ontario: University of Waterloo Press;1991.

[17] Wu G, Ladin Z. The effect of inertial load on human joint force and moment during locomotion. In: *Proc 2nd Intl Symp on 3-D Anal of Human Mvmt*. Poitier, France: June 30–July 3, 1993.

[18] Bell AL, Pederson DR, Brand RA. A comparison of the accuracy of several hip center location prediction methods. *J Biomech*, 1990;23:617–721.

[19] Stivers K, Tylkowski C, Howell V. Prediction of the hip joint center location from the relative motion between the thigh and pelvis. In: *Proc 6th Annual East Coast Gait Conf*, East Lansing, Mich: Michigan State University, 1990:72–74.

[20] Antonsson EK, Mann RW. The frequency content of gait. *J Biomech* 1985;18:39–47.

[21] Winter D. *Biomechanics and Motor Control of Human Movement* 2nd ed. New York, NY:John Wiley & Sons Inc;1990.

[22] Angeloni C, Leardini A, Capello A. Smoothing of motion data: A new self-tuning algorithm with initial and final state optimization. In: *Proc Eighth Mtg Euro Soc Biomech*; Rome: June 21–24, 1992.

[23] Lanshammar H. On practical evaluation of differentiation techniques for human gait analysis. *J Biomech* 1982;15:99–105.

[24] Lanshammar H. On the precision limits for derivatives numerically calculated from noisy data. *J Biomech* 1982;15:459–470.

[25] Lesh MD, Mansour JM, Simon SR. A gait analysis subsystem for smoothing and differentiation of human motion data. *J Biomech Eng* 1979;101:205–212.

[26] Verstraete M, Soutas-Little R. A method for computing the three-dimensional angular velocity and acceleration of a body segment from three-dimensional position data. *J Biomech Eng* 1990;112:114–118.

[27] Dempster WT, Gaughran RL. Properties of body segments based on size and weight. *Am J Anat* 1955;120:33–54.

[28] Drillis R, Contini R. Body segment parameters. Technical Report No. 1166.03. Vocational Rehabilitation Administration, Dept Health, Education & Welfare, New York, NY:1966.

[29] Jensen R. Body segment mass, radius and radius of gyration proportions of children. *J Biomech* 1986;19:359–368.

[30] Lamontagne M, McFaull S. Determination of the moment of inertia of human lower leg using the small oscillation technique. In: *Proc 2nd N Amer Congr on Biomech*; Chicago, Ill: August 24–28, 1992.

[31] Moran DW, Yamaguchi GT. Determining subject-specific musculoskeletal geometric and mass properties from magnetic resonance images. In: *Proc 2nd N Amer Congr on Biomech*; Chicago, Ill: August 24–28, 1992.

[32] Riegger-Krugh C. Determination of fetal limb segmental weights from measurements obtainable from ultrasound imaging. In: *Proc 2nd N Amer Congr on Biomech*; Chicago, Ill: August 24–28, 1992.

[33] Sarfaty O, Ladin Z. A video-based system for the estimation of the inertial properties of body segments. *J Biomech* 1993;26:1011–1016.

[34] Tupling S, Pierrynowski M. Segment inertial proportions of young female athletes. In: *Proc 2nd N Amer Congr on Biomech*; Chicago, Ill: August 24–28, 1992.

[35] Angeloni C, Cappello A, Magnani G, Leardini A. New weighted least squares and smoothing scheme for kinematic analysis: Application to instantaneous helical axis determination. In: *Proc 2nd Intl Symp on 3-D Anal of Human Mvmt*; Poitier, France: June 30–July 3, 1993.

[36] Spoor CW, Veldpaus FE. Rigid-body motion calculated from spatial coordinates of markers. *J Biomech* 1980;13:391–393.

[37] Veldpaus FE, Woltring HJ, Dortmans L. A least-squares algorithm for the equiform transformation from spatial marker coordinates. *J Biomech* 1988;21:45–54.

[38] Wang X, Rezgui M, Verriest J. Using the polar decomposition theorem to determine the rotation matrix from noisy landmark measurements in the study of human joint kinematics. In: *Proc 2nd Intl Symp on 3-D Anal of Human Mvmt*; Poitier, France: June 30–July 3, 1993.

[39] Blankevoort L, Huiskes R, DeLange A. Helical axes of passive knee joint motions. *J Biomech* 1990;23:1219–1229.

[40] Holzreiter S. Calculation of the instantaneous centre of rotation for a rigid body. *J Biomech* 1991;24:643–647.

[41] Ladin Z, Mansfield P, Murphy M, Mann RW. Segmental analysis in kinesiological measurements. In: *Proc SPIE Symposium Vol 1356, Image-Based Motion Measurement, 1st World Congress of Biomechanics*, San Diego, Ca: August 31–September 1 1990.

[42] Shiavi R, Limbird T, Frazer M, Stivers K, Strauss A, Abramovitz J. Helical motion analysis of the knee—1. Methodology for studying kinematics during locomotion. *J Biomech* 1987;20:459–469.

[43] Shiavi R, Limbird T, Frazer M, Stivers K, Strauss A, Abramovitz J. Helical motion analysis of the knee—2. Kinematics of uninjured and injured knees during walking and pivoting. *J Biomech* 1987;20:653–665.

[44] Ploeg EL, Engsberg JR. Transformation from location-time data of surface markers to location-time data of joint centers. In: *Proc 2nd N Amer Congr on Biomech*; Chicago, Ill: August 24–28, 1992.

[45] Ronsky J, Nigg B. Error in kinematic data due to marker attachment methods. In: *Proc 13th Intl Congr on Biomech*; Perth, Australia: December 9–13, 1991.

[46] Söderqvist I, Wedin P. Determining the movements of the skeleton using well-configured markers. *J Biomech* 1993;26:1473–1477.

[47] Stivers K, Ariel G, Vorobiev A, Wise J, Probe J. Length normalization for rigid-body movement. In: *Proc 2nd Intl Symp on 3-D Anal of Human Mvmt*; Poitier, France: June 30–July 3, 1993.

[48] Truppe M. Real-time display of marker movement relative to the skeletal structure. In: *Proc Eighth Mtg Euro Soc Biomech*; Rome: June 21–24, 1992.

[49] Robertson D, Barden J, Dowling J. Response characteristics of different Butterworth low-pass digital filters. In: *Proc 2nd N Amer Congr on Biomech*; Chicago, Ill: August 24–28, 1992.

[50] Stivers K, Wise J, Ariel G, Vorobiev A, Probe J. Modified segment length normalization. In: *Proc 2nd Intl Symp on 3-D Anal of Human Mvmt*; Poitier, France: June 30–July 3, 1993.

David A. Winter
Janice J. Eng
Milad Ishac

Chapter 4

Three-Dimensional Moments, Powers, and Work in Normal Gait

Implications for Clinical Assessments

4.1. INTRODUCTION

In the past decade kinetic analyses of normal and pathological gait have become more widely accepted. Using standard inverse dynamics techniques, many kinetic variables can be estimated: joint reaction forces, moments of force, and mechanical powers. The vast majority of such analyses of normals has focused on planar analyses in the plane of progression. Ground reaction forces have been reported in detail [1,2], as have intra- and intersubject averages of normal moments-of-force [3–6] and normal joint mechanical powers [7,8]. Although moment and power analyses of individual patients are over a decade old [9,10] it is not until recently that they have begun to be used routinely in clinical assessments [11–13]. Ground reaction force patterns of a wide variety of patients have been reported [14–17]. However, ground reaction forces are outcome measures and by themselves give us no insight into the detailed cause of the pathological gait patterns at the motor level.

Three-dimensional (3-D) commercial systems have become available over the past five years, yet it is surprising that reports of 3-D kinetics are rare. Many gait labs are claiming to carry out 3-D kinematics, but without complete 3-D anatomical calibrations followed by full 3-D data collection and complete 3-D biomechanical modeling, it is not possible to gain 3-D moments and mechanical powers. Some gait labs yield 3-D kinematics of all joints of the lower limb [18], while others have limited their 3-D kinematics to the pelvis and trunk but have limited their kinetics to the sagittal plane [13]. Some limited reports have reported intrasubject profiles of 3-D moments of the lower limb for three subjects [19] and for one subject [20], while two lower-limb amputees have moment and power profiles of their prosthetic limbs reported [21]. Unfortunately, this latter report had 18 ensemble-averaged power profiles crammed into one fourth of the page, making it virtually

71

impossible to interpret. One major study on 29 subjects reported the 3-D moment patterns during natural, slow, and fast walking; variable patterns were seen at the knee in the sagittal plane and at the ankle in the frontal and transverse planes [22]. No power profiles in 3-D for normal gait have been reported in the literature.

The purpose of this chapter is to report the detailed power profiles for nine subjects, each of which has been averaged over five repeat trials. The focus of the results will be new information revealed by the patterns in the frontal plane that relate to lateral balance. Some differences are also apparent in the mechanical power patterns, especially at the hip as analyzed in 3-D versus the two-dimensional (2-D) plane-of-progression profiles previously reported. The balance role of the hip abductors/adductors in steady state gait, during initiation and termination of gait, and during quiet standing is emphasized.

4.2. METHODOLOGY

The details of the 3-D instrumentation, subject preparation, spatial calibration, modeling, and data collection protocol are reported elsewhere [23]. The anatomical calibration to define the principal axis system of each segment was somewhat different and is described in detail here. The subject was required to stand erect with the foot and pelvis principal axes parallel to all three axes of the global reference system (GRS). The protocol and the location of markers is presented in the Appendix and in Figure 4-1. The subjects were instrumented with a 16-channel biotelemetry system (14 EMG and 2 foot switches) plus reflective markers to define the following segments: feet, legs, thighs, pelvis, thorax, and head. This nine-segment model was tracked by three CCD cameras (two sagittal and one frontal) as the subjects walked at their natural cadence along an 11-m walkway over two AMTI (Advanced Mechanical Technology, Inc.) force platforms. Marker coordinate data were low-pass filtered using a critically damped, fourth-order Butterworth zero-lag filter. Cutoff frequencies of 6 Hz were used. The global 3-D coordinates and force-platform data were used to calculate the kinematic and kinetic variables in the nine-segment model. The electromyography (EMG) profiles are not reported in this chapter.

4.3. RESULTS

Because of the large number of curves in 3-D space, we have grouped them by joint and have omitted the angular velocity profiles; their polarity is discussed and can be inferred from the polarities of the moment and power curves. All intersubject profiles were normalized to body mass [6] prior to ensemble averaging in order to reduce variability. All moment curves are internal moments and carry the same descriptions as the muscles that generate the moments; in other words, a flexor moment is generated by flexor muscles.

4.3.1. Ankle Moments and Powers

The sagittal moment (Figure 4-2) is very characteristic of what has been reported previously in scores of planar studies: a small dorsiflexor moment (for a controlled lowering of the foot to the ground) followed by an increasing and large plantarflexor moment peaking

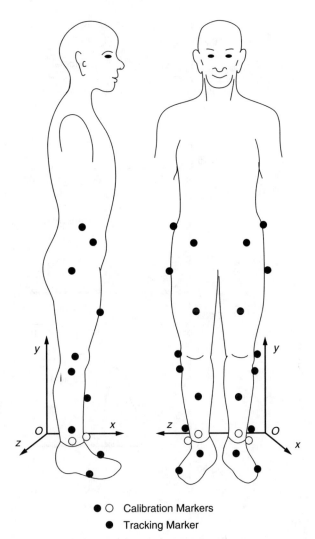

Figure 4-1. Location of reflective markers for 3-D trajectory of nine-segment model. Each segment has three independent noncolinear markers, and anatomical calibration required addition of four markers that were removed for walking trials.

●○ Calibration Markers

● Tracking Marker

at push-off. In the transverse plane, a small but regular external rotation pattern is evident during stance and might be the result of a small contribution from the plantarflexors in late stance, after the heel is off the ground. In the frontal plane, there is a small evertor moment immediately after heel contact, which reverses to invertor and back to evertor during late push-off. The associated power profiles in Figure 4-3 demonstrate that the plane-of-progression powers are totally dominant; the transverse ankle power is minuscule and inconsistent; the frontal plane power shows a very small absorption burst during push-off but was evident in only six of the nine subjects. The sagittal plane bursts are labeled as defined by D. A. Winter [24], with the work values compared with those reported in D. A. Winter et al. [25]. The negative A1-S work was 0.096 J/kg and the dominant positive A2-S push-off burst was 0.39 J/kg. The A1 burst was almost the same as that reported previously (0.116 J/kg) but the A2 burst was larger than that reported in 2-D studies (0.29 J/kg).

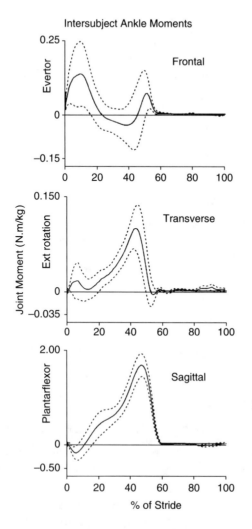

Figure 4-2. Three-dimensional internal ankle moments (N = 9,
n = 45) for nine adult subjects. Intersubject ensemble
average resulted from intrasubject ensemble average of
five repeat trials. See text
for discussion.

4.3.2. Knee Moments and Powers

The knee moment profiles normalized to body mass (Figure 4-4) were fairly consistent.
In the plane-of-progression, the knee exhibited profiles very similar to those reported from
planar studies [6]. There were minor differences in the magnitude of the peaks. The knee
extensor peak at weight acceptance was 0.45 N.m/kg, lower than 0.62 N.m/kg previously
reported. Also, the flexor peak at 40 percent of stride was higher (0.4 N.m/kg versus 0.27
N.m/kg). However, because of the fairly large intersubject variability, these differences
were not statistically significant. The differences were probably due to the definition of the
knee joint center in the 3-D model versus the planar location as defined by a marker located
in the midline of the lateral epicondyle of the femur. The distinct knee flexor moment
in late swing was virtually identical to that reported previously. In the transverse plane,
there was a small but distinct external rotation moment during weight acceptance, followed
by an internal rotation moment during push-off. These moments appear to be passive, as
indicated by the fact that they were attenuated versions of the pattern generated by the
hip external-internal rotators (see later discussion related to Figure 4-6). The frontal plane

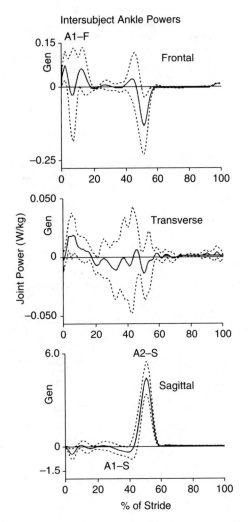

Figure 4-3. Three-dimensional intersubject ankle joint power profiles (N = 9, n = 45) for same subjects as reported in Fig. 4-2. See text for discussion.

moment pattern was entirely abductor during all of stance and reflected the gravitational loading of the condyles by the center of mass (COM) of head, arms, and trunk (H.A.T.) being medial of the knee joint center. Some of this moment was likely passive due to the loading of the medial condyles but was also active due to the tension in the iliotibial tract, itself due to continuous activity of the hip abductors (gluteus medius, tensor fasciae latae) during stance.

The power profiles at the knee (Figure 4-5) were essentially the same as previously reported in planar studies [8,25]. The four bursts reported previously (K1 . . . K4) were labeled here along with an early K0-S burst, which results from knee flexors (hamstrings) causing a short duration knee flexion immediately after heel contact (HC). All five of these bursts were seen in all nine subjects. There were two small but inconsistent bursts (not labeled) between 20 and 45 percent of stride, which were due to fluctuations in the small knee angular velocity during this midstance period. The work done by the muscles during each of these phases showed some differences with that previously reported. K1-S was slightly smaller (0.04 J/kg versus 0.048 J/kg); K2-S was larger (0.031 J/kg versus 0.019 J/kg). However, the absorption by the quadriceps in late stance and early swing (K3-S) was

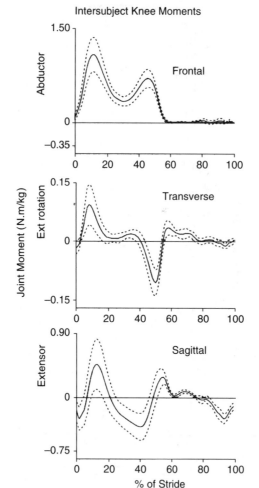

Figure 4-4. Three-dimensional intersubject internal knee moments (N = 9, n = 45) for same subjects as reported in Fig. 4-2. See text for discussion.

much larger (0.128 J/kg versus 0.047 J/kg), as was K4-S (0.141 J/kg versus 0.114/J/kg). Again, these differences can be attributed to definition of the knee joint center as defined in the 3-D versus the 2-D model.

The power profiles in the transverse plane were very small, with only one consistent negative burst during weight acceptance; this small loss in energy (0.009 J/kg) appeared to be due to passive structures resisting the external rotation of the knee. In the frontal plane there was a small and relatively consistent (eight out of nine subjects) generation (0.03 J/kg) as the abductors caused a small knee abduction during the first half of stance. During the latter half of stance a small absorption pattern was seen (0.021 J/kg) as these same abductor muscles allowed the joint to adduct slightly.

4.3.3. Hip Moments and Powers

At the hip, the differences between the 3-D and planar profiles were more significant. At the outset the ranges of movement of the hip joint were greater, especially in extension during late stance prior to toe-off (TO). There were two reasons for this difference. First, the

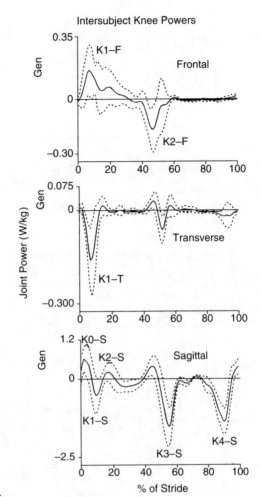

Figure 4-5. Three-dimensional intersubject knee power profiles (N = 9, n = 45) for same subjects as reported in Fig. 4-2. See text for discussion.

location of the hip joint in 3-D space is more medial than that defined by a greater trochanter reference. In 2-D space we defined the hip joint location in the plane-of-progression to be 3 cm superior and 1 cm posterior of the greater trochanter marker [26]. Also, in the 3-D model the hip joint was the angle between the femur and pelvis, while 2-D models routinely define the hip angle between the trunk and femur. This greater hip extension results in an increase in hip extensor velocity early in stance, with a commensurate alteration in the associated hip powers.

The hip moment profiles (Figure 4-6) have essentially the same patterns as that reported previously [6] but with significantly larger magnitudes. The initial hip extensor moment peaked at 1.2 N.m/kg, which was significantly larger than previously reported (0.6 N.m/kg). Also, the flexor peak in late stance was larger (1.03 N.m/kg versus 0.41 N.m/kg). These differences can be attributed to the parallax error of the hip location defined by a greater trochanter location. The more correct 3-D location placed the hip joint more medial; thus from the side camera it was more anterior during early stance and more posterior during late stance. The transverse moments were very consistent but small. An external rotator peak of 0.21 N.m/kg was evident at weight acceptance, followed by an almost equal (0.20

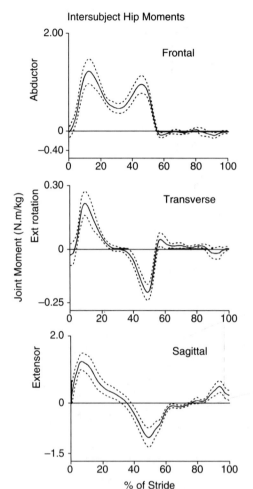

Figure 4-6. Three-dimensional intersubject internal hip moment profiles (N = 9, n = 45) for same subjects as reported in Fig. 4-2. See text for discussion.

N.m/kg) internal rotator peak in late stance. These patterns control the transverse rotation of the pelvis during single support. The frontal plane abductor pattern during almost all of stance was almost identical to that reported previously [27] and was responsible for the balance of the upper body in the frontal plane against the forces of gravity acting medial of the hip joint.

The power patterns at the hip (Figure 4-7) show one major difference from that reported in earlier planar studies. There was a large and consistent H1-S burst (0.31 J/kg) in this 3-D study versus a small and highly variable pattern (0.11 J/kg) from 2-D studies [25]. This H1-S burst results from high activity of the hip extensors during the first half of stance as the hip joint extends from its flexed position at HC. This burst has been described as a *push-from-behind* and definitely contributes to forward propulsion. The negative work burst (H2-S) associated with the deceleration of the backward rotating thigh was also larger than the 2-D studies reported (0.12 J/kg versus 0.043 J/kg). Similarly, the H3-S pull-off burst was higher (0.145 J/kg) in this 3-D study than in the 2-D study (0.089 J/kg). Thus all three major power bursts were larger, as a result of the higher estimated moments.

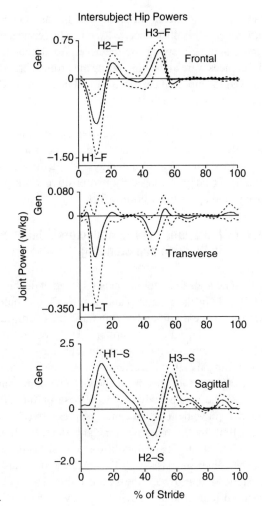

Figure 4-7. Three-dimensional intersubject hip power profiles (N = 9, n = 45) for same subjects as reported in Fig. 4-2. See text for discussion.

The transverse plane hip powers were small and somewhat inconsistent. The frontal plane powers were consistent across all nine subjects and reflect the role of the hip abductors during stance. During weight acceptance they acted eccentrically (H1-F) to absorb energy in controlling the drop of the pelvis and upper body (0.081 J/kg). Then in midstance they did positive work (H2-F) and caused a rise in the pelvis and upper body (0.031 J/kg). Finally, just prior to TO they did positive work (H3-F = 0.057 J/kg) and further raised the pelvis to increase the height of the contralateral hip prior to swing.

4.4. DISCUSSION

4.4.1. Summary of Major 3-D/2-D Differences and New Profiles

At the ankle there were no significant functional differences between the 3-D and 2-D analyses in either the moment or power profiles. At the knee the moment-of-force profiles showed no significant difference but the associated power profiles showed one statistical difference. This difference was a much larger negative work done during the K3 phase (late stance and early swing) by the eccentrically contracting quadriceps. The most important differences were at the hip. While the profiles had almost the same shape, the 3-D estimates showed the hip moment extensor and flexor peaks during stance were approximately twice the magnitude of the 2-D moments. As a result of these higher estimates, the work done by the hip muscles in all their phases (H1 . . . . . H3) was proportionally higher.

The work done in the transverse and frontal planes at all three joints was not functionally significant except at the hip in the frontal plane. Here we saw the stance limb hip abductors acted to absorb energy early in stance as they controlled the drop of the pelvis and upper body, followed by two positive work phases as these same muscles raised the pelvis and upper body prior to TO.

4.4.2. Importance of Hip Abductors/Adductors in Walking and Standing

The high abductor moment required at the hip (≈ 60 N.m) to maintain upright posture of H.A.T. in the frontal plane suggests we should look at the role of these same muscles in transient gait and in standing. In steady state walking this large abductor moment is required during single support. However, during transient conditions such as periods of double support, these same muscles have a major role in balancing the total body by controlling its lateral acceleration. During initiation and termination of gait, the hip abductors/adductors have been shown to be dominant in controlling mediolateral (ML) balance of the whole body about the base of support [23]. Prior to TO of the swing foot, the ML movement of the center of pressure (COP) is controlled by loading/unloading of each limb by the hip abductors/adductors, while the anteroposterior (AP) control is under ankle plantarflexor-dorsiflexor control. Thus to achieve the desired initial acceleration of the center of mass (COM) forward and toward the stance limb, the COP must move posteriorly and toward the swing limb. The posterior COP change is accomplished by reduced plantarflexor activity. However, the small lateral shift of COP is not controlled at the ankle. Rather, the shift results from a momentary loading of the swing limb by its hip abductors and unloading of the stance limb by decreasing its hip abductors. Once the COM has a forward velocity toward the stance limb, the COM must be accelerated forward and away from the stance limb. Thus a sudden loading of the stance limb by increased activity of its hip abductors occurs, which simultaneously unloads the swing limb and results in a rapid shift of the COP to the stance foot. The body COM is now accelerated forward and away from that stance limb. This fine and exact control of the net COP is even more critical during termination of gait [23]. Termination is seen to be the reverse of initiation, in that the net COP must be controlled to predict in advance the trajectory of the COM toward its future quiet stance position. Again the AP control comes from the ankle plantarflexors, while the critical ML control is dominated by the hip abductor/abductors.

Even during quiet standing the balance of the inverted pendulum is not an "ankle strategy" as inferred by many researchers [28]. AP control is achieved at the ankle, but the ML control is seen to be entirely at the hip; a hip load/unload is evident [29]. Again this ML control of the COP is achieved by the hip abductors/adductors.

4.4.3. Implications for Clinical Assessments

The fact that there were significant differences in the plane-of-progression moments and powers, especially at the hip joint, points to the need for 3-D inverse dynamics. Equally important are the frontal plane moments and powers, especially at the hip, which are critical in determining balance of the upper body in patients. A normalized database of these 3-D profiles is becoming mandatory to allow clinicians to pinpoint atypical motor patterns in patients [11–13,31], thereby focusing the clinician's attention on decisions regarding the cause of those atypical patterns. Based on his or her judgment, a decision will have to be made whether the atypical pattern is a primary problem or an adaptation to a primary problem [10]. Only then can proper rehabilitation or surgery be planned.

Appendix: Protocol and Location of Markers

The original subject calibration was reported in Y. Jian et al. [23] but was simplified to reduce the number of markers necessary to define the calibration position and to reduce the dependence of the actual marker placement in determining the local axes system. Markers on the midankle and the lateral malleolus were the only markers used in addition to the tracking markers for the calibration of the pelvis, thigh, legs, and feet. To simplify the calibration procedure, the principal axes of the pelvis and the foot segment were positioned to be parallel with the global reference system (GRS). The feet of the subjects were positioned at a standing width in which a marker halfway between the medial and lateral malleoli (midankle marker) was directly above a point halfway between the medial and lateral femoral condyles. Therefore, the foot and knee joint centers were aligned such that their global z coordinate was coincident with the global z coordinate of the midankle marker. A further simplification used a marker on the iliac crest to represent the hip joint x coordinate. In general, the principal reference systems were arranged such that the y axis ran the length of the segment from distal to proximal, the z axis ran from the left to the right side of the body and the x axis ran from posterior to anterior. This arrangement was the same for all segments, on both sides of the body. It was assumed that these principal axes also represented the anatomical axes for each segment. The origin of the principal axis system for each segment was fixed at the segment center of mass (COM). This point was assumed to lie on the long y axis of the segment. The distance between the COM and the distal end of the segment was calculated as a fraction of the distance between anatomical landmarks at either end of the segment. The exact landmarks and fractions used are as presented by D. A. Winter [30]. The moments of inertia were later calculated using regression equations [29]. These values will have slight errors as the anatomical reference systems in this study were not aligned exactly with the principal axes assumed by the authors.

1. *Pelvis*: The principal axes were aligned parallel to the global axes. The principal sagittal (xy) plane intersected the z axis at the midpoint of the two midankle markers. The hip joint was defined using fractions of the distance between the two ASIS (Bell et al., 1990). Thus, the hip joint y coordinate was located 30 percent of the inter–ASIS distance distal to the ASIS and the hip joint z coordinate was 45 percent of the distance lateral to the COM location. The hip joint x coordinate was defined as the x coordinate of the iliac crest. The L3/L4 joint was directly above the COM at the y height of the iliac crest.

2. *Thigh*: The long axis (principal y) extended from the hip joint center to an adjusted lateral femoral condyle marker. The z coordinate of the lateral femoral condyle marker had been adjusted to lie midway between the lateral and medial femoral condyles. The principal z axis was parallel to the global z. The principal x axis was defined as the cross product of the y and z axes. The knee joint was positioned on the principal y axis of the thigh, 2.5 cm distal from the lateral femoral condyle.

3. *Shank*: Since the subject was positioned with the ankle joint center and the knee joint center aligned with the same global z coordinate, a line joining the two joint centers at the level of the fibular head marker and the lateral malleoli marker defined the long y axis of the shank. The principal z axis was parallel to the global z axis. The principal x axis was defined as the cross product of the y and z axes. The ankle joint was defined along the principal y axis of the shank and set to be 1 cm distal to the level of the lateral malleolus.

4. *Foot*: The principal axes were parallel to the GRS. Thus, it was important to align the midankle marker, the heel, and the middle toes along a line parallel to the global x axis.

References

[1] Andriacchi TP, Ogle JA, Galante JO. Walking speed as a basis for normal and abnormal gait measurements. *J Biomech* 1977;10:261–268.

[2] Chao EY, Laughman RK, Schneider E, Stauffer RN. Normative data of knee joint motion and ground reaction forces in adult level walking. *J Biomech* 1983; 16:219–233.

[3] Cappozzo A, Figura F, Marchetti M, Pedotti A. The interplay of muscular and external forces in human ambulation. *J Biomech* 1976;9:35–43.

[4] Pedotti A. A study of motor coordination and neuromuscular activities. *Biol Cybernet* 1977;26:53–62.

[5] Winter DA. Overall principle of lower limb support during stance phase of gait. *J Biomech* 1980;13:923–927.

[6] Winter DA. Kinematic and kinetic patterns in human gait: Variability and compensating effects. *Hum Mvmt Sci* 1984;3:51–76.

[7] Winter DA, Robertson DGE. Joint torque and energy patterns in normal gait. *Biol Cybernet* 1978;29:137–142.

[8] Winter DA. Energy generation and absorption at the ankle and knee during fast, natural, and slow cadences. *Clin Orthop Rel Res* 1983;175:147–154.

[9] Winter DA. Use of kinetic analyses in the diagnostics of pathological gait. *Physio Canada* 1981;33:209–214.

[10] Winter DA. Concerning the scientific basis for the diagnosis of pathological gait and for rehabilitation protocols. *Physio Canada* 1985;37:245–252.

[11] Olney SJ, Jackson VG, George SR. Gait re-education guidelines for stroke patients with hemiplegia using mechanical energy and power analyses. *Physio Canada* 1988;40:242–248.

[12] Olney SJ, Griffin MP, Monga TN, McBride ID. Work and power in gait of stroke patients. *Arch Phys Med Rehabil* 1991;72:309–314.

[13] Rose SA, Õunpuu S, DeLuca PA, Strategies for the assessment of pediatric gait in the clincial setting. *Phys Ther* 1991;71:961–980.

[14] Smidt GL, Wadsworth JB. Floor reaction forces during gait: Comparison of patients with hip disease and normal subjects. *Phys Ther* 1973;53:1056–1062.

[15] Stallard J, Dounis E, Major RE, Rose GK. One leg swing through gait using two crutches: An analysis of the ground reaction forces and the gait phases. *Acta Orthop Scand* 1980;51:71–77.

[16] Skinner HG, Effeney DJ. Gait analysis in amputees. *Am J Phys Med Rehabil* 1985;64:82–89.

[17] Seliktar R, Mizraki J. Some gait characteristics of B/K amputees and their reflection on the ground reaction forces. *Eng in Med* 1986;15:27–34.

[18] Kadaba MP, Ramakrishnan HK, Wootten ME. Measurement of lower extremity kinematics during level walking. *J Orthop Res* 1990;8:383–392.

[19] Apkarian J, Naumann S, Cairns B. A three-dimensional kinematic and dynamic model of the lower limb. *J Biomech* 1989;22:143–155.

[20] Kadaba MP, Ramakrishnan HK, Wootten ME, Gainey J, Cochran GVB. Repeatability of kinematic, kinetic, and electroymyography data in normal adult gait. *J Orthop Res* 1989;7:849–860.

[21] Colborne GR, Naumann S, Longmuir PE, Berbrayer D. Analysis of mechanical and metabolic factors in the gait of congenital below-knee amputees. *Am J Phys Med Rehabil* 1992;71:272–278.

[22] Andriacchi TP, Mikosz RP. Musculoskeletal dynamics, locomotion and clinical applications. In: Mow VC, Hayes WC eds. *Basic Orthopaedic Biomechanics*. New York, NY: Raven Press;1991.

[23] Jian Y, Winter DA, Ishac MG, Gilchrist L. Trajectory of the body COG and COP during initiation and termination of gait. *Gait and Posture* 1993;1:9–22.

[24] Winter DA. Biomechanical motor patterns in normal walking. *J Mot Behav* 1983;15:302–330.

[25] Winter DA, Patla AE, Frank JS, Walt SE. Biomechanical walking pattern changes in the fit and healthy elderly. *Phys Ther* 1990;70:340–347.

[26] McFadyen B, Winter DA, Scott S, Fuglevand AJ. Towards better estimates of hip and ankle joint centres. In: *Proc 5th Cdn Soc Biomech Conf*; Ottawa, Ontario: August, 1989.

[27] MacKinnon CD, Winter DA. Control of whole body balance in the frontal plane during human walking. *J Biomech* 1993;26:633–644.

[28] McCollum G, Leen TK. Form and exploration of mechanical stability limits in erect stance. *J Mot Behav* 1989;21:225–244.

[29] Winter DA, Prince F, Stergiou P, Powell C. Medial-lateral and anterior-posterior motor responses associated with centre of pressure changes in quiet standing. *Neurosci Res Commun* 1993;12:141–148.

[30] Winter DA. *Biomechanics and Motor Control of Human Movement*. 2nd ed. New York, NY: John Wiley and Sons, Inc., 1990.

[31] Gage JR. The clinical use of kinetics for evaluation of pathological gait in cerebral palsy. *J Bone Joint Surg Am* 1994;76:622–631.

Richard P. Mikosz
Thomas P. Andriacchi
Ken N. Kuo

Chapter 5

The Use of Kinetic Data for Research and Clinical Applications in Human Motion Analysis

5.1. INTRODUCTION

The use of kinetic data for research and clinical applications in human motion analysis is very important in understanding the biomechanics of human motion and in assessing the biomechanics of various clinical pathologies [1–3]. Gait analysis is especially useful in assessing the gait of children with cerebral palsy [4–6]. Gait analysis can provide useful information in identifying contributions from other joints involved in producing the dynamic deformity. Gait parameters in general can be divided into three groups: time-distance, kinematic, and kinetic.

Time-distance parameters offer the researcher and clinician information such as walking speed, stride length, and cadence [7,8]. Stride length is dependent on the subject's walking speed and stature and is a sensitive indicator of walking abnormalities. Since stride length depends on walking speed and stature, it is important when comparing measurements between normals and individuals with walking disabilities to account for differences in walking speed and stature.

Kinematics, a subdivision of dynamics, is the study of motion. Kinematics is used to relate displacement, velocity, acceleration, and time without reference to the cause of the motion. In the analysis of human locomotion, kinematic techniques have been used to study body movements in both two-dimensional and three-dimensional space. While there are many types of kinematic measurements that can be used to measure locomotion, relative segmental angular motions have been used most frequently [9]. Relative segmental angular measurements have been applied extensively in measurement of walking and other activities of daily living. The anatomical definitions of angular joint movements are potentially ambiguous.

Kinetics is the study of the relation existing between the forces acting on a body, the mass of the body, and the motion of the body. Kinetics is used to predict the motion caused by given forces or to determine the forces required to produce a given motion [10]. An understanding of the kinetics of human movement is fundamental to the understanding of the musculoskeletal system [11]. The motion of the musculoskeletal system is the result of a balance between external and internal forces acting on it [12].

The purpose of this chapter is to point out the importance of the use of kinetic data for research and clinical applications in human motion analysis. In addition, this chapter will focus on relevant gait parameters used for assessing gait to evaluate ambulatory function preoperatively. Examples will be used to illustrate important gait parameters.

5.2. TIME-DISTANCE PARAMETERS

Time-distance measurements include measures of walking speed, cadence, and stride length. These are all important measures of normal and abnormal walking. Walking speed is the person's rate of travel determined by identifying the time required to cover a designated distance. Speed is defined as the magnitude of the velocity, and it is a scaler quantity [13].

Stride length is defined as the distance between consecutive unilateral heel-strikes and is one of the simplest and most sensitive indicators of walking abnormalities. Stride length depends on walking speed; thus, in comparing measurements among normals and individuals with walking disabilities, it is important to account for differences in walking speed [14–16]. The relationship between stride length and walking speed for normal individuals is relatively linear and reproducible. The following example illustrates the use of stride length in a population of spastic cerebral palsy patients with an apparent equinus deformity of the ankle. Figure 5-1 shows the stride length for a normal population and for the spastic cerebral palsy population. The stature of both populations were within 1-standard deviation and therefore stride length is not normalized to stature in this example. The stride length for the cerebral palsy population is shorter compared to the normal population at higher

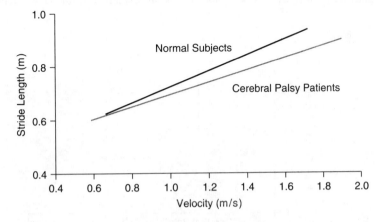

Figure 5-1. Regression analysis of stride length versus velocity for a spastic cerebral palsy population with an apparent equinus deformity of the ankle and a normal age-matched population.

walking speeds. At 1.0 m/s, the stride length for the normal population is approximately 0.73 m. The stride length for the cerebral palsy population at 1.0 m/s is approximately 0.69 m. This represents a 5 percent difference in stride length between the two populations (not statistically different, $p > 0.05$). At higher walking speeds (1.7 m/s) there is approximately a 9 percent change in the stride length for the two populations. It is noteworthy that the ranges of walking speeds between the normal population and cerebral palsy population are similar (ranging from 0.6 to 1.8 m/s).

The time-distance parameters, while efficient in evaluating quantitative changes in the overall characteristics of walking, do not provide specific information that can be related to the cause of the walking abnormality.

5.3. KINEMATICS

Relative segmental angles during gait have been described for normal gait. Angular measurements have most frequently been described for the hip, knee, and ankle joints [17,18]. These measurements are obtainable using both electrogoniometric and optical methods [19–21].

Measurement of joint kinematics can be used to help quantify specific joint involvements in walking disability. In particular, relative segmental angles quantify changes in patterns of motion related to specific joints. Consider again the example of the gait of patients with spastic cerebral palsy with dynamic equinus ankle deformity. In addition to the shorter-than-normal stride lengths, these patients have reduced midstance knee flexion (Figure 5-2). The normal midstance knee flexion is approximately 20 degrees at an average speed of 1.0 m/s, whereas patients with spastic cerebral palsy tend to walk with approximately 10 degrees of midstance knee flexion. The loss of midstance knee flexion is possible due to a flexion contracture of the hamstring muscles. This contributes to the reduction of the dynamic range of knee motion. Although the reduction in midstance knee flexion offers information about the specific phase of the gait cycle, at present it does not provide an explanation for the existence of this adaptation.

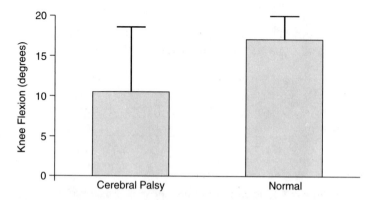

Figure 5-2. Stance phase knee flexion (degrees) for a spastic cerebral palsy population with an apparent equinus deformity of the ankle and normal age-matched population.

5.4. KINETICS

An understanding of the kinetics of human movement is fundamental to the understanding of the musculoskeletal system. The motion of the musculoskeletal system is the result of a balance between external and internal forces acting on it.

Before one can begin to analyze the forces acting during human movement, some basic definitions and assumptions must be made. In most studies of locomotion, the limb segments are assumed to be rigid. This simplifies the analysis since the structure is assumed not to deform under load. Forces acting on the rigid body may be classified as either external forces or internal forces. External forces represent the action of other bodies on the rigid body under consideration. Internal forces are responsible for holding together the component parts that make up the rigid body. Moments about an axis measure the tendency of a force to impart to the body a motion of rotation about a fixed axis. A moment of a force is expressed in units of Newton meters.

Inertia is a body's resistance to acceleration. Inertial resistance to linear acceleration depends on geometry and mass (and is generally referred to as *mass moment of inertia*). The mass moment of inertia must be referenced to a coordinate system. A more detailed discussion of mass moment of inertia can be found in a basic text on mechanics [13].

The analysis of forces and motion is a branch of mechanics called *dynamics*. Newton's second law of motion links the kinematics of a body to the kinetics. Newton's second law makes it possible to calculate forces acting on the musculoskeletal system from measurements of motion and segment mass. Usually, for locomotion studies, the foot-ground reaction forces are also measured. The external moment acting at the knee joint is indicative of the net muscle activity. The contribution of antagonistic muscle activity increases the load at the joint since the force in the agonist muscles must increase to counteract the contribution to the internal moment due to the antagonistic muscle activity. Thus, if no antagonistic muscle activity were present, the moment magnitude and direction would reflect the lower bound of muscle force and joint force. The presence of any antagonistic activity would increase both muscle and joint force. The external moment can be used to indicate net muscle activity during gait [11].

The following example illustrates the application of kinetics in evaluating ambulatory function and surgical treatment planning for patients with spastic cerebral palsy and an equinus deformity of the ankle.

5.4.1. Example: Patients with Spastic Cerebral Palsy and Dynamic Equinus Ankle Deformity

Treatment planning for patients with spastic cerebral palsy and an equinus deformity of the ankle is often complicated by the difficulty in determining the degree of hamstring involvement in the dynamic deformity [22]. The dynamic nature of the deformity is only briefly apparent during the stance phase of gait.

In this example, gait analysis is useful in identifying contributions from other joints producing the dynamic deformity [23]. The quantification in evaluation of the joint moment during locomotion can be useful in attempting to identify both the nature and the cause of the functional abnormality in patients with spastic cerebral palsy. Fourteen consecutive patients with an equinus deformity of the foot were selected for tendo-achilles lengthening on the basis of clinical examination. Ten patients were hemiplegic and four patients were diplegic. The patients were tested while walking the length of a 10-m walkway over a range of walking speeds. Instrumentation included an optoelectronic system for movement analysis, a force platform, and a microcomputer for data acquisition.

All patients had an abnormal pattern of ankle plantar-dorsiflexion moments during stance phase. This pattern differed from the normal pattern (Figure 5-3) in that the magnitude of the first peak of the ankle dorsiflexion moment occurring just after heel-strike was significantly higher than normal. Two different groups emerged based on the flexion-extension moment patterns at the knee (Figure 5-4). Seven patients demonstrated a moment that predominantly tended to extend the knee during stance phase (extension group). A second group had a moment that predominantly tended to flex the knee during stance phase (flexion group). The patients in the extension group had a significantly lower heel-strike knee flexion angle (Figure 5-5) than patients in the flexion group ($p < 0.05$). Patients in the extension group maintained a straighter knee throughout stance phase, with a minimum knee flexion angle of 6.7 ± 5 compared to 22.1 ± 16.8 for the flexion group (Figure 5-6). It was interesting to note that the clinical measure of the popliteal angle and range of dorsiflexion motion of the ankle obtained from clinical examination showed no significant difference between the two groups. Electromyography (EMG) is a relevant gait parameter; however, when in the assessment of the gait of children with spastic cerebral palsy, it offers little information since both antagonistic and agonistic muscle activity are present at the same time.

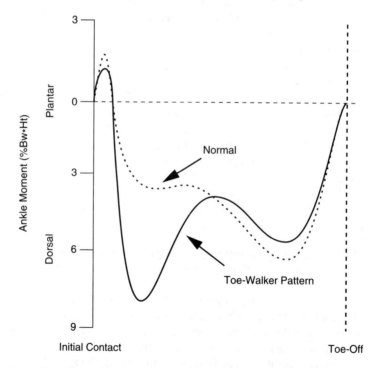

Figure 5-3. The ankle plantar-dorsiflexion moment pattern for a spastic cerebral palsy population with an apparent equinus deformity of the ankle ("toe-walker pattern") and a normal age-matched population. The ankle moment is normalized to the subject's weight and height and is reported as a percentage of body weight times height.

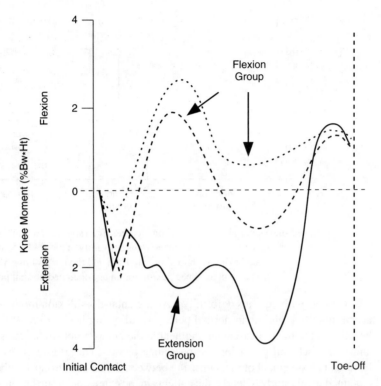

Figure 5-4. The knee flexion-extension moment patterns for a spastic cerebral palsy population with an apparent equinus deformity of the ankle. Moment patterns at knee joint were divided into flexion and extension groups. Knee moment is normalized to the subject's weight and height and is reported as a percentage of body weight times height.

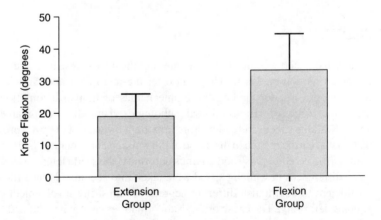

Figure 5-5. Initial contact knee flexion (degrees) for a spastic cerebral palsy population with an apparent equinus deformity of the ankle. Initial contact knee flexion is shown for extension and flexion groups.

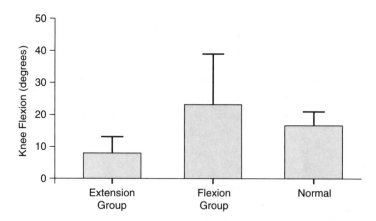

Figure 5-6. Stance phase knee flexion (degrees) for a spastic cerebral palsy population with an apparent equinus deformity of the ankle. Stance phase
knee flexion is shown for extension and flexion groups. Also shown
is stance phase knee flexion for an age-matched normal population.

Patients with equinus deformity have a plantar-dorsiflexion moment at the ankle that
has an initially higher-than-normal peak just following heel-strike. Patients separated on
the basis of the flexion-extension moment at the knee demonstrated substantially different
ability to reach full extension during stance phase. These differences suggest differing
degrees of involvement of the hamstring between the flexion group and the extension group
as defined in this study. Clearly, the patients in the extension group had nearly full extension
during stance phase and are therefore likely to have less involvement of a spastic hamstring
during the midstance of gait than those patients in the flexion group. Thus the gait test
identified differences among a patient population that was not detected clinically. The
nature of the gait differences have important implications to the treatment planning for this
patient population.

5.5. CONCLUSION

Kinetic data such as joint moments are significant for research and clinical application
in human motion analysis. They can offer the researcher and clinician information that
is important in understanding the biomechanics of human locomotion and in assessing
the biomechanics of various clinical pathologies. Time-distance parameters such as stride
length, walking speed, and cadence are important measures but do not provide specific information that can be related to the cause of the walking abnormality. In the example of patients
with spastic cerebral palsy and equinus deformity, the stride length was shorter than normal
when differences in walking speed were taken into account. Measuring time-distance was
insufficient to distinguish differing degrees of hamstring involvement contributing to the
equinus deformity. The cause of these abnormalities cannot be obtained from time-distance
measurements alone.

Measurement of joint kinematics offers the researcher and clinician data that allow
them to quantify the specific joint involvement in walking disability. In the example of
patients with spastic cerebral palsy with equinus deformity of the ankle, there was a reduction
of approximately 50 percent in midstance knee flexion in the extension group compared

to normal. Although measurement of joint kinematics can provide a quantitative measure of the functional adaptation to the specific joint, it does not provide an explanation for the existence of this adaptation.

Measurements of joint kinetics, specifically moments at the joints, offer the clinician and researcher information related to the nature of the functional abnormality by isolating the involvement of the muscle group responsible. The magnitude and direction of the flexion-extension moment can be related to muscular function and to joint loading.

References

[1] Andriacchi TP, Galante JO, Fermier RW. The influence of total knee replacement design on walking and stairclimbing. *J Bone Joint Surg Am* 1982;64-A:1328–1335.

[2] Andriacchi TP, Kramer GM, Landon GC. The biomechanics of running and knee injuries. In: Finerman G ed. *American Academy of Orthopaedic Surgeons, Symposium on Sports Medicine, The Knee*. St. Louis, Missouri: CV Mosby Company;1985: 23–32.

[3] Lai K-A, Kuo KN, Andriacchi TP. Relationship between dynamic deformities and joint moments in children with cerebral palsy. *J Ped Orthop* 1988;8(6):690–695.

[4] Rose SA, DeLuca PA, Davis III RB, Õunpuu S, Gage JR. Kinematic and kinetic evaluation of the ankle after lengthening of the gastrocnemius fascia in children with cerebral palsy. *J Ped Orthop* 1993;13(6):727–732.

[5] Gage JR, Fabian D, Hicks R, Tashman S. Preoperative and postoperative gait analysis in patients with spastic diplegia: A preliminary report. *J Ped Orthop* 1984;4(6): 715–725.

[6] Gage JR. Gait analysis for decision-making in cerebral palsy. *Bulletin of The Hospital for Joint Diseases Orthopaedic Institute* 1983;XLIII(2):147–163.

[7] Larsson LE, Miller M, Norlin R, Tkaczuk H. Changes in gait patterns after operations in children with spastic cerebral palsy. *Proc Intl Orthop (SICOT)* 1986;10:155–162.

[8] Norlin R, Odenrick P. Development of gait in spastic children with cerebral palsy. *J Ped Orthop* 1986;6(6):674–680.

[9] Blankervoort L, Huiskes R, DeLange A. The helical axes along the envelope of passive knee joint motion. In: *Proc 32nd Annual Mtg Orthop Res Soc* 1986;12:410.

[10] Bresler B, Frankel JP. The forces and moments in the leg during level walking. In: *Trans ASME*, 1953;48A:62.

[11] Andriacchi TP, Strickland AB. Gait analysis as a tool to assess joint kinetics. In: Berme N, Engin AE, Correia Da Silva KM, eds. *Biomechanics of Normal and Pathological Human Articulating Joints*. NATO ASI Series E (93). Dordrecht: Martinus Nijhoff;1985:83–102.

[12] Cappozzo A, Figura F, Marchetti M. The interplay of muscular and external forces in human angulation. *J Biomech* 1976;9(1):35–43.

[13] Beer FP, Johnston Jr ER. *Vector Mechanics For Engineers: Dynamics*. 5th ed. New York: McGraw-Hill Inc;1988.

[14] Andriacchi TP, Ogle JA, Galante JO. Walking speed as a basis for normal and abnormal gait measurements. *J Biomech* 1977;10:261–268.

[15] Grieve DW. Gait patterns and the speed of walking. *J Biomed Eng* 1968;3:119–122.

[16] Shapiro A, Susak Z, Malkin C, Mizrahi J. Preoperative and postoperative gait evaluation in cerebral palsy. *Arch Phys Med Rehabil* 1990;71:236–240.

[17] Grood ES, Suntay WJ. A joint coordinate system for the clinical description of three-dimensional motions: Application to the knee. *J Biomech Eng* 1983;105:136–144.

[18] Lamoreux L. Kinematic measurements in the study of human walking. *Bull Prosthetic Res* 1971;3.

[19] Chao EYS. Justification of triaxial goniometer for the measurement of joint rotation. *J Biomech* 1980;13:989–1006.

[20] Kettlekamp DB, Johnson RJ, Smidt GL, Chao EYS, Walker M. An electrogoniometric study of knee motion in normal gait. *J Bone Joint Surg Am* 1970;52A(4):775–790.

[21] Kinzel GL, Hall Jr AS, Hillberry BM. Measurement of the total motion between two body segments—I. Analytical development. *J Biomech* 1972;5:93–105.

[22] Brunt D, Scarborough N. Ankle muscle activity during gait in children with cerebral palsy and equinovarus deformity. *Arch Phys Med Rehabil* 1988;69:115–117.

[23] Ackman JD, Mikosz RP, Kuo KN, Lubicky JP, Harris GF, Andriacchi TP. Clinical implications of gait variations in spastic cerebral palsy patients with dynamic equinus ankle deformity. In: *Proc 37th Annual Mtg Orthop Res Soc* 1991:16(1):260.

Christopher L. Vaughan
Gary D. Brooking
Kenneth S. Olree

Chapter 6

Exploring New Strategies for Controlling Multiple Muscles in Human Locomotion

6.1. INTRODUCTION

Bipedal gait is an important hallmark of human evolution. Despite complex control systems, human gait is characterized by smooth, regular, and repeating movements. It therefore provides an appropriate focus to elucidate the flexible control strategies used by a biological system, and moreover, there is the potential for applying these strategies to robotic design. While much is known about individual components of human locomotion, it is significant that there is no widely accepted hypothesis for how the process works. The long-term goal of our research is to develop and test an integrated theory of bipedal gait that combines computational models of the neural control and musculoskeletal effector systems.

There are three theoretical models that provide the foundation for the work described here. Basic research in the spinalized cat preparation has shown that the initiation and timing of muscle action seems to be the work of a network of interneurons in the spinal cord that provides a cyclic pattern of signals [1]. This primitive and localized circuit, which we have called a spinal oscillating network (SON), is the first theoretical model. Once the neural drive has activated the muscles, they develop tension, and the musculoskeletal system operates in a functional milieu that is governed by the theory of Newtonian mechanics (our second model). The link between the neural control system (SON theory) and musculoskeletal effector system (Newtonian theory) has hardly been explored. We believe that artificial neural network (ANN) theory, especially with the incorporation of biologically based design features and feedback structures, can provide this vital link.

In this chapter we first review the research literature that provides the foundation for much of our own thinking. Second, we describe three projects that integrate our most recent research. Third, we lay out our research agenda for the next few years, delineating the steps that will be required to accomplish successful testing of our theoretical model of human locomotion. Finally, we consider some of the possible clinical applications of the technology and speculate on future trends in this field.

6.2. NEURAL CONTROL OF HUMAN LOCOMOTION

6.2.1. Neuronal Oscillators

Beginning with the pioneering research on mammalian walking by T. G. Brown [2], it has become increasingly evident that such rhythmic movements, both in the vertebrates and in the invertebrates, are generated by neuronal circuits that, in the isolated central nervous system (CNS), can generate neuronal activity patterns closely resembling those observed in nearly intact animals [3,4]. Rapid progress in the identification of specific neuronal oscillators that generate animal locomotor rhythms has occurred only recently, and most completely, with the investigation of the circuits underlying invertebrate movements. For example, there now exist published circuit diagrams of the neuronal oscillators underlying locomotory rhythms in leeches, insects, and marine mollusks, to name only the best described preparations [5,6]. Several of these circuits have been analyzed extensively through modeling studies [5]. In the recent past, research on vertebrate locomotor circuits has also progressed rapidly [7]. Detailed neuronal circuits that underlie vertebrate locomotion are now available for larval frogs [8] and for the lamprey [9]. S. Grillner [10] has suggested that there are a number of neuronal modules (possibly corresponding to spinal segmental levels, which he has referred to as a central pattern generator, or CPG), each of which can be made to produce a rhythmic output. He has further speculated on the unit CPG hypothesis, which suggests a very versatile motor organization, able to combine different components in a variety of ways. While an independent control of parts could be utilized, for instance, in the volitional control of independent ankle, knee, or hip movements or even individual muscle groups, activation of the entire CPG network will normally give rise to locomotion [10]. Rather than CPG, we prefer to use the concept of an SON in the current chapter.

6.2.2. Spinal Cord Circuitry

The identities of the neurons that comprise the SON remain largely unknown, but they do appear to be coextensive with interneurons that receive primary afferent input [11]. Although SONs can function without sensory input, this input can modify and reset the output to the alpha motoneurons [12]. Figure 6-1 illustrates the current knowledge of spinal cord circuitry: both the proprioceptive feedback and the descending commands converge on a matrix of interneurons [11]. Among these interneurons are at least some distinct subtypes with predictable input patterns (e.g., Renshaw cells, propriospinal cells, Ib inhibitory interneurons, reciprocal inhibitory interneurons) that allow a complex distribution of input signals [13]. We believe that this matrix of connections between the spinal interneurons, which links the sensors and actuators, can provide the necessary framework for us to build our ANN model of bipedal gait.

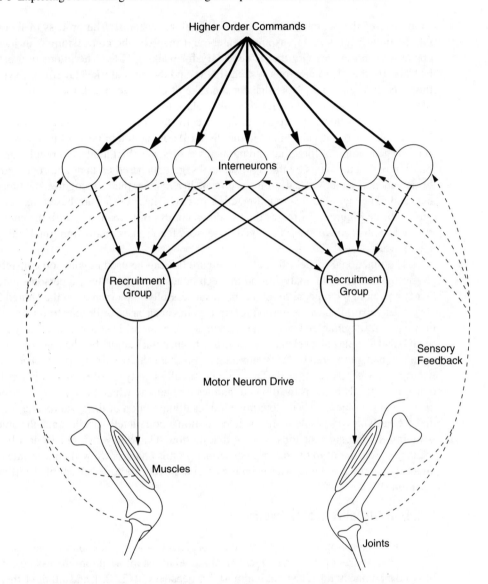

Figure 6-1. Spinal integration, in which both the descending commands and
proprioceptive feedback converge on a matrix of interneurons [11].
Among the interneurons are some distinct subtypes: Renshaw cells;
propriospinal cells, Ib inhibitory interneurons, and reciprocal inhibitory interneurons.

6.2.3. A Cause-and-Effect Model of Bipedal Gait

Upright bipedal gait is an important characteristic of the human condition, and yet
too often this ability to walk is taken for granted. When the locomotor apparatus malfunc-
tions, and walking ability is impaired, available options seldom account for the underlying

complexity of the neural, muscular, and skeletal subsystems. The process of locomotor programming occurs in supraspinal centers and involves the conversion of an idea into a pattern of muscle activity that is necessary for walking [14]. The interaction between the CNS, the peripheral nervous system (PNS), and the musculoskeletal effector system is illustrated in Figure 6-2. Note that for the sake of clarity, feedback loops have not been included. The sequence of events that takes place for walking to occur, therefore, can be summarized as follows: (1) registration and activation of the gait command in the CNS; (2) transmission of the gait signals to the PNS; (3) contraction of muscles that develop tension; (4) generation of forces at, and moments across, synovial joints; (5) regulation of the joint forces and moments by the rigid skeletal segments based on their anthropometry; (6) displacement (i.e., movement) of the segments in a manner that is recognized as functional gait; and (7) generation of ground reaction forces. These events are based on cause and effect. While Figure 6-2 stresses the top-down control of human gait, with the cascade of events described above, the role played by sensory feedback is vitally important and should not be overlooked.

The functional model illustrated in Figure 6-2 can be used to gain some insight into physiology, methods of analysis, and the techniques utilized to study a person's gait [15]. Dynamic gait in the bipedal robot has been successfully implemented in the United States [16] and in Japan [17], where the control strategy has been based on driving torques applied at the joints with angular feedback. The mathematical relationship between electromyography (EMG) and the musculoskeletal system awaits further elucidation, but the Newtonian model of human gait, pioneered by W. Braune and O. Fischer [18] over a century ago, has received widespread acceptance [15,19]. There are essentially two types of problems in rigid body dynamics [20]. The first is the direct dynamics problem, in which the forcing functions are known and the objective is to determine the resulting motion of the system. The second is the inverse dynamics problem, in which the motion is completely specified and the objective is to find the forcing functions causing that motion. Gait analysis normally involves this second approach, but in the research described in this chapter, we will concentrate on the direct dynamics problem. The equations to be solved are a set of coupled differential equations [21].

6.2.4. Artificial Neural Networks

ANN theory, one example of computational neuroscience, has come about through the efforts of scientists to create a mathematical model of the information-processing capabilities of the human brain. The field is almost five decades old [22,23], and although there was some activity in the 1960s [24–26] it has only become widely accepted as an area of serious research endeavor with the relatively recent efforts of J. J. Hopfield [27], J. A. Anderson [28], D. E. Rumelhart el al. [29], S. Grossberg [30], and others. As the name implies, an ANN is a group of many *neurons* (sometimes referred to as *units* or *processing elements*) that are interconnected and distributed in layers. The operation of the network is normally divided into two different phases [31]. First, in response to a given input stimulus, a process of changes in the synaptic weights (and other pertinent parameters) takes place. This phenomenon is called *learning*. The second function of an ANN is to *recall*, or to process an input stimulus and generate an output signal. What distinguishes one ANN mode! from another are their respective learning and recall mechanisms, the activation functions, the numbers of layers and neurons, and the distribution of connections. Robotic manipulators have utilized ANNs to replace direct dynamics algorithms [32], while applications of ANNs to study real biological systems have started to appear within the past few years [33–35].

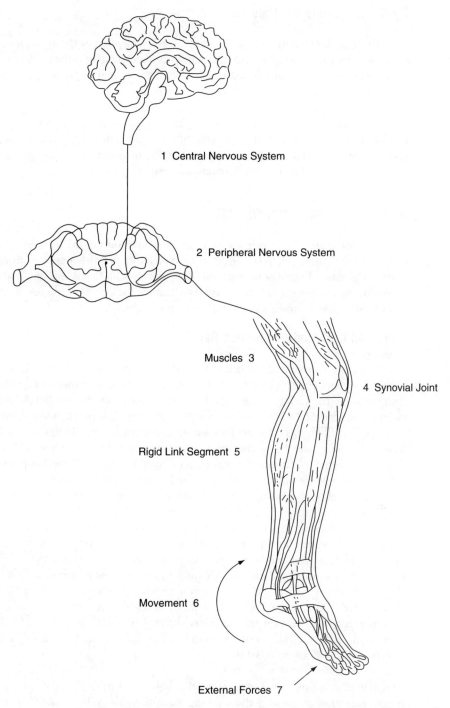

1 Central Nervous System

2 Peripheral Nervous System

Muscles 3

4 Synovial Joint

Rigid Link Segment 5

Movement 6

External Forces 7

Figure 6-2. The sequence of events necessary for human locomotion to occur. (While this cause-and-effect model stresses "top down" control of human gait, the important role played by sensory feedback should not be overlooked.) This figure has been reproduced, with permission, from C. L. Vaughan et al. [15].

6.2.5. Integrating the Theories

The argument has thus come full circle: ANNs, inspired by the example of the central nervous system, now have the potential to help us understand how the CNS itself functions. We believe that biologically based ANNs have the potential to provide a robust model of the oscillating and trajectory networks that control human gait. While some authors have suggested one advantage of ANNs is that hidden properties emerge when simulations are run [36], it is our contention that while the weights and interconnections store the functionality and memory of the system, they provide little insight into the overall functioning of the system. We will address this problem in our future research by developing a series of networks in smaller blocks to gain functional insight.

6.3. OUR RESEARCH FINDINGS TO DATE

There are three areas in which we have been working during the past few years that are relevant to the current chapter. These are: an ANN model of human gait using EMGs as input to the network; analyzing bilateral EMG signals with factor analysis; and developing a biologically based neuron that incorporates features lacking in current ANN designs. We describe these three projects in the following paragraphs.

6.3.1. An ANN Model of Human Gait

The basic structure of our network consisted of an array of several neurons and inter-connections between all elements from consecutive rows, as shown in Figure 6-3(a). We therefore hypothesized that input signals (EMG) could be used to predict the output signals (joint moments). The ANN was implemented with the back-propagation algorithm, which is composed of two stages: a feedforward step, where neuronal outputs are specified; and a feedback stage, where the connection weights and bias terms are updated [37,38]. The two steps are repeated for several patterns (sets of input and output values) until the difference between the network output and the expected values is below a specified tolerance value. This learning phase is illustrated in the left hand flow chart of Figure 6-3(b). In the EMG to joint moment mapping of Figure 6-3(a), the input signals are the EMG values for 16 muscles (gluteus medius and maximus, semitendinosus, biceps femoris, erector spinae, sartorius, rectus femoris, vastus lateralis, adductor longus and magnus, tibialis anterior, extensor digitorum longus, medial and lateral gastrocnemius, soleus, and peroneus) on the right side of the body. All training data (16 EMG and 3 joint moment patterns) were obtained from D. A. Winter [19]. Successful training of the network [left hand side of Figure 6-3(b)] took about 100,000 iterations, by which time the error (difference between actual and predicted joint moments) was below a predetermined threshold of 0.025. Simulating any abnormality took no more than a fraction of a second since all this required was a single feedforward loop [right side of Figure 6-3(b)].

Two abnormalities were simulated: a 30 percent reduction in soleus activity, and complete elimination of the rectus femoris. Figure 6-4(a) depicts the network prediction for the reduction in soleus activity during the entire gait cycle. It shows a clear decrease in plantarflexor (extensor) ankle moment during most of the stance phase and particularly before toe-off. This agrees with what we might expect since the soleus reaches maximum

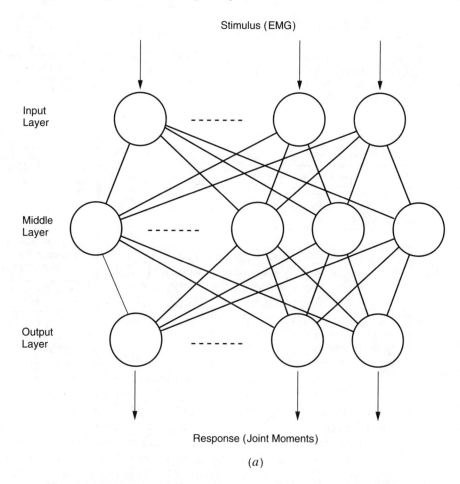

Stimulus (EMG)

Input Layer

Middle Layer

Output Layer

Response (Joint Moments)

(*a*)

Figure 6-3. (*a*) Basic architecture for a three-layer artificial neural network. Sixteen EMG patterns provide stimulus to the input layer of neurons; these are fully connected to the middle (or hidden) layer of neurons, which in turn are connected to the output layer. Response (or output) from this network is a set of three joint moments. (*b*) This flowchart illustrates the two important activities that take place after an artificial neural network has been built: training, shown on the left from Start to branch point 1; and simulation, shown on the right from 1 to Stop. Both (*a*) and (*b*) have been adapted from F. Sepulveda et al. [37].

activity during the latter part of stance phase, between 40 percent and 60 percent of the gait cycle. Figure 6-4(*b*) shows the joint moment predictions for a simulated elimination of the rectus femoris, a bi-articulate muscle that acts both as a hip flexor and knee extensor. The response is an increase in hip extensor and a decrease in knee extensor moments shortly after heel-strike, which corresponds to what we might expect. Despite the apparent success of this network, a number of shortcomings still exist: There are no feedback loops; the physical arrangements of muscles are ignored; and time is not an explicit variable in the

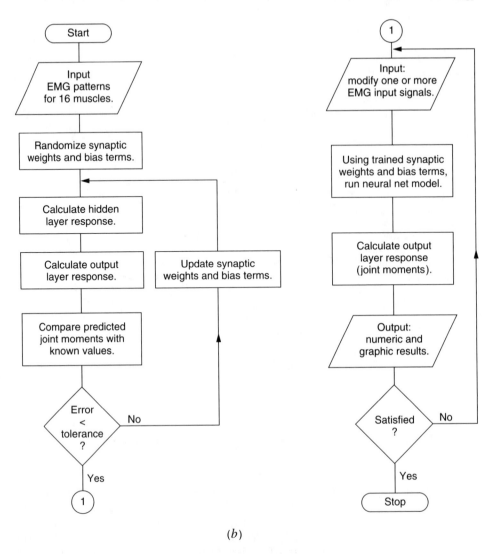

(b)

Figure 6-3. *(Continued)*

model. The speculative nature of computer simulation is both its appeal and weakness [39], but rigorous validation still tends to be an extremely difficult task [40]. Relatively few workers in the field of human gait biomechanics have attempted simulations of pathological conditions [41].

6.3.2. Bilateral EMG Signals and Factor Analysis

We have explored the application of multivariate statistical techniques to the 16 unilateral EMG signals presented by D. A. Winter [19] and have demonstrated that as few as 4 patterns can account for 91.5 percent of the variance in the original data set [15,42]. We rotated the eigen vectors so that they represented the most basic orthogonal features

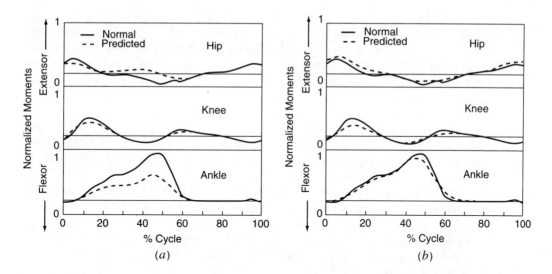

Figure 6-4. (*a*) The artificial neural network simulates a 30% reduction in soleus activity. The network predicts a reduction in the plantarflexor moment at the ankle. (*b*) The artificial neural network simulates the elimination of rectus femoris activity. The network predicts an increase in the hip extensor moment in early stance, and a decrease in knee extensor moment. Both (*a*) and (*b*) have been adapted from F. Sepulveda et al. [37].

of the original data set and could therefore be linked to specific phases of the gait cycle, thereby allowing us important physiological insights [42]. These data, which were in good agreement with other studies in the literature [43,44], suggested that in the control of human gait there are not multiple different "motor programs" for each of the many muscles of the lower limbs, but rather a few basic patterns that in some combination can describe all the necessary EMG signals.

We have recently extended this work and have gathered data for 16 bilateral EMG muscle signals (erector spinae, gluteus maximus, gluteus medius, rectus femoris, hamstrings, adductor magnus, tibialis anterior, and gastrocnemius on the left and right sides) on 10 subjects performing four distinct locomotor activities (forward walking, backward walking, ascending and descending stairs). Our analysis produced five factors for each of the four activities and accounted for at least 97.4 percent of the variance in the data [45]. Whereas previous studies, including our own [42], had shown that four factors were sufficient to represent the EMG patterns for forward walking, we believe that the introduction of a fifth factor was the result of our bilateral study. We interpreted this factor to be a coordinating factor that maintains the 180-degree phase shift between the left and right sides. The other four factors could be grouped as pairs that are shifted 180 degrees in phase. Based on the muscles that loaded most heavily on these factors, and the role of these muscles in the gait cycle [42], we interpreted them to be the *loading response* and *propulsion factors* for the left and right sides.

Figure 6-5(*a*) and (*c*) illustrate orthogonal factors 1 and 2 for forward walking, which represent loading response on the left and right sides respectively (note that the data are presented with respect to the gait cycle for the right side). The ensemble average EMG data for the rectus femoris muscles, which stabilize the hip and knee joints just after heel-strike (i.e., the loading response) have been plotted in Figure 6-5(b) and (d) for comparison purposes. Figure 6-5(e) and (g) illustrate orthogonal factors 3 and 4 for forward walking which represent propulsion on the left and right sides respectively. The ensemble average EMG data for the gastrocnemius muscles, which propel the body forward just before toe-off (i.e. the propulsion phase) have been plotted in Figure 6-5(f) and (h) for comparison purposes. Figure 6-5(i), the coordinating factor, shows six turning points with each maximum being followed by a corresponding minimum 50 percent later in the cycle. The right tibialis anterior EMG, which loads highly (in a positive direction) on this factor, has been plotted in Figure 6-5(j) for comparison.

The findings presented in Figure 6-5 lend credence to our hypothesis that the central nervous system has a strategy to reduce the high dimensionality that exists in the control of multiple muscles in human gait. In fact, we have shown that the 16 muscle patterns can be represented by a mere 5 patterns. Since 4 of these patterns occur as pairs shifted by 50 percent of the cycle (loading response and propulsion), the number of patterns can be further reduced to just 3 [45].

6.3.3. Biologically Based ANN Structures

Recent studies have shown that artificial neural networks (ANNs) have great potential for both biomechanical modeling and simulation [37]. However, the success of these studies has been limited by the present ANN architectures and designs, which have many deviations from biological neurons, some of which are listed below:

1. Traditionally, the accepted functional unit for most ANN computations is the neuron [22], and these rigidly structured models allow for little or no variation in the characteristics of different neurons [46].
2. Input and output signals are not frequency modulated as in the biological case.
3. Biological limitations, such as fatigue and excitability of a synaptic junction, are ignored.
4. Update laws are too rigid, which results in digital good/bad judgment of an output, rather than an analogue better/worse judgment.
5. Most ANN architectures do not allow for variations in time (i.e., they are not spatiotemporal).

It is clear that although many of the exact features of biological systems are not yet known, much of what is known about biological neurons has been excluded from present ANNs. We have developed a biologically based neuron that incorporates many of the biological features that are lacking [47]. Figure 6-6 shows the schematic representation of two model neurons linked together to make an oscillator. The model can be described in three sections: the synapse, the neuronal output, and learning.

Biological communication is based on the action potential (AP), which is a high voltage spike lasting about 1 ms. Throughout our model, the time of the AP is used as a single unit of time (i.e., the AP lasts for one time unit). In our model, as can be seen in Figure 6-7(a), an AP arriving at a synapse causes a rise in the local synaptic voltage (synapse output signal), which is analogous to the effect of vesicles being released in the neuron. This voltage will then decay with time. The following incoming AP adds to the present local synaptic voltage. To model the synaptic fatigue, the effect that an incoming AP has on

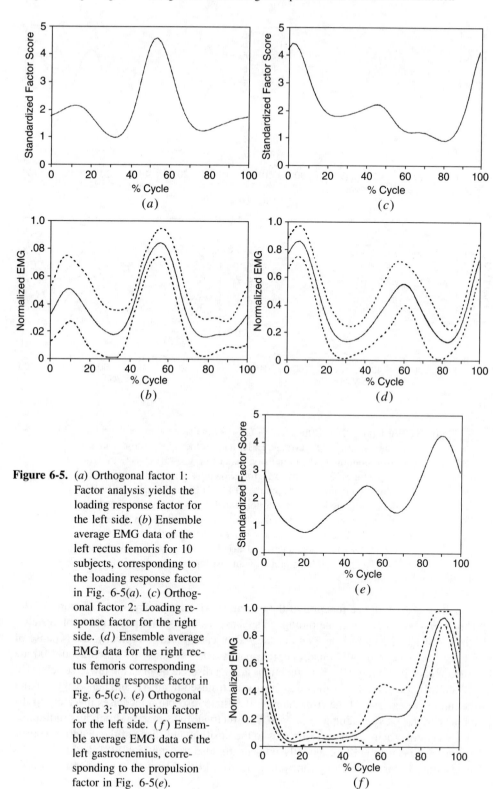

Figure 6-5. (a) Orthogonal factor 1: Factor analysis yields the loading response factor for the left side. (b) Ensemble average EMG data of the left rectus femoris for 10 subjects, corresponding to the loading response factor in Fig. 6-5(a). (c) Orthogonal factor 2: Loading response factor for the right side. (d) Ensemble average EMG data for the right rectus femoris corresponding to loading response factor in Fig. 6-5(c). (e) Orthogonal factor 3: Propulsion factor for the left side. (f) Ensemble average EMG data of the left gastrocnemius, corresponding to the propulsion factor in Fig. 6-5(e).

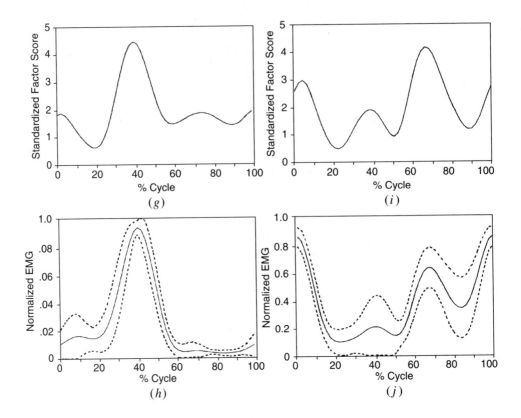

Figure 6-5. *(Continued) (g)* Orthogonal factor 4: Propulsion factor for the right
side. (*h*) Ensemble average EMG data of the right gastrocnemius,
corresponding to the propulsion factor in Fig. 6-5(*g*). (*i*) Orthogonal factor 5: Coordinating factor, showing six turning points, with
maxima and minima shifted by 50%. (*j*) Ensemble average EMG
data of the right tibialis anterior, which loads highly (in a positive
direction) on the coordinating factor. The left tibialis anterior, not
shown here, loads highly in a negative direction on this factor. These
figures have been adapted from data in K. S. Olree and C. L. Vaughan
[45] and have all been plotted with respect to the gait cycle for the
right side.

the synaptic strength is a function of the incoming AP's frequency, seen in Figure 6-7(*b*).
This phenomenon exists in the biological synapse, as it has a limited number of vesicles,
which restricts the number and rate of the APs it can process. Typically, the synapse of
a large motor neuron will contain approximately 1000 vesicles, of which about 200 are
used for each incoming AP. These functions are not discrete quanta: the fewer vesicles that
remain in storage, the lower the number of vesicles used in an AP, and hence, the smaller
the initial voltage rise. Likewise, the rate of vesicle resorption increases inversely to the
number of vesicles remaining. For each time interval, the synaptic strength is multiplied
by a weighting factor. This is analogous to the position and shape of the dendritic spines,
which have been found to efficiently prevent impulse transmission [48], and might thus
be responsible for the learning function in neurons [49]. The weight is different for each

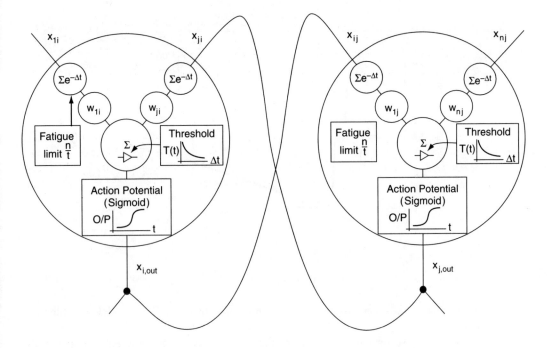

Figure 6-6. A schematic representation of two model neurons linked together to make an oscillator [47].

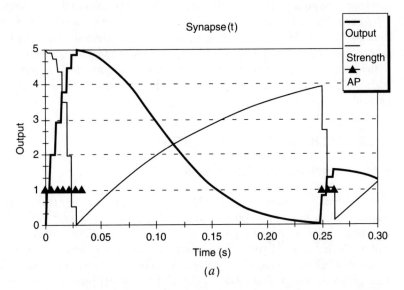

(a)

Figure 6-7. (*a*) Synaptic output from the model neuron, plotted as a function of time. The curve illustrates the effect of fatigue on the output of the synapse. (*b*) Incoming action potentials (APs), demonstrating synaptic fatigue. The parameters ρ and σ are time constants that determine the synaptic strength, and are based on real biological neurons [47].

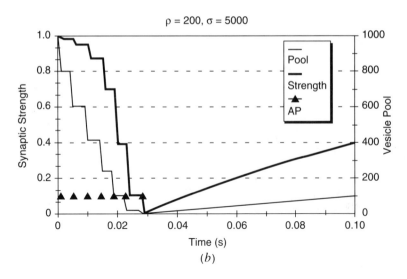

Figure 6-7. (*Continued*)

synapse and has a range from -1 to 1. This makes it possible to model an inhibitory input.

The adaptive or learning nature of the ANN results from being able to update the weighting factors. For temporal connections in the network, a "good" or desirable output may not be due to the present inputs of the individual synapses, but rather to the signal pattern that happened prior to the favorable output [50]. For our model this was implemented using a *fatigue function* of the synapse and an *excitability function* of the neuron. Fatigue is a direct measure of how active that synapse has been in the past; the more fatigued it is, the more it has been activated. Excitability is a measure of how active the neuron has been in the past. In order to control the modification of the weights, a *performance value* was added. This performance value has been implemented according to the objectives of the network.

6.4. OUR RESEARCH AGENDA FOR THE FUTURE

6.4.1. Overall Design of the System

As discussed previously, and illustrated in Figure 6-1, our current knowledge of the mammalian spinal cord proposes that both the descending commands and proprioceptive feedback signals converge on a matrix of interneurons. G. E. Loeb et al. [11] have suggested that researchers should consider the possible matrix of connections between sensors and actuators as a blank slate, to be explored without preconceived notions. We have adapted their proposed hierarchical model of the relationship between an open-loop controller and a closed-loop regulator for motor control (Figure 6-8). We have modeled the matrix of interneurons in the spinal cord by a cascade of three neural networks: a spinal oscillating network; a trajectory generating network; and a trajectory regulating network. Although these three networks are conceptually distinct processes from a control engineering perspective, and will be implemented separately in our model, they might actually reflect different

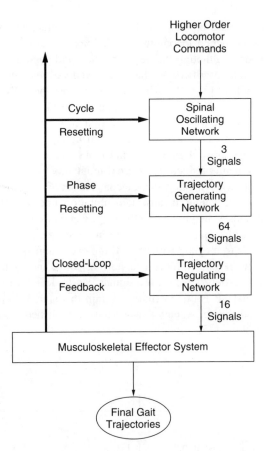

Figure 6-8. A hierarchical model of the human locomotor apparatus describes the relationship between an open-loop controller and closed-loop regulator. The matrix of interneurons in the spinal cord (*cf.* Fig. 6-1) has been modeled by a cascade of three neural networks: a spinal oscillating network; a trajectory generating network; and a trajectory regulating network. Output from the final network is a set of 16 muscle-activation signals that serve as input to the Newtonian model of the musculoskeletal effector system. This figure has been adapted from the ideas proposed by G. E. Loeb et al. [11].

emergent properties of the same group of interneurons [11]. The output from the trajectory regulating network will be the muscle actuation signals. These serve as input to the Newtonian model of the musculoskeletal effector system. The sensory feedback from this model includes the joint angles and joint angular velocities, while each muscle group will have a sensor for combined length and velocity (Ia muscle spindle afferent), force (Ib Golgi tendon organ), and activation (efference copy via the Renshaw cell, RC). We now describe the major components of our system in more detail.

6.4.2. Design of the Spinal Oscillating Network (SON)

A central goal of neuroethologists is to characterize animal behavior by describing the mechanisms whereby synaptic interactions between physiologically characterized neurons serve to control movements. To explain the neuronal origins of rhythmic movements many questions must be answered, including one that is addressed in this chapter: What is the nature of the spinal oscillator that generates the rhythmic signals? In humans, this question has not been addressed directly, as it has in the invertebrates or in lower vertebrates. However, it is significant that for the entire range of animals for which the neural origins of locomotion have been investigated, there is a single distinct mechanism that appears to generate the fundamental oscillations, namely, reciprocal inhibition between individual neurons or between pools of nearly identical neurons. The specific central neural circuits that generate locomotor oscillations in mammals, and in particular humans, remain unknown, although the neuroanatomy and some physiology of the mammalian spinal cord is well described. We have reviewed various models of the mammalian neural locomotor oscillator [51,52] and have chosen to base the SON on our previous studies of a biologically based ANN [47] and factor analysis of bilateral EMG [45]. In order to achieve a simple oscillator, we have combined four of the biological neurons shown in Figure 6-6 into a network. The inputs for each neuron included the outputs from all the neurons (including itself), as well as an external input. The external inputs were set to zero for all except one neuron, since its external input was used as a trigger to start the oscillations. With specified synaptic values, a constant set of weights can be calculated to ensure oscillations; i.e., one weight to cause self-inhibition, one weight to cause a strong excitatory input from its closest neighbor, and the other weights set to a low value. The output that was obtained from the four oscillating neurons is shown in Figure 6-9. Note how a single input pulse leads to a cyclic pattern of firing every unit time step from the four neurons. Using this network and weights as a starting point, and by introducing variations into synaptic values, different frequency signals can be learned by training the network with the desired signal. It is our intention to train this spinal oscillating network initially with the three fundamental signals that we have established from the factor analysis study on forward walking [45].

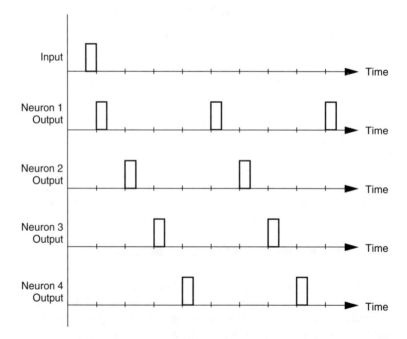

Figure 6-9. A single input to a network of four biologically based neurons (*cf.* Fig. 6-6) leads to oscillating output from each neuron. When some synaptic parameters are changed, the network can be retrained to provide oscillating outputs with different frequencies.

6.4.3. Design of the Trajectory Generating and Regulating Networks

With reference to Figure 6-8, the output from the spinal oscillating network (SON) will be the three fundamental patterns that we identified in our previous study [45] and illustrated in Figure 6-5. These three signals will therefore serve as the input to the trajectory generating network. There will be a total of 64 output trajectories from this network:

8 joint angles

8 joint angular velocities

16 length plus velocity signals (Ia spindles)

16 force signals (Ib Golgi tendon organs)

16 activation signals (Renshaw Cells)

As with the SON, we will use the biologically based neuron [47] as our building block for this network, which will be trained with the data generated for the Newtonian model (Section 6.4.4). The trajectory regulating network will have 128 signals as input: 64 from the trajectory generating network and 64 via closed loop feedback (Figure 6-8). This network will also be constructed from our basic building block neuron, and it too will be trained with the data generated for the Newtonian model.

6.4.4. Design of the Newtonian Model

Our mechanical model of the bipedal walker will consist of the following:

16 muscles	Erector spinae, gluteus maximus, gluteus medius, adductor magnus, hamstrings, rectus femoris, tibialis anterior, and gastrocnemius bilaterally
7 segments	Upper body including pelvis plus thigh, calf, and foot, bilaterally
6 joints	Hip, knee, and ankle joints, bilaterally
8 angles	Flexion/extension and abduction/adduction at hip joints, flexion/extension at knee joints, and plantar/dorsiflexion at ankle joints, bilaterally

We plan to build a forward dynamics model to explain how the muscles produce movement [20,21]. As seen from Figure 6-10, the body produces movement by transforming the neuromuscular excitations ($EMG_1 \ldots EMG_16$), the muscle force trajectories ($F_1 \ldots F_16$) and the muscle joint torque trajectories ($T_1^{mus} \ldots T_8^{mus}$) into joint angular accelerations ($\ddot{\Phi}$), velocities ($\dot{\Phi}$), and displacements (Φ). The relationship between the kinetics and kinematics is given by the dynamical equations of motion (referred to as the forward multijoint dynamics in Figure 6-10), and we will use the same strategy for formulating and solving these equations as established by the group at Stanford University [21,41]. Once the model has been formulated, then appropriate biomechanical data (body segment parameters, segment kinematics, ground reaction forces, and EMG trajectories) will be gathered. Finally, we will compute the neuromuscular excitation trajectories ($EMG_1 \ldots EMG_{16}$) that, when applied to the forward dynamics model, give the best fit to the measured data.

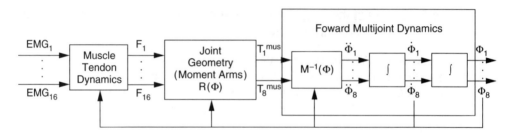

Figure 6-10. Forward dynamics analysis of musculoskeletal system transforms
neuromuscular excitations (16 EMG signals) to provide joint angular acceleration, velocities, and accelerations [21].

6.5. CLINICAL APPLICATIONS AND FUTURE TRENDS

We are confident that we can demonstrate the applicability of the SON and trajectory
generating and regulating network theories to human gait, despite there being no easy
method of validation. We have been unable to find any references to work on humans who
have had a complete lesion of their spinal cord, but we presume that it would be feasible
(although probably not ethical) to confirm the existence of such networks in these persons.
Our previous work [37,38] and that of others [11,52] give us some confidence that ANN
theory will be useful in modeling SONs for human locomotion. The ability of the Newtonian
model to provide appropriate sensory feedback (muscle length, joint angle, ground pressure)
will be a key component in determining success. The model, which is quite speculative, will
allow us to ask the "what if?" questions. By "corrupting" parts of the ANN we may be able
to simulate certain conditions or pathologies. This will allow us to explore, for example,
how bipedal robots accommodate uneven terrain or faulty joint actuators [16], why children
with cerebral palsy walk with high levels of agonist/antagonist co-contraction [53], or why
adults with osteoarthritis of the knee develop significant varus deformities [54].

Very few theories of human gait have been proposed, and those theories have not been
subjected to close scrutiny [38]. We suggest that a fertile area of future research would be
to test such theories both experimentally and using computer simulation techniques [55].
As proposed in this chapter, we believe that theories of human gait should not look at the
musculoskeletal system in isolation, but should try to integrate the neural control system as
well. Despite the promise of computer simulation as an adjunct to clinical decision making,
this has yet to be accomplished. We are confident that as models become more realistic,
algorithms easier to implement, and computers faster and more powerful, this promise
might still be fulfilled before the year 2000. Clinicians and engineers concerned with
understanding human locomotion will surely be limited only by their own imaginations.

References

[1] Perret C. Centrally generated pattern of motoneuron activity during locomotion in the
cat. In: Roberts A, Roberts B eds. *Neural Origin of Rhythmic Movement*. Cambridge,
England: Cambridge University Press;1980:405–422.

[2] Brown TG. The intrinsic factors in the act of progression in the mammal. *Proceedings of the Royal Society: London* 1911;84:308–319.

[3] Bullock TH. The origins of patterned nervous discharge. *Behaviour* 1961;17:48–59.

[4] Delcomyn F. Neural basis of rhythmic behavior in animals. *Science* 1980;210:492–498.

[5] Selverston AI. *Model Neural Networks and Behavior*. New York, NY: Plenum Press; 1985:3–548.

[6] Friesen WO. Neural control of leech movements. In: Jacklet JW ed. *Neuronal and Cellular Oscillators*. New York, NY: Marcel Dekker;1989:267–316.

[7] Cohen AV, Rossignol S, Grillner S. *Neural Control of Rhythmic Movements in Vertebrates*. New York, NY: John Wiley & Sons Inc;1988:500 pp.

[8] Roberts A. The neurons that control axial movements in a frog embryo. *Amer Zool* 1989;29:53–63.

[9] Grillner S, Wallen P, Brodin L, Lansner A. Neuronal network generating locomotory behavior in lamprey: Circuitry, transmitters, membrane properties and simulation central pattern generators for locomotion, with special reference to vertebrates. *Annual Reviews in Neuroscience* 1991;14:169–200.

[10] Grillner S. Neurological bases of rhythmic motor acts in vertebrates. *Science* 1985;228:143–149.

[11] Loeb GE, Levine WS, He J. Understanding sensorimotor feedback through optimal control. In: *Cold Spring Harbor Symposia on Quantitative Biology*, Cold Spring Harbor Laboratory Press; 1990:791–803.

[12] Conway BA, Hultborn H, Kiehn O. Proprioceptive input resets central locomotor rhythm in the spinal cat. *Experimental Brain Research* 1987;68:643.

[13] McCrea DA. Spinal cord circuitry and motor reflexes. *Exercise and Sports Science Reviews* 1986;14:105.

[14] Enoka RM. *Neuromechanical Basis of Kinesiology*. Champaign, Ill: Human Kinetics Publishers;1988.

[15] Vaughan CL, Davis BL, O'Connor J. *Dynamics of Human Gait*, Champaign, Ill: Human Kinetics Publishers;1992.

[16] Hemami H, Zheng YF, Hines MJ. Initiation of walk and tiptoe of a planar nine-link biped. *Math Biosc* 1982;61:163–189.

[17] Kato I, Fujie M, Yoshida T, Ichiyu K, Eng D. Development of the legged walking robot. *Hitachi Review* 1987;36(2):71–78.

[18] Braune W, Fischer O. Der Gang des Menschen, *Abhandlungen der Mathematisch-physische Klasse der Kongl. Sachsischen Gesellschaft der Wissenschaften*, Parts I to IV. Leipzig: S. Hirzel;1895.

[19] Winter DA. *The Biomechanics and Motor Control of Human Gait*. Ontario, Canada: The University of Waterloo Press;1987.

[20] Vaughan CL, Hay JG, Andrews JG. Closed loop problems in biomechanics, Parts I and II. *J Biomech* 1982;15:197–210.

[21] Zajac FE. Muscle coordination of movement: A perspective. *J Biomech* 1993;26(Supplement 1):109–124.

[22] McCulloch WS, Pitts W. A logical calculus of the ideas immanent in nervous activity. *Bull Math Biophys* 1943;5:115–133.

[23] Hebb DD. *The Organization of Behavior*. New York, NY: John Wiley & Sons Inc; 1949.

[24] Rosenblatt F. *Principles of Neurodynamics*. Washington, DC: Spartan Books;1961.

[25] Widrow B, Smith FW. Generalization and information storage in networks of Adaline neurons. In: Yovits MC, Jacobi GT, Goldstein GD, eds. *Self-Organizing Systems*. Washington, DC: Spartan Books;1962.

[26] Minsky M, Papert S. *Perceptrons*. Cambridge, Mass: MIT Press;1969.

[27] Hopfield JJ. Neural networks and physical systems with emergent collective computational abilities, *Proc Natl Acad Sci USA* 1982;79:2554–2558.

[28] Anderson JA. Cognitive and psychological computation with neural models, *IEEE Trans Sys Man Cyb* 1983;13:799–815.

[29] Rumelhart DE, Hinton GE, Williams RJ. Learning representations by back propagation errors. *Nature* 1986;323:533–536.

[30] Grossberg S. ed. *Neural Networks and Artificial Intelligence*. Cambridge, Mass: MIT Press;1988.

[31] Rumelhart DE, McClelland DL, and the PDP Research Group. *Parallel Distributed Processing: Explorations in the Microstructure of Cognitions*. Cambridge, Mass: MIT Press;1986.

[32] Kawato M, Furukawa K, Sizuki R. A hierarchical neural-network model for control and learning of voluntary movement. *Biol Cybernet* 1987;57:169–185.

[33] Zipser D, Andersen RA. A back-propagation programmed network that simulates response properties of a subset of posterior parietal neurons. *Nature* 1988;331:679–684.

[34] Massane L, Bizzi E. Generation of limb trajectories with a sequential network. *International Joint Conference on Neural Networks*. New York, NY: IEEE Press;1989;2:345–349.

[35] Wells DM, Vaughan CL. A 3-D transformation of a rigid link system using back propagation. *International Joint Conference on Neural Networks*. New York, NY: IEEE Press;1989; 2:630.

[36] Mitchell IJ, Brotchie JM, Brown GDA, Crossman AR. Modeling the funtional organization of the basal ganglia: A parallel distributed processing approach. *Movement Disorders* 1991;6(3):189–204.

[37] Sepulveda F, Wells D, Vaughan CL. A neural network representation of electromyography and joint dynamics in human gait, *J Biomech* 1993;26:101–109.

[38] Vaughan CL, Sussman MD: Human gait: from clinical interpretation to computer simulation. In: Grabiner M ed. *Current Issues in Biomechanics*. Champaign, Ill: Human Kinetics Publishers;1993:53–68.

[39] Vaughan CL. Computer simulation of human motion in sports biomechanics. *Exercise and Sports Sciences Reviews* 1984;12:373–416.

[40] Panjabi M. Validation of computer models (letter). *J Biomech* 1979;12:238.

[41] Yamaguchi GT. Performing whole-body simulations of gait with 3-D, dynamic musculoskeletal models. In: Winters JM, Woo SLY eds. *Multiple Muscle Models*. New York, NY: Springer-Verlag;1990:663–679.

[42] Davis BL, Vaughan CL. Phasic behavior of EMG signals during gait: Use of multivariate statistics. *J Electromyog Kinesiol* 1993;3(1):51–60.

[43] Patla AE. Some characteristics of EMG patterns during locomotion: Implications for the locomotor control process. *J Mot Behav* 1985;17:443–461.

[44] Wootten ME, Kadaba MP, Cochran GVB. Dynamic electromyography. I. Numerical representation using principal component analysis. *J Orthop Res* 1990;8:247–258.

[45] Olree KS, Vaughan CL. Fundamental patterns of bilateral muscle activity in human locomotion. *Biological Cybernetics*, 1995;73(in press).

[46] Shepherd GM. The significance of real neuron architectures for neural network simulations. In: Schwartz EL ed. *Computational Neuroscience*. Cambridge, Mass: MIT Press;1990:84–96.

[47] Brooking GD, Vaughan CL. Control of human movement with artificial neural nets: A biologically based neuron. *Proceedings of IVth International Symposium on Computer Simulation in Biomechanics*. Montlignon, France;1993:CSB10-13.

[48] Koch C, and Poggio T. Electric properties of dendritic spines. *Trends in NeuroScience* 1983;March:80–83.

[49] Callatay AM. *Natural and Artificial Intelligence*. New York, NY: North-Holland; 1992:27–109.

[50] Hecht-Nielsen R. *Neurocomputing*. Reading, Pa: Addison-Wesley;1990:2–10.

[51] Miller S, Scott PD. The spinal locomotor generator. *Experimental Brain Research* 1977;30:387–403.

[52] Patla AE. Analytic approaches to the study of outputs from central pattern generators. In: Cohen, AV, Rossignol S, Grillner S eds. *Neural Control of Rhythmic Movements in Vertebrates*. New York, NY: John Wiley & Sons Inc;1988:455–486.

[53] Vaughan CL, Bowsher K, Sussman MD. Spasticity and gait: knee torques and muscle co-contraction. In: Sussman MD ed. *The Diplegic Child: Evaluation and Management*. Rosemont, Illinois: American Academy of Orthopaedic Surgeons;1992:45–58.

[54] Wang JW, Kuo KN, Andriacchi TP, Galante JO. The influence of walking mechanics and time on the results of proximal tibial osteotomy. *J Bone Joint Surg Am* 1990;72A(6):905–909.

[55] Pandy MG, Berme N. Quantitative assessment of gait determinants during single stance via a three-dimentional model: 2. Pathological gait. *J Biomech* 1989;22: 725–733.

Chapter 7

Scott L. Delp

Computer Modeling and Analysis of Movement Disabilities and Their Surgical Corrections

7.1. INTRODUCTION

The outcomes of surgeries performed to correct movement abnormalities are unpredictable and sometimes unsuccessful. This problem exists, in part, because the development and testing of new operative techniques rely almost entirely on clinical trials (i.e., trying surgeries on patients) in which the means to quantify surgical changes or to predict postoperative results do not exist. The use of motion analysis equipment to quantify movement abnormalities and to assess surgical results is a major step toward providing a rational basis for the treatment of persons with movement disabilities. I believe that the design and development of improved treatments for movement disabilities can proceed even more effectively if clinical trials and motion studies are augmented by computer models that explain and predict the functional consequences of surgical interventions.

We have developed a graphics-based computer model of the lower extremity to study how various surgical procedures affect muscle function. This model has been used to analyze tendon transfers [1,2], tendon lengthenings [3a], osteotomies [4], and total joint replacements [5,6]. Based on these investigations, we have identified four areas in which musculoskeletal models can be particularly helpful for gaining insights into the causes of movement abnormalities and the consequences of common treatments. These four areas are (1) quantifying how muscle moment arms are altered by surgeries, (2) characterizing how surgical alterations affect muscle force-generating capacities, (3) estimating muscle lengths during normal and pathologic movement, and (4) visualizing the interactions between muscle activity, joint kinematics, ground reaction forces, and other kinematic and kinetic parameters. This chapter presents examples to highlight each of these areas.

This chapter is not intended to be a comprehensive review of musculoskeletal modeling. Rather, it provides an overview of our experience using musculoskeletal models to study movement abnormalities and their corrections. It begins with a brief description of the graphics-based model of the human lower extremity that we have used in several applications. Examples are then presented that illustrate the utility of the model by providing clinically relevant results. Finally, the limitations of our model are discussed in the context of its current applications. Analysis of these limitations suggests areas of future research.

7.2. MODEL OF THE LOWER EXTREMITY

We have developed a three-dimensional (3-D) biomechanical model of the human lower extremity that estimates the lengths and moment arms of the major muscles over a wide range of body positions [1]. Given muscle activations, the force and joint moments that each muscle develops can also be estimated. Using a computer graphics workstation, the model can be altered to study how various surgical procedures, such as osteotomies, tendon transfers, or tendon lengthenings, affect the moment arms and force-generating characteristics of the muscles. The model can also be used in conjunction with motion analysis data to study muscle function during movement. The model represents an adult male with a height of approximately 1.8 m and a mass of 75 kg.

The model consists of three items: 3-D representations of the bones, kinematic descriptions of the joints, and a model of each muscle-tendon complex. To acquire bone surface data for the pelvis and femur, we first marked the surfaces of bones with a mesh of polygons and then determined the coordinates of the vertices using a three-dimensional digitizer (Polhemus Navigation Sciences, Colchester, Vermont). Data describing the shank and foot bones were provided by D. L. Stredney [7]. Based on the anatomical landmarks of these bone surface models, we defined the origin-to-insertion paths of 43 muscle-tendon complexes. Each muscle-tendon path was represented as a series of line segments. In some cases, origin and insertion were sufficient for describing the muscle path. In other cases, where the muscle wraps over bone or is constrained by retinacula, intermediate *via points* were introduced to represent the muscle path more accurately. When it was necessary to constrain the muscle to wrap over bone or underlying structures in a particular range of motion, *wrapping points* were introduced into the muscle path in the appropriate range of motion. Muscles with broad areas of attachment, such as the gluteus medius, were divided into separate muscle compartments to represent more accurately the geometry of the muscle.

The lower extremity was represented as seven rigid segments: (1) pelvis, (2) femur, (3) patella, (4) tibia/fibula, (5) talus, (6) foot, comprising the calcaneus, navicular, cuboid, cuneiforms, and metatarsals, and (7) phalanges. The relative motions of these segments were defined by models of the hip, knee, ankle, subtalar, and metatarsophalangeal joints.

The hip was characterized as a ball-and-socket joint. The transformation between the pelvic and femoral reference frames is thus determined by successive rotations of the femoral frame about three orthogonal axes fixed in the femoral head. We developed a single-degree-of-freedom model to characterize motion of the knee in the sagittal plane. It is similar to the model described by G. T. Yamaguchi and F. E. Zajac [8], and accounts for the kinematics of both the tibiofemoral joint and the patellofemoral joint. Tibiofemoral kinematics were determined as follows: the femoral condyles were represented as an ellipse;

the tibial plateau was represented as a line segment (Figure 7-1). The transformation from the femoral reference frame to the tibial reference frame was then determined so that the femoral condyles remain in contact with the tibial plateau throughout the range of knee motion. The tibiofemoral contact point depends on the knee angle and was specified according to data reported by R. Nisell et al. [9]. Assuming that the length of the patellar ligament (ℓ_{pl} in Figure 7-1) is constant, the angle between the patellar ligament and the tibia (ϕ in Figure 7-1) determines the translation vector from the tibial reference frame to the patellar reference frame. Rotation of the patella with respect to the tibia (β in Figure 7-1) was specified according to experimental measurements of patellar rotation [10]. We represented the ankle, subtalar, and metatarsophalangeal joints as revolutes, with axes as described by V. T. Inman [11].

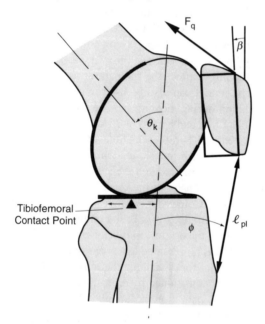

Figure 7-1. Geometry for determining knee moments and kinematics in the sagittal plane. θ_k is the knee flexion angle; ϕ is the patellar ligament angle; β is the angle between the patella and the tibia; F_q is the quadriceps force; ℓ_{pl} is the length of the patellar ligament. From these kinematics, the moment of the quadriceps force about the instant center of knee rotation can be computed. Figure from [1].

The isometric force-generating property of each muscle-tendon complex was estimated by scaling a generic, Hill-type model of muscle and tendon [12]. The generic model is based on dimensionless force-length curves of active and passive muscle. These curves are scaled by four parameters that are unique to each muscle-tendon complex: peak isometric muscle force, optimal muscle-fiber length, pennation angle, and tendon slack length. Peak isometric force was estimated by multiplying the physiologic cross-sectional area data reported by R. A. Brand et al. [13] by a "specific tension" of 25 N/cm². Optimal fiber lengths (the fiber length at which active muscle force peaks) and pennation angles (the angle between the tendon and the muscle fibers at their optimal length) were derived from studies of muscle architecture [14,15]. Tendon slack lengths (the length at which tendon begins to develop force when stretched) were derived by S. L. Delp et al. [1].

The accuracy of the lower-extremity model has been tested extensively to identify the limitations of the model and to determine the range of conditions over which the model may be appropriately used. For instance, we have compared moment arms computed with the model to moment arms measured in anatomical studies [16,17]. We have also compared maximum isometric joint moments computed with the model to maximum isometric moments measured over a range of body positions. For example, the maximum isometric moment generated by the ankle plantarflexors was compared to plantarflexion strength measurements (Figure 7-2). Similar to Figure 7-2, we compared the moments computed with the model to moments at the knee [18–22], hip [17,18,23–26], and subtalar [27] joints. These comparisons revealed that the model accurately represents the normal moment-generating capacities of the muscles over a wide range of body positions [6,28]. It is extremely important to test the accuracy of the model in the context of each new application. Tests of the model that are specific to the applications presented here are included with the examples below.

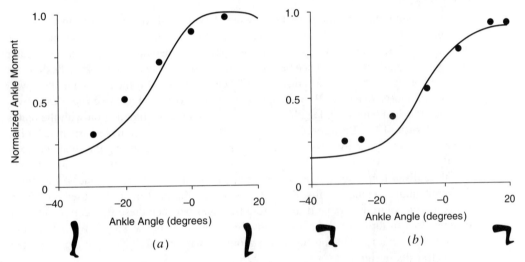

Figure 7-2. Maximum isometric ankle moment versus ankle angle. Moments computed with the model (solid curve) are compared to the maximum isometric moments reported by Sale et al. [53] (dots) with the knee extended (*a*) and flexed (*b*). Experimental and computed moments are normalized by the maximum active moment with the knee extended.

7.3. ANALYSIS OF THE RECTUS FEMORIS TRANSFER

Analysis of the computer model can help determine how muscle moment arms are altered by tendon transfer surgeries. Patients with movement abnormalities are often treated with tendon transfer surgeries aimed at altering joint moments and correcting gait abnormalities. Using a computer graphics workstation, one can alter the origin-to-insertion path of any muscle-tendon complex by graphically adjusting its origin, insertion, or intermediate via points to study how these geometric changes affect the moment arms of the muscle about a joint. This process was used to study the rectus femoris transfer [2]; this procedure is commonly used to treat *stiff-knee gait*, a condition characterized by decreased range of knee motion.

Decreased range of knee motion during the swing phase is a common movement disorder. In some cases, stiff-knee gait is thought to be caused by overactivity of the rectus femoris muscle [29,30]. The rectus femoris, which produces a flexion moment about the hip and an extension moment about the knee, is normally active for a short burst at the beginning of the swing phase. In some patients with stroke or cerebral palsy, however, the rectus femoris has prolonged or continuous activity during the swing phase, which restricts knee flexion [30–32].

J. Perry originally suggested transferring the distal tendon of the rectus femoris in patients with prolonged swing phase activity to treat decreased swing phase knee flexion after hamstring lengthening [30]. The surgery is now done in conjunction with hamstring lengthenings to avoid decreased knee flexion postoperatively. This tendon transfer is accomplished by surgically releasing the distal attachment of the rectus femoris from the patella, freeing it from surrounding tissue, and reattaching it to one of several sites posterior to the knee.

D. H. Sutherland et al. reported that swing phase knee flexion increased an average of 16 degrees after transfer of the rectus femoris in patients with decreased swing phase knee flexion [32]. J. R. Gage et al. reported that postoperative knee range of motion was greater during gait (i.e., stance phase knee flexion was decreased and swing phase knee flexion was increased or maintained) when hamstring lengthenings were performed in combination with the rectus femoris transfer [29]. S. Õunpuu et al. reported that swing phase knee flexion was maintained when hamstring lengthenings were performed in combination with the rectus femoris transfer [33]. Because of this documented success, the rectus femoris transfer has become widely used to avoid or correct inadequate knee flexion during the swing phase of gait.

The distal tendon of the rectus femoris is typically transferred to one of four sites: the semitendinosus, the gracilis, the sartorius, or the iliotibial tract. We used the lower-extremity model to determine if there are differences between these four commonly used transfer sites in terms of the postoperative moment arms at the knee. We believe that accurate descriptions of the postoperative geometry will provide a basis for more effective tendon transfer design.

7.3.1. Modeling the Tendon Transfer

To ascertain how the musculoskeletal geometry of the rectus femoris transfer could be accurately represented in the computer model, we performed an anatomical study during which the origin-to-insertion path of the rectus femoris was digitized after the muscle was transferred to each of the four sites. The left leg of one alcohol-preserved cadaver was prepared for digitizing by making an incision from the anterior superior iliac spine to the patella. An incision this large would not be made in an actual surgery; however, it was necessary to expose the entire muscle-tendon complex so that it could be digitized. The skin was removed, but the fascia surrounding the muscles was left intact on the upper two thirds of the thigh to maintain normal anatomical constraints. As in an actual surgery, the distal third of the rectus femoris was freed from surrounding tissue and transferred, as described by J. R. Gage et al. [29]. Once the distal end of rectus femoris was attached to one of the tendon transfer sites, tacks were inserted along the muscle between the origin and the new insertion to mark the points that would be digitized. Indentations were made in the head of each tack so that the tip of the digitizer could be placed at the same point during each digitizing trial. The knee and hip were maintained in 0 degrees flexion.

An Optotrak/3010 digitizing system (Northern Digital, Waterloo, Canada) was used to collect the coordinates that describe the path of rectus femoris after transfer. Three cameras mounted on a rigid frame tracked the 3-D position of infrared-emitting diodes (IREDs). A digitizing probe that houses sixteen IREDs and software that extrapolates the 3-D coordinates of the probe's tip were used to record the position of the center of the tacks along each muscle-tendon path.

Digitized coordinates that describe the rectus femoris path after transfer to each site were displayed on a graphics workstation (Figure 7-3). Since the model characterizes the kinematics of the hip and knee, it enabled the moment arms of rectus femoris after transfer to each site to be computed for a variety of body positions. The moment arm (MA) of the rectus femoris was computed as the partial derivative of muscle-tendon length ($\partial \ell$) with respect to knee angle ($\partial \theta$). That is,

$$MA = \partial \ell / \partial \theta \qquad (7\text{-}1)$$

[34]. Knee flexion moment arm versus knee angle curves were calculated for each of the four transfer sites.

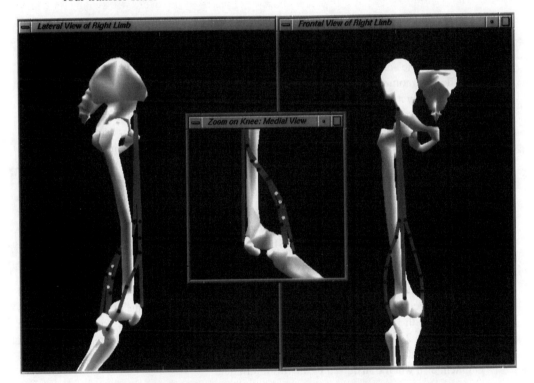

Figure 7-3. Biomechanical model of the rectus femoris before and after transfer to four different sites. The path of the rectus femoris is represented by a series of points: the muscle origin, insertion, and intermediate via points (dots defining the muscle-tendon path). From this representation, the muscle moment arms about the hip and knee can be computed. The left window shows a lateral view; the inset shows a medial view; the right window shows an anterior view. Figure from [2].

To test the computer model, knee flexion moment arms were measured in two alcohol preserved cadavers by recording tendon displacement over a range of knee flexion angles.

The distal end of rectus femoris was attached to each tendon transfer site, and tendon displacement was measured over a range of knee flexion angles. A locking brace mounted on the leg controlled the knee flexion angle during the tendon displacement measurements. The tendon displacement versus knee angle data for each site were fit with a fourth order polynomial that minimized the sum of the squared residuals. Thus, muscle-tendon length (ℓ) was expressed as a function of knee angle (θ):

$$\ell = C_0 + C_1\theta + C_2\theta^2 + C_3\theta^3 + C_4\theta^4 \qquad (7\text{-}2)$$

where C_0–C_4 were the coefficients determined by the least squares fit. Equation (7-2) was differentiated with respect to θ to determine the moment arm versus knee angle curves from the experimental data.

7.3.2. Results

We found substantial differences in the knee flexion moment arms between the four transfer sites (Figure 7-4). Results from the model and the two specimens show the rectus femoris has the largest moment arm after transfer to the semitendinosus, followed by the gracilis and the sartorius. When rectus femoris is transferred to semitendinosus, the peak knee flexion moment arm is approximately 4.5 cm; when transferred to gracilis, the peak is approximately 3.5 cm; and when transferred to sartorius, the peak is approximately 2.5 cm. The moment arm versus knee angle curves measured in the male and female specimens have the same shape for each transferred case, although the peak moment arm is consistently greater (by $\approx$ 5 mm) for the female specimen than the male specimen. The magnitudes of the peak knee flexion moment arms computed with the model are within 2 mm of the male specimen. However, the peak moment arm calculated with the model differs by as much as 8 mm from the peak moment arms measured in the female specimen. The knee flexion moment arm curves calculated using the model have the same relative magnitudes as the measured moment arms (i.e., semitendinosus has the largest knee flexion moment arm, followed by gracilis and sartorius). However, the moment arms calculated with the model peak at a more flexed knee position and vary less with knee angle than the measured moment arms.

The moment arm of the rectus femoris after transfer to the iliotibial tract is very small for both specimens and the model (Figure 7-4, dashed line labeled IT). The moment arm estimated with the model varies between a 6-mm extension moment arm with the knee extended to a 2-mm flexion moment arm with the knee flexed. The moment arms measured in the two cadavers indicate that the rectus femoris has a slight (0–5 mm) knee extension moment arm when transferred to the iliotibial tract.

7.3.3. Clinical Implications

Stiff-knee gait is thought to be caused by overactivity of the rectus femoris muscle in some cases [29,30]. The excessive knee extension moment generated by an overactive rectus femoris during the swing phase of gait may be eliminated by a transfer. If this were the only mechanism by which the transfer improved knee flexion, however, one would expect that the release of the rectus femoris, without transfer, would be as effective as the rectus femoris transfer. This is not the case. Gait analysis has demonstrated that the rectus femoris transfer increases knee range of motion more than the release alone [32,35].

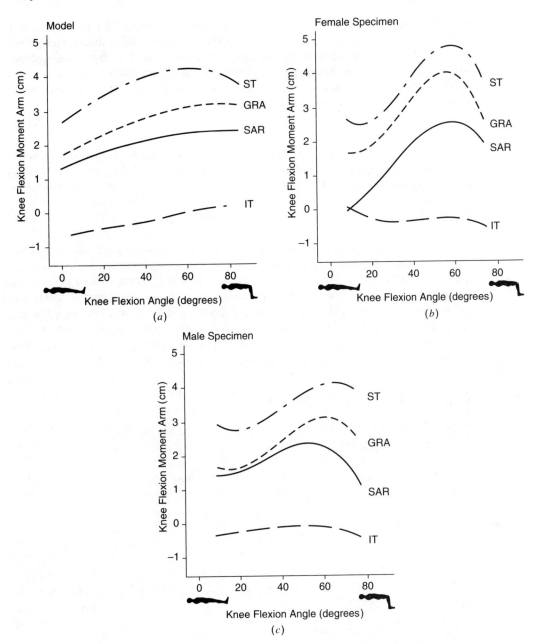

Figure 7-4. Knee flexion moment arm versus knee flexion angle of the rectus femoris after transfer to each of the four sites: (*a*) model, (*b*) female specimen, (*c*) male specimen. The curve marked ST is the moment arm after transfer to semitendinosus. GRA is the moment arm after transfer to gracilis. SAR is the moment arm after transfer to sartorius. IT is the moment arm after transfer to the iliotibial tract. Positive moment arms indicate knee flexion. Negative moment arms indicate knee extension. Note substantial differences in the moment arms between the transfer sites. Figure from [2].

The rectus femoris transfer may be more effective than the release for three reasons: (1) the transferred rectus femoris may develop knee flexion moment during swing and actively contribute to knee flexion, (2) the transfer may better preserve the capacity of the rectus femoris to generate flexion moment about the hip, which could contribute to knee flexion via dynamic coupling (i.e., accelerations of one joint caused by moments about another joint [36]), and (3) the transfer may keep the rectus femoris from reattaching to the patella, which has been observed during surgeries subsequent to a rectus femoris release. Transferring rectus femoris to any of the four tendon sites may decrease knee extension moment. Transfers to all sites also may prevent reattachment to the patella and preserve moment-generating capacity of the rectus femoris as a hip flexor. However, transferring to semitendinosus, gracilis, or sartorius may possibly allow transferred rectus femoris to generate a knee flexion moment, if it is active during swing. In contrast, rectus femoris transferred to the iliotibial tract does not have the possibility of actively flexing the knee.

It is often assumed that transferred muscles act as independent actuators, which transmit force only through their own tendons and not through surrounding musculature. Thus, if the distal tendon of the rectus femoris passes posterior to the instantaneous axis of rotation (e.g., after transfer to the semitendinosus), it is assumed that the muscle generates a flexion moment about the knee when activated. However, fascial attachments or scar tissue formed between the proximal part of the rectus femoris and the surrounding vasti that remain following surgery might allow some transmission of force through the remaining knee extensors. The extent to which muscles act as independent actuators remains an important question concerning the function of muscles before and after transfer.

7.4. SIMULATION OF TENDON LENGTHENINGS

Musculoskeletal modeling can also be used to study how lengthening tendon affects the force-generating capacity of muscles [3]. Patients with neuromuscular disorders are often treated with tendon-lengthening surgeries aimed at increasing range of joint motion and reducing forces that are disruptive to movement. For example, the Achilles tendon is commonly lengthened to correct an equinus deformity (toe walking) in stroke [37] and cerebral palsy patients [38]. Also, the hamstrings might be lengthened in patients who walk with excessive knee flexion, or a crouch gait [39]. While tendon lengthenings sometimes improve posture and walking, they often compromise the capacity of the muscles to generate force and produce moments about the joints. After a tendon is lengthened, the muscle fibers might be too short to develop active force. Patients who cannot generate sufficient muscle forces and joint moments can be left with weak or dysfunctional legs. For instance, overlengthening of the Achilles tendon can weaken the plantarflexors and result in excessive dorsiflexion during the stance phase of gait [38,40].

Understanding how tendon lengthening affects the force-generating capacity of each muscle is needed to help design effective tendon surgeries. We have used the lower-extremity model to quantify the sensitivity of the maximum isometric force developed by each lower-extremity muscle to changes in tendon length (i.e., to calculate how much force decreases from increasing tendon length). These results indicate how much each of these tendons should be lengthened to achieve a certain decrease in muscle force.

7.4.1. Modeling Tendon Lengthenings

The computer model of the lower extremity described in Section 7.2 was used to study how tendon lengthening affects muscle force production. Muscles were assumed to be fully activated to estimate the maximum isometric force generated by each muscle for a range of body positions. Tendon lengthenings were simulated by increasing the tendon length of each muscle-tendon complex and computing the change in the maximum isometric muscle force generated at a specific body position. Since the maximum isometric force varies with joint angle, the change in force (for a given change in tendon length) depends on body position. Consequently, the changes in the muscle forces were computed at many body positions. For clarity, however, the results presented here were computed at one body position: 10 degrees flexion of the hip, 20 degrees flexion of the knee, and 10 degrees dorsiflexion of the ankle. This position was chosen because it occurs in many functional activities, and was found to be representative of the changes in muscle force-generating capacities for many other positions.

7.4.2. Results

The computer simulations showed that the decrease in the isometric force-generating capacity for a given increase in tendon length is different for each muscle. Conversely, the increase in tendon length needed to reduce muscle force by a certain amount (e.g., 50 percent) is different for each muscle (Figure 7-5). Notice that there is a wide variation among the muscles in the sensitivity of force to a change in tendon length. For example, soleus force decreased 50 percent with only a 1.2-cm increase in tendon length. Biceps femoris (long head) and iliopsoas, on the other hand, required a 4-cm increase in tendon length to decrease force by 50 percent. In general, the forces developed by the muscles that cross posterior to the ankle are more sensitive to a change in tendon length than are the forces generated by the muscles that cross the hip. This variation in the sensitivity of the muscle forces to changes in tendon length is caused by differences in the architecture of each muscle-tendon complex. That is, each muscle has a different optimal fiber length, tendon length, and pennation angle, and thus responds differently to tendon lengthening (see [3] for an analysis of the effects of each parameter).

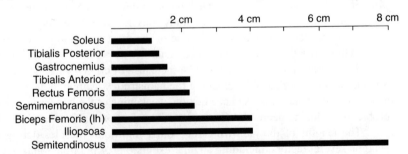

Figure 7-5. Change in tendon length needed to reduce muscle force by 50% [3]. Forces in these commonly lengthened tendons were calculated with 10° hip flexion, 20° knee flexion, and 10° dorsiflexion. Tendon lengths were scaled to a 1.8-m adult skeleton.

7.4.3. Clinical Implications

The simulations indicate that the forces developed by some muscles (particularly the ankle plantarflexors) are very sensitive to changes in tendon length. That is, small changes in tendon length result in large changes in muscle force. In contrast, other muscles (e.g., iliopsoas, semitendinosus) are much less sensitive to change in tendon length and must be lengthened more to achieve a significant decrease in force.

These results have practical implications with regard to tendon lengthenings. The observation that tendon lengthening decreases the force-generating capacity of the soleus more than gastrocnemius suggests that lengthening the Achilles tendon enough to correct a contracted gastrocnemius might weaken the soleus greatly. Lengthening the soleus and gastrocnemius independently, rather than lengthening their common tendon, accounts for the differences in the architectures of these two muscles. Independent lengthening might therefore help avoid excessive weakening of the soleus and provide a more effective means to restore range of motion while maintaining plantarflexion strength [3a].

The results presented here can also be applied to understand the force-generating capacity of muscles used in tendon transfers. If the force developed by a muscle is sensitive to changes in tendon length, then it is also sensitive to changes in origin-to-insertion length. That is, if the maximum isometric force of a muscle decreases a certain amount from lengthening its tendon 2 cm, then its force would decrease by the same amount if a tendon transfer decreased its origin-to-insertion length 2 cm. Thus, the sensitivity results (i.e., Figure 7-5) apply to both tendon lengthenings and tendon transfers. Furthermore, if a muscle that is sensitive to length change (e.g., tibialis posterior) is to generate active force after a transfer, the transfer must be performed in such a way that the muscle fibers are near optimal length in the range of motion where peak force is needed. This might be difficult to accomplish for a muscle with short fibers. By contrast, muscles that are less sensitive to length change (e.g., rectus femoris) are more likely to generate active force after a transfer, even if the origin-to-insertion length is changed substantially.

7.5. ASSESSMENT OF MUSCLE LENGTHS DURING CROUCH GAIT

Musculoskeletal modeling can be used in conjunction with experimental measurements of normal and pathologic kinematics to study muscle function during movements, such as normal and crouch gait. Crouch gait, one of the most common movement abnormalities among children with cerebral palsy, is characterized by persistent knee flexion during stance. Short hamstrings are often thought to be the cause of crouch gait and persistent crouch is often treated by surgically lengthening the hamstrings. Although hamstring lengthenings usually decrease stance phase knee flexion, weakening of the hamstrings can create several problems, including decreased swing phase knee flexion and increased hip flexion [39,41].

The lengths of the hamstrings and other multijoint muscles during movement depend on several factors, including angular excursions of multiple joints and the geometric relationships of the muscles and bones (i.e., muscle moment arms). We have used the lower-extremity model to estimate the lengths of the hamstrings and other multijoint muscles during normal and crouch gait in order to gain insight into the possible causes of this movement abnormality.

All subjects who participated in this study underwent gait analysis at Children's Memorial Medical Center in Chicago. A Vicon motion analysis system (Oxford Metrics, Oxford,

England) was used to determine 3-D kinematics of 10 normal subjects and 10 subjects with crouch gait (knee flexion > 25 degrees during the entire stance phase). All of the crouch-gait subjects had a diagnosis of spastic cerebral palsy, were over age 7, had no previous surgery, and walked without orthoses or other assistance.

The gait kinematics were used in connection with the biomechanical model of the lower extremity to estimate the changes in hamstrings and psoas lengths that occur over the gait cycle. A single muscle representation of the hamstrings was constructed using a weighted average of the muscle attachment coordinates for the semitendinosus, semimembranosus, and biceps femoris long head, with physiologic cross sectional area as the weighting factor. A model of the psoas was constructed using an average origin on the anterior lumbar spine, a via point near the pelvic brim, and an insertion point on the lesser trochanter.

Calculated muscle lengths were normalized by the muscle length at anatomical position and then plotted versus gait cycle for each subject. The normalized muscle lengths for each crouch gait subject were compared to the muscle lengths estimated from the normal gait kinematics (Figure 7-6). Analysis of the muscle length calculations revealed that many of the crouch gait subjects had hamstrings that were of normal length or longer than normal [as in Figure 7-6(a)]. This is consistent with results reported by S. A. Hoffinger

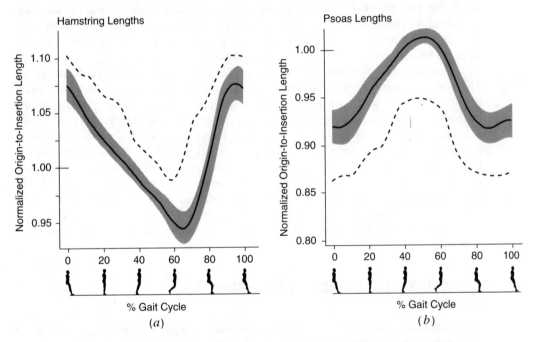

Figure 7-6. Normalized muscle lengths during normal and crouch gait. The lengths of (a) the hamstrings and (b) psoas were estimated based on gait kinematics of 10 normal subjects. The solid curve is the mean for the normal subjects, and shaded region indicates ± one standard deviation. The dotted curve shows the muscle lengths estimated based on the kinematics of one subject with crouch gait. Note that the hamstrings are longer than normal (above the shaded region) and the psoas is shorter than normal (below the shaded region). Muscle lengths are normalized by their lengths at the anatomical position (0° hip flexion, abduction and rotation, and 0° knee flexion).

et al. [42]. Analysis of the model also suggested that many of the crouch gait subjects walked in such a way that their psoas were shorter than normal [as in Figure 7-6(*b*)]. These preliminary results suggest that, in some patients, it might be more important to increase the length of the hip flexors than to increase the length of the hamstrings. Decreasing excessive hip flexion might decrease hamstring tension and enable knee extension.

7.6. SCIENTIFIC VISUALIZATION AND MOTION ANALYSIS

Analyzing plots of joint angles, joint moments, ground reaction forces, and electromyographic recordings have been the mainstay of quantitative motion analysis for the past two decades. Although these plots provide useful information, I find it difficult to see the relationships between the many variables collected in motion study and to pinpoint the causes of a movement abnormality by looking at the array of plots generated in a typical motion analysis. It is also difficult to communicate these relationships to individuals who are not experienced in biomechanics, such as patients or parents.

I believe that well-designed 3-D animations of human movement can help us to understand the causes of complex movement disabilities and to communicate those findings to others. Recent advances in computer graphics technology have made it possible to visualize relationships in multivariable systems in many areas of science. Human motion analysis is no exception. While it is difficult to demonstrate the value of 3-D animations in a static medium, such as a book, several important advantages are listed here.

First, in a computer animation motion can be observed from any angle, at any speed. This is not possible with video-based analysis. Second, body segments can be eliminated if they obstruct the view of other segments. This can be taken to the extreme by eliminating all the body segments except one, say the pelvis, to observe its motion independently. Third, animation allows one to visualize electromyographic activity of the muscles and ground reaction forces in the context of the joint kinematics (Figure 7-7). We have found this to be extremely helpful in discovering the causes of movement abnormalities. Finally, since color-keyed plots of joint angles, velocities, moments, and powers are also available via the computer display, an animation system is an excellent tool for interpreting these data as well. In the future, reports from motion studies will be supplemented by a videotape created from a 3-D animation that demonstrates the major abnormalities and their probable causes.

7.7. SOME CURRENT LIMITATIONS OF MUSCULOSKELETAL MODELING

There are numerous limitations associated with using computer models to analyze movement abnormalities and their surgical corrections, many of which have been discussed in previous publications [3,43,44]. Some of the major limitations of the computer modeling approach described in this article are discussed below.

The lower-limb model used here represents an adult male. However, children are often treated with tendon transfer surgeries. Although use of an adult-sized model to study surgical procedures performed on children can introduce serious errors in some situations, it might be reasonable in other situations, such as the rectus femoris transfer. One would

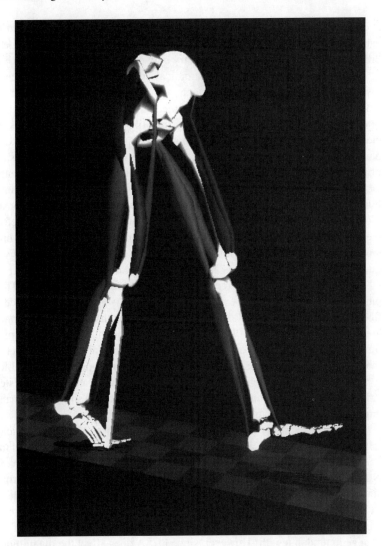

Figure 7-7. One frame from an animation in which the ground reaction force and EMG activity (viewed as changing muscle color) can be viewed with the joint motions.

expect children to have smaller moment arms than adults, due to smaller bone dimensions, but the relationships between knee moment arms after transfer of the rectus femoris presented in Section 7.3 are likely to be similar in children. Because the sartorius inserts on the tibia anterior to gracilis and semitendinosus, it should have the smallest knee flexion moment arm of the three medial transfers. Gracilis inserts on the tibia between sartorius and semitendinosus and should have a moment arm that is greater than sartorius, but less than semitendinosus. Semitendinosus has the most posterior insertion on the tibia and should therefore have the largest knee flexion moment arm, as our results indicate. We expect that these relationships would hold in children, since the anatomy of the muscle insertions is consistent with adults. To gain confidence in computer models used to study a wider variety of movement disabilities in children, additional studies are needed to characterize differences in musculoskeletal geometry between children and adults.

The computer model and anatomical specimens we use represent normal musculoskeletal geometry. However, patients with movement disabilities sometimes have bony deformities that could affect muscle moment arms and influence the results presented here. For example, if the distal femur, the proximal tibia, and the relationships between the muscles about the knee are altered, the relative magnitudes of the knee flexion moment arms presented in Figure 7-4 might be inaccurate. Also, deformities at the hip, such as subluxation of the femoral head, femoral anteversion, or a valgus femoral neck can affect the moment arms of muscles crossing the hip. Our estimations of normalized hamstrings lengths during normal and crouch gait depend on accurate representations of the relationships between the moment arms of the hamstrings about the hip and knee. Since bony deformities can alter these relationships substantially, we caution against using our results to understand muscle length changes in patients with substantial bony abnormalities. Future work is needed to quantify how bony deformities alter the mechanical actions of muscles.

The fidelity of muscle force estimations is limited by the accuracy of the muscle-tendon parameters used in the lower-extremity model (peak isometric muscle force, optimal muscle-fiber length, pennation angle, and tendon slack length). Estimates of muscle-fiber length are particularly important. Because three independent investigations of lower-extremity muscle architecture have reported remarkably consistent fiber lengths [14,15,45], we feel that the fiber lengths incorporated into the computer model are reasonable representations for normal subjects. Measurements of pennation angle are very consistent [14,15]. The values used in the computer model are adequate, especially since small changes in pennation angle have little effect on muscle force production [12].

Measured values for physiologic cross-sectional area (PCSA), which are used to estimate peak muscle force, are less consistent. J. A. Friederich et al. found that "normalized" PCSA values measured in six cadavers had an average standard deviation of 29 percent [14]. Normalized PCSA measured by P. W. Brand et al. [46] in 15 cadaver arms had an average standard deviation of 26 percent (calculated from mass fraction in Table 1 of [46]). Since PCSA does not affect the percentage change in force for a given change in tendon length, variability in this parameter does not affect the relative sensitivities of muscle force to a change in tendon length. However, since PCSA does affect the magnitude of muscle force production, this parameter must be estimated accurately in order to determine maximum force-generating capacity.

Since no experimental measurements of tendon slack length have been reported, a study was undertaken to assess the accuracy of the tendon length estimates used in the computer model. This study showed that the estimates of tendon length for muscles with high ratios of tendon length to fiber length (e.g., soleus, tibialis posterior, gastrocnemius) are reliable [1]. Estimates of tendon length for muscles with small ratios of tendon length to fiber length (e.g., iliopsoas, semitendinosus) are less reliable. However, since force is less sensitive to changes in tendon length for these muscles, accurate estimates are less critical since an error in tendon length has a smaller effect on muscle force generating characteristics.

An important limitation of the current computer model is that it does not account for the effects of muscle-tendon adaptation that can accompany central nervous system (CNS) pathology and immobilization after surgery. It has been suggested that inadequate addition of sarcomeres during growth can cause muscle contractures in children with cerebral palsy [47]. Immobilization after surgery can decrease the peak force of a muscle [48], alter the number of sarcomeres in a muscle fiber [48,49], and change the elasticity of tendon [50]. Peak muscle force, muscle fiber length, and tendon elasticity were kept constant in our initial simulations of tendon lengthenings. Our results should therefore be interpreted as the acute changes in the muscle force generating capacities that result from lengthening tendon, not the changes that might result from muscle-tendon adaptation. Future work is needed to characterize alterations in muscle properties exhibited by persons with CNS pathology and to understand how muscle-tendon remodeling alters muscle force-generating characteristics postoperatively.

Finally, even if one knew exactly how the musculoskeletal system changed with tendon transfer, tendon lengthening, or other surgical alterations, the functional result of these surgeries would still be somewhat unpredictable because of abnormal muscle activation patterns that often accompany CNS pathology [51,52]. Our studies to date have focused on the lengths, moment arms, and force-generating capacities of the muscles because they are affected directly by surgery. The current model cannot be used to study more complex issues, such as how surgery indirectly affects muscle force production through its influence on neural control patterns.

7.8. CONCLUSIONS

Current models of the neuromusculoskeletal system have important limitations. However, when used appropriately, models are powerful tools for analyzing the fundamental causes of movement abnormalities and revealing the biomechanical consequences of surgical treatments. I suggest that computer simulations performed in connection with clinical studies and quantitative motion analysis will improve our understanding of muscle function and our capacity to provide effective treatments for movement disorders.

Acknowledgments

We gratefully acknowledge Lori Kinzy, Abraham Komattu, Carolyn Moore, Wendy Murray, Randy Perkins, Deborah Ringwelski, Rosemary Speers, Kim Statler, and Paul Trykovski for help in the anatomical experiments, computer modeling, and data analysis; Eugene Bleck, Norris Carroll, Luciano Dias, Sylvia Õunpuu, Jacquelin Perry, George Rab, and Felix Zajac for their helpful suggestions related to movement deformities and musculoskeletal modeling; Steve Piazza and Allison Arnold for their helpful comments on the manuscript; and Idd Delp for help with the illustrations. The model used to create the animation shown in Figure 7-7 was created by Lisa Schutte using software provided by MusculoGraphics Inc., Evanston, Illinois. This work was supported by the Whitaker Foundation, the Baxter Foundation, NSF Grant BCS-9257229, and the Rehabilitation Research and Development Service, Department of Veterans Affairs.

References

[1] Delp SL, Loan JP, Hoy MG, Zajac FE, Topp EL, Rosen JM. An interactive, graphics-based model of the lower extremity to study orthopaedic surgical procedures. *IEEE Trans Biomed Eng* 1990;37:757–767.

[2] Delp SL, Ringwelski D, Carroll NC. Transfer of the rectus femoris: Effects of transfer site on moment arms about the knee and hip. *J Biomech* 1994;27:1201–1211.

[3] Delp SL, Zajac FE. Force- and moment-generating capacity of lower extremity muscles before and after tendon lengthening. *Clin Orthop* 1992;284:247–259.

[3a] Delp SL, Statler K, Carroll NC. Preserving plantarflexion strength after surgical treatment for contracture of the triceps surae: A computer simulation study. *J Orthop Res* 1995 13(1);96–104.

[4] Delp SL, Bleck EE, Zajac FE, Bollini G. Biomechanical analysis of the Chiari pelvic osteotomy: Preserving hip abductor strength. *Clin Orthop* 1990;254:189–198.

[5] Delp SL, Komattu AV, Wixson RL. Superior displacement of the hip in total joint replacement: Effects of prosthetic neck length, neck-stem angle, and anteversion angle on the moment-generating capacity of the muscles. *J Orthop Res* 1993;12(6):860–870.

[6] Delp SL, Maloney WJ. Effects of hip center location on the moment-generating capacity of the muscles. *J Biomech* 1993;26:485–499.

[7] Stredney DL. The representation of anatomical structures through computer animation for scientific, educational, and artistic applications. Columbus:Ohio State University, 1982:Masters thesis.

[8] Yamaguchi GT, Zajac FE. A planar model of the knee joint to characterize the knee extensor mechanism. *J Biomech* 1989;22:1–10.

[9] Nisell R, Nemeth G, Ohlsen H. Joint forces in extension of the knee. *Acta Orthop Scand* 1986;57:41–46.

[10] van Eijden TMGJ, de Boer W, Weijs WA. The orientation of the distal part of the quadriceps femoris muscle as a function of the knee flexion-extension angle. *J Biomech* 1985;18:803–809.

[11] Inman VT. *The joints of the ankle*. Baltimore, Md: Williams & Wilkins Publishing Co;1976.

[12] Zajac FE. Muscle and tendon: Properties, models, scaling, and application to biomechanics and motor control. *CRC Crit Revs Biomed Eng* 1989;17:359–411.

[13] Brand RA, Pedersen DR, Friederich JA. The sensitivity of muscle force predictions to changes in physiologic cross-sectional area, *J Biomech* 1986;19:589–596.

[14] Friederich JA, Brand RA. Muscle fiber architecture in the human lower limb. *J Biomech* 1990;23:91–95.

[15] Wickiewicz TL, Roy RR, Powell PL, Edgerton VR. Muscle architecture of the human lower limb. *Clin Orthop* 1983;179:275–283.

[16] Grood ES, Suntay WJ, Noyes FR, Butler DL. Biomechanics of the knee-extension exercise: Effect of cutting the anterior cruciate ligament. *J Bone Joint Surg Am* 1984; 66-A:725–734.

[17] Nemeth G, Ekholm J, Arborelius U, Harms-Ringdahl K, Schuldt K. Influence of knee flexion on isometric hip extensor strength. *Scand J Rehabil Med* 1983;15:97–101.

[18] Inman VT, Ralston HJ, Todd F. *Human Walking*. Baltimore, Md: Williams & Wilkins Publishing Co;1981.

[19] Lindahl O, Movin A, Ringqvist I. Knee entension: Measurement of the isometric force in different positions of the knee joint. *Acta Orthop Scand* 1969;40:79–85.

[20] Murray MP, Baldwin JM, Gardner GM, Sepic SB, Downs WJ. Maximum isometric knee flexor and extensor muscle contractions. *Phys Ther* 1977;57:637–643.

[21] Scudder GN. Torque curves produced at the knee during isometric and isokinetic exercises. *Arch Phys Med Rehabil* 1980;61:68–72.

[22] van Eijden TMGJ, Weijs WA, Kouwenhoven E, Verberg J. Forces acting on the patella during maximal voluntary contraction of the quadriceps femoris muscle at different knee flexion/extension angles. *Acta Anat* 1987;129:310–314.

[23] Cahalan TD, Johnson ME, Liu S, Chao EYS. Quantitative measurements of hip strength in different age groups. *Clin Orthop* 1989;246:136–145.

[24] Murray MP, Sepic SB. Maximum isometric torque of hip abductor and adductor muscles. *Phys Ther* 1968;48:1327–1335.

[25] Olson VL, Smidt GL, Johnston RC. The maximum torque generated by the eccentric, isometric, and concentric contractions of the hip abductor muscles. *Phys Ther* 1972;52:149–158.

[26] Waters RL, Perry J, McDaniels JM, House K. The relative strength of the hamstrings during hip extension. *J Bone Joint Surg Am* 1974;56A:1592–1597.

[27] Tropp H. Pronator muscle weakness in functional instability of the ankle joint. *Int J Sports Med* 1986;7:291–294.

[28] Delp SL. Surgery simulation: A computer graphics system to analyze and design musculoskeletal reconstructions of the lower limb. Stanford Calif: Stanford University, 1990:PhD thesis.

[29] Gage JR, Perry J, Hicks RR, Koop S, Werntz JR. Rectus femoris transfer as a means of improving knee function in cerebral palsy. *Dev Med Child Neurol* 1987;29:159–166.

[30] Perry J. Distal rectus femoris transfer. *Dev Med Child Neurol* 1987;29:153–158.

[31] Waters RL, Garland DE, Perry J, Habig T, Slabaugh P. Stiff-legged gait in hemiplegia: Surgical correction. *J Bone Joint Surg Am* 1979;61-A:927–932.

[32] Sutherland DH, Santi M, Abel MF. Treatment of stiff-knee gait in cerebral palsy: A comparison by gait analysis of distal rectus femoris transfer versus proximal rectus release. *J Ped Orthop* 1990;10:433–441.

[33] Õunpuu S, Muik E, Davis RB, Gage JR, DeLuca PA. Rectus femoris surgery in children with cerebral palsy. Part I: The effect of rectus femoris transfer location on knee motion. *J Ped Orthop* 1993;13:325–330.

[34] An KN, Takakashi K, Harrigan TP, Chao EY. Determination of muscle orientation and moment arms. *J Biomech Eng* 1984;106:280–282.

[35] Õunpuu S, Muik E, Davis RB, Gage JR, DeLuca PA. Rectus femoris surgery in children with cerebral palsy. Part II: A comparison between the effects of the transfer and release of the distal rectus femoris on knee motion. *J Ped Orthop* 1993;13:331–335.

[36] Zajac FE, Gordon ME. Determining muscle's force and action in multi-articular movement. *Exercise and Sport Sciences Reviews* 1989;17:187–230.

[37] Mooney V, Goodman F. Surgical approaches to lower-extremity disability secondary to strokes. *Clin Orthop* 1969;63:142–152.

[38] Bleck EE. *Orthopaedic Management in Cerebral Palsy*. Philadelphia Pa: MacKeith Press, 1987.

[39] Thometz J, Simon S, Rosenthal R. The effect on gait of lengthening of the medial hamstrings in cerebral palsy. *J Bone Joint Surg Am* 1989;71A:345–353.

[40] Waters RL, Perry J, Garland D. Surgical correction of gait abnormalities following stroke. *Clin Orthop* 1978;131:54–63.

[41] Ray RL, Ehrlich MG. Lateral hamstring transfer and gait improvement in the cerebral palsy patient. *J Bone Joint Surg Am* 1979;61A:719–723.

[42] Hoffinger SA, Rab GT, Abou-Ghaida H. Hamstrings in cerebral palsy crouch gait. *J Ped Orthop* 1993;13:722–726.

[43] Brand RA, Pederson DR. Computer modeling of surgery and a consideration of the mechanical effects of proximal femoral osteotomies. *The Hip. Proceeding of the Twelfth Open Scientific Meeting of the Hip Society* St Louis Mo: CV Mosby Company; 1984:193–210.

[44] Johnston RC, Brand RA, Crowninshield RD. Reconstruction of the hip: A mathematical approach to determine optimum geometric relationships. *J Bone Joint Surg Am* 1979; 61A:639–652.

[45] Weber E. *Wagner's Handworterbuch der Physiologie*. Braunscheig, Vieweg: 1846.

[46] Brand PW, Beach RB, Thompson DE. Relative tension and potential excursion of muscles in the forearm and hand. *J Hand Surg* 1981;6:209–219.

[47] Truschelli D, Lespargot A, Tardieu G. Variation in the long-term results of elongation of the tendo achillis in children with cerebral palsy, *J Bone Joint Surg Br* 1979; 61B:466–469.

[48] Williams PE, Goldspink G. Changes in sarcomere length and physiological properties in immobilized muscle. *J Anat* 1978;127:459–468.

[49] Tabary JC, Tabary C, Tardieu C, Tardieu G, Goldspink G. Physiological and structural changes in the cat's soleus muscle due to immobilization at different lengths by plaster casts. *J Physiol (Lond)* 1972;224:231–244.

[50] Woo S-Y, Gomez MA, Woo Y-K, Akeson WH. Mechanical properties of tendons and ligaments. II. The relationships of immobilization and exercise on tissue remodeling. *Biorheology* 1982;19:397–408.

[51] Perry J, Hoffer M. Preoperative and postoperative dynamic electromyography as an aid in planning tendon transfers in children with cerebral palsy, *J Bone Joint Surg Am* 1977;59A:531–537.

[52] Perry J, Waters RL, Perrin T. Electromyographic analysis of equinovarus following stroke. *Clin Orthop* 1978;131:47–53.

[53] Sale D, Quinlan JE, Marsh E, McComas AJ, Belanger AY. Influence of joint position on ankle plantarflexion in humans. *J Appl Physiol* 1982, 52:1636–1642.

Steven M. Kidder
Gerald F. Harris
Faruk S. Abuzzahab, Jr.
Jeffrey E. Johnson

Chapter 8

A Biomechanical Model for Foot and Ankle Motion Analysis

8.1. INTRODUCTION

The foot and ankle represent an important link in the human locomotor chain. They provide initial active compensation for uneven terrain, maintenance of balance, and absorption of energy at foot contact.

The process of locomotion involves the entire body, with each segment of the locomotor chain contributing biomechanically. Abnormalities of the joints or structures of any element in the kinematic chain can result in redistributed stresses on other segments, and particularly at the ankle, knee, and hip [1]. A better quantitative description of the kinematics and kinetics of the foot and ankle during ambulation could increase our understanding of this complex structure with resulting improvements in treatment.

The bony anatomy of the foot and ankle is generally described in terms of the hindfoot, midfoot, and forefoot segments. The hindfoot includes the calcaneus and talus; the midfoot includes the navicular and cuboids; and the forefoot includes the cuneiforms, metatarsals, and phalanges. Anatomic division into these segments is only approximate. Motion and position of any segment can profoundly influence other segments. This coupling effect is most evident during stance phase when the foot is bearing weight.

Motion of the foot and ankle is accomplished through several joints. The major joints are the talocalcaneal (subtalar), talocrural (ankle joint), transverse tarsal (midtarsal), tarsometatarsal, and metatarsophalangeal. Hindfoot motion involves the subtalar, midtarsal, and talocrural joints, with the talocrural joint accounting for most of the sagittal mobility [2].

The subtalar joint is responsible for movement in the coronal and transverse planes. Orientation of the subtalar joint determines the position and motion of the midfoot and forefoot, and accounts for the majority of transverse plane hindfoot rotation [3]. The subtalar joint also allows supination of the foot at foot-off. The unequal length of the metatarsals necessitates this supination for maintenance of the vertical foot position [4]. Biplanar motion measured at the subtalar joint requires an axis that is angled approximately 42 degrees from horizontal and anywhere from 16 to 23 degrees from vertical [3,5]. This axis moves as the ankle joint articulates during gait.

The midtarsal joint consists of the articulations of the calcaneocuboid and talonavicular joints. As the foot rolls off of the heel and onto the forefoot, the midtarsal joint allows inversion of the heel, which in turn increases the midtarsal joint rigidity as the cuboid becomes fixed [4,6,7]. This midfoot locking mechanism provides a foot "lever" during stance phase weight bearing. Conversely, eversion of the heel allows more flexibility in the joint during non–weight bearing.

The line along the metatarsophalangeal joints is known as the metatarsophalangeal break. The angle of this axis distributes weight across the metatarsal heads at roll-off and provides dynamic stability [6]. It is the oblique orientation of this axis that causes foot supination at foot-off [4]. The tarsometatarsal joints allow limited flexion-extension motion, with the first and fifth metatarsal possessing pronation-supination ability. These joints allow supination and pronation of the forefoot [5,8,9].

Current methods of foot and ankle analysis include a combination of physical exam, observation, and radiographs. Physical exam and radiographic data provide range of motion and static alignment information that, although helpful, does not address the condition of dynamic weight bearing during ambulation. Observation of gait is useful, but subject to interpretation and based largely upon the observer's experience. Observation does not reveal gait kinetics, nor a three-dimensional (3-D) perspective of multijoint motion [10].

Quantitative study of normal ambulation has led to a better understanding of gait. Systems for assessment have demonstrated value in presurgical assessment and postsurgical evaluation of abnormal gait patterns. Similar usefulness could be found in the description and analysis of foot and ankle motion. These require a biomechanical model of the structure and a suitable instrumentation system to acquire marker coordinate data.

Several biomechanical models for foot and ankle motion have been proposed, with the majority of published work focusing on the ankle joint. Much of this work has been carried out on cadaver specimens and has employed static test methods lacking the continuous motion of actual gait. The foot is frequently considered to be a single rigid body [11,12] with some of the more sophisticated models addressing the more complex triplanar motion. Most systems disregard the more distal segments of the foot. While helpful in determining ranges of motion, the kinematic studies only approximate the actual joint loading conditions.

Many motion analysis systems model the foot as a simple rigid body with a single hinge or revolute joint at the ankle [11,12]. These models provide a good estimation of gross ankle flexion-extension and internal-external rotation, but lack an accurate description of inversion-eversion.

In 1992, A. K. Singh et al. [13] used time-lapse photography and light emitting diodes attached to cadaver ankles to determine the orientation of the talocrural angle. A single hinge axis model was assumed, and subtalar joint motion was not included. V. T. Inman et al. [14] modeled motion of the hindfoot with a double-hinged model as well as a hinged joint and pivot model. Investigation of hindfoot motion was also conducted by M. J. Muelle and B. J. Norton in 1992 with a video-based system as a subject walked on a treadmill [15]. Calcaneal alignment relative to the tibia in the coronal plane was described. J. Apkarian et al. [16] provided a 3-D model of the lower leg that included the pelvis, thigh, lower leg, and foot segments, each with coordinate axes. Unlike hinged-joint models, this system was modeled with three-degree-of-freedom joints. Marker locations were like those of M. P. Kadaba et al. [11], with a third marker at the heel. Ankle motion measurement was more reliable and included inversion-eversion data. The addition of a force plate allowed estimation of joint moments. In 1988, S. Siegler et al. [17,18] investigated the kinematics and kinetics of the ankle with a six-degree-of-freedom apparatus. Fresh lower limbs were fitted with sonic emitters at the talus and calcaneus. Pneumatic actuators were then used to position the calcaneus while forces and moments were computed. A joint coordinate system similar to that of E. S. Grood and W. J. Suntay [19] was used to describe relative rotation and displacement. Siegler concluded that both the talocrural and subtalar joints produced motion in all three clinical planes. Plantarflexion-dorsiflexion was reported to occur primarily at the talocrural joint with increasing subtalar contribution at extreme ranges of motion. Inversion-eversion of the hindfoot contributed mainly to the subtalar joint, while internal and external rotation contributions were approximately equal. R. W. Soutas-Little et al. [20] applied a similar system to describe ankle motion during running with two high-speed cameras. Calculations using the joint coordinate system and an Euler rotation system were compared for hindfoot motion. A four-camera cine system used by N. Murphy et al. [21] tracked hindfoot motion by embedding markers in the talus and malleolus of a fresh cadaver leg. The authors suggested a helical axis motion description of ankle joint kinematics. In 1991 S. Ortloff et al. [22] utilized a noninvasive method to study subtalar joint motion. Computerized axial tomography (CAT) scans were made of ankle specimens in specified clinical positions and digitized to assimilate 3-D images, including geometric and mass properties used to define the principal axes. Translations and Euler rotations between the talus and calcaneus were described. A. Lundberg et al. [23–25] placed tantalum markers in the foot and ankle of eight volunteers in a stereoradiographic study. Data was collected with subjects in static weight-bearing stance. The findings generally agreed with those of Siegler regarding motion contributions of the individual joints. However, a limited range of dorsiflexion in the arch was seen when the hindfoot was plantarflexed. For foot rotation, the studies indicated that all of the joints contributed motion.

In a study of midfoot motion, T. J. Ouzounian et al. [26] tested 10 lower leg specimens with reference pins inserted in the midfoot bones. Dorsiflexion and plantarflexion was simulated, and marker locations were determined using a three-space tracker. Rotations of the bones were calculated using direction cosines, but the motion was not well related to standard clinical planes.

A. Wanivenhaus et al. [27] reported on the motion of the first metatarsal joint in 100 cadaver specimens. The feet were manually compressed while the position of the bones was determined radiographically by the orientation of implanted Kirschner wires.

8.2. MATERIALS AND METHODS

8.2.1. Instrumentation

Many reported studies utilize radiographic exposure with invasive radiopaque markers to obtain position and orientation data of the foot and ankle. Although acceptable and effective when applied statically, these methods are invasive and expose the subject to radiation.

Video-based methods for motion analysis are noninvasive, offer high rates of data acquisition, and can be implemented with reasonable accuracy using standard cameras and available computer technology. In this study, a Vicon-based motion analysis system (Oxford, England) was utilized to capture 3-D marker coordinate data from subjects during normal ambulation. The system incorporated five cameras and an Advanced Mechanical Technology, Inc. (AMTI) force plate (Newton, Massachusetts). The cameras were oriented around a 2.6 m × 0.9 m × 0.62 m capture volume. Infrared strobes were synched to the cameras and used to illuminate retroreflective markers on the foot and ankle. The markers were 15.9 mm in diameter. Double-sided adhesive tape was used to fix the marker bases to the subject's skin. The camera frame rate was 60 Hz and the analog data collection rate was 600 Hz. Markers that were not detected due to low reflectivity, movement beyond the capture volume, high acceleration, close proximity to other markers, and contralateral foot swing resulted in periods of missing data or marker "drop-out." Cameras were placed to minimize occurrences of drop-out. The criteria selected for acceptance required that drop-out periods not exceed 10 frames (167 ms). An interpolation routine was used to estimate these small missing sections.

8.2.2. Biomechanical Model

A four-segment rigid-body model without joint constraints was developed to describe the kinematics of the foot and ankle during ambulation. The complexity of motion in the foot and ankle and paucity of published quantitative information about joint center locations makes assumptions about these points questionable. For this reason, a general rotational model without joint location constraints was adopted. This assures accurate orientation (rotation) information for clinical study. The initial model is also suitable for development of a kinetic model when combined with information regarding joint centers.

The four rigid-body foot-model segments were defined by the bones with markers attached (Figure 8-1): (1) the tibia (segment 1), (2) the hindfoot defined by the calcaneus (segment 2), (3) the forefoot marked by the 1st and 5th metatarsal (segment 3), and (4) the

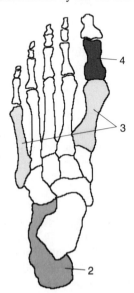

Figure 8-1. Model segments (Segment 1 not shown).

proximal hallux (segment 4). As markers are only positioned on the tibia, calcaneus, first and fifth metatarsal, and proximal hallux, relative motion of other bones of the foot cannot be known for certain. Additional considerations must be made to satisfy rigid-body model conditions. For example, the tibia segment includes the tibia and fibula, while the forefoot segment is considered to include all the metatarsals. Obviously, there will be some relative motion of the metatarsals making this a less attractive assumption.

In order to describe foot and ankle segment orientation, a minimum of three non-colinear marker locations were needed. A minimum of 12 markers was required for the four-segment foot and ankle model. Segment numbers, marker numbers, abbreviated designations, and anatomical locations of the markers are described in Table 8-1. The 15 marker positions are depicted anatomically in Figure 8-2.

TABLE 8-1 ANATOMICAL MARKER POSITIONS

Marker	Anatomical location
1	Medial surface of the anterior tibia
2	Medial malleolus
3	Lateral malleolus
4	Tuberosity of the calcaneus
5	Medial calcaneus
6	Lateral calcaneus
7	Medial tuberosity of the navicular
8	Antero-superior process of the calcaneus
9	Medial base of the 1st metatarsal
10	Tuberosity of the 5th metatarsal laterally
11	Medial head of the 1st metatarsal
12	Lateral head of the 5th metatarsal
13	Anteriorly directed hallux marker
14	Laterally directed hallux marker
15	Superiorly directed hallux marker

The global (lab-referenced) coordinates of the markers are obtained with the Vicon system. These 3-D coordinates are then used to construct a local (body-fixed) set of mutually orthogonal axes. The relative orientations of the body-fixed axes are used to express motion clinically. A method for expressing a distal segment orientation relative to the next proximal segment was used in this study. A method was needed to depict rotational motion about clinically meaningful axes (i.e., sagittal, coronal, and transverse planes). Partly due to widespread clinical acceptance in whole-body gait applications, and following analysis of other methods of 3-D orientation description (Grood and Suntay, helical axis, direction cosines [28]), the Euler (Cardan) angle system was selected for this study [28]. The Euler angles describe a set of three successive (nonindependent) rotations about predefined orthogonal coordinate axes. It is important to note that the order of the rotations is critical and must be clearly defined.

A method utilizing sequences of independent rotations and a floating axis [19] was considered, but because of cadaveric studies demonstrating that in the foot and ankle the primary plane of rotation differs by segment, this method was ruled out. The system of E. S. Grood and W. J. Suntay is most effective when primary motion occurs in a single plane. In the

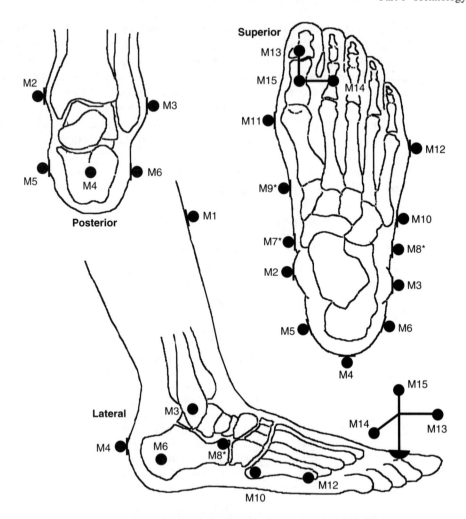

Figure 8-2. Retroreflective marker positions. Note: asterisks (*) indicate additional markers positioned to provide redundancy to reduce dropout effects.

case of foot and ankle motion, the floating axis is difficult to understand. Similarly, helical-axis and direction-cosine methods of motion description were also difficult to represent in clear clinical terms, and were not selected for this study.

The four-segment foot and ankle model assumed no fixed axes of rotation between body segments. This eliminated the need for assumption or computation regarding fixed centers, while providing accurate orientation data. Calculation of 3-D instantaneous centers, for example, can be made difficult if even a small amount of error is introduced. Formulation of future kinetic models will require, however that axes locations be specified.

At each time step, kinematic analysis of foot and ankle motion produced 12 separate angular values: 3 Eulerian angles for each of the 4 modeled segments (Table 8-2).

In selection of the order of rotations, it was determined that the first derotation is most accurately expressed if about the axis with the largest rotational component. From clinical

TABLE 8-2   ANGULAR CONVENTIONS FOR MODEL SEGMENTS

Anatomic plane	Sign convention
Segment 1 (Tibia)	
Sagittal	(+) Forward - proximal tibia moving anterior of the distal tibia. (−) Backward
Coronal	(+) Abduction - distal tibia moving lateral with respect to proximal tibia (−) Adduction
Transverse	(+) External rotation of the tibia with respect to the lab coordinates (−) Internal rotation
Segment 2 (Hindfoot)	
Sagittal	(+) Dorsiflexion (−) Plantarflexion
Coronal	(+) Eversion (−) Inversion
Transverse	(+) External rotation (−) Internal rotation
Segment 3 (Forefoot)	
Sagittal	(+) Dorsiflexion (−) Plantarflexion
Coronal	(+) Valgus (−) Varus
Transverse	(+) Abduction (−) Adduction
Segment 4 (Hallux)	
Sagittal	(+) Dorsiflexion (−) Plantarflexion
Coronal	(+) Pronation (−) Supination
Transverse	(+) Valgus (−) Varus

data, it was noted that the largest motion component for the tibia and hallux exists in the sagittal plane, while motion of the hindfoot is generally split between sagittal and coronal planes [16,29]. Because of the orientation of the capture volume and greater horizontal resolution of the cameras, the transverse plane data is the least accurate. The order of derotations selected for this study were sagittal, coronal, and then transverse. Subject to the results of initial studies, future versions might employ an altered derotational sequence.

Local coordinate axes were developed for each model segment based upon the global (laboratory) referenced 3-D marker coordinates. The construction of each segment coordinate axes set was unique to the segment. The x axis was constructed such that it pointed anteriorly, the y axis medially/laterally, and the z axis, superiorly.

The 3-D marker coordinates were used to construct a segment rotation matrix referenced to the lab coordinate system. The constructions for these coordinate axes are as follows (see the Appendix for nomenclature).

The origin of the tibial body coordinate system is located midway between markers 2 and 3. The tibial origin (**t**) is defined as:

$$\mathbf{t} = \begin{bmatrix} \dfrac{m_{2x} + m_{3x}}{2} \\ \dfrac{m_{2y} + m_{3y}}{2} \\ \dfrac{m_{2z} + m_{3z}}{2} \end{bmatrix} \tag{8-1}$$

Note that the medial/lateral sense is reversed for left and right feet in order to maintain consistent clinical rotations.

The unit vector, $\mathbf{t}_2'$ is defined as pointing laterally from the origin of **t** to marker 3 for the left foot (marker 2 for the right):

$$\mathbf{t}_2' = \begin{bmatrix} m_{3x} - t_x \\ m_{3y} - t_y \\ m_{3z} - t_z \end{bmatrix}' \quad \text{(left foot)} \tag{8-2}$$

$$\mathbf{t}_2' = \begin{bmatrix} m_{2x} - t_x \\ m_{2y} - t_y \\ m_{2z} - t_z \end{bmatrix}' \quad \text{(right foot)} \tag{8-3}$$

The unit vector, $\mathbf{t}_1'$ is formed by crossing $\mathbf{t}_2'$ with the unit vector from the origin of **t** to marker 1:

$$\mathbf{t}_1' = \mathbf{t}_2' \times \begin{bmatrix} m_{1x} - t_x \\ m_{1y} - t_y \\ m_{1z} - t_z \end{bmatrix}' \tag{8-4}$$

Unit vector $\mathbf{t}_3'$ is formed by $\mathbf{t}_1'$ crossed with $\mathbf{t}_2'$:

$$\mathbf{t}_3' = \mathbf{t}_1' \times \mathbf{t}_2' \tag{8-5}$$

The rotation matrix (**T**) for the tibial segment is constructed from the three unit vectors:

$$\mathbf{T} = [\mathbf{t}_1' \ \mathbf{t}_2' \ \mathbf{t}_3']$$
$$\text{or}$$
$$\mathbf{T} = \begin{bmatrix} t_{1x}' & t_{2x}' & t_{3x}' \\ t_{1y}' & t_{2y}' & t_{3y}' \\ t_{1z}' & t_{2z}' & t_{3z}' \end{bmatrix} \tag{8-6}$$

The origin of the hindfoot coordinate system (**H**) is located midway between markers 5 and 6. The hindfoot origin, **h**, is defined as:

$$\mathbf{h} = \begin{bmatrix} \dfrac{\mathbf{m}_{5x} + \mathbf{m}_{6x}}{2} \\[2ex] \dfrac{\mathbf{m}_{5y} + \mathbf{m}_{6y}}{2} \\[2ex] \dfrac{\mathbf{m}_{5z} + \mathbf{m}_{6z}}{2} \end{bmatrix} \tag{8-7}$$

The unit vector $\mathbf{h}_1'$ is pointing anteriorly from marker 4 through the origin, **h**:

$$\mathbf{h}_1' = \begin{bmatrix} \mathbf{h}_x - \mathbf{m}_{4x} \\ \mathbf{h}_y - \mathbf{m}_{4y} \\ \mathbf{h}_z - \mathbf{m}_{4z} \end{bmatrix}' \tag{8-8}$$

Unit vector $\mathbf{h}_3'$ is formed by crossing $\mathbf{h}_1'$ with the vector from marker 5 to 6 for the left side and from marker 6 to 5 on the right side:

$$\mathbf{h}_3' = \mathbf{h}_1' \times \begin{bmatrix} \mathbf{m}_{6x} - \mathbf{m}_{5x} \\ \mathbf{m}_{6y} - \mathbf{m}_{5y} \\ \mathbf{m}_{6z} - \mathbf{m}_{5z} \end{bmatrix}' \quad \text{(left foot)} \tag{8-9}$$

$$\mathbf{h}_3' = \mathbf{h}_1' \times \begin{bmatrix} \mathbf{m}_{5x} - \mathbf{m}_{6x} \\ \mathbf{m}_{5y} - \mathbf{m}_{6y} \\ \mathbf{m}_{5z} - \mathbf{m}_{6z} \end{bmatrix}' \quad \text{(right foot)} \tag{8-10}$$

Unit vector $\mathbf{h}_2'$ is formed by $\mathbf{h}_3'$ crossed with $\mathbf{h}_1'$:

$$\mathbf{h}_2' = \mathbf{h}_3' \times \mathbf{h}_1' \tag{8-11}$$

The rotation matrix (**H**) for the hindfoot segment is constructed from the three unit vectors:

$$\mathbf{H} = [\mathbf{h}_1' \ \mathbf{h}_2' \ \mathbf{h}_3']$$

or

$$\mathbf{H} = \begin{bmatrix} \mathbf{h}_{1x}' & \mathbf{h}_{2x}' & \mathbf{h}_{3x}' \\ \mathbf{h}_{1y}' & \mathbf{h}_{2y}' & \mathbf{h}_{3y}' \\ \mathbf{h}_{1z}' & \mathbf{h}_{2z}' & \mathbf{h}_{3z}' \end{bmatrix} \tag{8-12}$$

Forefoot unit vector $\mathbf{f}_1'$ is defined as pointing from marker 10 to 12:

$$\mathbf{f}_1' = \begin{bmatrix} \mathbf{m}_{12x} - \mathbf{m}_{10x} \\ \mathbf{m}_{12y} - \mathbf{m}_{10y} \\ \mathbf{m}_{12z} - \mathbf{m}_{10z} \end{bmatrix}' \tag{8-13}$$

Unit vector $\mathbf{f}_3'$ is found by crossing $\mathbf{f}_1'$ with the vector from marker 11 to 12 for the left foot and marker 12 to 11 for the right foot:

$$\mathbf{f}_3' = \mathbf{f}_1' \times \begin{bmatrix} m_{12x} - m_{11x} \\ m_{12y} - m_{11y} \\ m_{12z} - m_{11z} \end{bmatrix}' \quad \text{(left foot)} \tag{8-14}$$

$$\mathbf{f}_3' = \mathbf{f}_1' \times \begin{bmatrix} m_{11x} - m_{12x} \\ m_{11y} - m_{12y} \\ m_{11z} - m_{12z} \end{bmatrix}' \quad \text{(right foot)} \tag{8-15}$$

Crossing $\mathbf{f}_3'$ with $\mathbf{f}_1'$ produces $\mathbf{f}_2'$:

$$\mathbf{f}_2' = \mathbf{f}_3' \times \mathbf{f}_1' \tag{8-16}$$

The rotation matrix (**F**) or the forefoot segment is constructed from the three unit vectors:

$$\mathbf{F} = [\mathbf{f}_1' \ \mathbf{f}_2' \ \mathbf{f}_3']$$

or

$$\mathbf{F} = \begin{bmatrix} f_{1x}' & f_{2x}' & f_{3x}' \\ f_{1y}' & f_{2y}' & f_{3y}' \\ f_{1z}' & f_{2z}' & f_{3z}' \end{bmatrix} \tag{8-17}$$

Hallux unit vector $\mathbf{b}_1'$ is directed from marker 15 to marker 13:

$$\mathbf{b}_1' = \begin{bmatrix} m_{13x} - m_{15x} \\ m_{13y} - m_{15y} \\ m_{13z} - m_{15z} \end{bmatrix}' \tag{8-18}$$

For the left foot, $\mathbf{b}_3'$ is defined by crossing $\mathbf{b}_1'$ with the unit vector from marker 15 to marker 14. For the right side, $\mathbf{b}_3'$ is produced by crossing $\mathbf{b}_1'$ with the vector from marker 14 to marker 15:

$$\mathbf{b}_3' = \mathbf{b}_1' \times \begin{bmatrix} m_{14x} - m_{15x} \\ m_{14y} - m_{15y} \\ m_{14z} - m_{15z} \end{bmatrix}' \quad \text{(left foot)} \tag{8-19}$$

$$\mathbf{b}_3' = \mathbf{b}_1' \times \begin{bmatrix} m_{15x} - m_{14x} \\ m_{15y} - m_{14y} \\ m_{15z} - m_{14z} \end{bmatrix}' \quad \text{(right foot)} \tag{8-20}$$

Unit vector $\mathbf{b}_2'$ is defined as $\mathbf{b}_3'$ crossed with $\mathbf{b}_1'$:

$$\mathbf{b}_2' = \mathbf{b}_3' \times \mathbf{b}_1' \tag{8-21}$$

The rotation matrix (**B**) for the hallux is constructed:

$$\mathbf{B} = [\mathbf{b}_1' \ \mathbf{b}_2' \ \mathbf{b}_3']$$

or

$$\mathbf{B} = \begin{bmatrix} b_{1x}' & b_{2x}' & b_{3x}' \\ b_{1y}' & b_{2y}' & b_{3y}' \\ b_{1z}' & b_{2z}' & b_{3z}' \end{bmatrix} \tag{8-22}$$

This construction resulted in a set of oblique axes. Therefore, matrix **B** was multiplied by a correction matrix, $\mathbf{R}_{\text{geometric correction}}$, (based upon the geometry of the fixed triad) to orient the coordinate system more closely with the long axis of the toe.

In order to properly align the marker-based coordinate systems with the underlying bony anatomy, a final rotation matrix was determined with the use of radiographic data. A clinical series of X-rays was chosen to provide correlation between the instrumented foot posture and that examined radiographically. Subjects walked at a freely selected cadence and then halted several times until a representative stance phase foot posture was obtained. The plantar foot position was then recorded on graph paper, and this template was used in X-ray to repeat the weight-bearing stance position of the foot. The radiographic views used in this study were (1) anterior-posterior (AP) view, (2) lateral view (LAT), and (3) hindfoot alignment view (HA). The radiographic exposures produce minimal radiation exposure to the extremities and are often requested as part of a clinical exam. Thus, use of the X-ray series in this study causes no substantial increased risk to a clinical subject. This X-ray series allowed determination of the following angles [30]:

1. (AP) BM-C—Angle between a line connecting the medial and lateral malleoli and the long axis of the calcaneus.
2. (AP) C-MT(2)—Angle between the long axis of the calcaneus and long axis of the second metatarsal.
3. (AP) MT-P(1)—Angle between the long axis of the first metatarsal and the long axis of the proximal hallux.
4. (LAT) T-C—Angle between the long axis of the tibia and a line along the posterior aspect of the calcaneus.
5. (LAT) C-MET(1)—Angle between the posterior aspect of the calcaneus and the long axis of the first metatarsal.
6. (LAT) MT-P(1)—Angle between the long axis of the first metatarsal and long axis of the proximal hallux.
7. (HA) T-C—Coronal plane hindfoot angle between the long axis of the tibia and the major axis of the calcaneus.

Certain measurements are difficult to obtain even with the help of X-rays. For example, the rotation of the hallux in the coronal plane is difficult to determine either radiographically or clinically. Clinical measurement is subject to the shape of the toenail and an inability to see the hallux bone. Radiographic determination of this angle using a standing sesamoid view is unreliable as it places the foot into a very unnatural position (with the toes in extreme dorsiflexion). This would be a position difficult to duplicate in the motion analysis lab, and a position many subjects with pathology would have difficulty achieving and maintaining. Rotation of the forefoot in the coronal plane is also difficult to determine either clinically or radiographically. No radiographic view exists that would allow determination of this angle. Measurement of the arch has been suggested as a form of clinical measurement, but this method is subject to the position of the plantar fascia and fatty tissue. The tibial sagittal and coronal angles with respect to the floor can be determined from the lateral and hindfoot X-rays respectively. The rotation in the transverse plane with respect to the lab is not a well-defined angle clinically and will likely need to be determined by a physical therapist at the time of testing.

During testing, a brief "snapshot" of data was taken of the foot fully instrumented with markers and standing in the same position on the graph paper used when the X-rays were taken. An iterative process was used to create rotation matrices that when multiplied by the matrices described above, would result in angles measured in the X-rays. That is, a kinematic analysis of the relative position of the model segments during this stance test would match the radiographic data. This provided a correlation between the somewhat arbitrary segment coordinate axes orientation due to marker position and the actual position of the underlying bony anatomy.

The coordinate data collected with the video system is referenced to the lab coordinate system. Thus the segment rotation matrices (transformation matrices) are described with respect to the global or laboratory system. For a vector $\mathbf{q}$, referenced in global coordinates, the following can be demonstrated:

$$\begin{bmatrix} q_x \\ q_y \\ q_z \end{bmatrix} = \mathbf{A} \begin{bmatrix} r_{Ax} \\ r_{Ay} \\ r_{Az} \end{bmatrix} \text{ and } \begin{bmatrix} q_x \\ q_y \\ q_z \end{bmatrix} = \mathbf{B} \begin{bmatrix} r_{Bx} \\ r_{By} \\ r_{Bz} \end{bmatrix} \tag{8-23}$$

$\mathbf{r_A}$ and $\mathbf{r_B}$ are the vectors of $\mathbf{q}$ expressed in their relative coordinate systems and $\mathbf{A}$ and $\mathbf{B}$ are 3×3 transformation matrices. Therefore:

$$\mathbf{Ar_A} = \mathbf{Br_B}$$

$$\text{or} \tag{8-24}$$

$$\mathbf{r_A} = \mathbf{A^T Br_B}$$

where $\mathbf{A^T A} = [\mathbf{I}]$

Note that the coordinates of one system can be expressed in terms of the other by multiplying the transpose of the reference system rotation matrix ($\mathbf{A^T}$) by the rotation of the other system ($\mathbf{B}$). This requires that both sets of direction cosines are referenced to the common, global coordinate system. Thus, at each time step, the local coordinate system rotation matrix for the proximal segment is transposed and multiplied by the distal coordinate system rotation matrix. This results in a 3×3 matrix, $\mathbf{R}$, which can be "derotated" to determine the relative angular orientation of the two model segments (Equations 8-26, 8-27, 8-28). This process is repeated for each segment (the proximal coordinate system for tibial rotations was the lab coordinate system).

The derotational sequence (sagittal, coronal, transverse) correlated to rotations about the proximal y, x, and z axes. The assembled rotation matrix, $\mathbf{R}$, was expressed as $\mathbf{R} = \mathbf{R_z R_x R_y}$:

$$\mathbf{R} = \begin{bmatrix} cy\,cz + sx\,sy\,sz & cx\,sz & -sy\,cz + sx\,cy\,sz \\ -cy\,sz + sx\,sy\,cz & cx\,cz & sy\,sz + sx\,cy\,cz \\ cx\,sy & -sx & cx\,cy \end{bmatrix} \tag{8-25}$$

where ci = the cosine of the rotation about the i-th axis
$\quad si$ = the sine of the rotation about the i-th axis

The three Eulerian angles, y, x, and z, were calculated as:

$$x \text{ (coronal)} = \sin^{-1}(-\mathbf{R}_{32}) \tag{8-26}$$

$$z \text{ (transverse)} = \sin^{-1}\left(\frac{\mathbf{R}_{12}}{\cos(x)}\right) \tag{8-27}$$

$$y \text{ (sagittal)} = \sin^{-1}\left(\frac{\mathbf{R}_{31}}{\cos(x)}\right) \tag{8-28}$$

The arcsin terms were used instead of the arccos terms because they return an angular value between −90 and 90 degrees. In some planes of motion, a negative sign is incorporated either so that results match an orthopaedic convention or to compensate for the different rotational directions for right and left feet.

To reduce marker detection noise and resulting error, a digital filter was applied to the coordinate data. Spectral analysis of raw data demonstrated that the majority of power fell below 6 Hz. Some noise was noticed at 15 Hz; likely a result of the camera sampling rate. Consequently, a 6-Hz cut-off was chosen for the filter. Because of the low sampling frequency (60 Hz) and a short data set (approximately 1 to 1.5 s, or 60 to 90 frames), an infinite impulse response (IIR) filter with Butterworth response was developed. A bilinear transform was used to ensure stability.

8.3. RESULTS

Kinematic data is presented for five normal adult subjects, aged 20 to 40 years. A minimum of three trials per side were collected for each subject. Each subject was instructed to walk at a comfortable pace and was positioned such that a single stride fell within the capture volume.

The average kinematic data from five normal adult subjects are presented in Figure 8-3. The four rows of graphs correspond to the four modeled segments, tibia (first), hindfoot (second), forefoot (third), and hallux (fourth). The three columns correspond to the three clinical planes of motion, sagittal, coronal, and transverse. Additionally, four trials (two per side) of kinematic data are presented for three planes of motion (Figures 8-4, 8-5, 8-6).

Tibial motion (Figure 8-3, row 1) is expressed relative to the lab coordinate system and in the sagittal plane demonstrates a negative angle (ankle forward of the knee) at initial contact. The angle then increases in a positive direction (knee moving forward of the ankle) throughout stance phase, peaking shortly after foot-off. A smooth return in the negative direction is seen during swing phase in preparation for foot contact. In the coronal plane, the tibia shows a relatively neutral position (perpendicular to the floor) through early and midstance. An increase in abduction (knee moving medial of the ankle) occurs just prior to foot-off and into early swing. A return to a neutral position is shown from mid to late swing. Direct comparison to other work is difficult, but these motions seem to correlate with the current understanding of the events of the gait cycle [31]. Transverse plane motion of the tibia demonstrates an increase in external rotation through swing phase. The leg rotates internally from late swing phase throughout foot contact to approximately 15 percent of the gait

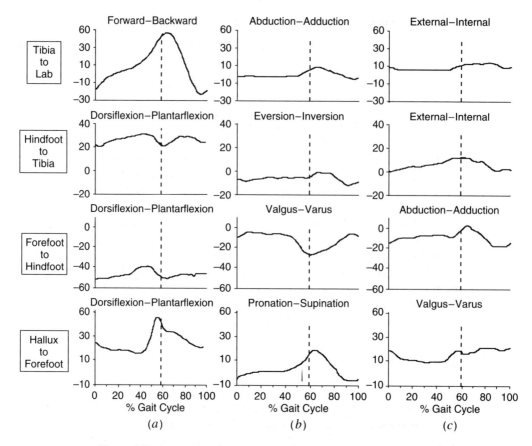

Figure 8-3. Average motion patterns collected from five normal adult subjects:
(*a*) sagittal plane, (*b*) coronal plane, and (*c*) transverse plane. Note:
Vertical dashed line indicates foot-off.

cycle. During midstance the leg rotates externally, which continues through midswing before returning to internal rotation in preparation for foot contact. This pattern agrees with previously reported motion of the tibia, with internal rotation of the entire limb beginning at initial contact and continuing through the loading response [31]. The tibia has been shown to have a markedly accelerated internal rotation during the loading response of early stance phase [32].

The sagittal plane hindfoot motion pattern (Figure 8-3, row 2) indicates an increase in dorsiflexion through swing phase as the foot prepares for foot contact. The hindfoot begins to plantarflex during late swing and this plantarflexion increases after foot contact. At the beginning of midstance the hindfoot motion reverses and begins to dorsiflex until late stance when the hindfoot plantarflexes during foot-off. The patterns and ranges of motion obtained for the sagittal plane in this study agree with previous work [11,14,16,33–36]. S. D. D'Andrea et al., using a similar four-segment model of the foot, reported a similar motion pattern and range of motion [37]. Motion of the hindfoot in the coronal plane shows an increase in hindfoot inversion at foot-off, which moves to a neutral or slightly everted position shortly before foot contact. Through most of stance phase, a relatively neutral position is maintained, with a movement back into inversion just prior to foot-off. The overall patterns and ranges agree with reported normal data [16,33,34,37]. Transverse

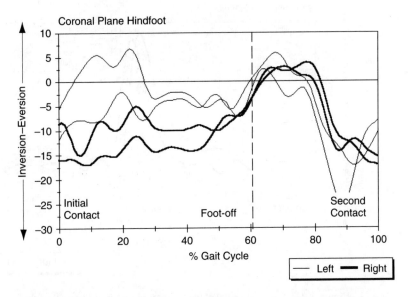

Figure 8-4. Relative coronal plane hindfoot motion for one normal adult, four trials (two per side).

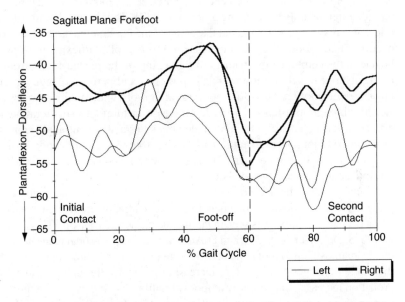

Figure 8-5. Relative sagittal plane forefoot motion for one normal adult, four trials (two per side).

plane hindfoot motion shows a steady movement into internal rotation throughout swing phase to the beginning of midstance. At midstance the hindfoot begins external rotation, which continues through foot-off.

Sagittal plane forefoot motion (Figure 8-3, row 3) demonstrates relative plantar flexion at foot-off, which changes to a more dorsiflexed position approaching foot contact. The total range of motion of this segment is small, measuring approximately 10 degrees. Little data

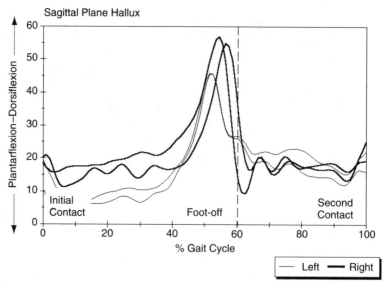

Figure 8-6. Relative sagittal plane hallux motion for one normal adult, four trials (two per side).

is available for this motion segment. D'Andrea et al. reported a similar motion pattern but recorded significantly greater ranges of motion [37]. The gradual dorsiflexion motion during midstance may represent a gradual flattening of the longitudinal arch as the body progresses over the stance foot. The sharp increase in forefoot plantarflexion prior to foot-off might be due to the combined mechanism of tightening of the plantar fascia from the "windlass mechanism" and activity in the tibialis posterior and peroneus longus muscles. Coronal plane forefoot motion shows forefoot varus at foot-off, with rotation towards forefoot valgus steadily through midstance. A sudden increase in forefoot varus rotation occurs at foot-off. Transverse plane forefoot motion demonstrates a near neutral position at foot-off with an abduction motion occurring in early swing followed by adduction of the forefoot that increases through foot contact. During the load response period of early stance phase, forefoot adduction changes to abduction, which continues through foot-off.

Sagittal plane hallux motion (Figure 8-3, row 4) shows dorsiflexion at foot-off with a progressive plantarflexion movement to a more neutral position at midstance. A rapid transition back to dorsiflexion is seen in late stance phase and foot-off. This data correlates well with G. S. DeLozier et al. [34], and D'Andrea et al. [37]. Coronal plane hallux motion shows that from midswing to foot contact there is an increase in hallux supination. At foot contact the motion changes to pronation, increasing gradually throughout stance phase. Hallux pronation increases more rapidly at foot-off until midswing, when it returns to a supination motion. Transverse plane hallux motion demonstrates motion of the hallux in a varus direction from shortly after foot contact through midstance, with a rapid movement back to valgus at foot-off. The hallux remains in a relative valgus position throughout swing phase.

8.4. CONCLUSIONS AND DISCUSSION

The results indicate that the four-segment kinematic model could provide quantitative information regarding motion of the foot and ankle. From trial to trial, the data has been demonstrated to be repeatable for a single subject. Variability noted in the kinematic data when averaged across several subjects is not unexpected and will require analysis of a larger population for validation. Some variation in the system can be attributed to the differences in foot structure among subjects as detected in the X-ray data. To quantify this variability, a technique such as that applied by Kadaba et al. is considered [12].

Error sources contributing to variability include soft tissue movement and uncertainty in the spatial location of the markers due to instrumentation error. The actual contribution of each of these sources is currently being studied, but additional cameras, higher resolution sensors, and further enhancements should reduce this error in the future.

The size and weight of the hallux marker is also of some concern. Due to the hallux marker inertia, some of the motion observed in the hallux data could be due to marker motion relative to the toe, or motion of the toe induced by the mass of the triad. A lighter triad would reduce this error.

The rigid-body model assumptions are well justified when applied to the tibia and hallux. However, motion of the hindfoot can only be isolated to motion of the calcaneus relative to the tibia. The motion of intermediate bones, such as the talus and navicular, cannot be measured with the present system. It is possible that comparison of motion data from subjects who have had joint fusions to that of normals might lend additional insight. The rigid-body assumption for the forefoot is also not entirely justified. Some of the motion observed on the plots is probably due to relative movement between the metatarsals. Incorporation of more markers on the forefoot and additional model segments might reduce some of this error.

Appendix: Equation Notation

- Small bold letters represent 3×1 vectors (e.g., **a**):

$$\mathbf{a} = \begin{bmatrix} a_x \\ a_y \\ a_z \end{bmatrix} \tag{8-29}$$

- Capital bold letters represent 3×3 matrices (e.g., **M**):

$$\mathbf{M} = \begin{bmatrix} a_x & b_x & c_x \\ a_y & b_y & c_y \\ a_z & b_z & c_z \end{bmatrix} \tag{8-30}$$

- Numerical subscripts on vectors indicate the marker number associated with that vector (e.g., $\mathbf{m}_{12}$ is the vector pointing to marker 12).
- Subscripted x, y, and z indicate the x, y, and z vector components (e.g., $\mathbf{m}_{8x}$ is the x coordinate or x vector component of marker 8).
- A prime (') represents a (3×1) unit vector quantity where:

$$\mathbf{a}' = \frac{\mathbf{a}}{|\mathbf{a}|} \tag{8-31}$$

$$\text{and } |\mathbf{a}| = \sqrt{\mathbf{a}_x^2 + \mathbf{a}_y^2 + \mathbf{a}_z^2}$$

Unit vectors of segment rotation matrices are designated by the small letter primed. For example, segment 1, the tibial segment, has a rotation matrix designated **T**.

The unit vectors are $\mathbf{t_1}'$, $\mathbf{t_2}'$, and $\mathbf{t_3}'$. Each unit vector has x, y, and z components represented by subscripts. In the same example, the components of unit vector $\mathbf{t_2}'$ are $\mathbf{t_{2x}}'$, $\mathbf{t_{2y}}'$, and $\mathbf{t_{2z}}'$, or:

$$\mathbf{t_2'} = \begin{bmatrix} t_{2x}' \\ t_{2y}' \\ t_{2z}' \end{bmatrix} \tag{8-32}$$

and therefore,

$$\mathbf{T} = \begin{bmatrix} t_{1x}' & t_{2x}' & t_{3x}' \\ t_{1y}' & t_{2y}' & t_{3y}' \\ t_{1z}' & t_{2z}' & t_{3z}' \end{bmatrix} \tag{8-33}$$

References

[1] Mann RA. Surgical implications of biomechanics of the foot and ankle. *Clin Orthop* 1980;146:111–118.

[2] Scott SH, Winter DA. Talocrural and talocalcaneal joint kinematics and kinetics during the stance phase of walking. *J Biomech* 1991;24(8):743–752.

[3] Close JR, Inman VT, Poor PM, Todd FN. The function of the subtalar joint. *Clin Orthop* 1967;50:159–179.

[4] DuVries HL, Mann RA, eds. *Surgery of the Foot. DuVries Surgery of the Foot*. St Louis Mo: CV Mosby Company;1978.

[5] Hicks JH. The mechanics of the foot. I. The joints. *J Anat* 1953;87:345–357.

[6] Donatelli R, Wolf SL eds. *The Biomechanics of the Foot and Ankle*, Philadelphia, Pa: FA Davis Co; 1990.

[7] Morris JM. Biomechanics of the foot and ankle. *Clin Orthop* 1977;122:10–17.

[8] Nuber GW. Biomechanics of the foot and ankle during gait. *Clin in Sports Med* 1988;7(1):1–13.

[9] Shepard E. Tarsal movements. *J Bone Joint Surg Br* 1951;33B(2):258–263.

[10] Harris GF, Wertsch JJ. Procedures for gait analysis. *Arch Phys Med Rehabil* 1994;75:216–225.

[11] Kadaba MP, Ramakrishnan HK, Wootten ME. Measurement of lower extremity kinematics during level walking. *J Orthop Res* 1990;8:383–392.

[12] Kadaba MP, Ramakrishnan HK, Wootten ME, Gainey J, Gorton G, Cochran GVB, Repeatability of kinematic, kinetic, and electromyographic data in normal adult gait. *J Orthop Res* 1989;7(6):849–860.

[13] Singh AK, Starkweather KD, Hollister AM, Jatana S, Lupichuk AG. Kinematics of the ankle: A hinge axis model. *Foot and Ankle* 1992;13(8):439–446.

[14] Inman VT, Ralston HJ, Todd F. *Human Walking*, Baltimore, Md: Williams and Wilkins Publishing Co.; 1981.

[15] Muelle, MJ, Norton BJ, Reliability of kinematic measurements of rear-foot motion. *Phys Ther* 1992;72(10):731–737.

[16] Apkarian J, Naumann S, Carins B. A three-dimensional kinematic model of the lower limb. *J Biomech* 1989;22:143–155.

[17] Chen J, Siegler S, Schneck CD. The three-dimensional kinematics and flexibility characteristics of the human ankle and subtalar joints - Part II: Flexibility characteristics. *J Biomech* 1988;110(4):364–373.

[18] Siegler S, Chen J, Schneck CD. The three-dimensional kinematics and flexibility characteristics of the human ankle and subtalar joints - Part I: Kinematics. *J Biomech* 1988;110(4):364–373.

[19] Grood ES, Suntay WJ. A joint coordinate system for the clinical description of three-dimensional motions: Application to the knee. *J Biomech* 1983;105:136–144.

[20] Soutas-Little RW, Beavis GC, Verstraete MC, Markus TL. Analysis of foot motion during running using a joint coordinate system. *Medicine and Science in Sports and Exercise* 1987;(3):285–293.

[21] Murphy N, Allard P, Aissaoui R. Helical motion analysis of the ankle. In: *Proc 2nd North Amer Congress on Biomech* 1992:501-502; Chicago, Ill: August 24–28.

[22] Ortloff S, Harris GF, Wynarsky G, Smith J, Shereff M. Noninvasive biomechanical analysis of joint motion. *Proceedings of the IEEE Engineering in Medicine and Biology Society 13th International Conference*, volume 13, October 31–November 3, 1991.

[23] Lundberg A, Goldi I, Kalin B, Selvik G. Kinematics of the ankle/foot complex: Part 1: Plantarflexion and dorsiflexion. *Foot and Ankle* 1989;9(4):194–200.

[24] Lundberg A, Svensson OK, Bylund C, Goldie I, Selvik G. Kinematics of the ankle/foot complex - Part 2: Pronation and supination. *Foot and Ankle* 1989;9(5):248–253.

[25] Lundberg A, Svensson OK, Bylund C, Selvik G. Kinematics of the ankle/foot complex - Part 3: Influence of leg rotation. *Foot and Ankle* 1989;9(6):304–309.

[26] Ouzounian TJ, Shereff MJ. In vitro determination of midfoot motion. *Foot and Ankle* 1989;10(3):140–146.

[27] Wanivenhaus A, Pretterklieber M. First tarsometatarsal joint: Anatomical biomechanical study. *Foot and Ankle* 1989;9(4):153–157.

[28] Goldstein H. *Classical Mechanics 2nd ed.*, New York, NY: Addison-Wesley, 1980.

[29] Perry J. Anatomy and biomechanics of the hindfoot. *Clin Orthop* 1983;177:9–15.

[30] Steel MW, Johnson KA, DeWitz MA, Ilstrup DM. Radiographic measurements of the normal adult foot. *Foot and Ankle* 1990;1(3):151–158.

[31] Perry J. *Gait Analysis: Normal and Pathological Function*, Thorofare, NJ; Slack Inc., 1992.

[32] Levens AS, Inman VT, Blosser JA. Transverse rotation of the segments of the lower extremity in locomotion. *J Bone Joint Surg Am* 1948;30A:859–872.

[33] Buck P, Morrey BF, Chao EYS. The optimum position of arthrodesis of the ankle: A gait study of the knee and ankle. *J Bone Joint Surg Am* 1987;69A(7):1052–1062.

[34] DeLozier GS, Alexander IJ, Narayanaswamy R. A method for measurement of integrated foot kinematics. In: *Proc 1st Int Symp on 3-D Anal of Human Mvmt*. Montreal, Quebec, Canada: July, 1991.

[35] Mazur JM, Schwartz E, Simon SR. Ankle arthrodesis: Long-term follow-up with gait analysis. *J Bone Joint Surg Am* 1979;61A(7):964–975.

[36] Stauffer RN, Chao EYS, Brewster RC. Force and motion analysis of the normal, diseased, and prosthetic ankle joint. *Clin Orthop* 1977;127:189–196.

[37] D'Andrea SD, Tylkowski C, Losito J, Arquedas W, Bushman T, Howell V. Three-dimensional kinematics of the foot. In: *Proc 8th Annual East Coast Gait Conf*, Rochester, Minn: May 5–8, 1993: 109–110.

Faruk S. Abuzzahab, Jr.
Gerald F. Harris
Steven M. Kidder
Jeffrey E. Johnson
Joseph Nery

Chapter 9

Foot and Ankle Motion Analysis System Instrumentation, Calibration, and Validation

9.1. INTRODUCTION

Human walking is a complex phenomenon that involves an assortment of interconnected musculoskeletal activities. It has been determined that walking is a learned activity that is taught at an early age and developed individually through maturity. The foundation for mature gait patterns has been established by the age of 7 to 9 years [1]. As a result, these patterns represent a form of personal identification similar to one's signature. Small changes in the general rhythmic walking pattern can be made to conform to an individual's needs and desires. Although unique, this pattern is relatively constant and repeatable [1–3]. Conscious control can alter the internal rhythm as needed to overcome obstacles, move faster, or cease motion entirely. External inputs including the variable shapes and characteristics of terrain and footwear also contribute to demonstrated changes in normal ambulatory patterns.

The human foot and ankle complex has been subjected to detailed investigation by clinicians and anatomists for many years. As the final segment in the locomotor chain, the foot provides support to the body during ambulation by distributing gravitational and inertial loads. Pathology and structural changes in the foot and ankle can cause irregular loading and pain in more proximal parts of the body [4].

This study was designed to better understand the dynamics of foot and ankle motion, through the design of an instrumented system to track independently the tibia, hindfoot, forefoot, and hallux segments during gait [5–7]. Currently, there are no reports of foot segment tracking during both stance and swing phases of gait, although similar methods have been used to describe more proximal body segment motion (pelvis, hip, knee, and ankle) [2,3,8,9]. Most reports of human motion describe the foot as a single rigid body

[2,3,9–13]. A more descriptive model of the foot requires recognition and definition of the major biomechanical segments and joint articulations.

The primary foot and ankle motion segments include the hindfoot, forefoot, and hallux, with articulation between adjacent segments and between the hindfoot and tibia/fibula [14]. Multisegmental articulations include:

1. The talocrural or ankle and subtalar joints between the tibia and hindfoot
2. Talonavicular and talocuboid joints between the hindfoot and forefoot
3. The metatarsophalangeal joint between the forefoot and hallux

Many of these articulations possess complex motion characteristics because of multiplanar contact at the joint surfaces [15,16]. It has been reported that characterization of the ankle in the sagittal plane by a single axis is inaccurate at initiation and termination of stance phase [16]. In a series of cadaveric motion studies, J. R. Engsberg (1987) and S. Siegler et al. (1988) concluded that ankle and subtalar joint motion was multiplanar [17,18]. A. Lundberg (1989) confirmed these results in a study of adult feet with implanted radio-opaque markers [11]. Testing methodology involved placing each subject in a stationary apparatus while stereoradiographic images were taken of the foot and ankle. Lundberg examined the talonavicular joint in the same study and showed that it possessed multiplanar motion characteristics [11]. Shape changes in the longitudinal arch altering the relative positions of the hindfoot and forefoot as well as changes in transverse plane orientation have been demonstrated during dorsiflexion of the foot from a plantarflexed position to neutral [11]. The arch of the foot "flattened out" as the foot was rotated from a plantarflexed to neutral position. The study also reported that this behavior was associated with 10 to 40 percent of the observed external foot rotation during plantarflexion.

A foot and ankle analysis system should accurately capture multisegmental data during both swing and stance phases in order to faithfully characterize the complex intersegmental motion patterns of the foot during gait [19]. A video-based system was described by I. J. Alexander et al. (1990) to track motion of the tibia, calcaneus, forefoot, and hallux during stance phase [14]. In 1993, S. D. D'Andrea et al. reported on the three-dimensional (3-D) motion patterns of an adult subject during stance using a video-based system [20]. Unfortunately, both systems were unable to track motion during swing phase. More recently, F. S. Abuzzahab et al. demonstrated a system for dynamic 3-D analysis of foot and ankle motion during both stance and swing phases [21–23]. S. M. Kidder et al. demonstrated the ability of that system to track foot and ankle motion in normal adult subjects when used with an appropriate biomechanical model [5–7]. Practical clinical application requires that the system be capable of tracking extended and unusual ranges of segmental motion during both stance and swing phases of gait.

9.2. MATERIALS AND METHODS

9.2.1. Instrumentation

A Vicon (Oxford Metrics, Ltd. Oxford, England) motion analysis system utilizing five cameras was used to acquire foot and ankle motion data. This system used a Micro-VAX 3100 computer (DEC, Maynard, Massachusetts) operating from a VMS platform. The computer was connected to a PDP-11 data acquisition unit by a thin Ethernet link. The data acquisition unit was responsible for collecting and temporarily storing data as well as providing a synchronization pulse for each of the cameras. The cameras were designed to detect reflected infrared light from specially designed spherical markers placed on anatomic landmarks. The infrared source was provided by light emitting diode (LED) strobes surrounding each camera lens. The strobes illuminated the target markers, which were covered with 3M 7610 reflective tape (St. Paul, Minnesota). The infrared light provided adequate marker illumination without the distraction of visible light. Each camera was equipped with an optical filter selective of light in the infrared spectrum ($\lambda \approx 860$ nm). The reflected image from each marker was digitized by the data acquisition unit. The use of spherical markers ensured that the centroid location of each marker was independent of camera view angle. Each 3-D sphere (target marker) transforms into a two-dimensional (2-D) circle (digital planar image) of the same radius. A direct linear transformation method was used to describe the position of each marker in space [24,25].

In order to track foot and ankle motion, spherical markers were covered with reflective tape and placed over known anatomic locations. A 15.9-mm diameter nylon marker was selected because it offered an adequate reflective surface for identification without obscuring neighboring markers. The nylon material is durable, lightweight, and capable of withstanding a wide variety of loads without distortion. Each marker was carefully covered with retro-reflective tape in a manner that ensured near uniform diameter. This was achieved by cutting small elliptical strips of tape and applying them to the surface of each marker without overlap. Four rigid-body segments were used to map geometrically the foot and ankle structure. The four segments were: hallux or great toe (H), forefoot (FF), hindfoot or calcaneus (HF), and tibia or leg (T). Three markers were placed on each body segment in order to allow complete rigid-body tracking (Table 9-1). Because of the small size of the hallux, a marker triad was rigidly attached to that segment. It consisted of a small metal base and three 1.60-mm diameter wires affixed to the markers (Figure 9-1).

TABLE 9-1   TARGET MARKER LOCATIONS

Marker	Marker Position	Identifier
1	Medial surface of the anterior tibia	MSAT
2	Medial malleolus	MMAL
3	Lateral malleolus	LMAL
4	Tuberosity of the calcaneus	TCAL
5	Medial calcaneus	MCAL
6	Lateral calcaneus	LCAL
7	Tuberosity of the fifth metatarsal laterally	T5ML
8	Medial head of the first metatarsal	MH1M
9	Lateral head of the fifth metatarsal	LH5M
10	Hallux marker in the x-direction	XHAL
11	Hallux marker in the y-direction	YHAL
12	Hallux marker in the z-direction	ZHAL

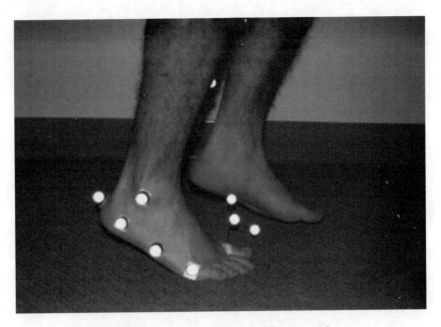

Figure 9-1. Subject instrumented with target markers.

9.2.2. Capture Volume and System Calibration

The capture volume is a region of space common to the field of view of all cameras, which is defined by the position of a set of reference markers. The reference markers were attached to four suspended chains (five markers on each chain) placed vertically at the corners of the region (Figure 9-2). The capture volume dimensions were 2.4 m long by 0.5 m wide by 0.6 m high. Volume length allowed one full stride length for a normal adult subject ranging from 1.0 to 1.7 m [26]. Since stride length is a measurement of the distance that a point on the foot traverses during the gait cycle (i.e., heel-strike to heel-strike or toe-off to toe-off), it was necessary to expand the volume to compensate for the length of the foot. An additional factor was also included to allow for deviations from the normal ranges. The volume width was selected to accommodate a normal adult base of support, which was limited to the width of the force plate embedded in the walkway. The height was chosen so that the most proximal marker on the tibia would remain well within the defined volume.

Five brass spheres (15.9-mm diameter) were attached to each of four lengths of ball-chain suspended from the laboratory ceiling. Four of the markers were mounted at 200-mm intervals. The final marker was attached at a center-to-center distance of 30 mm with respect to the next closest marker and was used for identification of the specific marker chain. These identification markers were affixed to the lower end of three of the chains and at the upper end of the fourth. This ensured a unique camera view of the volume independent of location or angle. The marker positions on the chain were measured with a micrometer and located within ± 0.1 mm of tolerance.

Coordinates of the markers were measured from the origin of a laboratory-oriented Cartesian system for clinical convenience. These data were entered into a calibration file

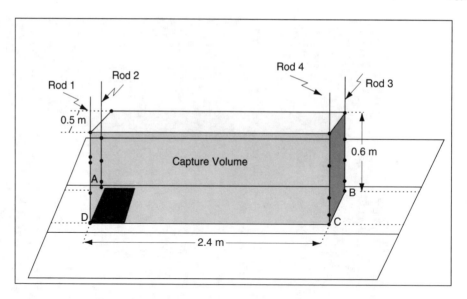

Figure 9-2. System capture volume and calibration chains.

on the computer. The point directly beneath one of the calibration chains served as the origin of the laboratory coordinate system. The coordinate system was oriented such that the length and width of the walkway were coincident with the representative x and y axes of the system. The z axis was defined to be orthogonal to the plane of the walkway, extending vertically from the floor to the ceiling. The x and y coordinates of the reference markers were obtained by attaching a plumb-bob to the ceiling suspension points of the calibration chains. The center of the bob corresponded to the calibration chain center, and its position was marked on the walkway floor. These points were referenced with respect to the system origin and trigonometrically cross-checked to lie within 0.5 mm of the noted locations.

In order to remove as many of the inherent system inaccuracies as possible, a linearization process was performed on each of the cameras used for data acquisition. Camera and system error sources included lens curvature and deformation, focal length uncertainty, inaccurate aperture setting, changes due to thermal expansion/contraction and other non-linearities inherent in video scanning [27]. The field of view of each camera was directed toward a flat matrix of known reflective disc locations. Data acquisition was performed and a linearization matrix was constructed to correct for these errors.

System resolution was calculated from static and dynamic test results [8,27]. A rigid steel rod was used in the static test with two 15.9-mm diameter target markers mounted to each end. The markers were separated by a constant distance of 132.80 ± 0.02 mm (micrometer tolerance). This rod was used in a series of tests which were performed at each corner and at the center of the capture volume while alternately oriented along each of the three axes of the laboratory coordinate system. Marker images were sampled for a period of 4 s at a sampling frequency of 60 Hz at each position/orientation. System resolution was calculated through the use of an algorithm that computed the difference between the measured (empirical) distance between the markers and the computed distance. An additional factor was included to account for round-off errors, micrometer, and computed marker location tolerance errors [28].

$$R = |D - \frac{1}{n}\sum_{i=0}^{n-1} d_i| \pm t\left(\frac{s}{\sqrt{n}} + \epsilon_r + \epsilon_m\right) \tag{9-1}$$

where D = measured (empirical) distance
$\quad\quad d_i$ = computed distance
$\quad\quad n$ = total number of samples
$\quad\quad s$ = sample standard deviation
$\quad\quad t$ = t-test coefficient
$\quad\quad \epsilon_r$ = round-off error
$\quad\quad \epsilon_m$ = measurement error

T-test coefficients were obtained from statistical tables [29]. Round-off error was computed as:

$$\epsilon_r = \frac{5}{10^m} \tag{9-2}$$

where m = the number of significant digits

Accuracy was determined as:

$$A = \left(1 - \frac{|x_w - \frac{1}{n}\sum_{i=0}^{n-1} d_i|}{\frac{1}{n}\sum_{i=0}^{n-1} d_i}\right) \times 100\% \tag{9-3}$$

where A = system accuracy as a percentage
$\quad\quad x_w$ = "worst" data point

The measured value of the distance contains unresolvable errors (primarily due to the resolution of the micrometer). As a result, the absolute separation distance of the markers in these tests was not known. The average value of the computed distances was used as an estimate of the true distance [28].

In order to define the dynamic resolution and accuracy, a pendulum apparatus was developed using two brass retro-reflective markers connected by a thin tether at a distance of 594.0 ± 0.5 mm. The pendulum was placed in the center of the capture volume. Dynamic testing was performed by perturbing the free end of the pendulum from a rest position and allowing it to swing in the sagittal and coronal planes of the capture volume. The amount of perturbation was limited to restrict the total arc length of the pendulum to approximately 620 mm. This provided a period of 4 s or a frequency of 0.25 Hz. Data were then captured for 4 s at a sampling rate of 60 Hz. Accuracy and resolution was determined using Equations 9-1 and 9-3.

9.2.3. Subject Testing

One normal male subject (25 years of age, 175 cm height, weighing 60 kg) was instrumented and tested with the system. The subject had no prior surgery or a history of foot pain or disorders. Twelve reflective markers were placed over bony prominences on the foot, ankle, and distal portion of the lower leg with doublesided adhesive tape (Table 9-1). The marker locations were consistent with the requirements for the biomechanical model used for describing the kinematic behavior of foot and ankle motion [5].

The subject was instructed to walk at a natural, freely selected pace following initial placement at one end of the capture volume. Data acquisition was performed in a manner that captured one complete, unilateral gait cycle. Approximately 10 data collection trials were completed for each foot. Multiple trials were necessary due to the medial placement of target markers on the foot and ankle complex. These markers had a tendency to be blocked from camera view during contralateral foot swing. As a result, any trials with 10 or more successive (60 Hz) frames of missing data were excluded from the study. Several steps were taken to minimize the occurrence of marker dropout, which included optimization of camera placement, careful camera linearization, and accurate camera calibration. Marker segment data were used to describe the rigid-body kinematics of the segmental foot and ankle structure in terms of Eulerian angles acting about the clinical (anatomic) planes of motion [5–7].

9.3. RESULTS

9.3.1. Capture Volume Definition

The process of optical data acquisition began with the establishment of a reference frame for data acquisition. The coordinates of each target marker in the reference frame were calculated using a micrometer and a tape measure. The marker locations were referenced to the global laboratory coordinate system with the assistance of a trigonometric correction algorithm.

The calibration residual was defined as the difference between the least-squares average of the measured and computed marker locations from each camera. Although it is impossible to draw definite conclusions from the residual values, the calibration residual is capable of describing the relative measurement accuracy of the process. Zero-value residuals are indicative of perfect conditions, while larger values might indicate errors in the calibration procedure or faulty instrumentation. An acceptable commercial system residual value should not exceed 0.1 percent of the largest dimension of the capture volume, or 2400 mm [30]. Since system calibration was performed prior to data acquisition, it was impossible to obtain constant values due to slight variations in camera position from day to day. Typical residual values were less than 2.0 mm, or 0.083 percent of the largest dimension of the capture volume.

9.3.2. Resolution and Accuracy

Using a specially designed and calibrated steel rod, the system was used to calculate the location of two static markers affixed to either end of the rod. This was done 60 times per second for 4 s (240 samples). The distance from the laboratory coordinate system origin to the center of the computed marker locations was represented by Cartesian vectors. The distance between markers was computed by calculating the vector difference between the two marker position vectors. The magnitude of the resultant vector was rounded to the nearest 0.01 mm, which was represented by the round-off error factor ϵ_r, in Equation 9-1 of 0.005 mm. Another factor used for the computation of the measurement error was based upon the resolution of the micrometer (± 0.02 mm) and represented by ϵ_m in the same equation.

In order to determine the accuracy of the static test given by Equation 9-3, identification of the least accurate (computed) separation distance between target markers was required. This was accomplished by sorting the computed target marker distances, d_i, in ascending order. The worst computed distance was located at either the beginning or the end of this array of data. A simple comparison test was employed between the measured separation distance and these end-point values. Accuracy was expressed as a percentage. A computer program was written to expedite and automate these calculations. A synopsis of system resolution and accuracy data is provided in Table 9-2. For purposes of statistical comparison, the t-test coefficient used in the static resolution expression was computed at the 0.05 and 0.01 levels of significance.

TABLE 9-2 STATIC TEST RESOLUTION AND ACCURACY

Location	Level of significance	x-axis Resolution (mm)	Acc. (%)	y-axis Resolution (mm)	Acc. (%)	z-axis Resolution (mm)	Acc. (%)
1	$\rho = 0.05$	0.43 ± 0.06	99.1	0.88 ± 0.06	98.8	1.27 ± 0.08	99.3
	$\rho = 0.01$	0.43 ± 0.08	99.1	0.88 ± 0.08	98.8	1.27 ± 0.11	99.3
2	$\rho = 0.05$	0.78 ± 0.08	99.1	1.11 ± 0.08	99.0	0.13 ± 0.18	98.7
	$\rho = 0.01$	0.78 ± 0.10	99.1	1.11 ± 0.10	99.0	0.13 ± 0.23	98.7
3	$\rho = 0.05$	0.64 ± 0.07	99.0	0.81 ± 0.10	98.8	1.42 ± 0.15	98.3
	$\rho = 0.01$	0.64 ± 0.09	99.0	0.81 ± 0.13	98.8	1.42 ± 0.19	98.3
4	$\rho = 0.05$	0.47 ± 0.08	98.8	0.44 ± 0.08	98.8	0.73 ± 0.04	99.7
	$\rho = 0.01$	0.47 ± 0.10	98.8	0.44 ± 0.10	98.8	0.73 ± 0.05	99.7
Center	$\rho = 0.05$	0.92 ± 0.06	98.7	1.49 ± 0.10	98.8	1.33 ± 0.05	99.2
	$\rho = 0.01$	0.92 ± 0.08	98.7	1.49 ± 0.13	98.8	1.33 ± 0.07	99.2

System resolution and accuracy were also determined for the dynamic tests in a similar manner through a modification of the static-test computer program. Marker separation distance for the pendulum apparatus used in the dynamic tests was measured with a device with 0.5 mm of accuracy (ϵ_m). Round-off error (ϵ_r) was set at a value of 0.05 in Equation 9-1 to compensate for the coarse measurements. Results for the dynamic tests are provided in Table 9-3. The t-test coefficients used in the dynamic resolution expression were computed at the 0.05 and 0.01 levels of significance.

TABLE 9-3 DYNAMIC TEST RESOLUTION AND ACCURACY

Plane	Level of significance	Resolution (mm)	Accuracy (%)
Sagittal (x-z)	$\rho = 0.05$	0.1 ± 0.89	99.4
	$\rho = 0.01$	0.1 ± 1.2	99.4
Coronal (y-z)	$\rho = 0.05$	0.6 ± 0.82	99.5
	$\rho = 0.01$	0.6 ± 1.1	99.5

9.3.3. Spectral Characteristics

Spectral analysis of a time-domain signal involves a transformation of the data to the frequency domain. This is typically performed through the use of a *fast Fourier transformation* (FFT). Such an operation is useful in system analysis through its ability to provide information regarding the noise content of a known signal. The resolution of the Fourier transformation is directly dependent upon the number of samples taken (number of data points) and the rate at which the samples were collected (sampling frequency). Since the sampling frequency was constant (60 Hz), the duration of data collection became the limiting factor in the resolution of this procedure. The bandwidth of signal following the transformation was dependent on the sampling frequency used to collect the data. For reasons beyond the scope of this discussion, the Fourier transformation cannot provide frequency information beyond one-half the sampling frequency. Frequencies beyond this limit will appear as aliased signals (within the acceptable limits of frequency data but at incorrect locations). Digital sampling theory stipulates that the lowest acceptable sampling frequency required to reproduce an analog signal should be twice the highest frequency component [31]. However, faithful signal reproduction can fail at this critical sampling frequency if digital readings correspond to the nodes of the analog waveform. It is recommended, therefore, that a sampling frequency of 5 to 10 times the highest analog frequency be used in conjunction with appropriate low-pass filtering techniques to assure proper signal replication.

A spectral analysis was performed on data collected on a stationary marker positioned at the center of the capture volume. The reasoning behind choosing this location was that it represented an optimally distant point from all calibration marker locations while remaining within the capture volume. The calibration process optimized the capture volume bounded by the calibration chains. The center position should be indicative of the "worst" location for data acquisition. The position of the stationary marker was spectrally analyzed after acquiring 4 s of data at 60 Hz (240 samples). The collected data were analyzed for each of the three global coordinate directions. A final analysis was performed on the magnitude of the displacement data to determine the combined effects of the position vectors. Each data set was normalized by computing the mean of the data. This value was subtracted from each point in the relevant data set in order to provide a zero-mean distribution. The effect of this procedure on the FFT algorithm is elimination of zero-frequency (DC offset) in each signal while providing a better indication of the frequencies present (Table 9-4).

Spectral content of the global x component of the stationary marker position vector appeared to be composed of white or random noise [Figure 9-3(a)]. The spectral amplitudes were relatively small compared to the y and z components and were widely distributed across the entire spectrum. The y component was characterized by several distinct, high-amplitude peaks across the spectrum [Figure 9-3(b)]. The most dominant of these peaks appeared at 30 Hz. Similar peaks were observed in both the z component and combined magnitude analyses [Figure 9-3(c) and d)].

One contributor to high-frequency components embedded in the video signal is video interlacing. Television video screens are composed of 525 horizontal lines, which are

TABLE 9-4 MAJOR FREQUENCIES IN SPECTRAL ANALYSIS OF THE STATIC MARKER POSITION VECTOR

Location	Frequency (Hz)	Amplitude
	10.8	0.07
x	8.2	0.11
	2.6	0.08
	30.0	0.47
	21.8	0.27
y	19.2	0.39
	16.4	0.14
	2.6	0.18
	30.0	0.59
z	10.8	0.07
	8.2	0.06
	30.0	0.09
Combined	19.2	0.17
	8.2	0.11

scanned at 30 Hz to compose a single video frame. Each 30-Hz frame is subsequently divided into two 60-Hz fields, which scan alternate horizontal lines first (odd field) and then those that are missed second (even field). These fields do not lie exactly between one another and result in a high-frequency image vibration along the vertical component of the camera image plane [32]. All of the camera positions had the vertical axis of their image plane aligned with the z axis of the global coordinate system. Thus, the spectral peak at 30 Hz was likely due to the camera interlace characteristic.

A similar form of reasoning can be used to explain the presence of the 30-Hz component in the data obtained from the y-axis component. All of the cameras were positioned with a slight downward tilt to their field of view, bringing their line of focus beneath the horizontal (x-y) plane. Pure motion along the y axis of the global coordinate system would appear in both the horizontal and vertical planes of the camera. As a consequence, slight deviations along the vertical image plane of the camera could be resolved into the y axis of the system.

9.3.4. Subject Test Results

Typical displacements in mm are depicted for each global vector component of a target marker placed on the medial malleolus in Figure 9-4. Three separate trials are displayed on each graph and represent complete gait cycles (toe-off to toe-off of the same foot). In each trial, the subject progressed toward a force plate embedded in the walkway. A complete strike and release of the instrumented foot on this plate defined the termination of the gait cycle. Observation of the kinematic pattern produced by this marker reveals a distinct and

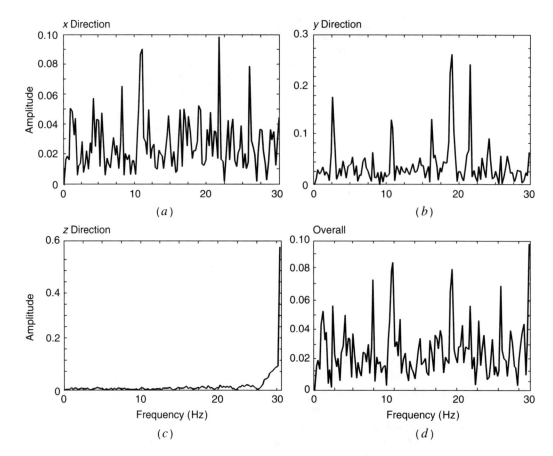

Figure 9-3. Spectral analysis of stationary marker: (*a*) *x* direction, (*b*) *y* direction, (*c*) *z* direction, and (*d*) overall.

repeatable pattern consistent with a comparably placed marker in a motion analysis system
described by M. P. Kadaba et al. [2,8]. Lack of synchronization in the time domain between
trials produced a phase shift. Similar conclusions were drawn regarding the kinematic
behavior of the remaining markers on the foot.

Marker dropout usually occurred during midswing when the medial markers (medial
malleolus, medial calcaneus, and medial head of the first metatarsal) were obscured from the
cameras by the contralateral limb. This phenomenon was minimized through careful placement of the cameras about the capture volume, precise system calibration, and linearization.
Meticulous construction of the target markers increased the ability of the system to acquire
their images as well. However, some instances of missing data were accepted under the
condition that they be limited to less than 10 frames (167 ms). This missing information
was interpolated based on data prior to and after the break. This procedure assumes that
the data on both sides of the break are consistent; an incorrect assumption during toe-off
and heel-strike. With the exception of data interpolation during the beginning and end of
stance phase, which was not necessary in this study, this method is generally acceptable
and offers an accurate representation of segmental motion.

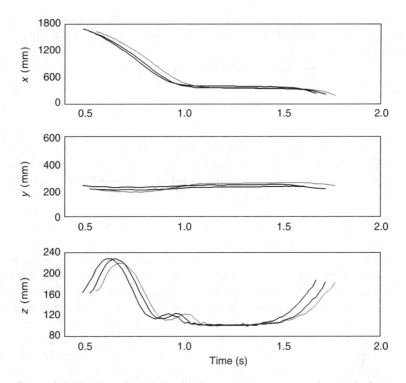

Figure 9-4. Position of medial malleolus marker (mm) versus time (s) in three planes.

9.4. DISCUSSION

9.4.1. System Error

The single factor that had the greatest effect on the ability of the system to accurately reconstruct target marker images was the calibration process. The coordinates of the target markers on each of the calibration chains were calculated through direct measurement techniques. Each chain was assumed to have constant x and y global coordinate values over the entire length. This was based upon the orthogonality criteria of the global z axis to the floor of the walkway. Unfortunately, the floor exhibited a 16-mm drop with respect to the 2.4-m walk space. Hence, an orthogonal ray extending from the floor would not be perfectly coincident with the defined global z axis. This information can be used to further reduce error with subsequent use of the system.

The motion analysis system employed a double edge detection algorithm to compute the centroid of each target marker within the capture volume. This was performed by computing the centroid of a "best fit" circle drawn through the captured data. Faulty marker construction and marker surface degradation are important factors regulating the ability of the system to accurately calculate the centroid. Gaps and overlap between the individual pieces of reflective tape covering the surface of each marker can add significant variability to the overall consistency of the marker diameter. These deviations can be detected in both dynamic and static settings. When combined with the frame interlace behavior of the system, the perceived location of a compromised target marker could change on a frame-by-frame basis.

Another error source contributing to the position estimate variability of each marker could be attributed to marker surface degradation. The reflective tape covering each marker was found to be susceptible to damage through routine handling. The tape was quite porous, which allowed dirt and oil to become embedded in it. This translated to a diminished capacity to reflect incident light. If the surface degradation was concentrated to a specific location on the marker, the reflectivity of this location would become diminished. Should this particular area be situated at an edge of a marker, the calculated center would become shifted. This is a likely scenario given the multiple camera angles combined with the dynamic nature of the testing protocol. Each marker was carefully checked for any noticeable flaws prior to and during testing. Any problematic markers were discarded and replaced as necessary.

The camera linearization process provided a contour map of lens distortion for each camera, which was instrumental in reducing errors inherent in each camera. This was achieved through proper alignment and measurement of each camera with respect to the linearization grid. The grid was carefully affixed to a flat, planar surface in a uniform manner to avoid the possibility of compromising the integrity of this procedure.

The system characterization was based upon the results of static and dynamic tests involving two target markers. In each of these processes, the results were directly dependent upon accurate measurement of the separation distance between the markers. This factor was not as significant in the static tests as in the dynamic. The markers used for the dynamic tests were separated by a slightly elastic tether. Changes in tension during these tests from the periodic motion produced minor variations in marker separation. The apparatus used in the test impaired the ability to accurately locate the center of rotation of the system. It is recommended that future investigations regarding the dynamic performance of this system be performed with a rigid gimbal apparatus similar to the rod used in the static test.

The results of the system characterization tests indicated that the sagittal plane resolution exceeded that of the coronal and transverse planes. This is a reflection of the resolution of the image plane of the cameras used. Each camera had greater pixel resolution along its horizontal image plane. Four of the cameras were oriented in a manner such that the sagittal plane motion component (global x-z plane) was maximized in the field of view. This resulted in a greater discretization of the global x components. This effect could be altered through reorientation of the cameras, but this would impede the ability of the system to track all of the markers used in subject testing.

9.5. SUMMARY

Studies of lower extremity kinematics have demonstrated the ability of the Vicon motion analysis system to quantitatively describe human motion [33,34]. This project demonstrated the ability of the Vicon system to track successfully foot and ankle motion during gait. In order to describe accurately the segmental foot and ankle motion characteristics during both stance and swing phases, many small markers were placed over a relatively small anatomical region. This required the addition of a fifth camera to minimize marker dropout. Spectral characteristics of the system indicate the necessity for low-pass filtering of the trajectory data (6-Hz stop band) prior to performing data analysis.

References

[1] Inman VT, Ralston HJ, Todd F. *Human Walking*, Baltimore: Williams and Wilkins Publishing Co.;1981.

[2] Kadaba MP, Ramakrishnan HK, Wooten ME. Measurement of lower extremity kinematics during level walking. *J Orthop Res* 1990;8:383–392.

[3] Kadaba MP, Ramakrishnan HK, Gainey J, Gorton G, Cochran GV. Repeatability of kinematic, kinetic and electromyographic data in normal adult gait. *J Orthop Res* 1989;7:849–860.

[4] Radin EL, Yang KH, Riegger C, Kish VL, O'Connor JJ. Relationship between lower limb dynamics and knee joint pain. *J Orthop Res* 1991;9:398–405.

[5] Kidder SM, Harris GF, Wynarski GT, Johnson JE, Alexander I, DeLozier G, Abuzzahab FS. A four-segment model for clinical description of foot and ankle motion. *Proc IEEE Eng Med Bio Soc*, Paris, France; 1992;14:52–53.

[6] Kidder SM, Harris GF, Abuzzahab, Jr FS, Johnson JE. A four-segment model for clinical description of foot and ankle motion. *Proc IEEE Eng Med Bio Soc*, San Diego, Ca, 1993;3:1065–1066.

[7] Kidder SM, Harris GF, Johnson JE, Abuzzahab FS. A kinematic model for clinical description of foot and ankle motion. *Proc 8th Annual East Coast Clinical Gait Laboratory Conf*, Rochester, Minn;1993:111–112.

[8] Kadaba MP, Wootten ME, Ramakrishnan HK, Hurwitz D, Cochran GVB. Assessment of human motion with VICON. *ASME Biomech Symp* 1987;84:335–338.

[9] Õunpuu S, Gage JR, Davis RB. Three-dimensional lower extremity joint kinetics in normal pediatric gait. *J Ped Orthop* 1991;11:341–349.

[10] Dul J, Johnson GE. A kinematic model of the human ankle. *J Biomed Eng* 1985;7:137–143.

[11] Lundberg A. Kinematics of the ankle and foot: In vivo roentgen stereophotogrammetry. *Acta Orthop Scand* (Supplementum) 1989;233:1–24.

[12] Nissan M, Whittle MW. Initiation of gait in normal subjects: A preliminary study. *J Biomed Eng* 1990;12:165–171.

[13] White SC, Yack HJ, Winter DA. A three-dimensional musculoskeletal model for gait analysis. Anatomical variability estimates. *J Biomech* 1989;22:885–893.

[14] Alexander IJ, Campbell KR. Dynamic assessment of foot mechanics as an adjunct to orthotic prescription. In: Donatelli R ed. *The Biomechanics of the Foot and Ankle*, Philadelphia, Pa: FA Davis Co;1990:148–152.

[15] Scott SH, Winter DA. Biomechanical model of the human foot: Kinematics and kinetics during the stance phase of walking. *J Biomech* 1993;26:1091–1104.

[16] Scott SH, Winter DA. Talocrural and talocalcaneal joint kinematics and kinetics during the stance phase of walking. *J Biomech* 1991;24:743–752.

[17] Engsberg JR. A biomechanical analysis of the talocalcaneal joint in vitro. *J Biomech* 1987;20:429–442.

[18] Siegler S, Chen J, Schneck CD. The three-dimensional kinematics and flexibility characteristics of the human ankle and subtalar joints—part 1: Kinematics. *J Biomech Eng* 1988;110:364–373.

[19] Harris GF. Analysis of ankle and subtalar motion during human locomotion. In: Stiehl J ed. *Inman's Joints of the Ankle*, 2nd ed. Baltimore, Md: Williams and Wilkins Publishing Co;1991:75–84.

[20] D'Andrea SD, Tylkowski C, Losito J, Arguedas W, Bushman T, Howell V. Three-dimensional kinematics of the foot. *Proc 8th Annual East Coast Clinical Gait Laboratory Conf*, Rochester, Minn;1993:109–110.

[21] Abuzzahab FS, Harris GF, Kidder SM, Johnson JE, Alexander IJ, DeLozier GS. Development of a system for dynamic 3-D analysis of foot and ankle motion. *Proc IEEE Eng Med Bio Soc*, Paris, France, 1992;14:110–111.

[22] Abuzzahab FS, Harris GF, Kidder SM, Johnson JE. A system for foot and ankle motion analysis during gait. *Proc 8th Annual East Coast Clinical Gait Laboratory Conf*, Rochester, Minn;1993:137–138.

[23] Abuzzahab FS, Harris GF, Kidder SM, Johnson JE. A clinical system for foot and ankle motion analysis. *Proc IEEE Eng Med Bio Soc*, San Diego, Ca, 1993;3:1067–1068.

[24] Abdel-Aziz YI, Karara HM. Direct linear transformation from comparator coordinates into object space coordinates in close-range photogrammetry. *American Society of Photogrammetry Symposium on Close-Range Photogrammetry*, Falls Church, Va;1971:1–18.

[25] Antonsson EK. A three-dimensional kinematic acquisition and intersegmental dynamic analysis system for human motion. Cambridge, Mass: Massachusetts Institute of Technology;1982: PhD dissertation.

[26] Whittle MW. *Gait analysis: An introduction.* Oxford, England: Butterworth-Heinemann Ltd;1991:136.

[27] Whittle MW. Calibration and performance of a 3-dimensional television system for kinematic analysis. *J Biomech* 1982;15:185–196.

[28] Hall JL, Naim M. Instrument statics. In: Nachtigal CL ed. *Instrumentation and Control: Fundamentals and Applications.* New York, NY: John Wiley and Sons, Inc;1990:62.

[29] Ott L. *An Introduction to Statistical Methods and Data Analysis.* Boston, Mass: PWS-Kent Publishing Company;1988:A5.

[30] *AMASS: ADTECH Motion Analysis Software System*, Adelphi, Md: ADTECH;1988.

[31] Domanski SJ, Marsh J, McQuilken MA, Kauffman LA. Electronic devices and data conversion. In: Nachtigal CL ed. *Instrumentation and Control: Fundamentals and Applications*, New York, NY: John Wiley and Sons, Inc;1990:167.

[32] Goode BL. Shriner's Hospital for Crippled Children, Houston Unit, Personal Communication, June 5, 1994.

[33] Ramakrishnan HK, Kadaba MP, Wootten ME. Lower extremity joint moments and ground reaction torque in adult gait. In: Stein JL ed. *Biomechanics of Normal and Prosthetic Gait*, ASME Annual Winter Meeting 1987;BED-4.

[34] Ramakrishnan HK, Masiello G, Kadaba MP. On the estimation of three-dimensional joint angular motion in gait analysis. *Trans 35th Annual Mtg Orthop Res Soc*, Las Vegas, Nev, 1990;36:244.

George Wynarsky
Gerald F. Harris

Chapter 10

A Mathematical Description of Three-Dimensional Joint Kinematics Using a Noninvasive Imaging Technique

10.1. INTRODUCTION

An accurate definition of complex joint motion is essential for understanding normal and pathological bone and joint kinematics. A detailed and thorough method to study joint motion should have the following characteristics: (1) it should consider all six degrees of freedom (three translations and three rotations) to define three-dimensional (3-D) motion completely, (2) it should be noninvasive in nature to preserve all intact structures and to have potential clinical applications, and (3) it should provide an accurate mathematical definition of the joint motion. Many previous studies of joint kinematics have not adequately satisfied these characteristics; in particular, most six degrees of freedom kinematic studies have used invasive methods [1–4].

In the past decade, 3-D reconstructions based on series of parallel sections derived from computerized tomography (CT) scans or magnetic resonance images (MRI) have been used to visualize skeletal structures and to design and manufacture custom implants. More recently, 3-D reconstructions have been used to examine the spatial relationship between bones of a joint, particularly for the human wrist. S. J. Bresina et al. [5] described carpal bone motion as the wrist was moved through radial-ulnar deviation and flexion-extension. Six-degree-of-freedom kinematic data was obtained by an electromagnetic tracking system which monitored the position of K-wires inserted into the carpal bones. Correlation of position data with 3-D surface reconstructions of the carpal bones showed that the instantaneous center of rotation was not fixed in the head of the capitate. R. J. Belsole et al. [6] used 3-D volumetric reconstructions to determine carpal bone location and orientation of three wrists in five anatomic positions. Translations were determined by the location of the volumetric centroid of each carpal bone. Spatial orientations were defined by direction cosines of the three principal axes of each carpal bone referenced to the principal axes of the radius. D. P. Levinson and M. M. Dale [7] determined the structural properties of the wrist complex using 3-D reconstructions derived from CT scans. Volumes, centroids, and principal axes were computed for 21 wrists without using implanted or anatomical markers. This data was used to establish the "normal" spatial configuration of the carpal complex and to examine pathological deviations from the norm. P. F. Justin et al. [8] used 3-D solid modeling reconstructions to predict the range of motion of the wrist following a proximal row carpectomy. This study showed that volumes, principal moments of inertia, and principal axes of carpal bones were reproducible in various wrist positions and that this technique is suitable for describing wrist kinematics.

R. C. Hallgren et al. [9] used solid model reconstructions in combination with roentgen stereophotogrammetry to examine lumbar spine position and mobility. However, position changes were defined by using embedded balls as reference markers. J. E. Herzenberg et al. [10] used 3-D reconstructions derived from histological serial sections to determine the rotational alignment of the hindfoot bones. Although body axes were used to monitor bone rotations, it is not clear how these axes were determined and no quantification of bone orientation is presented.

The general concept of using principal axes to monitor rigid-body orientation has been described previously [11–13]. For example, N. M. Alpert et al. [11] used the principal axes transformation technique to register images of whole brain volumes based on image data from CT and MRI. However, a detailed mathematical definition of body position using this technique has not been presented. G. T. Wynarsky et al. [14] presented preliminary results of subtalar joint kinematics using principal axes to monitor bone orientation. This chapter describes three frequently used mathematical methods of defining joint kinematics based on computer model reconstructions of bones using noninvasive imaging techniques. The methods described in this chapter have general applicability; their use will be developed and illustrated here by examining subtalar joint motion.

10.2. METHODS

10.2.1. Specimen Imaging

The methods described in this study were developed for two general rigid bodies. Although both bodies can move, one was considered to be fixed and the motion of the second body was determined relative to the first. Three fresh-frozen foot and lower-leg specimens were used to develop the technique. The calcaneus was fixed to a Plexiglas box frame with nylon threaded rods. The tibiotalar joint was fixed in a neutral position with threaded fiberglass rods used to control kinematic coupling with the subtalar joint. Thus, the calcaneus was considered to be the fixed body and the talus was the moving body. The proximal tibia was manually ranged from maximum clinical inversion to maximum clinical eversion using a mechanical jig (Figure 10-1). The only joint load was due to the weight of the specimen preparation. Each specimen was imaged with a GE 9800 Quick CT Scanner in the coronal plane at 1.5-mm increments in six discrete positions: maximum inversion, 2/3 inversion, 1/3 inversion, neutral, 1/2 eversion, and maximum eversion.

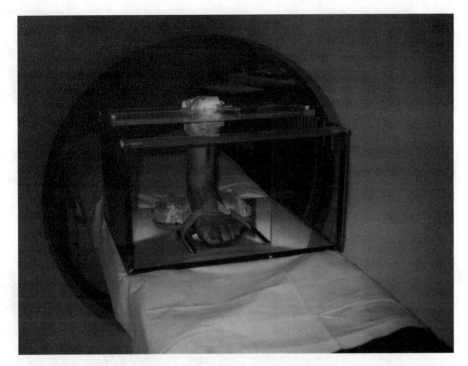

Figure 10-1. Specimen in mechanical jig used to create discrete joint positions (neutral shown) and CT scanner used for imaging.

10.2.2. Solid Model Reconstruction

Each CT slice was digitized manually and the data entered into a CADKEY solids modeling program. The slice boundaries (outlines) of the talus and calcaneus were described as closed cubic spline functions. Each spline was then connected to the adjacent slice spline(s) with linear functions to create 3-D geometric reconstructions of each bone (Figure 10-2). Next, the volume, mass, and center of mass (CM) of the talus and calcaneus were computed. Since only kinematic properties were desired, a uniform bone density distribution was assumed; thus, the mass and center of mass (CM) were equivalent to volume and center of volume (centroid), respectively.

10.2.3. Modeling Accuracy

Accuracy estimates of the solid model reconstructions were determined by simple comparisons of geometric property values (volume, moments of inertia, etc.) from two modeling programs, CADKEY and ARIES. More detailed accuracy estimates of the solid model reconstructions were not considered. (H. J. G. Gundersen and E. B. Jensen [15] describe techniques to measure the coefficient of error for volume estimates from serial sampling.) Consistency of geometric property computations for different joint positions was tested by comparing principal moments of inertia at each position. Accuracy of digitization

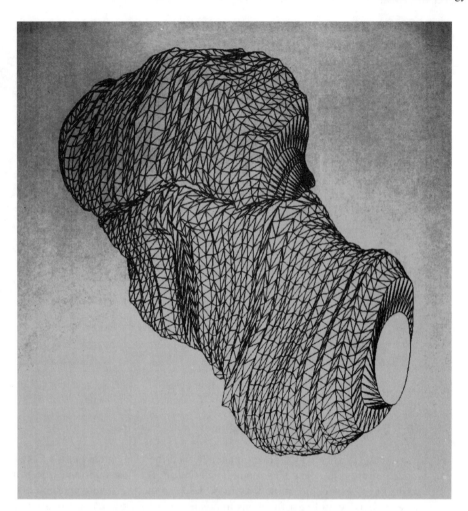

Figure 10-2. Solid model reconstructions of the talus and calcaneus.

was examined by comparing the surface area and volume values of four simple cylinders with different cross sections. Repeatability of the CT tracing and digitization process was examined by comparing surface area and volume values of a four-slice segment of each bone determined from three trials.

10.2.4. Definition of Spatial Position

A complete description of 3-D spatial position requires that both the location and orientation of a rigid body be defined. The spatial locations and rigid-body translations of each body were defined by CM coordinates. Determination of body orientation required several steps. The solids modeling program computed the mass inertia tensor for each body position. Diagonalization of the inertia tensor and solution of the eigenvalue problem yielded the three principal moments of inertia (eigenvalues) and their corresponding principal axes (eigenvectors). Changes in rigid-body orientation can be monitored by changes in the orientation of the three principal axes. Because the CM and the principal axes are fixed in a body, they provide a singular reference for describing all six degrees of free-dom of motion. (Rigid bodies possessing at least one plane of symmetry will not have a unique set of principal axes; however, this limitation would not apply to human bones.) The CM coordinates and principal-axis orientations are invariant with respect to each local body coordinate system. Thus, bone translations and rotations can be completely defined at discrete joint positions. Once the CM coordinates and principal-axis orientations are established for the range of joint motion considered, each discrete body position can be defined mathematically in various ways; three commonly used kinematic descriptions of rigid bodies are presented in the following sections.

10.2.5. Direction Cosines; Relative Position

The CM coordinates and principal-axis direction cosines of the moving (m) and fixed (f) bodies (talus and calcaneus, respectively) were first described with respect to a fixed Cartesian reference frame $\{u\}$ at each joint position (i) by

$$\{\mathbf{r}_m\}_{(i)} = x_m \mathbf{I} + y_m \mathbf{J} + z_m \mathbf{K} \qquad (10\text{-}1a)$$

$$\{\mathbf{r}_f\}_{(i)} = x_f \mathbf{I} + y_f \mathbf{J} + z_f \mathbf{K} \qquad (10\text{-}1b)$$

and

$$\{u'_m\}_{(i)} = [DC_m]_{(i)}\{u\} \qquad (10\text{-}2a)$$

$$\{u'_f\}_{(i)} = [DC_f]_{(i)}\{u\} \qquad (10\text{-}2b)$$

where $\{\mathbf{r}\}$ = position vector defining CM coordinates

$\{u'\}$ = body-fixed principal axes $\{x', y', z'\}$

$\{u\}$ = fixed global coordinate system $\{X, Y, Z\}$

$[DC]$ = direction cosine matrix defining orientation of body principal axes

To describe relative position of the two bodies, the moving-body CM coordinates were defined with respect to the fixed-body CM by

$$\{\mathbf{r}_{m/f}\}_{(i)} = \{\mathbf{r}_m\}_{(i)} - \{\mathbf{r}_f\}_{(i)} \qquad (10\text{-}3)$$

To describe relative orientation of the two bodies, the moving-body principal axes were defined with respect to the fixed-body principal axes. Solving Equation (10-2b) for $\{u\}$ and substituting into Equation (10-2a) yields

$$\{u'_m\} = [DC_m]_{(i)}[DC_f]_{(i)}^T\{u'_f\} \qquad (10\text{-}4a)$$

or

$$\{u'_m\} = [DC_{m/f}]_{(i)}\{u'_f\} \qquad (10\text{-}4b)$$

where

$$[DC_{m/f}]_{(i)} = [DC_m]_{(i)}[DC_f]_{(i)}^T \qquad (10\text{-}4c)$$

Since the above operations involve orthogonal coordinate transformations, the inverse and transpose of the direction cosine matrices are equivalent, $[DC]^{-1} = [DC]^T$. The rows of

$[DC_{m/f}]_{(i)}$ define the nine direction cosines, which describe the orientation of the moving-body principal axes (talus) relative to the fixed-body principal axes (calcaneus) at any position (i).

10.2.6. Euler Angles

The relative orientation given by Equation (10-4c) can also be described by Euler angles, a standard method to define 3-D rigid-body rotations. For example, E. Y. S. Chao [16] showed how 3-D joint rotation can be defined by Euler angles and a triaxial goniometer. Using a rotation sequence $Z(\gamma)$, $Y(\beta)$, $X(\alpha)$ about the fixed-body principal axes [17], the correspondence between the direction cosine and Euler transformation matrices at any position (i) is given by

$$[DC_{m/f}]_{(i)} = [ET]_{(i)} \qquad (10\text{-}5a)$$

where

$$[ET]_{(i)} = \begin{bmatrix} \cos\beta\cos\gamma & \cos\beta\sin\gamma & -\sin\beta \\ \cos\gamma\sin\beta\sin\alpha - \sin\gamma\cos\alpha & \sin\gamma\sin\beta\sin\alpha + \cos\gamma\cos\alpha & \cos\beta\sin\alpha \\ \cos\gamma\sin\beta\cos\alpha + \sin\gamma\sin\alpha & \sin\gamma\sin\beta\cos\alpha - \cos\gamma\sin\alpha & \cos\beta\cos\alpha \end{bmatrix}$$
$$(10\text{-}5b)$$

Each term of the overdetermined Euler matrix can be solved for the appropriate Euler angle at each joint position. For the subtalar joint, a set of three Euler angles (α, β, γ) was determined for each discrete clinical position, from maximum inversion to maximum eversion. Each set of Euler angles describes the relative orientation of the talar principal axes with respect to the calcaneal principal axes. Translations were defined by the relative CM coordinates described previously (Equation 10-3).

10.2.7. Clinical-Plane Angles

Although Euler angles provide a standard description of 3-D orientations, they may be difficult to visualize and utilize clinically. To facilitate the description of complex 3-D motion, the joint coordinate system developed by E. S. Grood and W. J. Suntay [18] was used as an alternative definition of bone orientation in terms of clinically relevant planes.

In order to implement the Grood and Suntay system and utilize body principal axes, several preliminary coordinate relations must be established. Because human bones are irregularly shaped bodies, their principal axes $\{u' = x', y', z'\}$ do not in general align with a convenient coordinate system. Thus, it is convenient to establish another body-axis system $\{u'' = x'', y'', z''\}$ related to the principal axes and aligned with the fixed global Cartesian system $\{u = X, Y, Z\}$ when the body is in the neutral (n) position (Figure 10-3). Thus, the two body-fixed sets of axes can be related by

$$\{u''\}_{(i)} = [DC]_{(n)}^{T}\{u'\}_{(i)} \qquad (10\text{-}6)$$

where $[DC]_{(n)}^{T}$ = direction cosine matrix relating body-fixed axes $\{u''\}$ to principal axes $\{u'\}$

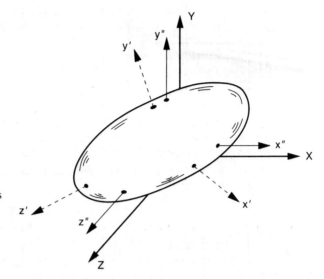

Figure 10-3. Body-fixed principal axes (x', y', z'); body-fixed axes related to principal axes (x'', y'', z''); global Cartesian reference axes (X, Y, Z).

Since both sets of axes are body-fixed, the relation (Equation 10-6) between $\{u''\}$ and $\{u'\}$ is invariant and holds for all positions (i). Substituting for $\{u'\}_{(i)}$ using Equation (10-2a), the $\{u''\}$ axes can be related to the original global system by

$$\{u''\}_{(i)} = [DC]^T_{(n)}[DC]_{(i)}\{u\} \tag{10-7}$$

Thus, in the neutral body position (i = n), the $\{u''\}$ body axes are aligned with the global axes $\{u\}$ and the product $[DC]^T_{(n)}[DC]_{(n)}$ reduces to the identity matrix. In other body positions, the $\{u''\}$ axes partially define changes in body orientation in standard clinical planes. For the subtalar joint, these planes were flexion-extension, inversion-eversion, and internal-external rotation.

Next, it is convenient to define the $\{u''\}$ body axes in each bone such that two of their axes coincide with the body-fixed (e_1, e_3) and reference (e_1^r, e_3^r) axes of the Grood and Suntay joint coordinate system (Figure 10-4). For the body-fixed axes, the e_1 unit vector coincides with the x_t'' axis of the talus, and the e_3 unit vector coincides with the y_c'' axis of the calcaneus. For the reference axes, the e_1^r unit vector coincides with the z_t'' axis of the talus, and the e_3^r unit vector coincides with the z_c'' axis of the calcaneus. The e_2 unit vector of this nonorthogonal joint coordinate system is a "floating" axis; it is always perpendicular to both body-fixed axes (e_1, e_3), moves relative to both axes, and is not fixed to either body (Figure 10-4). The clinical angle rotations and sign conventions are defined below. In the anatomic neutral body position, all angles have zero value (θ, Ψ, $\phi = 0$).

  Plantarflexion/dorsiflexion

$$\cos\theta = e_2 \cdot e_1^r \tag{10-8a}$$

$$\text{sign} : \cos\theta = e_2 \cdot j_t \qquad \begin{array}{l} (-) = \text{plantarflexion} \\ (+) = \text{dorsiflexion} \end{array} \tag{10-8b}$$

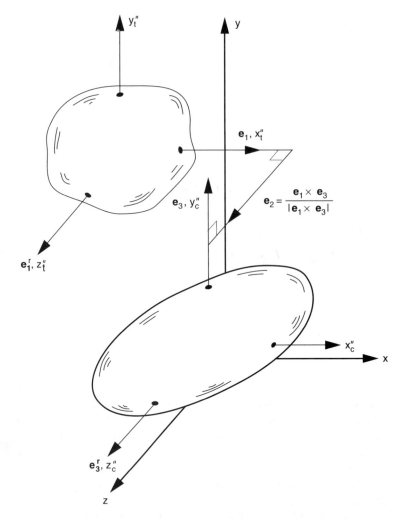

Figure 10-4. Generalized Grood and Suntay (1983) joint coordinate system: t = talus (moving body); c = calcaneus (fixed body); $\mathbf{e}_1, \mathbf{e}_3, \mathbf{e}_1^r, \mathbf{e}_3^r$ = body-fixed vectors; $\mathbf{e}_2$ = "floating" axis.

Inversion/eversion

$$\cos \Psi = \mathbf{e}_1 \cdot \mathbf{e}_3 \tag{10-9a}$$

$$\Psi = \Psi - 90° \qquad \begin{array}{l} (-) = \text{eversion} \\ (+) = \text{inversion} \end{array} \tag{10-9b}$$

Internal/external rotation

$$\cos \phi = \mathbf{e}_2 \cdot \mathbf{e}_3^r \tag{10-10a}$$

$$\text{sign} : \cos \phi = \mathbf{e}_2 \cdot \mathbf{i}_c \qquad \begin{array}{l} (-) = \text{external rotation} \\ (+) = \text{internal rotation} \end{array} \tag{10-10b}$$

Since the CM coordinates are invariant for each body, relative bone translations were defined by Equation (10-3) and the Grood and Suntay [18] joint translations were not utilized.

10.2.8. Helical-Axis Parameters

Three-dimensional rigid-body motion can also be defined by a finite helical (screw) axis analysis. For example, C. W. Spoor and F. E. Veldpaus [19] described 3-D rigid-body motions by helical axes based on data from spatial coordinates of body markers. E. J. van Langelaan [2] described relative talotibial and tarsal movements using sets of helical axes. Any rigid-body motion can be represented as a rotation about an axis defined in 3-D space, and a translation along that axis. The helical-axis parameters that describe a finite rigid-body displacement are presented in Figure 10-5. For a full range of motion, helical-axis parameters can be calculated for an entire series of consecutive body positions.

An analytical development of the helical-axis parameters for motion between two bodies has been presented by G. L. Kinzel et al. [20]. As derived by Kinzel et al., the finite movement of a rigid body from position (i) to position (i + 1) is given by

$$[A]_{(i)} = [B]_{(i+1)}[B]_{(i)}^{-1} \qquad (10\text{-}11)$$

where [A] = helical-axis transformation matrix whose elements are given functions of the helical-axis parameters (to be determined)

[B] = coordinate transformation matrix; defines a discrete position of the moving body relative to the fixed body.

Input values for matrices $[B]_{(i)}$ and $[B]_{(i+1)}$ in Equation (10-11) can be obtained by various six-degree-of-freedom methods. For example, G. L. Kinzel et al. [21] used an instrumented spatial linkage to define positions of a canine shoulder joint; S. Siegler et al. [3] used sonic digitizers to monitor positions of the ankle and subtalar joints; and R. A. Hart et al. [22] used acoustic transducers to track flexion of the human knee. In this study, values for the [B] matrices were determined from CM coordinates and principal-axis orientations computed by the solids modeling program. Specifically, the [B] matrix for any position (i) can be partitioned as

$$[B]_{(i)} = \left[\begin{array}{c|c} I & O \\ \hline \mathbf{r}_{m/f} & DC_{m/f}^{T} \end{array}\right] \qquad (10\text{-}12)$$

where $[\mathbf{r}_{m/f}] = \begin{bmatrix} x_{cm} \\ y_{cm} \\ z_{cm} \end{bmatrix}$ = CM coordinates of moving body relative to fixed body

$[DC_{m/f}]^{T}$ = direction cosine matrix defining principal axes of moving body relative to fixed body given by Equation (10-5).

$[I] = [1]$
$[O] = [0]$

Values for $[B]_{(i)}$ and $[B]_{(i+1)}$ were input for each discrete position of the moving body and the helical-axis parameters were determined from [A](i) (Equation 10-11) for the entire range of joint motion (maximum inversion to maximum eversion).

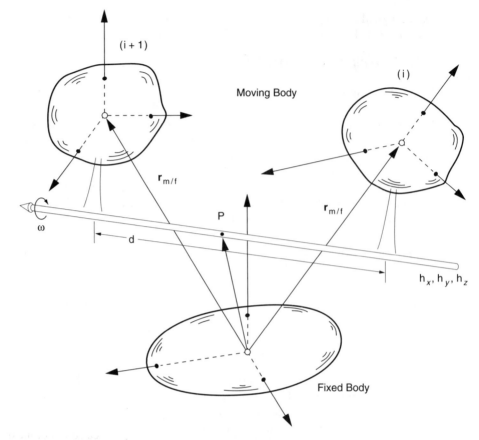

Figure 10-5. Definition of helical-axis parameters for a finite increment of motion from position (i) to position (i + 1).

h_x, h_y, h_z = direction cosines defining spatial orientation of
helical axis
ω = angle of rotation about helical axis
d = translation along helical axis
$P = P_x, P_y, P_z$ = location of arbitrary point on
helical axis

10.3. RESULTS

10.3.1. Model Accuracy

The accuracy of the 3-D geometric reconstructions for each bone was determined by comparing the values of the volume, surface area, centroid location, and principal moments of inertia computed independently by two solids modeling programs, CADKEY and ARIES (Table 10-1). Differences in values between the two programs were very

TABLE 10-1 COMPARISON OF GEOMETRIC PROPERTY VALUES
BETWEEN TWO SOLIDS MODELING PROGRAMS

Talus	CADKEY	ARIES	% difference	Calcaneus	CADKEY	ARIES	% difference
Vol (cm^3)	49.78	50.93	−2.24	Vol (cm^3)	88.65	87.49	−1.16
S.A. (cm^2)	97.53	96.76	0.88	S.A. (cm^2)	149.90	152.02	−1.39
x_c (cm)	7.47	7.47	0.00	x_c (cm)	6.71	6.71	0.00
y_c (cm)	6.66	6.66	0.00	y_c (cm)	2.91	2.91	0.00
z_c (cm)	5.97	5.91	1.01	z_c (cm)	3.47	3.46	0.23
I_1 (cm^4)	87.45	87.09	0.41	I_1 (cm^4)	198.59	192.49	3.17
I_2 (cm^4)	136.74	141.60	3.43	I_2 (cm^4)	478.17	470.38	1.66
I_3 (cm^4)	156.52	159.96	2.15	I_3 (cm^4)	521.71	512.62	1.77

Vol = volume; S.A. = surface area; (x_c, y_c, z_c) = centroid coordinates; I_1, I_2, I_3 = principal moments
of inertia.

small, particularly in the location of the body centroid (average difference = 0.21 percent). The average difference for principal moments of inertia was 2.10 percent and the maximum differences were 3.43 percent (I_2) for the talus and 3.17 percent (I1) for the calcaneus. Consistency of geometric property computations for different joint positions was determined by comparing principal moments of inertia at each joint position (maximum inversion to maximum eversion). The mean values and standard deviations for specimen 1 were $I_1 = 87.05 \pm 2.70$cm^4, $I_2 = 143.22 \pm 4.04$cm^4, and $I_3 = 165.24 \pm 4.11$cm^4 and the corresponding coefficients of variation were 3.10 percent, 2.82 percent, and 2.49 percent, respectively. Accuracy of the digitization process was examined by comparing geometric property values determined experimentally and exact values for four different cylinders of known dimensions. The average differences between digitized and exact values were 1.00 percent for surface area and 1.59 percent for volume. Repeatability of the digitizing process was examined by calculating geometric properties of a four-slice segment of each bone in three trials. The means and standard deviations for the talar segment were 67.33 ± 0.78 cm^2 for surface area and 36.65 ± 1.50 cm^3 for volume; the corresponding coefficients of variation were 1.16 percent and 4.09 percent, respectively. For the calcaneal segment, the results were 109.38 ± 0.79 cm^2 for surface area and 59.50 ± 0.39 cm^3 for volume; the corresponding coefficients of variation were 0.72 percent and 0.66 percent, respectively.

10.3.2. Translations

The translations of the moving body (talus) were determined by changes in its CM coordinates relative to the CM coordinates of the fixed body (calcaneus) as given by Equation 10-3. Displacements of the talus from the neutral joint position are reported in Table 10-2. Although the general displacement is variable among the three specimens, the x-axis translation shows a consistent trend. The magnitude of x-axis (mediolateral) translations ranged from 3.8 to 5.8 mm. The talus moved in a medial to lateral direction relative to the fixed calcaneus as the subtalar joint was ranged from maximum inversion to maximum eversion (Figure 10-6b).

TABLE 10-2 CM TRANSLATIONS (MM) OF TALUS RELATIVE TO FIXED CALCANEUS; DEVIATIONS FROM NEUTRAL JOINT POSITION

Joint position	Specimen 1			Specimen 2			Specimen 3		
	x	y	z	x	y	z	x	y	z
Max inversion	1.3	2.7	−4.8	1.1	0.5	−0.7			
2/3 inversion	0.4	3.0	−3.2	0.1	0.3	0.6			
1/3 inversion	0.1	2.4	−3.8	0.0	0.3	−0.1	2.3	−0.4	−0.7
Neutral									
1/2 eversion	−0.1	0.0	1.0	−1.7	0.1	0.2	−2.3	−0.2	5.5
Max eversion	−3.9	1.4	−1.3	−2.7	0.0	0.2			

10.3.3. Direction Cosines

The orientations of the moving (talus) and fixed (calcaneus) bodies were first defined with respect to a global reference system by direction cosine matrices of the body principal axes. Relative orientation of the two bodies was defined by the direction cosines of the talar principal axes with respect to the calcaneal principal axes at each joint position (Equation 10-4b). The angle between any two principal axes can be computed from these direction cosines; however, due to the large quantity of these results, they are not reported here. Body orientations are reported in more compact form in terms of Euler angles, clinical-plane angles, and helical-axis parameters in the following sections.

(*a*)

Figure 10-6. Views of talus, with embedded principal axes, relative to fixed calcaneus: (*a*) posterior view, (*b*) medial view, and (*c*) anterior view. Maximum inversion, neutral, and maximum eversion positions are shown left to right, respectively in each photograph.

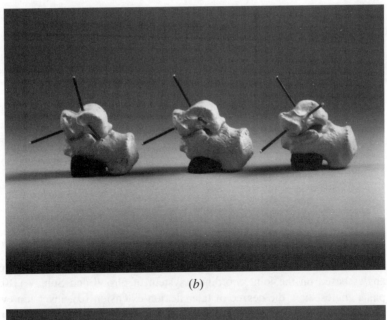

(b)

(c)

10.3.4. Euler Angles

The relative body orientations were expressed in terms of Euler angles with a rotation sequence of $z'(\gamma)$, $y'(\beta)$, $x'(\alpha)$ about the principal axes of the calcaneus. The rotations necessary to define the orientation of the talus with respect to the calcaneal principal axes are listed in Table 10-3. Euler angle results suggest that changes in talar orientation occurred primarily in two planes as the subtalar joint was ranged from maximum inversion to maximum eversion.

TABLE 10-3 EULER ANGLE ORIENTATIONS (DEGREES) OF TALUS RELATIVE TO CALCANEAL PRINCIPAL AXES; ROTATION SEQUENCE $z'(\gamma)$, $y'(\beta)$, $x'(\alpha)$

Joint position	Specimen 1			Specimen 2			Specimen 3		
	α	β	γ	α	β	γ	α	β	γ
Max inversion	155.5	−0.3	34.5	146.0	24.0	61.3			
2/3 inversion	155.1	4.9	38.8	145.1	32.6	67.6			
1/3 inversion	155.7	11.6	41.2	146.4	34.6	64.4	150.3	12.9	38.3
Neutral	151.4	23.4	52.9	147.4	34.6	65.9	152.0	23.6	44.0
1/2 eversion	148.2	29.7	54.7	146.3	44.9	71.8	144.6	39.3	50.6
Max eversion	147.9	36.6	57.9	147.9	45.5	71.1			

10.3.5. Clinical-Plane Angles

The orientations of the moving body were also expressed in terms of clinical-plane angles based on the joint coordinate system of Grood and Suntay [18]. The clinical-plane angles show the degree of talar flexion-extension (θ), inversion-eversion (Ψ), and internal-external rotation (ϕ); these are listed in Table 10-4. As with the Euler angles, these results show that the talus rotates primarily in the sagittal (θ) and coronal (Ψ) planes. The rotations in the transverse plane (ϕ) are inconsistent; the talus rotated externally in both inversion and eversion of the subtalar joint.

TABLE 10-4 CLINICAL-PLANE ANGLES (DEGREES); TALAR ORIENTATIONS RELATIVE TO CALCANEAL BODY {u″} AXES IN THE SAGITTAL (θ), CORONAL (ψ), AND TRANSVERSE (ϕ) PLANES

Joint position	Specimen 1			Specimen 2			Specimen 3		
	θ	Ψ	ϕ	θ	Ψ	ϕ	θ	Ψ	ϕ
Max inversion	24.5	−18.9	5.3	7.2	−8.7	2.3			
2/3 inversion	18.7	−15.4	2.3	−1.5	−2.3	3.0			
1/3 inversion	14.6	−10.2	−1.5	1.1	0.4	0.5	8.8	−7.4	3.7
Neutral									
1/2 eversion	−4.2	6.0	2.5	−8.6	8.5	2.5	−14.7	12.2	7.6
Max eversion	−9.3	11.9	3.2	−7.9	9.3	7.6			

10.3.6. Helical-Axis Parameters

The position changes of the talus were alternatively described in terms of helical (screw) axis parameters. The helical-axis direction cosines (h_x, h_y, h_z), rotations about the helical axis (ω), and translations along the helical axis (d) for each increment of joint motion are listed in Table 10-5. The locations of three points on the helical axis ($x - y$, $x - z$, and $y - z$ plane intercepts) relative to the calcaneal body axes were also computed but are not reported here. The direction cosines indicate that the helical axis had an oblique orientation relative to the calcaneal body axes and was not fixed as the foot was ranged from maximum inversion to maximum eversion. In general, the helical axis was located within or anterior to the body of the talus and pointed in a lateral, anterior, and superior direction.

TABLE 10-5 HELICAL AXIS PARAMETERS; TALUS RELATIVE TO FIXED CALCANEUS

Joint position	Specimen 1		
	h_x, h_y, h_z	ω	d
Max inversion to 2/3 inversion	−0.515, 0.577, 0.634	6.8	1.71
2/3 inversion to 1/3 inversion	−0.528, 0.782, 0.332	7.1	−0.55
1/3 inversion to neutral	−0.639, 0.281, 0.716	18.0	2.15
Neutral to 1/2 eversion	−0.885, 0.190, 0.426	7.6	1.43
1/2 eversion to max eversion	−0.767, 0.468, 0.438	7.8	1.79

Joint position	Specimen 2		
	h_x, h_y, h_z	ω	d
Max inversion to 2/3 inversion	−0.739, 0.281, 0.612	10.8	1.45
2/3 inversion to 1/3 inversion	0.325, −0.406, 0.854	−4.5	−1.65
1/3 inversion to neutral	0.303, 0.650, −0.697	1.3	0.72
Neutral to 1/2 eversion	−0.811, 0.244, 0.531	12.2	1.60
1/2 eversion to max eversion	0.341, −0.464, 0.818	1.4	0.29

Joint position	Specimen 3		
	h_x, h_y, h_z	ω	d
1/3 inversion to neutral	−0.487, 0.762, 0.427	11.9	1.68
Neutral to 1/2 eversion	−0.798, 0.297, 0.542	20.0	4.66

(h_x, h_y, h_z) = orientation (direction cosines) of helical axis; ω = rotation (degrees) about helical axis; d = translation (mm) along helical axis.

10.3.7. Summary of Results

The results demonstrate that the subtalar joint does not act as a simple hinge about a fixed oblique axis of rotation. This is illustrated best by the changing orientation of the helical-axis direction cosines as the joint moves from maximum inversion to maximum eversion. Posterior, medial, and anterior views of a model talus with embedded principal axes and a fixed calcaneus are shown in Figure 10-6. The maximum inversion, neutral, and maximum eversion joint positions are shown left to right, respectively. Since the calcaneus was fixed in these experiments, the anterior principal axis of the talus in maximum eversion (right) is pointing down. Foot inversion resulted in a 3-D translation of the talus, inversion and plantarflexion at the subtalar joint, and minimal external rotation. Foot eversion also resulted in a 3-D talar translation along with talar eversion, dorsiflexion, and minimal external rotation. It is not clear why the talus rotated externally in both inversion and eversion of the foot.

10.4. DISCUSSION

This chapter presents a general technique to describe six-degree-of-freedom bone and joint motion based on rigid-body kinematics. There are three significant features of these methods to define joint kinematics: (1) noninvasive imaging techniques are used to define the bones studied, (2) invariant body centroids and principal axes are used to monitor changes in body position, and (3) the resulting body translations can be expressed by simple changes in body-centroid coordinates and body orientations can be expressed in terms of direction cosines, Euler angles, clinical-plane angles (Grood and Suntay joint coordinate system), or helical-axis parameters. These three features are discussed in the following paragraphs.

First, most prior studies of bone and joint kinematics have utilized invasive techniques which can alter joint structures and would not be suitable for in vivo characterization of joint motion. The methods described here are based on noninvasive imaging techniques such as CT scans, MRI, or any system that yields volumetric data from which the 3-D shapes of the bones could be reconstructed. These imaging and geometric reconstruction techniques eliminate the need for invasive markers or labels, instrumented linkages, or other methods that rely on the tracking of specific body points. Also, these techniques have the potential for in vivo characterization of unaltered 3-D joint motion. They would allow the study of a normal clinical population or a specific pathologic condition without the restrictions of in vitro cadaver studies.

Second, most prior studies rely on invasive markers and/or anatomical landmarks to monitor changes in bone position. The methods of this study use body centroids and principal axes to define joint kinematics. Since the principal axes form an orthogonal set of invariant axes fixed in a body, they can be used to monitor changes in body orientation (moving body) or to serve as a reference frame (fixed body). Similarly, since the body centroids are invariant, they can be used to define absolute or relative body translations. Because the principal axes and centroids are fixed in each body, the need for anatomical landmarks or markers to define relative bone positions is eliminated.

Third, the joint motions determined by principal axes and body centroids can be mathematically described by several alternative methods. Once the principal-axis direction cosines are determined, body motions can be readily defined by the most convenient method for the particular joint studied. As noted by Hart et al. [22], Euler angles or the clinical-plane angles of Grood and Suntay [18] are simpler for the interpretation of joint rotations. Euler angles can be computed directly from the direction cosine matrices (Equations 10-5a and 10-5b) at each joint position. However, if the three successive Euler rotations do not correspond to clinically identifiable planes, it might be more convenient to use the clinical-plane angles based on the Grood and Suntay joint coordinate system. In contrast, Hart et al. [22] noted that helical-axis parameters are easier to compare because helical-axis positions and orientations transform as vectors while Euler angle comparisons require rotation matrix transformations. Kinzel et al. [20] noted that helical-axis parameters can be used to characterize the general behavior of joint motion. For example, the motion of a true hinge joint would yield collinear helical axes with zero displacements along the helical axis. The motion of a six degrees of freedom joint would result in a helical axis with changing orientation, angular rotation about the axis, and a translation along the axis.

The three mathematical descriptions of body orientation are precise; the accuracy of these methods depends on how well the bodies (bones) are mathematically reconstructed.

Comparisons of geometric properties computed by two modeling programs resulted in very small differences, indicating that essentially the same bodies were reconstructed by each program (Table 10-1). The greatest difference for any geometric parameter was 3.43 percent (I_2, talus). The average difference was 2.10 percent for principal moments and 1.70 percent for volume. In a study of carpal bones, Justin et al. [8] reported average differences between two modeling programs of 6.6 percent for principal moments and 3.14 percent for volume. The use of principal axes and body centroids to define body orientations and translations should be valid if these parameters can be consistently reproduced in each discrete body position. Since the orientations of the principal axes change with joint position, the best indicator of accuracy was the variation of the principal moments of inertia with joint position. The average coefficient of variation for the three principal moments of inertia was 2.80 percent. Thus, the principal axes were determined with reasonable accuracy in each discrete joint position. Lastly, the results of digitization accuracy and repeatability tests showed that the digitization process did not lead to any significant errors.

The primary goal of this chapter was to present a general noninvasive technique for the definition of bone and joint kinematics. Thus, only three specimens subjected to clinical inversion-eversion have been examined so far, and the motion of the subtalar joint cannot be fully characterized. Therefore, a detailed review and comparison of subtalar joint motion is not presented. Furthermore, the tibiotalar joint was locked to simplify joint motion; therefore, the present results cannot be compared directly with other studies. For example, the large sagittal-plane rotations (θ, Table 10-4) would occur to a greater extent at the ankle joint rather than the subtalar joint as shown by Siegler et al. [3]. Nonetheless, the overall results are consistent with previous studies of subtalar joint motion [1,3,23]. E. J. van Langelaan [2] determined the positions of foot and ankle bones of 10 specimens using X-ray stereophotogrammetric analysis. For the subtalar joint, motion occurred about discrete helical axes that changed position and orientation continuously. Siegler et al. [3] also showed that the subtalar joint does not act as an ideal hinge joint with a fixed axis of rotation. This finding is supported by the results of the present study. The orientation of the helical axis changed as the specimens were ranged from maximum inversion to maximum eversion. In contrast, S. H. Scott and D. A. Winter [24] suggested that under full body weight loads, the motion of the talocalcaneal joint can be defined as a monocentric single degree of freedom hinge joint.

While the results were very well matched between the three methods of motion description for all specimens, some specific results for specimen 2 showed some inconsistencies. The joint motion increments 2/3 to 1/3 inversion, 1/3 inversion to neutral, and 1/2 to maximum eversion resulted in a helical-axis orientation and direction inconsistent with the general pattern of the other motion increments and specimens. The direction cosines defining helical-axis orientation (Table 10-5) for these motion increments resulted in helical axes that were perpendicular to the general trend. The reasons for this discrepancy are unclear. However, it is interesting to note that the angular rotations were relatively small for each of these problematic motion increments. It has been shown that errors in determining helical-axis position and direction from anatomical landmark measurements are inversely proportional to the rotation magnitude [25,26]. Since the helical axis is undefined for pure translation, its position is very sensitive to measurement errors under small rotations [25]. While the particular source of error in the present study is undetermined, helical-axis position and direction appear to be similarly sensitive to small rotation magnitude.

At present, the methods developed in this study have several limitations. First, current methods use a large number of thin CT scan sections to reconstruct accurately the geometry of the bones, resulting in substantial procedure duration and radiation exposure. Also, the CT scan outlines were digitized manually. (Automated digitizing methods exist; however, they were not available to the authors for the present study.) Second, the present methods are useful for the general characterization of joint motion. However, to describe the relative position of a specific point (other than the body centroid) would require the consistent identification of a bony landmark relative to the center of mass. Third, the present methods reconstruct the entire volume of a particular bone. Thus, these methods are presently useful for small bones and joints, but would be impractical for entire long bones. A potential solution would be to scan only a portion of the bone (containing the joint) and locate the centroid and principal axes for that particular segment. If these segment geometric properties can be reproduced accurately and consistently, the number of scan slices could be reduced substantially. Another future consideration is the determination of accuracy with respect to slice direction and the shape of the bone. For example, an oblong bone must be scanned perpendicular to the long axis to be adequately reproduced.

The general methods described in this chapter might have many potential clinical applications. The in vivo characterization of 3-D joint motion could include the effects of normal muscular activity and intact soft tissues. The effects of 3-D loading on normal joint kinematics could be examined. Normal joint motion data could then serve as a baseline for the detection of irregular joint kinematics and to determine if surgical intervention could restore normal joint motion. On the basis of normal joint motion, the design of prosthetics and orthotics could be improved. Furthermore, these methods could be used for the quantitative examination of the effects of prosthetics, orthotics, or surgery on the resulting joint motion. Other potential applications could include the determination of bone and joint velocities and accelerations using high-speed MRI scanning techniques. The correspondence of two-dimensional radiograph images with 3-D reconstructions of bone and joint positions could also be investigated. These methods could be used to examine the spatial relationship of other joints and structures. For example, the effects of relative vertebral body positions in the spine during periods of back pain could be examined.

Acknowledgments

The authors wish to thank Stefan Ortloff, Dr. Judy Smith, and Dr. Nick Nigro for their contributions to this work.

Glossary

A	Helical-axis transformation matrix
B	Position matrix of moving body
CM	Center of mass (centroid)
c	Calcaneus
DC	Principal-axis direction cosine matrix
d	Translation along helical axis
ET	Euler angle transformation matrix
e	Unit vector in Grood and Suntay joint coordinate system
f	Fixed body
h_x, h_y, h_z	Helical-axis direction cosines

(i)	Joint position
m	Moving body
P	Arbitrary point on helical axis
r	Centroid position vector
t	Talus
u $= X, Y, Z$	Global Cartesian reference system
u' $= x', y', z'$	Body-fixed principal axes
u" $= x'', y'', z''$	Body-fixed axes related to principal axes
α, β, γ	Euler angles
θ, ψ, ϕ	Clinical-plane angles (Grood and Suntay joint coordinate system)
ω	Rotation about helical axis

References

[1] Engsberg JR. A biomechanical analysis of the talocalcaneal joint—In vitro. *J Biomech* 1987;20:429–442.

[2] van Langelaan EJ. Relative talotibial movements and relative tarsal movements. In: A kinematical analysis of the tarsal joints. *Acta Orthop Scand* (Suppl), 1983;204: 135–265.

[3] Siegler S, Chen J, Schneck CD. The three-dimensional kinematics and flexibility characteristics of the human ankle and subtalar joints - Part I: Kinematics. *J Biomech Eng* 1988;110:364–373.

[4] Siegler S, Wang D, Plasha E, Berman AT. Technique for in vivo measurement of the three-dimensional kinematics and laxity characteristics of the ankle joint complex. *J Orthop Res* 1994;12:421–431.

[5] Bresina SJ, Vannier MW, Logan SE, Weeks PM. Three-dimensional wrist imaging: Evaluation of functional and pathological anatomy by computer. *Clinics in Plastic Surgery* 1986;13:389–405.

[6] Belsole RJ, Hilbelink DR, Llewellyn JA, Stenzler S, Greene TL, Dale M. Mathematical analysis of computed carpal models. *J Orthop Res* 1988;6:116–122.

[7] Levinson DP, Dale MM. Wrist configuration: A study from computed carpal models. *Proc IEEE Eng Med Bio Soc* 1991;13:1964–1965.

[8] Justin PF, Wurster SS, Werntz JR, Dale M, Llewellyn JA. Solid model prediction of the range of motion of the wrist following a proximal row carpectomy. *Proc IEEE Eng Med Bio Soc* 1991;13:1966–1967.

[9] Hallgren RC, Reynolds HM, Soutas-Little RW, Hubbard RP, Rechtien JJ. 3-D analysis and display of sequential position data in the lumbar spine. *J Clin Eng* 1988;13:51–57.

[10] Herzenberg JE, Carroll HC, Christofersen MR, Lee EH. Three-dimensional computerized reconstruction of histologic serial sections for orthopedic research. *Orthopedics* 1988;11:1549–1555.

[11] Alpert NM, Bradshaw JF, Kennedy D, Correia JA. The principal axes transformation—A method for image reconstruction. *J Nucl Med* 1990;31:1717–1722.

[12] Gamboa-Aldeco A, Chen GTY. Correlation of 3-D surfaces from multiple modalities in medical imaging. *SPIE Proceedings* 1986:460–466.

[13] Faber TL, Stokely EM. Orientation of 3-D structures in medical images. *IEEE Trans Pat Anal and Mach Intel* 1988;10:626–633.

[14] Wynarsky GT, Harris GF, Ortloff S, Smith J, Shereff M. A noninvasive technique for the description of three-dimensional bone and joint kinematics. *Trans Orthop Res Soc* 1992;38:471.

[15] Gundersen HJG, Jensen EB. The efficiency of systematic sampling in stereology and its prediction. *J Microsp* 1987;147:229–263.

[16] Chao EYS. Justification of triaxial goniometer for the measurement of joint rotation. *J Biomech* 1980;13:989–1006.

[17] Goldstein H. *Classical Mechanics* 2nd ed. Reading, Mass: Addison-Wesley; 1970.

[18] Grood ES, Suntay WJ. A joint coordinate system for the clinical description of three-dimensional motions: Application to the knee. *J Biomech Eng* 1983;105:136–144.

[19] Spoor CW, Veldpaus FE. Rigid-body motion calculated from spatial coordinates of markers. *J Biomech* 1980;13:391–393.

[20] Kinzel GL, Hall AS, Hillberry BM. Measurement of the total motion between two body segments - I. Analytical development. *J. Biomech* 1972;5:93–105.

[21] Kinzel GL, Hillberry BM, Hall Jr AS, Van Sickle DC, Harvey WM. Measurement of the total motion between two body segments - II. Description of application. *J Biomech* 1972;5:283–293.

[22] Hart RA, Mote Jr CD, Skinner HB. A finite helical axis as a landmark for kinematic reference of the knee. *J Biomech Eng* 1991;113:215–222.

[23] Lundberg A, Svensson OK, Bylund C, Goldie I, Selvik G. Kinematics of the ankle/foot complex - Part 2: Pronation and supination. *Foot and Ankle* 1989;9:248–253.

[24] Scott SH, Winter DA. Talocrural and talocalcaneal joint kinematics and kinetics during the stance phase of walking. *J Biomech* 1991;24:743–752.

[25] Woltring HJ, Huiskes R, DeLange A, Veldpaus FE. Finite centroid and helical axis estimation from noisy landmark measurements in the study of human joint kinematics. *J Biomech* 1985;18:379–389.

[26] DeLange A, Huiskes R, Kauer JMG. Measurement errors in roentgen-stereo-photogrammetric joint-motion analysis. *J Biomech* 1990;23:259–269.

Kenton R. Kaufman
David H. Sutherland

Chapter 11

Future Trends in Human Motion Analysis

11.1. INTRODUCTION

The 20th century has been characterized by scientific advancement. The technological discoveries produced by scientific endeavors have benefited many people. Gait analysis is one field that has seen considerable advances in the application of technology. Since the pioneering work of W. Braune and O. Fisher [1], much effort has been put into developing the needed technology. Computerized movement tracking systems have replaced hand digitization. Advances in the aerospace industry have been utilized to develop force plates for kinetic analysis. Telemeterized electromyography (EMG) systems have replaced hand palpitation. Currently, the technology and knowledge have advanced to a level that permits rapid analysis.

The health care community is at a turning point. An increasing emphasis in medicine is being placed on determining the outcome of various clinical procedures. Current knowledge provides a scientific basis for clinical practice. A number of approaches and methods are applied by doctors, nurses, therapists, and other specialists to prevent a particular condition, ameliorate its effects, or change a given state. Accurate measures are needed to quantify the vast array of medical procedures that affect outcome. The objective measurement tools provided by gait analysis techniques are central to measurement of the patient's progress. The future of gait analysis will depend upon advances/changes made in three areas: (1) health care reform, (2) analytical techniques, and (3) interpretation techniques of gait studies.

11.2. HEALTH CARE REFORM

Health insurance provides people access to the health care system. It also protects them against financial catastrophe in the case of illness. The birth of modern health insurance came in 1929 when a group of school teachers made a contract with Baylor Hospital in Dallas, Texas, to provide health care services at a predetermined monthly cost [2]. This plan generally is acknowledged as the first Blue Cross plan. The Blue Cross plan provided a mechanism to insure that a patient would be able to pay for health care services received. During the 1950s, health insurance protection expanded rapidly and by the middle of the decade, 77 million people had hospital expense insurance [2]. During the next 20 years, health insurance broadened its scope and covered an increasing number of people. In 1966, the Medicare program for people aged 65 and over and the Medicaid program for people under the age of 65 were designed to share the cost of medical care for low-income people. Health care costs rose dramatically in the 1970s and 1980s (Figure 11-1). In 1960, the national expenditure for health care was 5.3 percent of the gross national product (GNP). By 1990, health care expenditure had risen to 12.2 percent of the GNP. Similarly, personal expenditure for medical care increased threefold during a similar time frame (Figure 11-2). In 1950, personal expenditure for medical care was 4.6 percent of total personal consumption expenditure and 4.3 percent of disposable income. By 1989, these expenditures had risen to 13.1 percent and 11.7 percent respectively [3]. The U.S. health care system is the most expensive in the world. Health care expenditure in the United States exceeded $600 billion—more than 12 percent of our gross domestic product—in 1990 (Figure 11-3). This is one-third more than any other industrialized nation. In addition to the U.S. system being the most expensive system in the world, U.S. health care costs are growing more rapidly than those in any other industrialized nation. The United States currently spends one-third more on health care than on education or defense (Figure 11-4).

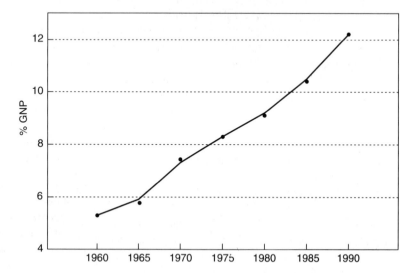

Figure 11-1. National expenditures for health care over past three decades, expressed as percentage of gross national product [3].

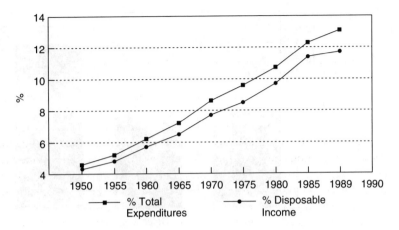

Figure 11-2. Personal expenditures for medical care over past four decades [3].

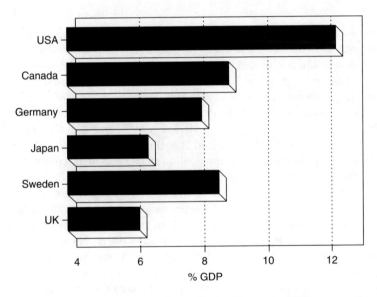

Figure 11-3. International expenditures for health care in 1990, expressed as percentage of gross domestic product [3].

Many options are debated, but it is not known how the nation will change its health care system. The hospital of the future will differ from the hospital of today. Health care delivery systems are changing. Initially, health maintenance organizations (HMOs) and later, preferred provider organizations (PPOs), were developed to provide a loose framework of health care delivery. The HMO delivery system provides a defined, comprehensive set of health services to a voluntarily enrolled population within a specified geographic service area. The PPO offers more flexibility than the HMO, giving consumers greater freedom in choosing providers, but, as with the HMO, it tries to achieve savings by directing patients to

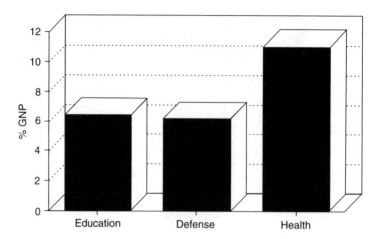

Figure 11-4. United States spending for health care, education, and defense in
1988 [3].

providers who are committed to cost-effective delivery of care. These health care delivery
systems seem to offer the potential for controlling costs by providing coherent networks to
obtain discount pricing and by integrating the financing and delivery of medical care.

During the past 5 to 10 years, the health care delivery system has evolved at a pace
that few expected. The most visible change has been the explosion of what have become
known as *managed care delivery systems*, of which HMOs and PPOs are the best-known
examples. It is projected that by 1995, over 90 percent of the population in the United
States will be covered by managed care (Figure 11-5). Managed care, and everything it
represents (cost containment, competition among providers, constraints on health services,
reimbursement decreases, and utilization review) has forever changed the traditional fee-for-
service model [4]. In the fee-for-service contract, a health care provider received payment
for each service rendered. This created an incentive to provide a high volume and range
of services. Managed care makes fixed payments per subscriber for all services, creating
the incentive to attract a high number of subscribers, but providing the fewest number
of services to each subscriber. The implication is that higher cost per patient will lower
profits. Managed competition is the extension of managed care. Managed competition
seeks to transfer the entire economic risk of health care from the insurance companies to
the health care provider. Individual patients obtain health care coverage from a provider
network that arranges service options by soliciting bids for specified services from health
care providers.

A paradigm shift in health care delivery is occurring. Buyers of health care are
changing from a health care system that manages "sickness" to a system that manages
"health." The evolution of the market is occurring most rapidly in the western United
States [5]. A market classification of localities in the United States is given in Table
11-1. The ranking in this table ranges from a fee-for-service environment (score = 1.0)
to a totally managed competition stage (score = 4.0). The movement toward universal
access and cost control of U.S. health care will certainly intensify in the future. Partners
in regionally integrated health service networks will include network hospitals, ambulatory
care sites, long-term care facilities, behavioral medicine programs, large multisite medical

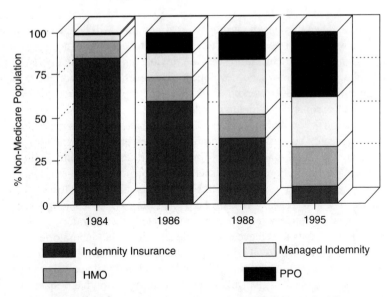

Figure 11-5. Evolution of health care delivery system in United States.

TABLE 11-1   HEALTH CARE MARKET CLASSIFICATION BY LOCATION

I. Unstructured		II. Loose framework		III. Consolidation		IV. Managed competition	
Nashville	1.5	Chicago	2.3	Los Angeles	3.2	Minneapolis/St. Paul	3.4
New Orleans	1.5	Salt Lake City	2.3	Orange	3.1		
Newark	1.5	Tucson	2.3	San Diego	3.1		
Oklahoma City	1.5	Houston	2.2	Worcester	3.0		
Toledo	1.5	Cincinnati	2.2	Portland	3.0		
Nassau	1.4	Dallas	2.2	Sacramento	3.0		
Galveston	1.4	Madison	2.2	San Francisco/	2.8		
Harrisburg	1.4	Cleveland	2.1	Oakland			
Little Rock	1.3	Washington, D.C.	2.1	Denver	2.7		
Chapel Hill	1.3	Baltimore	2.0	Seattle	2.4		
(Triangle)		Columbus	2.0				
Pittsburgh	1.3	Philadelphia	2.0				
Syracuse	1.3	Albany	1.9				
Augusta	1.2	St. Louis	1.9				
Lexington	1.2	Gainesville	1.9				
Omaha	1.2	Richmond	1.8				
Columbia	1.1	Atlanta	1.8				
Charlottesville	1.0	Indianapolis	1.7				
Morgantown, WV	1.0	Hartford	1.7				
		Birmingham	1.7				
		New York	1.6				
		Middlesex	1.6				

* Totally fee-for-service = 1.0; totally managed competition = 4.0.
Source: Alksne, 1993 [5]

groups and health plans of various types. Capitation will be the primary form of payment. This new model for health care delivery will alter economic incentives and provide terrific opportunities for organizations that are flexible and move quickly. Case management and practice guidelines will be developed. However, it is important to note that managed competition has never worked anywhere. The rapid expansion of HMOs in the past two decades has coincided with unprecedented cost increases. One-third of all Californians are enrolled in HMOs, and more than 80 percent of all employees are covered by some form of managed care. Yet costs in California are 19 percent above the national average and rising more rapidly. Massachusetts and Minnesota, the second and third highest HMO penetration states, have similarly undistinguished cost records [6].

The use of gait analysis in this scenario is uncertain. Most of the clinical gait laboratories are in the eastern half of the United States (Figure 11-6). Many of these changes in health care delivery might not have impacted gait laboratories yet. Thus, a window of opportunity exists to achieve a workable situation. Gait laboratories can play a key role in managed care scenarios. It is important that individuals involved in health care policy development, organization, and provision understand that gait analysis can be used to eliminate unnecessary surgery. P. A. DeLuca et al. [7] have shown that frequently the number of surgical procedures are reduced after a three-dimensional (3-D) gait analysis, when compared to a clinical examination and videotaping alone. Further, gait analysis will maximize the return when surgery is indicated by providing recommendations for multilevel surgery [8]. The use of an appropriately timed gait study should make it possible to develop a treatment plan for a patient that can be completed in one operative setting. Objective gait analysis data can be used to quantify the patient's functional status. Depending on the patient's functional status, bilateral multilevel surgery might be performed. When appropriately planned, no

Figure 11-6. Location of clinical gait laboratories in United States. (A clinical gait laboratory is defined as a laboratory that is receiving referrals from physicians, providing recommendations for treatment, and receiving third-party reimbursement for these services.)

further surgery will be needed. This reduction in the number of surgeries will lower the overall long-term cost of treating a patient.

One of the most important features of the new health care system will be a greater emphasis on prevention of disease and measurement of clinical outcome. Patient functional status before and after treatment will need to be studied. Payors are turning their attention from short-term savings to long-term predictable improvement in both cost and quality. Future efforts aimed at the development of suitable analytical techniques and methods for automation of data analysis are needed to make it easier for clinicians to identify and treat problems in human movement. Possible areas of work in analytical and interpretive techniques are described in the next two sections.

11.3. ANALYTICAL TECHNIQUES

A fundamental concern in the study of human locomotion is a description of the kinematics and kinetics involved. During the study of gait, a large number of measurements are taken. The experimental data are entered into an analytical model to obtain the values of variables not directly measurable. The analytical model is a link segment model. The human body is modeled as a system of articulated, rigid links which represent the lower limb segments and the upper body. By modeling the body as an ensemble of rigid-body segments, it is possible to calculate the movement and loads at any articulation.

11.3.1. Kinematics

In order to establish a mathematically workable model, Cartesian coordinate systems are established on each body segment [9–13]. These anatomically based axis systems are fixed in each body segment and move with it. The coordinates of bony landmarks are used to build a right-handed orthogonal coordinate system. The unique specification of anatomical coordinate systems requires a minimum of three noncolinear points that are defined with respect to surface landmarks associated with each segment. In order to obtain the joint movement, expressions have to be obtained relating the position of each segment in the model with respect to adjacent segments. Joint motions are usually 3-D. The anatomical description of the relative orientation of the two limb segments can be conveniently obtained by relating the two coordinate systems embedded in the proximal and distal body segments. The ability to describe joint orientation in 3-D space following traditional rigid-body motion theory is essential. For finite spatial rotation, the sequence of rotation is extremely important and must be specified for a unique description of joint motion. For the same amount of rotation, different final orientations will result from different sequences of rotation. However, with proper selection and definition of the axes of rotation between two bony segments, it is possible to make the finite rotation sequence independent or commutative. In the past 15 years, the concept of Eulerian angles has been adopted in the field of biomechanics to unify the definition of finite spatial rotation [14,15]. If a unit vector triad $(\mathbf{I},\mathbf{J},\mathbf{K})$ is attached to a fixed segment along the XYZ axes and another triad $(\mathbf{i},\mathbf{j},\mathbf{k})$ is fixed to the moving segment along the xyz axes (Figure 11-7), the relationship between them after any arbitrary finite rotation can be expressed by a rotational matrix in terms of three Eulerian angles, ϕ, θ, ψ

as follows:

$$
\begin{bmatrix} \mathbf{i} \\ \mathbf{j} \\ \mathbf{k} \end{bmatrix} = \begin{bmatrix} c\theta c\phi & c\theta c\phi & -s\theta \\ -c\psi s\phi + s\psi s\theta c\phi & c\psi c\phi + s\psi s\theta s\phi & s\psi c\theta \\ s\phi s\psi + c\psi s\theta c\phi & -s\psi c\phi + c\psi s\theta s\phi & c\psi c\theta \end{bmatrix} \begin{bmatrix} \mathbf{I} \\ \mathbf{J} \\ \mathbf{K} \end{bmatrix} \qquad (11\text{-}1)
$$

where s = sine
      c = cosine.

The Eulerian angles can be calculated based on the known orientation of these unit vector triads attached to the proximal and distal body segments.

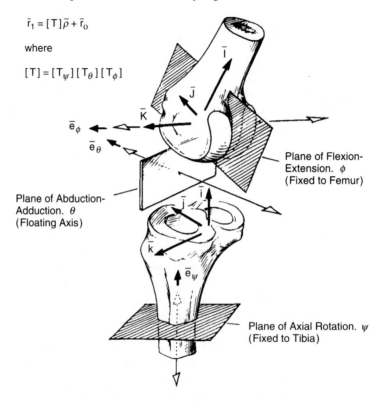

Figure 11-7. Description of knee joint motion using Eulerian angle system. Axis fixed to distal femur defines flexion/extension motion, ϕ. Axis fixed to proximal tibia along its anatomical axis defines internal-external rotation, ψ. Floating axis is orthogonal to other two axes and is used to measure abduction-adduction, Θ. (Reproduced with permission from the Mayo Clinic)

   For a more general unconstrained movement in space, three translations and three rotations are required to describe the joint motion. The displacement of a rigid body can take place along any one of an infinite number of paths. It is convenient to describe the displacement in terms of the simplest motion that can produce it. The most commonly used analytic method for the description of six-degree-of-freedom rigid-body displacement is the screw displacement axis [16–18]. The motion of the moving segment from one position to another can be defined in terms of a simultaneous rotation, Φ, around and a translation, τ, along a unique axis, called a screw displacement axis, which is fixed in the fixed segment (Figure 11-8). The screw displacement axis is a true vector quantity. However, the amount of the finite screw rotation is not a vector quantity, and the decomposition of it must be carefully interpreted because of the noncommutative nature of finite rotation. H. J. Woltring [19] recommended that the component rotations (flexion-extension, abduction-adduction, endo-exo rotation) be defined as a component of the product $\Phi = \Phi \mathbf{n}$, where $\mathbf{n}$ is the unit direction vector of the screw axis.

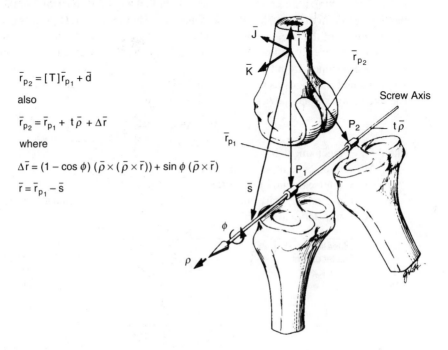

$$\bar{r}_{p_2} = [T]\bar{r}_{p_1} + \bar{d}$$

also

$$\bar{r}_{p_2} = \bar{r}_{p_1} + t\bar{\rho} + \Delta\bar{r}$$

where

$$\Delta\bar{r} = (1 - \cos\phi)(\bar{\rho} \times (\bar{\rho} \times \bar{r})) + \sin\phi(\bar{\rho} \times \bar{r})$$

$$\bar{r} = \bar{r}_{p_1} - \bar{s}$$

Figure 11-8. Screw displacement axis can be used to describe general spatial motion. Tibia moves from position 1 to position 2 by rotation about screw axis by an amount Φ and by translating along the screw axis by an amount τ. (Reproduced with permission from the Mayo Clinic)

11.3.2. Inverse Dynamics

Once the transformation matrices have been obtained, we can proceed to solve for the joint moments given the joint positions, velocities, and accelerations and the ground reaction forces. Typically, these formulations are based on the inverse dynamics approach [20], proceeding from known kinematic data and external forces and moments to arrive at expressions of the resultant intersegmental forces and moments. If the exact motion history of the system, especially accelerations, is available, then this type of problem presents little mathematical challenge and can be solved by applying the equations of motion derived for the system (Figure 11-9). An unconstrained rigid body has six degrees of freedom. Hence, six equations of motion are needed to specify its configuration. Three equations can be chosen to represent the translation of the rigid-body center of mass and three equations to represent the rotation about any point, A. In the case of the motion of a rigid body in three dimensions, the fundamental equations are:

$$\Sigma \mathbf{F_c} = m\, d(\dot{\mathbf{r}}_c)/dt$$
$$\Sigma \mathbf{M_A} = \dot{\mathbf{H}}_A + m(\dot{\mathbf{r}}_A \times \dot{\mathbf{r}}_c) \tag{11-2}$$

These fundamental equations express that the system of external forces, $\Sigma \mathbf{F_c}$, and moments, $\Sigma \mathbf{M_A}$, acting at the limb segment are equipollent to the system consisting of the linear momentum vector, $m\, d(\dot{\mathbf{r}}_c)/dt$, and the moment of momentum vector, $\dot{\mathbf{H}}_A + m(\dot{\mathbf{r}}_A \times \dot{\mathbf{r}}_c)$. Using measurements of the intersegmental load actions and the relevant kinematics, it is possible to compute the energy and power transmitted from one body segment to another. The joint powers are obtained from the scalar (dot) product of the intersegmental joint moment and the joint angular velocity as well as the intersegmental joint force and translational velocity. The rate of work done (power) can be calculated from:

$$\dot{W} = \mathbf{M} \cdot \omega + \mathbf{F} \cdot \mathbf{v} \tag{11-3}$$

where $\dot{W}$ = mechanical power
$\quad\ \mathbf{M}$ = intersegmental joint moment
$\quad\ \mathbf{F}$ = intersegmental joint force
$\quad\ \omega$ = angular velocity and
$\quad\ \mathbf{v}$ = translational velocity.

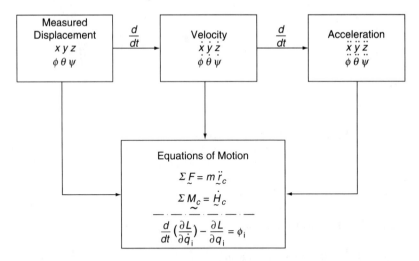

Figure 11-9. Solution process for inverse dynamics problem. Displacement information must be differentiated twice to yield acceleration. Either Newtonian or Lagranian formulations can be used to formulate the equations of motion. (Reproduced with permission from the Mayo Clinic)

Frequently, the component due to translation is assumed to be small and the second term ($\mathbf{F} \cdot \mathbf{v}$) is rarely included in joint power estimates for gait. This technique can be used to predict the transfer of energy from body segment to body segment through the muscles

[21]. The muscles can either generate mechanical energy or absorb mechanical energy by contracting concentrically or eccentrically, respectively.

11.3.3. Body Segment Mass Inertial Estimates

Estimates of body segment mass, center of mass, and moments of inertia are needed for these biomechanical models. These body segment parameters are used along with the segmental kinematics to compute the linear and angular momentum of the body segments. Estimates of these values are substituted into the Newton-Euler equations of motion to obtain an estimate of joint loads during physical activity. These body segment estimates are a big source of error in biomechanical models [22]. Future efforts need to be aimed at getting a subject's specific body segment parameters. Methods of obtaining inertial parameters of body segments can be classified into three groups: (1) regression equations, (2) geometrical approximation, and (3) direct measurement. Regression equations have been developed based on cadaver studies [23–25] and living subjects [26–28]. The regression equations have been developed through statistical analysis of the data. The regression equations based on cadaver studies typically lead to errors arising from differences in tissue composition and morphology between the cadaver samples and a given human subject [29]. The study by R. F. Chandler et al. [25] was the first study to determine the segmental principal axes of inertia. This study also provided verifiable comparisons of derived photometric values and directly measured values. On the basis of these comparative relationships, a series of predicted regression equations were developed for adult males [27] and adult females [28]. However, the sample sizes of these studies have been relatively small. The geometrical approximation method represents the shape of different body segments with standard geometric forms that are capable of simple mathematical description [30–34]. Errors reported using this technique are in the range of 3 percent to 5 percent. However, only partial validation of the predicted parameter values is possible, since only a few of them are measurable on living subjects. Efforts are under way to gain direct measurements of subject-specific body segment parameters using either computed tomography [35–37] or magnetic resonance imaging [38,39]. However, such techniques can involve high radiation levels (computed tomography) and require specialized, expensive instrumentation.

Future work should be aimed at obtaining inexpensive, fast, noninvasive, individualized estimates of the inertial properties of body segments. One possibility is a video-based system [34]. Error levels using this technique are on the order of 5 percent. Another possibility is the use of high-speed laser scanning. A 3-D laser scanner can obtain digitized images of a patient's limb in 10 seconds [40,41]. Markers placed near anatomic landmarks can be used as reference points. These data can be used to compute subject-specific body segment parameters.

11.3.4. Forward Dynamics

These biomechanical models of the musculoskeletal system have improved our understanding of the complex processes underlying movement. Traditional gait studies have typically been conducted to collect experimental data and analyze movement and forces. In the future, the forward dynamics model can be used more extensively to study how the body actually produces movement. The forward dynamics problem provides the motion of a multibody system over a given time period as a consequence of the applied forces and given initial conditions. Solution of the forward dynamics problem makes it possible to simulate and predict the body segment's motion. The resultant motion is a result of the forces that produce it. Numerical computation of movements produced by applied forces can lead to an improved understanding of the locomotor system.

Using models to synthesize gait can provide insight into the relationship between muscle forces or joint moments and the body segment motions that result. The equations that govern the motion of the body can be expressed as:

$$[\mathbf{H}(\theta)]\ddot{\theta} = \mathbf{C}(\theta, \dot{\theta}) + \mathbf{G}(\theta) + \mathbf{F_m}(\theta) \tag{11-4}$$

where $[\mathbf{H}(\theta)]$ is an n $\times$ n inertia matrix for an n degree of freedom model

$\mathbf{C}\,(\theta, \dot{\theta})$ is an n $\times$ 1 vector of coriolis and centrifugal terms

$\mathbf{G}\,(\theta)$ is an n $\times$ 1 vector of gravitational terms

$\mathbf{F_m}$ is an n $\times$ 1 vector of applied moments

$\theta, \dot{\theta}, \ddot{\theta}$ are all n $\times$ 1 vectors of angular displacement, velocity, and acceleration.

Solving directly for the vector of angular acceleration gives:

$$\ddot{\theta} = [\mathbf{H}(\theta)]^{-1}\{\mathbf{C}(\theta, \dot{\theta}) + \mathbf{G}(\theta) + \mathbf{F_m}(\theta)\} \tag{11-5}$$

Dynamic simulations of movement integrate this equation forward in time to obtain motion trajectories in response to neuromuscular inputs (Figure 11-10). The inputs can be either joint moments or muscle forces that act on the skeletal system to result in joint moments. Experimentally collected kinesiological data (i.e., body segment motion, ground reaction forces, and electromyographic data), can be used to compute the forward dynamics model inputs that give the measured motion trajectories. The simulated gait pattern can be studied to gain insight into the muscle coordination of the task.

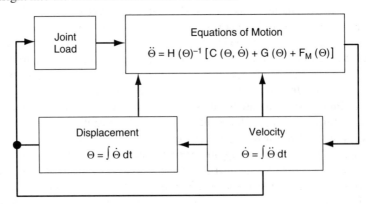

Figure 11-10. Solution process for the forward dynamics problem. Joint load can be taken directly from joint moments or can be calculated from a muscle-tendon model and a joint moment arm model that yield joint moments. Joint loads cause angular accelerations $\ddot{\theta}$. Equations of motion are integrated to yield joint velocities $\dot{\theta}$, and displacements, θ.

Currently available models for simulating human locomotion have tended to be simple [42–52]. State-of-the-art mathematical models of the musculoskeletal system need to be developed to predict gait patterns. The forward dynamics problem seeks the solution to a system of nonlinear ordinary differential equations (initial value problem). These differential equations are numerically integrated starting from the initial conditions. An important characteristic of this mathematical problem is that it is computationally intense. Because of this characteristic, it is very important to choose the most efficient method for solving this problem. Mathematical models have not been fully developed for several reasons:

1. The development of a dynamic model of the body that is sufficiently complex to encompass the multijoint, multibody, multimuscle characteristics of the human body requires considerable effort [53]. The problem is to develop a model that is phenomenologically correct without being overwhelmingly complex for practical applications.

2. The muscle excitation patterns required as input to such a model are not fully defined [54]. An improperly designed neural excitation pattern will simply result in inadequately coordinated body segment displacements.

3. The dynamic optimization algorithms to find iteratively an acceptable muscle excitation pattern are few and lack robustness [55].

4. The computational time required to find an adequate muscle excitation pattern is long [53].

5. The coordination principles provided by the neurological control systems in normal individuals is poorly understood. The additional challenges of understanding pathological neuromuscular control systems have yet to be addressed.

When fully developed, these models need to include representations of the (1) muscle tendon complex [56–60], (2) skeletal geometry [61,62], (3) kinematic models of the anatomic joints [63], and (4) inertial characteristics of the body segments [63]. Realistically developed theoretical models of the neuromusculoskeletal system will play a significant role in understanding locomotion.

Computer-based models are needed to study the biomechanical consequences of surgical reconstructions of the lower extremity. Upon review of data from a gait analysis study, surgical reconstruction is frequently recommended. Sometimes the reconstructive procedure compromises the capacity of muscles to generate forces and moments about the joints. Computer models are needed to predict the anticipated effects that surgical alterations to the musculoskeletal system will have on a patient's gait pattern. Relatively few researchers have developed computerized musculoskeletal models to plan orthopaedic reconstructive surgeries for correcting pathological gait. R. C. Johnston et al. [64] developed a computer model of the hip to evaluate effects of surgical alterations. J. Dul et al. [65] developed a biomechanical computer model to simulate tendon transfer surgeries to correct equinovarus. U. Lindgren and A. Seireg [66] studied the effects of mediolateral deformity, tibial torsion, and different centers of foot support during gait in patients with varus deformity of the knee. S. L. Delp et al. [62] developed a graphical model of the lower extremity to visualize the musculoskeletal geometry and manipulate model parameters to study the biomechanical consequences of orthopaedic surgical procedures. R. W. Mann [67] developed a surgical simulation model to determine the effect of skeletal system alterations on patients' specific gait patterns. Typically these surgical models compute static changes to isometric conditions but do not extend to dynamic movements such as gait. Future work is required to enhance these models. Future models should include the 3-D characteristics of the musculoskeletal geometry, as well as subjects' specific parameters. The musculotendinous aspects of the model need to be scaled to the individual being studied. The ability numerically to predict ambulation following changes to the musculoskeletal system is imminently feasible. However, it has not currently been implemented.

11.3.5. Muscle Force Measurement

Muscle forces reflect the underlying neurocontrol processes responsible for observed movement patterns. In addition, muscle forces play a major role in determining stresses in bones and joints. Thus, a knowledge of muscle forces is fundamental for improving the diagnosis and treatment of individuals with movement disorders. Interpretation of muscle function has routinely been based on analyses of electromyographic data obtained during gait studies [68–70]. More specific detailed knowledge of the muscle forces acting on the body will allow us to improve our ability to diagnose and treat patients with movement disabilities. It will also increase our understanding of muscle function during gait. Unfortunately, invasive techniques for measuring muscle forces are highly objectionable.

Techniques such as electromyography do not provide the quantitative accuracy needed. A fundamental relationship exists between the tension that a muscle is capable of developing and the length of the muscle. The total muscle tension is composed of both active and passive components. This well-known phenomenon is described by Blix's curve, which demonstrates the relationship of total muscle force, passive stretch force, and muscle contractile force to the length of the muscle [71]. Yet, the integrated electromyogram can only be proportional to the active component and will not account for the passive stretch of the muscle. Use of the integrated electromyogram as an indicator of the quantity of muscle contraction has another drawback. There is a significant delay between maximal electric activity in the muscle and maximal tension. The electromechanical delay has been estimated to be 30 to 90 ms [72–76], which would be approximately 3 to 9 percent of the gait cycle.

Measurement of intramuscular pressure is a conceivable solution. Intramuscular pressure is a mechanical variable that is proportional to muscle tension. Investigators have shown in studies on animals [77–79] and in humans [80–83] an approximately linear relationship between intramuscular pressure and muscle force during isometric muscle contraction. Further, estimation of muscle force from intramuscular pressure is not affected by changes in signal due to muscle fatigue [83,84]. Nevertheless, the absolute intramuscular pressure depends on the depth of the recording catheter within the muscle [78,84], the shape of the muscle [85], and the compliance of the surrounding tissue [86]. J. U. Baumann et al. [87] reported that intramuscular pressure is related to the active and passive components of muscle tension during gait. In the future, more work is needed in the use of intramuscular pressure to quantify muscle force. Improvements in microsensor technology can be used to facilitate these measurements.

11.3.6. Advances in Computer Power

The development of biomechanical models has increased dramatically in the last decade. These advances were made possible by the decreasing costs and simultaneous increase in computational capacity of computers. In 1937, Howard H. Aiken of Harvard University conceived the first large-scale automatic digital computer. In the late 1960s, computers operated at internal speeds about 20 to 100 times faster than their counterparts of 10 years earlier. By the 1980s, speeds were 1000 times faster than in the 1960s. Over the same period, storage capacities of computer memory increased by comparable factors [88]. Thus, since 1945 the speed of computers has approximately doubled every two years. The exponential increases in the computational power of computers makes biomechanical models of the musculoskeletal system possible. Beyond the purely technological improvements in memory and speed, user interface improvements have probably had an equally large effect on increases in productivity. The interface between the human and the computer has become easier to use and much more efficient. Computer programs of today feature pull-down menus, mouse-driven applications, and graphical input and display capabilities. These changes have resulted in user-friendly systems that aid in the assimilation and understanding of complicated biomechanical models.

11.4. TECHNIQUES FOR INTERPRETATION OF GAIT STUDIES

Despite the growing availability of technology, gait analysis has not yet become a common tool for the physician. Gait laboratories have been started when individuals and institutions were willing to make the investment in time, effort, and money to assemble and operate gait laboratory systems. Gait laboratories have flourished when a combination of physician input and referral was coupled with day-to-day expertise in the form of physical therapists or other health care specialists and with technical expertise in the form of engineers and other technical staff [89]. Several commercial gait systems are on the market. Increasing interest in gait analysis is emerging. Sixty-eight percent of the clinical gait analysis laboratories in the United States have been developed in the last five years [90]. This trend demonstrates that gait laboratories are becoming recognized as an important clinical tool in the assessment of gait abnormalities.

When new gait laboratories are started, they frequently make a sizable investment in equipment. Nevertheless, instrumentation alone cannot make gait analysis clinically relevant. Clinical gait analysis is the correlation and interpretation of the data. Taking care of patients in a gait laboratory requires turning data into information. The problem-solving process requires questioning the patient; performing a physical examination; obtaining kinematic, kinetic, and electromyographic data; and then linking the symptoms (complaints), signs (physical exam), and test results (gait data) to obtain a treatment plan. In this process, it is important to distinguish between functional deficits that contribute to the patient's problem and compensations that the patient adopts in an attempt to walk more normally. The future of gait analysis lies in the ability to process data quickly and identify the functional deficits of a patient. Classification methods are needed to characterize a patient's gait and direct the clinician reading the gait study to the movement abnormalities. The ability to develop computerized classification techniques will make gait analysis accessible to a wider audience with limited experience.

11.4.1. Classification Techniques

One of the main obstacles to automated gait analysis is the difficulty of distinguishing between normal and abnormal movements. A person's gait is classified as abnormal when the person's gait parameters deviate excessively from normal. The clinical application of gait analysis is aimed at identifying these inappropriate deviations. In its simplest form, the problem of classifying gait disorders is a problem of mapping a multivariate temporal pattern to the most likely known disorder. Robust analysis of these data requires consideration of interactions among a large number of highly coupled variables, and the time dependence of these variables. Two approaches have been utilized: statistical techniques and artificial intelligence techniques.

Several statistical techniques have been applied to the analysis of gait data. These include the "boot strap" method [89,91], the linear discriminant method [92–94], principal component analysis [95], and cluster analysis [96]. The bootstrap technique [97] was used to establish boundaries about the mean curve for normal subjects to mark the limits of normal variability [89,91]. These boundaries were designated as prediction regions. This technique was undertaken after initial attempts at setting boundaries for the variability within normal subjects using ensemble averages of one or two standard deviations failed. M. F. Kelly and E. N. Biden [98] compared the results of classification of knee motion by ensemble averaging versus bootstrapping. The motion curves of 39 normal 5-year-old children were classified using both techniques. The ensemble-averaging method utilizing ± 2 standard deviations misclassified 16 of 39 normal subjects as abnormal. In contrast, the bootstrapping method classified all subjects as normal. Bootstrap estimates of the prediction regions are of the form:

$$\hat{F}_h(\Theta) - m\hat{\sigma}_f(\Theta) \leq \tilde{F}_h(\Theta) \leq \hat{F}_h(\Theta) + m\hat{\sigma}_f(\Theta) \qquad (11\text{-}6)$$

where $\hat{F}_h(\Theta)$ = the least squares estimate of the subject's sum of harmonic coefficients
$\hat{\sigma}_f(\Theta)$ = the standard deviation of the harmonics
m = a positive number.

This technique has been applied clinically and has been shown to have a high sensitivity [99].

Methods of discriminant analysis have been shown to be effective in recognizing gait patterns of normal subjects and patients following total knee replacement surgery with a classification error rate of about 2 percent [92]. This technique has also been used to develop knee and hip performance indices with well-demonstrated utility [93,94].

Principal component analysis and cluster analysis techniques have been used as a stepwise pattern-recognition approach to identify patterns of gait deviations. Principal component analysis is used to reduce the enormous quantity of data obtained in a gait study to a parsimonious set of features that describe gait patterns accurately [95]. Principal component analysis results in a reduction in dimensionality of the original set of wave forms. Individual wave forms can be reconstructed using a linear combination of basis vectors modulated by weighting coefficients. Numerical representation using principal component analysis is important for two reasons [95]. First, it is a parsimonious representation of cyclic wave form data. Second, it may be very useful in identifying and classifying homogeneous subgroups within a larger patient population. Cluster analysis is used to place objects into groups or clusters suggested by the data, not defined a priori. Subjects in a given cluster tend to be similar to each other in some sense and subjects in different clusters tend to be dissimilar. These techniques have been used for classifying normal subjects [100], patients with cerebral palsy [101], and patients with anterior cruciate ligament (ACL) deficiency [102].

Methods based on statistical analysis will continue to play a role in processing of gait data. The strengths of statistical methods are that they (1) provide a mathematical foundation for the analysis, (2) accept experimental noise in the measurements, and (3) offer robust time-series analysis. The weaknesses of statistical methods are that they (1) ignore the physical meaning of the measurements and (2) treat each variable in isolation.

An alternative approach to the analysis of gait dynamics is to use artificial intelligence (AI) techniques to diagnose gait disorders. Two categories of AI that have been used successfully are knowledge-based systems and neural networks.

Knowledge-based systems are most commonly referred to as "expert systems" and are characterized by large amounts of domain-specific knowledge and methods that embody the clinician's problem-solving strategy [103–105]. Expert systems organize a knowledge base of facts that can be causally related by a reasoning program. The causal chain of reasoning can be used to explain the logical connection between gait parameters and gait functional deficits. The facts in the knowledge base are arranged in premise-conclusion pairs called *rules*. The rules serve the purpose of causally relating gait parameters and functional deficits. The rules are probabilistic in nature, so inferences made by the program are seldom "all or nothing." The strength of expert systems is that they encapsulate high-level knowledge from "experts," and they model interactions among variables. However, the drawback of expert systems is that they assume abnormal gait has been classified, and they only weakly model time.

A second method of AI is the neural network. Neural network designs are based on the structure of the human brain and try to emulate the way intelligent information processing occurs. The basic structure of a neural network is very simple. It consists of an array of elements usually called *nodes*, interconnections between these nodes, and some input/output scheme (Figure 11-11). The intelligent information properties of the network arise from the formation of the topology of the network, the learning rules of the nodes, and the particular type of nodes. Neural networks, despite their simplification of natural behavior, process information in novel ways. These networks have collective computational properties, such as association, generalization, differentiation, preferential learning, optimization, and fault tolerance. The use of these properties appears to have promise for the development of solutions to problems that have intractable or unknown algorithms and/or are too computationally intense. Neural networks follow an adaptive information-processing method well suited for modeling dynamic processes.

Neural networks are capable of performing pattern-recognition tasks useful in the analysis of gait dynamics [106,107]. The neural network has been shown by our laboratory to be capable of performing difficult temporal pattern processing tasks of gait kinematic data [108]. The specific type of neural network used was a modification of standard back propagation as described by J. L. Elman [109]. The network consisted of 12 input units, 10 hidden units, and 12 output units (Figure 11-11). The network was trained using a set of 25 simulated normal 7-year-old individuals. The simulated individuals were generated from the mean and variance data for the normal population [89]. For each time increment, 12 motion variables, which contained the sagittal, coronal, and transverse plane motions of the pelvis, hip, knee, and ankle, were input to the neural network. The output of the network was the 12-tuple of motion variables at time increment, $t + 1$. In this way, the network was trained to learn the temporal pattern of gait motion. The data set was subdivided into 50 time steps of each variable over a single gait cycle. After training was completed, the neural network was presented with gait patterns for 25 children at each age increment from 1 to 7 years of age. The difference between the new gait pattern (y') and the learned gait pattern (y) was analyzed where the output error was calculated as follows:

$$SS_{Error} = \Sigma_i \Sigma_j (y - y')^2 \tag{11-7}$$

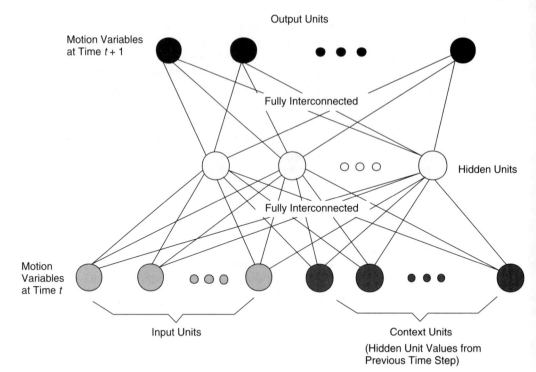

Figure 11-11. Basic structure of a neural network, consisting of elements
called nodes, interconnections between nodes, and an input/output
scheme. This particular network is called a *back propagation
network* and also has a set of hidden nodes. It was used for
temporal-pattern processing of gait kinematic data, which consisted of twelve motion parameters.

where i = number of individual data sets (25) at each age increment
       j = number of gait cycle divisions (50).

This total sum-squared error measures the deviation of each age group from 7-year-
old gait (Figure 11-12). These results provide evidence that gait stabilizes between the
ages of 3.5 and 4.0 years. This characteristic of gait development is supported both by
expert physicians [89] and previous statistical analysis [91]. This example demonstrates
that neural networks are capable of performing pattern-recognition techniques useful in the
analysis of gait dynamics. In the future, neural networks can be used to differentiate normal
and pathological gait. Neural networks can be constructed to recognize kinematic and
kinetic patterns of normal gait. A patient's gait data will be analyzed to yield a total sum-
squared error. If the value exceeds a threshold, the patient's gait will be further analyzed
to pinpoint the areas of gait deviations, based on the difference between the patient's gait
pattern and the learned normal gait pattern. Additional networks can be developed to
differentiate subcategories of gait abnormalities. Once the patient's gait has been identified
as abnormal, it can be analyzed by subsequent neural networks that are trained to recognize
predefined functional gait deficits. Thus it will be possible to identify the gait abnormalities
of a patient.

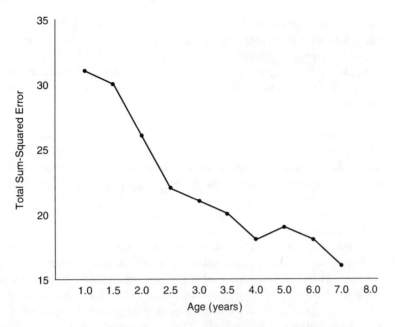

Figure 11-12. Deviations of age group kinematic data from normal seven-year-old gait. Deviations are expressed as a sum-squared error. Differences were determined using a back propagation neural network. Results provide evidence that gait kinematics stabilize between 3.5 and 4.0 years of age.

Similar to the other techniques for classification of gait data, the strengths and weaknesses of neural networks must be recognized. The advantages of neural networks are that they (1) capture the temporal structure of the gait variables, (2) model the interconnection among these variables, and (3) contain nonlinear processing elements. These advantages must be weighed against several disadvantages. First, neural networks require a large amount of data on which to be trained. Aside from normal subjects, this amount of data on select pathologies might not be available. Further, neural networks require extensive training time in order to assure stable operation. Finally, neural networks do not distinguish between signal and noise [110].

Experienced specialists are needed to ensure that techniques used for pathological gait classification are reasonable. Each of the methods (statistical techniques, expert systems, neural networks) offers advantages and disadvantages. The relative merits of each approach have not been fully investigated. In the end, it will be important to draw upon the strengths of all techniques in a productive and mutually supportive relationship in order to maximize the outcome.

11.4.2. Scientific Visualization

Recent developments in computer animation make it possible to apply advanced methods to visualize human movements. A highly dimensional space is needed to fully describe the complexities of human movement. The large volume of variables currently found in a typical clinical report should be replaced with a printout of a few graphic images that succinctly provide the needed information. It is difficult to fully appreciate and understand relationships between motion dynamics and physiologic or biomechanical variables without scientific graphic visualization.

Due to the complexity of gait-derived data, powerful visualization tools are needed. The ability to incorporate scientific visualization will provide unprecedented power to support the clinician's recommendations in a manner that the referring physician can intuitively understand and visualize. The popular scientific visualization techniques are (1) one-dimensional (1-D) plotting, (2) two-dimensional (2-D) plotting, (3) 3-D volume visualization, (4) imaging processing, and (5) animation [111]. Separate software packages are available to perform each of these techniques. However, as the need to solve complex problems becomes more acute, one package is needed that provides all of these capabilities to enhance productivity.

A scientific computing environment is needed that will allow the rapid transmission, archival, retrieval, and manipulation of images within a system equipped with analytical tools useful for clinical and research purposes (Figure 11-13). Tools are needed for data collection, analysis, and visualization. A suitable database of normal gait patterns is needed for comparison. The ultimate goal of this scientific visualization workstation is to provide a user-friendly, menu-driven environment that will facilitate the reporting of biomechanical data and integrate real-time animation of fully three-dimensional realistic graphical depictions of articulated body segments. This system should provide clinicians with the ability to visualize the correlation between collected biomechanical data and the actual human motion. Further, this system should provide the ability to simulate gait and compare the computer-generated simulation with experimentally collected data. The operator should be able to examine the data from any viewing angle, to zoom in or out, change the viewing perspective, or stop the motion. This system should have the ability to superimpose normal gait on a patient's gait in order to visualize differences. The system should also be able to align the bodies displayed to a common center of gravity or to a common point in the gait cycle [112]. It should be capable of "removing" extremities in order to improve visualization of other body segments. The two most important goals are the realistic appearance of the human figure and the convenient specification of the biomechanical data. This application should be user-friendly so that it can be used by colleagues who are not necessarily programmers but have expertise in their respective fields (e.g., medical doctors). The software environment should be capable of quick and easy customization to serve very specific needs.

Another key issue is the communication of the results. The clinician must be able to select only the most essential results for communication to the referring physician and the patient. Otherwise, the individuals will be overwhelmed by the plethora of numbers while comprehending little. Practical display of data will provide an economical and efficient method of communicating information [113]. When graphical portrayal of data is limited by dimensionality (i.e., three dimensions), other variations in the output such as color, sound, and shape can be used to help overcome this limitation. This application of technology should provide a mechanism to integrate all aspects of gait measurements and observations into a single tool for physician interpretation, diagnosis, and treatment recommendations.

11.4.3. Standardization of Gait Analysis Techniques

In the future, standardization of gait analysis techniques must be established so that data can be shared between laboratories for expert consultation. Several national organizations are developing ad hoc committees in an attempt to standardize techniques utilized and

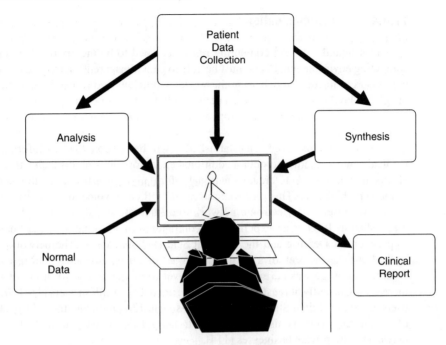

Figure 11-13. Proposed interactive computer graphics workstation for scientific
visualization of gait dynamics. All gait data will be encoded into
a 3-D dynamic graphical display of subject. Both experimental
and simulation data can be displayed and compared to a normal
database. This animated graphical image will facilitate interpretation and will be incorporated into a clinical report.

defined in appropriate studies in various clinical settings. An Ad Hoc Committee on Gait
Analysis has been formed by the American Academy for Cerebral Palsy and Developmental
Medicine. This committee is examining issues relevant to gait. The committee is attempting to address the need for standardization in gait analysis. It is defining requirements for
equipment and staff to perform gait analysis. It is examining definitions of appropriate
studies in various clinical settings, as well as the degree of reporting. It is developing standard nomenclature so that billing charges can be developed to cover services provided by
clinical laboratories.

Similar efforts are under way in Europe. The Computer-Aided Movement Analysis
in a Rehabilitation Context (CAMARC) project is being undertaken under the Advanced
Informatics in Medicine action of the Commission of the European Communities with
academic, industrial, public-health, and independent partners from Italy, France, the United
Kingdom, and the Netherlands. The aims of the project are: (1) assessment of existing
biomedical knowledge on movement analysis, (2) standardization of test protocols, (3)
assessment and implementation of relevant digital signal processing algorithms, (4) analysis
of marketing potential of new instrumentation, and (5) development of design criteria for
new devices. It is the hope of this group to develop standards and the appropriate interface
between the instrumentation and a suitable neuromusculoskeletal model. The combination
of movement data in an appropriate model of human movement is expected to provide
meaningful information for assessment of normal and pathological movement for diagnosis,
treatment planning, pretreatment and posttreatment comparison, and long-term follow-up.

11.4.4. Telecommunication

Distributed data and computing resources need to be incorporated in this scientific computing environment. Users must be able to gain transparent access to data and computing resources located anywhere in the world. Clinicians and researchers scattered around the globe should be connected via a network. Individuals operating computer software environments residing on their desk tops should be able to communicate with leading centers in gait analysis.

Once standards have been established, it will be possible to share information among medical centers in order to obtain additional expert opinions on difficult cases. Currently, efforts are being made to create a national information infrastructure—the so-called electronic superhighway. This electronic network will carry voice, data, and video in digital form. At present, an electronic network, the Internet, already exists. The Internet was established in 1969 as an experimental computer network organized and financed by the Department of Defense and the National Science Foundation. The network was created to facilitate the research of a small number of scientists, engineers, and researchers. No commercial usage was permitted at first. Over time, the number of users of Internet has increased. Currently, it is estimated that there are over 15 million users [114]. Most of these users are in the United States but there are users in 134 other countries [114]. The number of commercial users is also increasing. In early 1993, more than half of the registered networks were private businesses [114].

A nationwide communication system can be used in health care. High-performance computing and networking can be used to speed development of gait interpretation techniques, facilitate diagnoses from remote locations, and achieve enormous improvements in efficiency by aiding multicenter studies on treatment techniques. Major medical centers are obtaining state-of-the-art telecommunication capabilities [115]. Telecommunication includes the transmission of data, audio, and visual information. Telecommunication networks have made people throughout the world accessible within a matter of minutes or hours. It is no longer necessary for collaborators to be near one another. Current telecommunication systems provide two-way video and two-way audio. The image must be high-resolution and obtained in real time so that medical examinations can be performed. This connection will enable the transmission of information over high-bandwidth networks for immediate physician–physician consultation on particular cases. The security of all transmissions must be assured by scrambling the signal to maintain the confidentiality of all patient information. In the years ahead, fiberoptic transmission and high-definition television will be among the advancements that will strengthen the interchange of information. Telecommunication will also enable the sharing of digital data with large bandwidth requirements for research purposes. The ability to share information will facilitate the development of databases that will enable clinicians to obtain knowledge for the treatment of specific gait disorders.

11.5. SUMMARY

The ultimate goal of gait analysis should be to provide reliable, objective data on which to base clinical decisions. A gait analysis laboratory requires an interdisciplinary team of individuals with various educational backgrounds who contribute their skills. These individuals need to understand the underlying principles that are utilized to identify and correct neuromuscular deficiencies. Improvements will be made in the ability to obtain in vivo measurements of muscle function. Advances in computer technology, biomechanical models, gait classification techniques, and telecommunication will shape our future. Computer animation techniques will be used to visualize gait data. It is increasingly important that we consider the effectiveness of what we do and the role it plays in shaping the outcome of medical care. The future of gait analysis will require the ability to identify the critical tests, interpret data more quickly, predict the outcome of various clinical procedures, and quantify the outcome. Regional and national computer networks should be established whereby data can be exchanged to assimilate the knowledge necessary to predict the outcome of various surgical procedures. Techniques must be standardized in order to facilitate the exchange of data. Reforms in health care will require that we be able to manage costs while providing an important diagnostic service.

Acknowledgments

This work was supported in part by a grant from the National Institute of Health R01HD 31476. Appreciation is also expressed to Sherill Marciano, Evelyn Grass, and Shirley Meacham for their assistance with the manuscript.

References

[1] Braune W, Fischer O. *Der Gang des Menschen*. Leipzig: BG Tenbner:1895.

[2] Health Insurance Association of America. *Source book of health insurance data*. Washington, DC;1990.

[3] US Bureau of the Census. Statistical abstract of the United States. 112th ed. Washington, DC;1992.

[4] Gade C. Strategic Planning: Mayo faces changing times with an unchanged focus: The patient. *Mayo Alumni* 1993;29(2):4–13.

[5] Alksne J. Health care market evolution. Presented to the Children's Hospital and Health Center Board of Trustees Meeting. San Diego, Ca; February 17, 1993.

[6] Himmelstein D, Wolfe S, Woolhandler S. Mangled Competition. *Health Letter* 1993;9(5):1–4.

[7] DeLuca PA, Õunpuu S, Rose SA, Sirkin R. Alterations in cerebral palsy surgical decision-making based on three-dimensional gait analysis. *Dev Med Child Neurol* 1993;35(9) suppl 69:9.

[8] Nene AV, Evans GA, Patrick JH. Simultaneous multiple operations for spastic diplegia. *J Bone Joint Surg Br* 1993;75-B(3):488–494.

[9] Davis RB, Õunpuu S, Tyburski D, Gage JR. A gait analysis data collection and reduction technique. *Hum Mov Sci* 1991;10(5):575–587.

[10] Kadaba MP, Ramakrishnan HK, Wootten ME. Measurement of lower extremity kinematics during level walking. *J Orthop Res* 1990;8:383–392.

[11] Apkarian J, Naumann S, Cairns B. A three-dimensional kinematic and dynamic model of the lower limb. *J Biomech* 1989;22(2):143–155.

[12] Cappozzo A, Leo T, Pedotti A. A general computational method for the analysis of human locomotion. *J Biomech* 1975;8:307–320.

[13] Kaufman KR, An KN, Chao EYS. A dynamic mathematical model of the knee joint applied to isokinetic exercise. Spilker RL, Simon BR eds. In: *Computational Methods in Bioengineering*. New York, NY: ASME:Biomechanical Engineering Division 1988:9:157–167.

[14] Chao EYS. Justification of tri-axial goniometer for the measurement of joint rotation. *J Biomech* 1980;13:989–1006.

[15] Grood ES, Suntay WJ. A joint coordinate system for the clinical description of three-dimensional motions: Application to the knee. *J Biomech Eng* 1983;105:136–144.

[16] Kinzel GL, Hall AS, Hillberry BM. Measurement of the total motion between two body segments: Part I—Analytic development. *J Biomech* 1972;5:93–105.

[17] Spoor CW, Veldpaus FE. Rigid-body motion calculated from spatial coordinates of markers. *J Biomech* 1980;13:391–393.

[18] Woltring HJ, Huiskes R, DeLange A, Veldpaus FE. Finite centroid and helical-axis estimation from noisy landmark measurements in the study of human joint kinematics. *J Biomech* 1985;18(5):379–389.

[19] Woltring HJ. Analytical body-segment photogrammetry. In: *Models*, connection with experimental apparatus and relevant DSP techniques for functional movement analysis. Ancona, Italy: Dipartimento di Eletronica ed Automatica, Universita di Ancona, 1990.

[20] Chao EYS. Determination of applied forces in linking systems with known displacements: With special application to biomechanics. Iowa City: University of Iowa, 1971: PhD dissertation.

[21] Robertson DGE, Winter DA. Mechanical energy generation, absorption and transfer amongst segments during walking. *J Biomech* 1980;13:845–854.

[22] Cappozzo A, Berme N. Subject-specific segmental inertia parameter determination—A survey of current methods. In: Berme N and Cappozzo A, eds. *Biomechanics of Human Movement: Applications in Rehabilitation, Sports and Ergonomics*. Worthington, Ohio: Bertec Corp;1990:179–185.

[23] Dempster WT. Space requirements of the seated operator. WADC Technical Report 55-159. Wright-Patterson AFB; Ohio: AERO Medical Laboratory, 1955.

[24] Clauser CE, McConville JT, Young JW. Weight, volume, and center of mass of segments of the human body. *AMRL-TR-69-70* (AD 710 622). Wright-Patterson AFB, Ohio: Aerospace Medical Research Laboratory; 1969.

[25] Chandler RF, Clauser CE, McConville JR, Reynolds HM, Young JW. Investigation of inertial properties of the human body. *DOT HS-801*. Washington, DC: National Highway Traffic Safety Administration; 1975:430.

[26] Drillis RJ, Contini R. Body segment parameters. Technical Report No.1166.03 School of Engineering and Science, New York University, 1966.

[27] McConville JT, Churchill TD, Calepis I, Clauser CE, Cuzzi J. Anthropometric relationships of body and body segment moments of inertia. Technical Report No. AFAMRL-TR-80-119. Wright-Patterson AFB; Ohio: Aerospace Medical Research Laboratory; 1980.

[28] Young JW, Chandler RF, Snow CC, Robinette KM, Zehner GF, Lofber MS. Anthropometric and mass distribution characteristics of the adult female. Technical Report No. FAA-AM-83-16. Oklahoma City, Oklahoma: FAA Civil Aeromedical Institute; 1983.

[29] Yeadon RM, Morlock M. The appropriate use of regression equations for the estimation of segmental inertial parameters. *J Biomech* 1989;22:683–689.

[30] Hanavan EP. A mathematical model for the human body, Report No. AMRL-TR-102. Wright-Patterson AFB; Ohio: Aerospace Medical Research Laboratory; 1964.

[31] Jensen RK. Estimation of the biomechanical properties of three body types using a photometric method. *J Biomech* 1978;11:349–358.

[32] Jensen RK. Body segment mass, radius, and radius of gyration proportions of children. *J Biomech* 1986;19:359–368.

[33] Hatze, HA. A mathematical model for the computational determination of parameter values of anthropometric segments. *J Biomech* 1980;13:833–843.

[34] Sarfaty O, Ladin Z. A video-based system for the estimation of the inertial properties of body segments. *J Biomech* 1993;26(8):1011–1016.

[35] Huang HK, Woo SC. The evaluation of mass densities of the human body in vivo from CT scan. *Comput Biol Med* 1976;6:337–343.

[36] Zatsiorsky VM, Seluyanov VN. The mass and inertial characteristics of the main segments of the human body. In: Matsui H, Cobayashi K, eds. *Biomechanics VIII-B*. Champaign, Ill: Human Kinetics Publishers;1983:1152–1159.

[37] Zatsiorsky VM, Seluyanov VN. Estimation of the mass and inertial characteristics of the human body by means of the best predicted regression equations, In: Winter DA et al eds. *Biomechanics IX-B*. Champaign, Ill: Human Kinetics Publishers; 1985; 233–239.

[38] Martin PE, Mungiole M, Marzke MW, Longhill LM. The use of magnetic resonance imaging for measuring segment inertial properties. *J Biomech* 1989;22:367–376.

[39] Mungiole M, Martin PE. Estimating segment inertial properties: Comparison of magnetic resonance imaging with existing methods. *J Biomech* 1990;23:1039–1046.

[40] Ashley S, Rapid prototyping for artificial body parts. *Mech Eng* 1983;50–53.

[41] McMillan T. 3-D digitizing. *Computer Graphics World* January, 1989.

[42] Chow CK. Jacobson DH. Studies of human locomotion via optimal programming. *Math Biosci* 1971;10:239–306.

[43] Chow CK, Jacobson DH. Further studies of human locomotion: Postural stability and control. *Math Biosc* 1972;15:93–108.

[44] Townsend MA, Seireg A. The synthesis of bipedal locomotion. *J Biomech* 1972;5: 71–83.

[45] Mochon S, McMahon TA. Ballistic walking: An improved model. *Math Biosc* 1980;52:241–260.

[46] Onyshko S, Winter DA. A mathematical model for the dynamics of human locomotion. *J Biomech* 1980;13:361–368.

[47] Hatze HA. Quantitative analysis, synthesis and optimization of human motion. *Hum Mov Sci* 1984;3:5–25.

[48] Marshall RN, Jensen RK. A general Newtonian simulation of an N-segment open chain model. *J Biomech* 1985;18(5):359–367.

[49] Nagurka ML. Theoretical approach for optimal motion generation of a bipedal locomotion model. *Advances in Bioengineering* New York, NY: ASME;1986:115–116.

[50] Pandy MG, Berme N. A numerical method for simulating the dynamics of human walking. *J Biomech* 1988;21:1043–1051.

[51] Yamaguchi GT. Feasibility and conceptual design of functional neuromuscular stimulation systems for the restoration of natural gait to paraplegics based on dynamic musculoskeletal models. Stanford, Ca: Stanford University; 1989: PhD dissertation.

[52] Meglan DA. Enhanced analysis of human locomotion, Columbus, Ohio: Ohio State University; 1991: PhD dissertation.

[53] Zajac FE. Muscle coordination of movement: A perspective. *J Biomech* 1993;26(1): 109–124.

[54] Yamaguchi GT, Pandy MG, Zajac FE. Dynamic musculoskeletal models of human locomotion: Perspectives on model formulation and control. In: Patla A ed. *Adaptability of Human Gait: Implications for the control of locomotion.* Advances in Psychology Series No. 78. Amsterdam: Elsevier Science Publishers;1991:205–240.

[55] Pandy MG, Anderson FC, Hull DG. A parameter optimization approach for the optimal control of large-scale musculoskeletal systems. *J Biomech Eng* 1992;114: 450–460.

[56] Zajac FE. Muscle and tendon: Properties, models, scaling, and application to biomechanics and motor control. In: Bourne JR, ed. *CRC Critical Reviews and Biomedical Engineering* Boca Raton, Fl: CRC Press; 1989;17(4):359–411.

[57] Hoy MG, Zajac FE, Gordon ME. A musculoskeletal model of the human lower extremity: The effect of muscle, tendon, and moment arm on the moment-angle relationship of musculotendon actuators at the hip, knee, and ankle. *J Biomech* 1990;23:157–169.

[58] Kaufman KR, An KN, Chao EYS. Incorporation of muscle architecture into the muscle length-tension relationship. *J Biomech* 1989;22(8/9):943–948.

[59] Lieber RL, Brown CG, Trestik CL. Model of muscle-tendon interaction during frog semitendinosus fixed-end contractions. *J Biomech* 1992;25:421–428.

[60] Trestik CL, Lieber RL. Relationship between achilles tendon mechanical properties and gastrocnemius muscle function. *J Biomech Eng* 1993;115:225–230.

[61] Brand RA, Crowninshield RD, Wittstock CE. A model for lower extremity muscular anatomy. *J Biomech Eng* 1982;104:304–310.

[62] Delp SL, Loan JP, Hoy MG, Zajac FE, Topp EL, Rosen JM. An interactive graphics-based model of the lower extremity to study orthopedic surgical procedures. *IEEE Trans Biomed Eng* 1990;37(8):757–767.

[63] Yamaguchi GT, Zajac FE. A planar model of the knee joint to characterize the knee extensor mechanism. *J Biomech* 1989;22:1–10.

[64] Johnston RC, Brand RA, Crowninshield RD. Reconstruction of the hip: A mathematical approach to determine optimum geometric relationships. *J Bone Joint Surg Am* 1979;61A:639–652.

[65] Dul J, Shiavi R, Green N. Simulation of tendon transfer surgery. *Eng in Med* 1985;14: 31–38.

[66] Lindgren U, Seireg A. Influence of mediolateral deformity, tibial torsion, and foot position on femoral tibial load: Prediction of a musculoskeletal computer model. *Arch Orthop Trauma Surg* 1989;108:22–26.

[67] Mann RW. Computer-aided surgery. Proceedings of the 8th annual conference of RESNA: Memphis, Tenn; 1985:26–35.

[68] Perry J, Waters RL, Perrin T. Electromyographic analysis of equinovarus following stroke. *Clin Orthop* 1978;131:47–53.

[69] Sutherland DH, Cooper L, Daniel D. The role of the ankle plantar flexors in normal walking. *J Bone Joint Surg Am* 1980;62A:354–363.

[70] Waters RL, Frazier J, Garland DE. Electromyographic gait analysis before and after operative treatment for hemiplegic equinus and equinovarus deformity. *J Bone Joint Surg Am* 1982;64A:284–288.

[71] Blix M. Die langrund die spennung des muskels. *Skand Arch Physiol* 1894;5: 149–206.

[72] Cavanagh PR, Komi PU. Electromechanical delay in human skeletal muscle under concentric and eccentric contractions. *Europ J Appl Physiol* 1979;42:159–163.

[73] Long C. *Normal and Abnormal Motor Control in the Upper Extremities* Cleveland, Ohio: Case Western Reserve University, 1970;8. Thesis.

[74] Ralston HJ, Todd FN, Inman VT. Comparison of electrical activity and duration of tension in the human rectus femoris muscle. *Electro Clin Neurophys* 1976;16: 277–286.

[75] Norman RW, Komi PV. Electromechanical delay in skeletal muscle under normal movement conditions. *Acta Physiol Scand* 1979;106:241–248.

[76] Vos EJ, Mullender MG, van Ingen Schenau GJ. Electromechanical delay in the vastus lateralis muscle during dynamic isometric contraction. *Europ J Appl Physiol* 1990;60:467–471.

[77] Hill AV. The pressure developed in muscle during contraction. *J Physiol* 1948; 107:518–526.

[78] Kirkebö A, Wisnes A. Variation in tissue fluid pressure in rat calf muscle during sustained contraction on stretch. *Acta Physiol Scand* 1982;114:551–556.

[79] Sutherland DH, Woo SLY, Schoon J, Jemmott G, Akeson WH. The potential application of a small solid state pressure transducer to measure muscle activity during gait. *Trans Orthop Res Soc* 1977;2:289.

[80] Hargans AR, Sejersted OM, Kardel KR, Bloom P, Harmansen L. Intramuscular fluid pressure: A function of contraction force and tissue depth. *Trans Orthop Res Soc* 1982;7:371.

[81] Mubarak S, Hargans A, Owen C, Garetto L, Akeson W. The Wick catheter technique for measurement of intramuscular pressure. *J Bone Joint Surg Am* 1976;58A: 1011–1019.

[82] Owen CA, Garetto LP, Hargens AR, Schmidt DA, Mubarak SJ, Akeson WH. Relationship of intramuscular pressure to strengthen muscular contraction. *Trans Orthop Res Soc* 1977;2:246.

[83] Parker PA, Körner L, Kadefors R. Estimation of muscle force from intramuscular total pressure. *Med Bio Eng Comp* 1984;22:453–457.

[84] Körner L, Parker P, Almström C, et al. Relationship of intramuscular pressure to the force output and myoelectric signal of skeletal muscle. *J Orthop Res* 1984;2:289–296.

[85] Järvholm U, Palmerud G, Karlsson D, Herbertz P, Kadefors R. Intramuscular pressure and electromyography in four shoulder muscles. *J Orthop Res* 1991;9:609–619.

[86] Garfin SR, Tipton CM, Mubarak SJ, Woo SLY, Hargens AR, Akeson WH. Role of fascia in maintenance of muscle tension and pressure. *J Appl Physiol* 1981;51: 317–320.

[87] Baumann JU, Sutherland DH, Hänggi A. Intramuscular pressure during walking: An experimental study using the Wick catheter technique. *Clin Orthop* 1979;145: 292–299.

[88] Robinson L. *Encyclopedia Americana* 7:473. Danbury, Connecticut: Grolier; 1988.

[89] Sutherland DH, Olshen RA, Biden EN, Wyatt MP. Bax M ed. *The Development of Mature Walking*. London: MacKeith Press; 1988.

[90] Thomas SS. The gait analysis laboratory: An administrative manual for physicians and administrators. Results of master's thesis. 7th Annual East Coast Clinical Gait Laboratory Conference, Richmond, Va, Oct 31–Nov 2, 1991.

[91] Olshen RA, Biden EN, Wyatt MP, Sutherland DH. Gait Analysis and the Boot Strap. *Annal Stat* 1989;17(4):1419–1440.

[92] Donath M. Human gait pattern recognition for evaluation, diagnosis and control. Cambridge, Ma: Massachusetts Institute of Technology; 1978: PhD dissertation.

[93] Laughman RK, Stauffer RN, Ilstrup DM, Chao EYS. Functional evaluation of total knee replacement. *J Orthop Res* 1984;2:307–313.

[94] Kaufman KR, Chao EYS, Callahan TD, Askew LJ, Bleimeyer RR. Development of a functional performance index for quantitative gait analysis. *Biomed Sci Instrumentation* 1987;23:49–55.

[95] Wootten ME, Kadaba MP, Cochran GVB. Dynamic electromyography I: Numerical representation using principal component analysis. *J Orthop Res* 1990;8:247–258.

[96] Kadaba MP, Ramakrishnan HK, Jacobs D, Goode B, Scarborough N. Relationships between patterns of knee and ankle motion in spastic diplegic patients with dynamic ankle equinus. *Trans Orthop Res Soc* 1993;18(2):364.

[97] Efron B. *The Jack Knife, The Bootstrap, and Other Resampling Plans*. Philadelphia, Pa: Society for Industrial and Applied Math; 1982.

[98] Kelly MF, Biden EN. A comparison of two classification methods for gait data. *Trans Orthop Res Soc* 1989;14:241.

[99] Sutherland DH, Kaufman K, Ramm K, Ambrosini D. Clinical use of prediction regions for motion data. *Dev Med Child Neuro* 1992;34(9) suppl. 66:26–27.

[100] Wootten ME, Kadaba MP, Cochran GVB. Dynamic electromyography II: Normal patterns during gait. *J Orthop Res* 1990;8:259–265.

[101] Wong MA, Simon S, Olshen R. Statistical analysis of gait patterns of persons with cerebral palsy. *Stat Meth* 1983;2:345–354.

[102] Shiavi R, Zhang LQ, Limbird T, Edmondstone MA. Pattern analysis of electromyographic linear envelopes exhibited by subjects with uninjured and injured knees during free and fast speed walking. *J Orthop Res* 1992;10:226–236.

[103] Dzierzanowski JM, Bourne JR, Shiavi R, Sandell HSH, Guy D. Gaitspert: An expert system for the evaluation of abnormal human locomotion arising from stroke. *IEEE Trans Biomed Eng* 1985;32(11): 935–942.

[104] Simon SR, Bylander T, Weintraub M, Szolovits P, Hirsch DE. Doctor gait: An expert system for gait analysis. *Trans Orthop Res* 1989;14:245.

[105] Hirsch DE, Simon SR, Bylander T, Weintraub MA, Szolovits P. Using causal reasoning in gait analysis. In: Horne W ed. *Causal AI Models: Steps Toward Applications* New York, NY: Hemisphere Publications;1989:253–272.

[106] Holzreiter SH, Kohle ME. Assessment of gait patterns using neural networks, *J Biomech* 1993;26(6):645–651.

[107] Sepulveda F, Wells DM, Vaughan CL. A neural network representation of electromyography and joint dynamics in human gait. *J Biomech* 1993;26(2):101–109.

[108] Biafore S, Cottrell G, Focht L, Kaufman K, Wyatt M, Sutherland DH. Neural network analysis of gait dynamics. *Trans Orthop Res Soc* 1991;16(1):255.

[109] Elman JL. Finding structure in time. Center for Research in Language, Tech Report No. 8801. San Diego: University of California; 1988.

[110] Sartori DE. Neural networks, statistics and experimental designs. *Sci Comput Auto* 1992;8(11):4–6.

[111] Elgie H. What is Scientific Visualization? *Sci Comput Auto* March, 1993:34–35.

[112] Morris T, Larson G, Donath M. Real Time Animation of Human Walking for the Evaluation of Pathological Gait. *RESNA 9th Annual Conf* 1986;233–235.

[113] Tufte ER. *The Visual Display of Quantitative Information* Cheshire, Conn: Graphics Press; 1983.

[114] Schiller HI. Electronic highway to where? *National Forum* 1994;74(2):19–21.

[115] Parker BK, Telecommunication: When the sky's the limit. *Mayo Magazine* 1990;5(1):18–29.

Part 2

Clinical Applications

Methods and Practice

Chapter 12

David H. Sutherland
Kenton R. Kaufman

Human Motion Analysis and Pediatric Orthopaedics

12.1. INTRODUCTION

Orthopaedic surgeons are deeply involved in the treatment of patients with disorders of the musculoskeletal system. Scientific knowledge of the function of the musculoskeletal system is essential for effective treatment of disorders associated with it. Modern motion analysis has provided the most effective approach to meeting this fundamental need. Three-dimensional (3-D) motion analysis has developed into both a sophisticated research tool and an immense aid in preoperative planning and postoperative assessment. Technical advances in data collection, storage, and output have greatly reduced the time and human labor involved in making the results of clinical studies available for assessment of individual patients.

This chapter illustrates some of ways in which human motion analysis has influenced the field of pediatric orthopaedics. The general areas are in teaching, research, and patient care. The three areas merge in an ideal environment, each adding richness to the other. Teaching of human musculoskeletal function cannot overreach its scientific foundation, which can only be based on research. Unless clinical studies are performed, and the individuals responsible for providing treatment are involved, the questions asked by researchers might not be the most appropriate, thus depriving patients of the potential benefits of research.

12.2. EDUCATION

No individual without a basic knowledge of human gait should be considered adequately prepared for biomechanical engineering, orthopaedic surgery, physical medicine, neurology, developmental pediatrics, physical therapy, orthotics, or prosthetics. Ideally the teaching of human motion analysis should begin early in the professional schools, and continue throughout postgraduate training. In actuality, most orthopaedic surgeons are not chal- lenged to learn functional assessment of the musculoskeletal system until their residency rotation in pediatric orthopaedics. Then they learn manual muscle testing and observational gait analysis. If they are fortunate, they are exposed to the scientific analysis of gait. De- pending on the residents' interests and the training environment, progress will be slow or rapid. For training programs where motion analysis laboratories are not yet available, the methodology and biomechanical principles of motion analysis can still be mastered. Pow- erful teaching aids are being developed to stimulate the learning process. A good example of an effective teaching format is the videotape and interactive video disc on the subject of normal human walking, prepared by James Gage and his colleagues at Gillette Children's Hospital.* Similar efforts have been undertaken on the subject of pathological gait by Kit Vaughan[†] and Shelley Simon.[‡] The possibilities for teaching tools of this type are virtually unlimited. The advent of 3-D computer graphic programs opens opportunities to visually present biomechanical analyses. High-quality science and high-quality graphics must be blended to drive home biomechanical principles and to depict individual functional deficits. Good work is going on, but only the surface has been scratched.

12.3. RESEARCH

12.3.1. Growth and Development

Human motion analysis has added to the body of knowledge in the field of human growth and development. Several examples of insights gained from an NIH–supported study of the development of normal walking, carried out in our Motion Analysis Laboratory, will illustrate this point [1].

The average 1-year-old child demonstrates an absent or poorly developed initial heel- strike. A graph of the mean ankle dorsi-plantarflexion curve of forty-nine 1-year-old subjects shows only slight movement into plantarflexion after foot-strike [Figure 12-1(a)]. On the same curve the ankle remains in slight plantarflexion even at the time of maximum lift in swing phase. The mean curve of 39 normal 1.5-year-old subjects shows much greater plantarflexion following foot-strike, indicating greater initial heel contact [Figure 12-1(b)]. There is also increased dorsiflexion in swing phase.

The muscle phasic activity of the tibialis anterior in 1-year-old and 1.5-year-old sub- jects shows an immature pattern as compared with the other age groups through age 7 years (Figure 12-2). The onset of the electromyographic (EMG) action potentials is delayed in swing phase and their activity is prolonged in stance phase. These changes are attributed

*James Gage. Normal Walking. An Overview Based on Gait Analysis. Gillette Children's Hospital, 1992.
[†]Kit Vaughan. *Interactive Computer-based Program.* Univ. of Virginia Health Sciences Center, 1992.
[‡]Sheldon Simon. *Gait Analysis Interactive Learning Computer-based Program.* The Ohio State University. In press.

to neurologic immaturity caused by incomplete myelination and incomplete development of interneuronal connections.

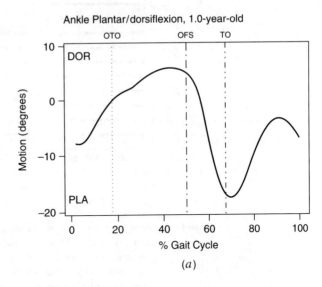

(a)

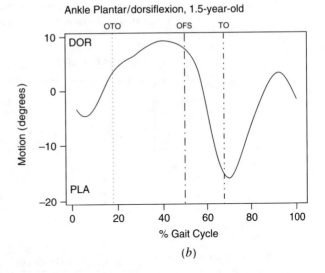

Figure 12-1. Mean ankle plantar/dorsiflexion curves of (a) 49 normal 1-year-old children and (b) 39 normal 1.5-year-old children. OTO represents opposite toe-off, OFS represents opposite foot-strike, TO represents toe-off. Reproduced with permission, Sutherland et al.: *The Development of Mature Walking*, MacKeith Press, 1988.

(b)

The percent of single stance is an indication of single limb weight bearing stability. The values are shown for each age group on the vertical axis, and the age in years and the numbers for each age group on the horizontal axis (Figure 12-3). Note that the greatest increases occur between ages 1 and 3.5 years.

Children in the youngest age groups walk with a wide base of support. That means that the distance between the ankles, measured in the coronal plane during double limb support, is nearly as wide as the span of the pelvis (Figure 12-4). The ratio of pelvic-span to ankle-spread becomes progressively greater until about 4 years of age.

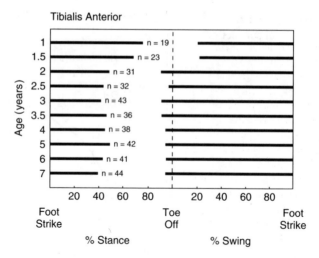

Figure 12-2. Mean times of onset and cessation of EMG activity in the tibialis anterior in each of 10 age groups. On and off times are expressed as percentages of stance and swing phases. All measurements were made using surface electrodes. Number of subjects in each age group is noted following point of cessation of stance-phase activity. Reproduced with permission, Sutherland et al.: *The Development of Mature Walking*, MacKeith Press, 1988.

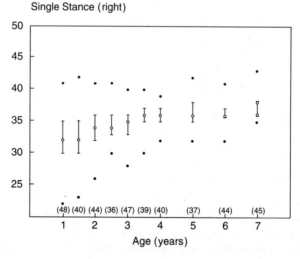

Figure 12-3. Duration of single-limb stance as percentage of gait cycle for the right side. Number of subjects along with age groups are listed on the horizontal axis. Percentage of gait cycle is shown on the vertical axis; vertical bar encompasses the middle 50% of subjects; box indicates median. Upper/lower markers show greatest/least values recorded. Reproduced with permission, Sutherland et al.: *The Development of Mature Walking*, MacKeith Press, 1988.

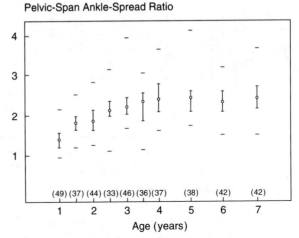

Figure 12-4. Pelvic-span/ankle-spread ratio in each of 10 age groups between 1 and 7 years of age. Square indicates the median value; vertical bar encompasses the middle 50% of subjects; upper/lower marks indicate greatest/least values recorded. (Reproduced with permission, Sutherland et al.: *The Development of Mature Walking*, MacKeith Press, 1988)

These facts and many others resulting from the study are helpful in differentiating normal from pathologic gait for children between 1 and 7 years of age.

12.3.2. Kinesiology

The application of gait analysis techniques to examine concepts of muscle function have been productive [2–8]. For example, an experimental study was carried out in our laboratory to determine the contribution of the plantarflexor muscle to gait [8]. Gait studies were done before and after nerve block of the tibial nerve. Paralysis of the plantarflexor muscles brought about an increase in ankle dorsiflexion and knee flexion during single-limb stance, a reduction in walking velocity, a reduction in single-stance percentage, a reduction in opposite step length, a decrease in the second peak of the vertical force curve, and a reduction in aft shear. While controversy exists about the accelerative function of the ankle plantarflexors during second double support (preswing), our study points to an accelerative function of the plantarflexor muscles limited to late single-limb stance (between 40 percent and 50 percent of the gait cycle). Electromyography revealed that the ankle plantarflexor muscles are inactive during preswing; thus, the plantarflexion that occurs during this period of rapid unloading of the limb is passive. It was concluded from this study that the gait deficit associated with paralysis of the plantarflexors is very great.

The alteration in vertical force can be seen in the mean vertical force curves of five normal subjects before and after nerve block of the tibial nerve. Note the reduction in the second peak and the reduction in single-stance percentage following tibial nerve block (Figure 12-5).

The information gained from the experimental study has been helpful in understanding the pathological gait in patients with lower lumbar and sacral level spinal defects.

12.3.3. Orthotics

It is common practice in a clinical gait assessment to evaluate the effectiveness of orthoses. The patients are studied with and without the orthosis and the gait parameters are compared. The result is that we sometimes find that an orthosis is unnecessary, or unsuited

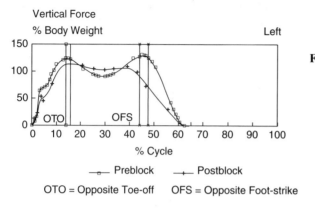

Figure 12-5. Mean vertical force curves of five normal subjects before and after paralysis block of tibial nerve by lidocaine block. (Adapted with permission, Sutherland et al.: "The role of the ankle plantarflexors in normal walking," *J Bone Joint Surg Am*, 1980;62A:354–363)

for the child because of inappropriate orthotic design. In other instances, improvements in gait accompany the wearing of the orthosis, thus validating the efficacy of the appliance.

We are currently conducting an NIH–sponsored study to develop an electronically controlled free knee brace [9]. Oxygen consumption measurements, carried out on a treadmill in the cardiology laboratory, show lower oxygen consumption for a normal subject walking on treadmill with the free knee brace functioning than with it locked (Figure 12-6).

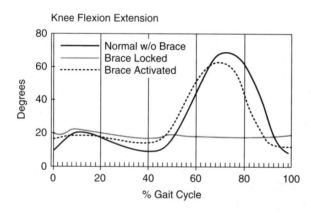

(*a*)

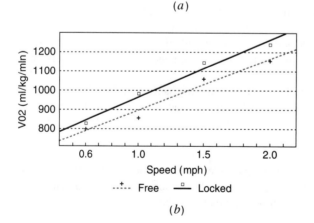

(*b*)

Figure 12-6. (*a*) Knee flexion/extension curve of one normal subject wearing an experimental free knee brace. With brace not activated, knee is locked; with solenoid automatically releasing braking mechanism, motion is very similar to knee motion without brace. (*b*) Oxygen consumption while treadmill walking with brace locked and with brace functioning to permit swing phase knee flexion.

We anticipate that patients requiring a locked knee brace for stance phase stability will expend less energy when they are provided with a brace that automatically unlocks for swing phase.

12.3.4. Prosthetics

A study of swing phase control with knee friction in juvenile amputees revealed that the excursion of the prosthetic shank was altered by changing the amount of knee friction, but the period of the shank remained the same. Consequently more symmetrical gait was achieved by alteration of the amount of friction, but matching of cadence was not achieved [10].

12.3.5. Genu Varum

A different kind of clinical problem is presented by children who are bowlegged. The pediatric orthopaedic surgeon must try to distinguish between those children who have physiologic genu varum, a relatively normal condition that will self-correct, and those children with Blount's disease. Those children in the latter category will worsen with time and require bracing or osteotomy to avoid catastrophic knee problems [5]. Prolonged severe pressure on the medial portion of the proximal tibial growth plate can produce growth arrest of the medial portion of the growth plate. We are conducting a study in our laboratory to measure the extrinsic adduction moment at the knee joint. The goal of this study is to better distinguish between the two conditions. The hypothesis is that if the external adduction moment is mild, there is a likelihood of self-correction, and further observation is appropriate. On the other hand, if the external adduction moment is excessive, early intervention by bracing or by surgery is indicated.

The adduction moments for a 2-year-old child with bilateral genu varum appear to be excessive, suggesting that this child is at risk for progressive deformity (see Figure 12-7 on page 226). This idea will remain a hypothesis until standards for adduction moments for children are determined. Adduction moments of more than 3.3 are considered excessive in adults [11]. There are as yet no published studies of adduction moments of children.

12.4. PATIENT CARE

It is in the area of pediatric patient care that the contributions from motion analysis are most visible. Cerebral palsy surgery prior to gait analysis was a guessing game pitting the experience of the surgeon against the complexities of a disorder of the motor control system, complicated further by muscle contractures and abnormal skeletal alignment. Without benefit of the knowledge of abnormalities of muscle function, floor reaction forces, and three-dimensional movements, the surgeon and the patient were frequently disappointed in the outcome of surgery. There has been substantial improvement with the advent of clinical gait analysis. To its everlasting credit, the American Academy for Cerebral Palsy and Developmental Medicine was the first national organization to embrace the concept of clinical gait analysis and to encourage those who were struggling to develop better and more rapid methods of measurement. It was also the first to apply the results in the care of individual patients. Instructional courses in gait analysis became a regular part of each

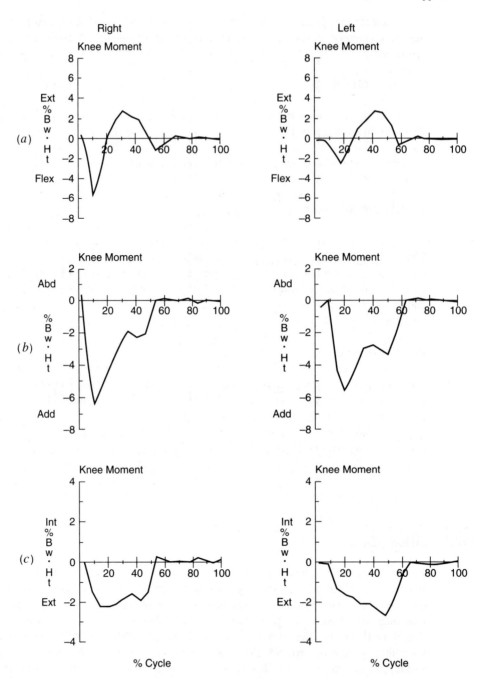

Figure 12-7. Three-dimensional external knee moments of a 2-year-old child
with excessive genu varum. Three sets of bilateral graphs represent
(*a*) flexion/extension, (*b*) adduction/abduction, and (*c*) rotation.

annual meeting of this organization in the decade of the 1970s, and these courses, from their inception to the present time, have been consistently well attended. Papers presented in this organization and in other national and international meetings are now frequently based on functional analysis.

Has all of this effort and cost made a difference in the care of individual patients? For one who has lived through the changes in care the answer is a resounding yes. Others will demand proof. Some examples of changes in treatment that have their origin in gait analysis can be given.

12.4.1. Rectus Femoris Spasticity in Cerebral Palsy

Rectus spasticity has been identified as the most frequent cause of stiff-knee gait in cerebral palsy. The functional problem that this creates is difficulty in clearing the foot in swing phase. Compensatory mechanisms, such as ipsilateral circumduction at the hip and contralateral vaulting, are required to clear the swinging foot. Gait analysis has helped identify the problem and in addition has been used to compare the result of surgical treatment [6,12–15]. The effects of proximal release, distal release, and distal transfer have been compared. Distal transfer of the rectus femoris has prevailed as the most effective surgical procedure. While distal release, proximal release, and distal transfer of the rectus femoris can all improve the dynamic range of knee flexion-extension in selected patients with cerebral palsy, only distal transfer can improve the timing of peak flexion in swing phase (see Figure 12-8 on page 228).

12.4.2. One-Stage Surgical Treatment in Cerebral Palsy

The usual strategy in the surgical treatment of patients with cerebral palsy prior to motion analysis was to perform isolated procedures at frequent intervals, thus subjecting the patients to multiple hospital admissions and time lost from schooling. The current strategy is now quite different. Following gait analysis, an operative plan is prepared that addresses all of the problems at each joint level, and the surgery is performed at one time [16].

12.5. ROLE OF CLINICAL GAIT ANALYSIS IN A MANAGED CARE ENVIRONMENT

All diagnostic methods and treatment protocols will be under scrutiny in the intense medical economic readjustments underway in the United States. All gait laboratories providing clinical gait analysis have an obligation to undertake outcome assessments and to be prepared to provide this information to health maintenance organizations. That is not a simple task, but failure to do this can result in denial of funding. The cost of one extra day in the hospital is approximately equivalent to the cost of a gait analysis. Furthermore, the wrong operation can result in no improvement or even a worsening of the patient's condition with the need for additional surgery. However, this type of a justification for the cost of gait analysis will not be sufficient to convince those who control the purse strings. We must provide objective evidence of the value of gait analysis by showing outcome measures

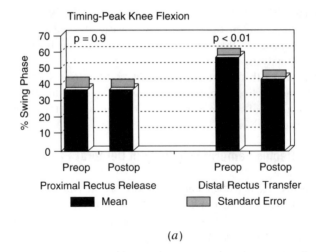

(a)

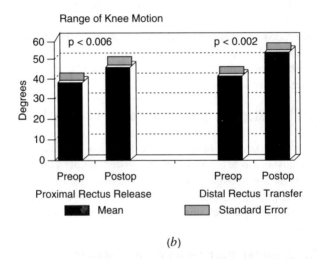

(b)

Figure 12-8. (a) Timing of peak knee flexion unchanged by proximal rectus
release but improved by distal rectus transfer. (b) Range of dynamic knee motion before and after rectus surgery in two groups
of patients. First group had undergone proximal release of rectus;
second group had been treated by distal rectus transfer [6].

following treatment that has been guided by gait analysis. What outcome measures are
appropriate for this task? The specific measurements that can be used in a modern gait
laboratory to address this question are: oxygen consumption and oxygen cost, walking
velocity, heart rate, dynamic joint angles, joint moments, and joint powers [17–19]. These
measurements give objective information about changes in the pattern and efficiency of
walking. When supplemented by the subjective response of the patient regarding satisfaction
with the outcome of treatment, the gait data provide powerful information regarding the
efficacy of treatment.

12.6. CONCLUSIONS

The field of pediatric orthopaedics has been positively influenced by motion analysis in a variety of ways. The teaching of biomechanical principles has been strengthened. The planning of care for patients with disorders of movement can now be based on scientific analysis. Many improvements in patient care have occurred. Patients with cerebral palsy, myelodysplasia, limb deficiencies, and congenital deformities are particularly appropriate for clinical gait studies. Thus far, patients with cerebral palsy have been the greatest beneficiaries of motion analysis. Undoubtedly this patient mix will widen as investigators apply their skills to the problems of patients with other diseases. How well this discipline fares in the present economic recession will depend upon the efficiency of the motion analysis laboratories, their ability to accurately define functional gait deficits and their causes, and their success in completing credible outcome studies that identify effective treatment regimens. Motion analysis will not disappear from the medical scene because it is uniquely capable of providing objective answers about pathological motion.

Acknowledgments

We wish to acknowledge the National Institutes of Health Grants 5R01 HD08520, HD 15801, and 5R01 HD 30150. We also wish to thank Sherill Marciano and Evelyn Grass for their assistance with the manuscript.

References

[1] Sutherland DH, Olshen RA, Biden EN, Wyatt MP. *The Development of Mature Walking.* Oxford: MacKeith Press;1988.

[2] Gage JR. *Gait Analysis in Cerebral Palsy.* Oxford: MacKeith Press;1991.

[3] Õunpuu S, Gage JR, Davis RB. Three dimensional lower extremity joint kinetics in normal pediatric gait. *J Ped Orthop* 1991;11(3):341–349.

[4] Perry J. *Gait analysis: Normal and Pathological Function.* Thorofare NJ: Slack Inc; 1992.

[5] Sutherland DH. *Gait Disorders in Childhood and Adolescence.* Baltimore, Md: Williams & Wilkins Publishing Co;1984.

[6] Sutherland DH, Santi MD, Abel MF. Treatment of stiff-knee gait in cerebral palsy: A comparison by gait analysis of distal rectus femoris transfer versus proximal rectus release. *J Ped Orthop* 1990;10:433–441.

[7] Sutherland DH, Kaufman KR. Motion analysis: Lower extremity. In: Nickel VL, Botte MJ, eds. *Orthopaedic Rehabilitation* 2nd ed: New York, NY: Churchill Livingstone; 1992:223–242.

[8] Sutherland DH, Cooper L, Daniel D. The role of the ankle plantar flexors in normal walking. *J Bone Joint Surg Am* 1980;62A:354–363.

[9] Malcolm LL, Sutherland DH, Cooper L, Wyatt M. A digital logic-controlled electromechanical orthosis for free knee gait in muscular dystrophic children. *Orthop Trans* 1981;5:90.

[10] Hicks R, Tashman S, Cary JM, Altman RF, Gage JR. Swing phase control with knee friction in juvenile amputees. *J Orthop Res* 1985;3(2):198–201.

[11] Prodromos, CC, Andriacchi TP, Galante JO. A relationship between gait and clinical changes following high tibial osteotomy. *J Bone Joint Surg Am* 1985;67A(8): 1188–1194.

[12] Gage JR, Perry J, Hicks RR, Koop S, Werntz JR. Rectus femoris transfer to improve knee function of children with cerebral palsy. *Dev Med Child Neurol* 1987;29: 159–166.

[13] Õunpuu S, Mink E, Davis RB III, Gage JR, DeLuca PA. Rectus femoris surgery in children with cerebral palsy, Part II: A comparison between the effect of transfer and release of the distal rectus femoris in knee motion. *J Ped Orthop* 1993;13(3):331–335.

[14] Perry J. Distal rectus femoris transfer. *Dev Med Child Neurol* 1987;29:153–158.

[15] Sutherland DH, Larsen LJ, Mann R. Rectus femoris release in selected patients with cerebral palsy: A preliminary report. *Dev Med Child Neurol* 1975;17:26–34.

[16] Nene AV, Evans GA, Patrick JH. Simultaneous multiple operations for spastic diplegia. Outcome and functional assessment of walking in 18 patients. *J Bone Joint Surg Br* 1993;75B(3):488–494.

[17] Rose J, Gamble JG, Medeiros J, Burgos A, Haskell WL. Energy cost of walking in normal children and in those with cerebral palsy: Comparison of heart rate and oxygen uptake. *J Ped Orthop* 1989;9:276–279.

[18] Sutherland DH. Outcome assessment in cerebral palsy: Has walking improved? In: Sussman M, ed. *The Diplegic Child: Evaluation and Management.* Rosemont, Ill:Am Acad Orthop Surg 1992:133–144.

[19] Waters RL, Hislop HJ, Campbell LT. Energy cost of walking in normal children and teenagers. *Dev Med Child Neurol* 1983;25:184–188.

Tom F. Novacheck

Chapter 13

Surgical Intervention in Ambulatory Cerebral Palsy

13.1. INTRODUCTION

The history of the treatment of cerebral palsy is a long and sometimes dubious one. Of course, consideration of the entire topic would require the pages of an entire book. Ambulatory dysfunction alone will be considered in this chapter. This chapter will focus on its surgical treatment. Upper extremity issues, spine deformity, or hip subluxation/dislocation will not be considered.

In the past surgeons have made decisions based on visual observation of gait and static physical examination of bone deformity and joint contracture [1,2]. Prior to gait analysis, treatment was aimed at the most obvious abnormality which often unmasked other more subtle problems because the balance between the multiple joints was upset. This led to multiple interventions over time (M. Rang's "birthday syndrome") [3]. The advent of gait analysis has altered this approach.

Gait analysis offers many benefits. Ultimately, normal gait is better understood. We have gained a significant qualitative and quantitative body of knowledge about normal gait. This provides the basis for the understanding and treatment of pathological gait. Reference to the original descriptions of this material is recommended for the reader unfamiliar with the basics of normal gait [4–7]. The author will review a few of the key points here.

Recognized prerequisites of normal gait [4] include:

1. Stability in stance
2. Sufficient clearance in swing
3. Appropriate prepositioning of the foot in terminal swing for initial contact
4. Adequate step length
5. Conservation of energy

In cerebral palsy gait, some or all of these normal attributes are lost. Gait analysis is then able to identify which of these prerequisites has been lost and to provide the information that the skilled interpreter uses to understand why.

In addition, with gait analysis one is able to:

1. Identify multiple abnormalities (bone and soft tissue) simultaneously
2. Identify them at multiple levels
3. Identify them in all three anatomical planes
4. Differentiate between primary gait deviations and coping responses
5. Safely perform multiple-level/multiple-plane intervention simultaneously

One must have an adequate understanding of the pathophysiology of cerebral palsy in order to treat the ambulatory problems caused by it. The primary lesion is in the central control system (the brain) and occurs due to an injury to the immature brain. The location of the lesion and etiology of the injury determines which abnormalities occur. The primary lesion produces peripheral manifestations. Some of these are:

1. Loss of selective motor control
2. Dependence on primitive reflex patterns for ambulation
3. Abnormal muscle tone
4. Relative imbalance between muscle agonists and antagonists
5. Deficient equilibrium reactions

These peripheral neurological findings reflect the central injury. For example, injuries to the pyramidal system cause spasticity while athetosis and rigidity are due to extrapyramidal system damage. Injuries to both systems lead to mixed tone patterns.

The impact of each of these abnormalities on any given patient's ambulatory function is as individual as the site and degree of the causative central nervous system (CNS) lesion. Sophisticated gait analysis can assist in the differentiation of the importance of each of these in the individual's gait pattern.

The primary CNS lesion is static. The secondary changes in the periphery (musculoskeletal system) due to that lesion are cumulative over time with growth and development. Some of the secondary changes include contracture, bone deformity, and joint subluxation/dislocation.

Pathological gait is typically characterized by primary anomalies and secondary coping responses or compensations [4,8]. Some of the prerequisites for normal gait (listed earlier) can be lost in cerebral palsy. In an effort to maintain maximum function and energy efficiency, compensations are made. The clinician must be able to distinguish between these, since treating the primary problem will eliminate the need for the secondary compensation. It will, therefore, disappear. Treating the secondary compensation would worsen the gait pattern. For example, a drop foot in swing will lead to inadequate swing phase clearance (one of the essential attributes of normal gait). The patient might employ any number of compensations such as vaulting on the contralateral side or circumduction, hip hike, or exaggerated hip and knee flexion on the ipsilateral side. If the surgeon fails to recognize these appropriate coping responses and inappropriate surgical correction is done, then the patient's function will worsen. On the other hand, if the drop foot is appropriately treated with an ankle-foot orthosis (AFO) or tendon transfer, the compensations will disappear as they are no longer necessary.

Because gait deviations can be complex three-dimensional (3-D) dynamic problems, preoperative evaluation must be detailed, specific, and complete. If one dissects the complex problem into its component parts, one can assess the problem accurately. The components of a complete preoperative evaluation of an individual with ambulatory problems due to cerebral palsy are listed in Table 13-1. It should be obvious that the evaluation is incomplete without assessment in each of the four listed areas. Therefore, assessment is not complete without the use of sophisticated gait analysis, and gait analysis alone does not constitute a complete assessment. This reflects the evaluation methodology used at Gillette Children's Hospital.

TABLE 13-1   COMPLETE PREOPERATIVE EVALUATION

1. Detailed history
   a. Birth
   b. Developmental
   c. Ambulatory function
2. Physical exam
   a. Bone deformity
   b. Joint contracture
   c. Tone pattern
   d. Selective control
   e. Muscle strength
3. Gait analysis
   a. Video
   b. Kinematics
   c. Kinetics
   d. Electromyography (EMG)
   e. Energy assessment
4. X-ray
   a. Spine
      Scoliosis
      Kyphosis/lordosis
   b. Pelvis
      Pelvic obliquity
      Hip subluxation/dislocation
      Acetabular dysplasia
      Coxa valga
   c. Feet (standing)
      Hindfoot varus/valgus
      Talonavicular subluxation ("midfoot break")
      Hallux valgus

As a result of this analysis, one will gain the most knowledge of the patient's disease process and the impact that it has on his or her function. One must consider the patient's level of daily function, balance, coordination, bone deformities, joint contractures, abnormal muscle tone, persistence of primitive gait patterns, selective motor control, muscle strength, and mental ability. Each of these areas must be considered individually and as part of the entire picture for that patient. The result of this evaluation frequently leads to a single stage, multiple level surgical treatment simultaneously correcting bone and soft tissue problems.

The remainder of the chapter will discuss separately each of these areas. First, a rather brief discussion of several neurological issues (balance, reliance on primitive patterns, and mental ability) will be given. The identification and treatment of musculoskeletal manifestations will constitute the majority of the remainder of the chapter.

13.2. NEUROLOGICAL ISSUES

13.2.1. Balance

One can gain insight into an individual's balance using gait analysis techniques. Some patients widen their base of support to compensate for imbalance. The width of the patient's base of support can be measured. Some employ a crouch gait pattern to compensate for instability while others lock their knees in hyperextension. In the former case, the ground reaction force (GRF) falls behind the knee joint center, requiring a muscle-generated knee extension moment to maintain an upright posture. In the latter case, the GRF falls anterior to the knee joint axis, allowing the posterior capsular structures to provide stability at that joint. Some will compensate for instability by using the arms for counterbalance. The comparison of data collected over multiple strides will reveal the degree of variability from one stride to the next. Significant variability suggests poor balance and/or poor control. The combination of injury to the central control areas for balance and the presence of musculoskeletal deformities that cause stance phase instability can lead to greater impairment.

13.2.2. Reliance on Primitive Patterns

Delayed onset of walking is common in cerebral palsy, and as a result, maturation of the gait pattern will be prolonged. Children might employ primitive gait patterns to compensate for their lack of selective motor control. Recognition of these patterns will avoid ineffective and sometimes detrimental treatment. These patterns are usually recognized as *mass flexion-mass extension*. To advance the trailing limb, the hip, knee, and ankle joints are flexed simultaneously while the stance phase limb is in an extension posture to maintain stability. The subject does not have selective control over any one of these joint movements. It is generally optimal to delay surgical intervention to allow further maturation of the central nervous system as gait will become less primitive. Unfortunately, if the central nervous system damage is too severe, selective motor control might never develop. While surgical treatment can be helpful in this situation, ultimate gains might be less than in those less impaired.

13.2.3. Mental Ability

The consideration of mental ability is crucial in the decision-making process. As with most surgical interventions, postoperative rehabilitation significantly affects the outcome. The surgical decision-making process is therefore altered dependent on this assessment. In general, a less aggressive surgical approach will be recommended if mental ability is thought to impair cooperation with the rehabilitation program. However, impaired mentation does not preclude surgical intervention.

13.3. IDENTIFICATION AND TREATMENT OF SPECIFIC MUSCULOSKELETAL DEVIATIONS

Table 13-2 lists the common abnormalities seen in ambulatory cerebral palsy. This is not an all-inclusive list of deviations. Only the most common are included. Each of these individual problems will be addressed separately. For each, the abnormality, its method of identification, indications for treatment, and current acceptable management will be discussed. This evaluation and treatment methodology is the one currently employed at Gillette Children's Hospital.

TABLE 13-2 COMMON DEVIATIONS IN AMBULATORY CEREBRAL PALSY

Bone deformities	Spastic/contracted muscles	Joint subluxations	Joint contractures
Increased femoral anteversion	Psoas	Hip	Hip flexion/adduction
External tibial torsion	Hamstrings	Talonavicular— abduction/supination	Knee flexion
Pes valgus or varus	Rectus femoris Gastrocnemius Posterior tibialis	Hallux valgus	Ankle equinus

13.3.1. Bone Deformity

Bone deformity is almost universally present. Unfortunately, it is often not adequately recognized, and its impact on gait dysfunction is frequently not appreciated. The importance of bone deformity lies in the creation of *lever arm disease* [4]. According to this concept, a muscle's ability to create a moment at a joint is diminished if the bone is deformed. For example, Figure 13-1 illustrates the effect of external foot rotation on the GRF. With a normal foot progression angle, the lever arm for the ankle plantarflexors is longer than if there is a significant external foot progression angle due to either pes planovalgus or external tibial torsion. If an external foot-progression angle exists because of an external tibial torsion, the plantarflexion moment produced by the gastrocsoleus is diminished because the length of the moment arm is diminished in the sagittal plane. Correction of this bone deformity has been shown to improve plantarflexion moment generation [9]. An example of the improvement in plantarflexor power generation is seen in Figure 13-2. When tibial derotational osteotomy to correct lever arm disease and external foot progression angle was performed, ankle plantarflexor power generation was normalized.

Femoral Anteversion. Excessive femoral anteversion is common and is frequently between 50 and 65 degrees. Multiple measurement methods have been described, but most often an estimate of anteversion by examination for maximum trochanteric prominence

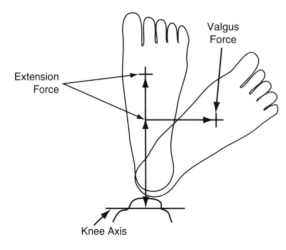

Figure 13-1. The plantarflexion/knee extension (PF/KE) couple. (Reprinted with permission of the author)

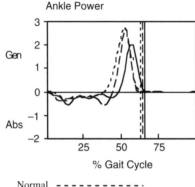

Figure 13-2. The effect of correction of external tibial torsion on ankle plantarflexor power generation.

is sufficient, and, in skilled hands, is accurate and repeatable [10,11]. The examination is performed on a patient in the prone position. The maximum trochanteric prominence is palpated while the hip is rotated through a full range of motion. When the trochanter is most prominent, the femoral neck is horizontal. In that position, the angle between the tibial shaft and a vertical line equals the femoral anteversion angle. The total arc of motion is also recorded and provides some insight into the degree of anteversion. Generally, anteversion is 10 to 20 degrees less than maximum internal rotation.

The other methods of assessment are radiographic and include the use of Magilligan X-rays [12] and computerized tomography (CT) scans [13]. These are generally not necessary, given the accuracy of the physical examination determination. Fluoroscopy can also be used to document the degree of anteversion either before surgery or as a final check at the time of surgery if there is any uncertainty about its severity. Under fluoroscopic guidance, in the prone position, the hip is internally rotated until the proximal femur is seen in its greatest profile. In that position (just as in the palpation for greatest trochanteric prominence), the femoral neck is horizontal. Once again, the angle between the shaft of the tibia and a vertical line represents the femoral anteversion.

The gait deviations that occur include increased hip internal rotation with a resultant internal foot progression angle. Coronal plane lever arm disease (abductor moment arm out of plane) occurs. Figure 13-3 illustrates this concept. In this example, anteversion is 60 degrees (45 degrees more than normal). If the foot progression angle is 10 degrees internal, then the femur is being held in 25 degrees more external rotation than normal, since the normal foot progression angle is 10 degrees external (if no other rotational deformities exist at other levels). This maldirection causes a functional shortening of the abductor moment arm by a factor of 0.9 (cosine of 25 degrees) because the greater trochanter (the insertion site of the hip abductors) is more posterior than normal and is out of the coronal plane.

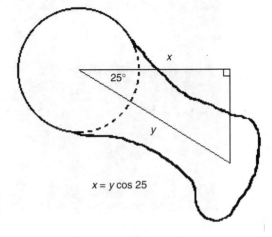

Figure 13-3. Coronal plane lever arm disease due to excessive femoral anteversion.

Correction is indicated if external rotation is insufficient to maintain a normal foot progression angle, the hip is subluxated, or the anteversion is greater than 40 to 45 degrees. Correction can be performed at the intertrochanteric or supracondylar levels.

For the intertrochanteric correction, the patient is usually positioned prone and AO blade plate fixation is used [14]. The site of the osteotomy is above the level of the lesser trochanter. By rotating the lesser trochanter more anterior, the psoas is loosened. (This might, in fact, obviate the need for surgical lengthening of the psoas.) The femur is derotated to 15 degrees anteversion while carefully maintaining 20 to 25 degrees internal rotation. Varus can be incorporated if necessary to improve coverage if subluxation is present. One must minimize excessive elevation of the greater trochanter with varusization to avoid abductor weakness. A spica cast is advisable if the quality of fixation is poor or if the infant-sized plate is used. Using short leg casts with a Denis-Browne bar to control rotation has been helpful in avoiding external rotation positioning in the immediate postoperative period, to improve comfort, and to augment rotational fixation at the osteotomy site. Prone positioning during surgery allows ease of estimation of the anteversion and the amount of derotation. A Steinmann pin parallel to the femoral neck in the transverse plane serves as a guide to the orientation of the proximal femur. The tibial shaft depicts the position of the distal femoral segment. Representative radiographs of intertrochanteric derotational femoral osteotomy are seen in Figure 13-4(*a*) through (*c*). Figure 13-4(*a*) shows a preoperative neutral anteroposterior (AP) radiograph of the hip. The distinction between femoral anteversion and coxa valga cannot be made on the basis of this X-ray. Lateral uncovering of the femoral head and mild subluxation (broken Shenton's line) are noted. Postoperative AP and lateral radiographs show the osteotomy and implant position following femoral varus derotational osteotomy. Lateral uncovering and subluxation are improved.

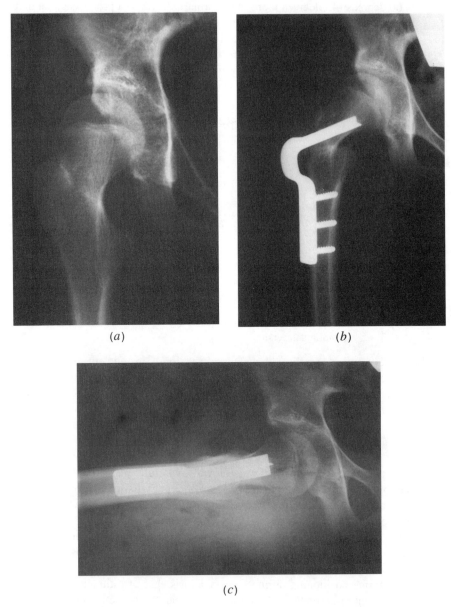

(a)   (b)

(c)

Figure 13-4. Femoral osteotomy technique in cerebral palsy.

Supracondylar correction is performed in the supine position and is occasionally used in the younger child (less than 6 years of age). K-wires are placed at a convergent angle equal to the desired degree of correction. Derotation is performed until the pins are parallel. Fixation is achieved with crossed, threaded Steinmann pins supplemented with a long leg cast.

External Tibial Torsion. External tibial torsion develops later than femoral anteversion. It is a result of an abnormal external rotation torque on the distal tibial physis. This is often due to the combination of poor clearance with resultant toe dragging and femoral anteversion. The consequence is an external foot progression angle. The plantarflexor moment arm is decreased leading to a decrease in the plantarflexion/knee extension (PF/KE) couple (second rocker) and push-off (third rocker) [9]. Figure 13-5(*a*) and (*b*) illustrates these kinematic abnormalities.

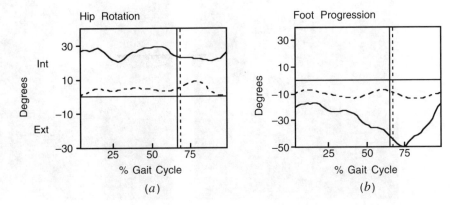

Figure 13-5. Transverse plane kinematic abnormalities due to combined excessive femoral anteversion and external tibial torsion. Normal motion is represented by dashed line; (*a*) pathological excessive internal hip rotation (due to increased femoral anteversion) and (*b*) external foot progression (secondary to tibial deformity) are depicted by solid lines.

Supramalleolar osteotomy of the tibia (with crossed Steinmann pins if less than 10 to 12 years of age or an AO T-plate if older) will correct the deformity. A fibular osteotomy might not be necessary and can be judged intraoperatively by the ability to achieve an adequate correction without dividing the fibula. A short leg cast is used in all patients. To prevent recurrence, one must correct the etiologic mechanism by performing a femoral derotation, hamstring lengthening, and rectus transfer if indicated. Postoperative AP and lateral radiographs in Figure 13-6(*a*) and (*b*) respectively, show osteotomies of the distal tibia and fibula in the early phases of healing. Internal fixation with an AO T-plate is also shown.

Correction is indicated if the malrotation causes instability in stance or if the plantarflexor moment is inadequate to prevent crouch gait. If the foot is malrotated, crouch can result and might be progressive as the soleus can no longer generate an adequate plantarflexor moment to control the forward movement of the tibia over the stationary foot. Figure 13-2 depicts the adverse effects of tibial malrotation on sagittal plane kinetics and the improvements that can be seen with correction of malrotation.

Pes Valgus. Pes valgus is almost always associated with midfoot break (subluxation of the talonavicular joint). The resultant gait deviations include external foot progression angle, inadequate lever arm for the ankle plantarflexors, and an unstable base of support. This deformity is not well detected in the gait lab kinematically unless a more sensitive

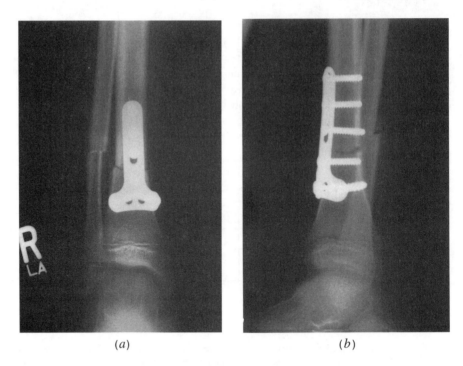

(a)   (b)

Figure 13-6. Supramalleolar tibial derotational osteotomy technique.

ankle/foot model is employed than that currently in use at Gillette Children's Hospital. Errors of excessive dorsiflexion in the sagittal plane ankle kinematic and external rotation of the foot in the transverse plane will be recorded. These errors are due to the inability of the current system to distinguish between ankle movement and abnormal, excessive talonavicular joint motion. Other labs might be able to assess this more completely by developing a more sophisticated foot and ankle assessment model [15]. Misinterpretation will be avoided by combining review of the videotape, X-rays, and the physical examination with the kinematic plots.

The deformity is caused by rotational abnormalities above (causing abnormal weight-bearing position), gastrocsoleus contracture, and/or peroneal spasticity. One can control this deformity with an AFO if the patient is young and the foot supple. Calcaneal lengthening or subtalar arthrodesis can be employed in the older child. By lengthening the lateral column, calcaneal lengthening seems to improve the forefoot abduction more completely and avoids the loss of subtalar motion created by fusion.

Subtalar arthrodesis is performed using the Princess Margaret Rose (W. G. Dennyson and R. Fulford) technique using an AO cannulated screw and iliac crest bone graft [16]. Postoperative management includes a short leg non–weight-bearing cast for three weeks. This is removed and X-rays are obtained to ensure appropriate position. Weight-bearing as tolerated for three weeks in a new short leg cast is then allowed. An AFO is then employed during the postoperative rehabilitation period.

Calcaneal lengthening [17], recently repopularized for use in cerebral palsy foot deformity by V. S. Mosca [18], is performed through a lateral oblique incision over the calcaneus. A Z-lengthening of the peroneus brevis and division of the lateral fibers of the plantar fascia

relieve soft tissue constraints to allow the lengthening achieved with the opening wedge osteotomy. The calcaneus is exposed subperiosteally just anterior to the middle talocalcaneal
facet. This includes elevation of the peroneal tendon sheath. A transverse osteotomy is performed with opening laterally greater than medially (a lamina spreader is helpful) leaving
the medial cortex intact to act as a hinge. A tricortical iliac graft is placed at the dorsal corti-
cal margin. Postoperative immobilization is similar to that used for the subtalar arthrodesis.
Representative radiographs are depicted in Figure 13-7(a) through (d).

The indications for correction are similar to those for tibial derotational osteotomy
since the pes planovalgus deformity with midfoot break causes lever arm disease with similar adverse effects on gait kinetics. In addition, one must correct causative factors to prevent
recurrence. This includes derotations above as indicated, gastrocnemius lengthening, peroneus brevis lengthening, and a rectus transfer if clearance is poor.

Pes Varus. While the pes planovalgus deformity with midfoot break is common
in diplegia and quadriplegia, the more frequent foot deformity in hemiplegia is that of pes
varus. This deformity can cause instability in stance due to excessive lateral weight bearing.
Overactivity of the posterior tibialis is generally the cause.

Correction can be obtained by soft tissue balancing alone in the younger patient,
potentially including posterior tibialis intramuscular lengthening (H. M. Frost) [19] and
plantar fascia release. Split posterior tibial tendon transfer (SPOTT) is another option [20].
In the older patient with fixed bone deformity, Dwyer lateral closing wedge osteotomy of
the calcaneus can be combined with the soft tissue rebalancing procedures to correct fixed
hindfoot varus [21].

Hallux Valgus. The etiologic mechanisms responsible for this deformity are similar
to those for external tibial torsion and pes valgus. These must be corrected. Soft tissue
procedures to correct the hallux valgus deformity have had high failure rates in young
patients with cerebral palsy [22]. McKeever first metatarsalphalangeal (MTP) fusion [23]
reliably corrects the deformity and prevents recurrence. After the deformity is corrected, a
single AO cannulated screw from the plantar surface of the proximal phalanx into the distal
metatarsal maintains the alignment until fusion occurs. Representative radiographs of this
correction are depicted in Figure 13-8(a) through (c).

13.3.2. Musculotendinous

As mentioned previously the primary CNS lesion is static. The secondary changes
in the musculoskeletal system due to increased tone are cumulative over time with growth
and development. Shortening (contracture) of the musculotendinous unit develops due to
an inadequate rate of growth in the muscle [24]. In the following sections, discussion will
center on both increased muscle tone and contracture for each of the musculotendinous
units in the lower extremities commonly affected by cerebral palsy.

Tonal Abnormalities. Spasticity is defined as ". . . a motor disorder characterized
by a velocity-dependent increase in tonic stretch reflexes (muscle tone) with exaggerated
tendon jerks, resulting from hyperexcitability of the stretch reflex" [25]. It is due to an
injury to the pyramidal tract. Other types of tonal abnormalities and movement disorders in

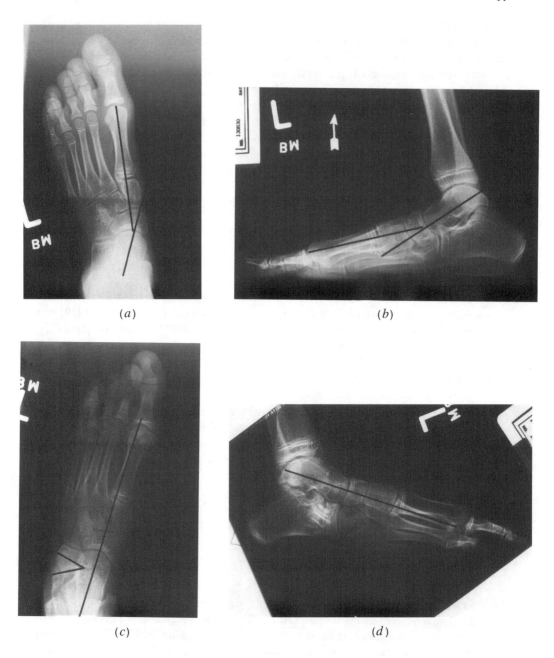

(a)

(b)

(c)

(d)

Figure 13-7. Calcaneal lengthening. (a) and (b) are preoperative standing AP and lateral radiographs of foot. Talar line and first metatarsal line are depicted. Talonavicular joint dorsal and lateral subluxation (midfoot break) is evident in abnormally increased divergence of these lines. (c) and (d) show postoperative AP and lateral radiographs following calcaneal lengthening osteotomy. V-shaped bone graft is outlined. Talar and first metatarsal relationship is normalized postoperatively.

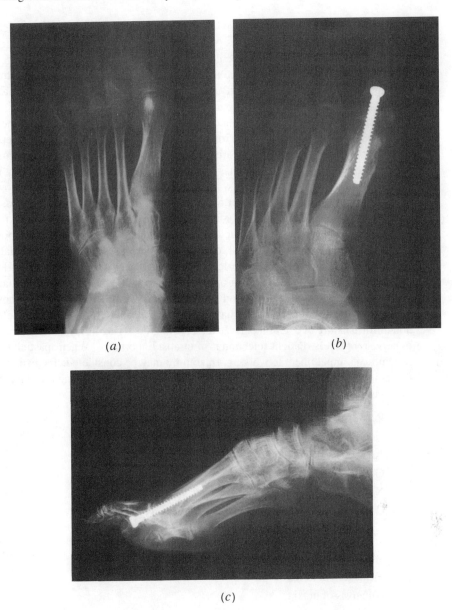

Figure 13-8. Hallux valgus: (*a*) depicts hallux valgus (bunion) deformity preoperatively; (*b*) and (*c*) are postoperative AP and lateral radiographs,
respectively. Correction of deformity and internal fixation are apparent.

cerebral palsy include rigidity, dystonia, athetosis, and ataxia. Rigidity is characterized by
constant increased tone throughout the range of motion and unlike spasticity, is independent
of the muscle spindles in the spinal reflex arc. It is due to an injury to the extrapyramidal system. Dystonia is characterized by fluctuating tone. Generally no contractures or
increased reflexes are seen. Athetosis is another type of extrapyramidal injury resulting
in purposeless/involuntary random movements. Current management strategies for these

tonal abnormalities are rapidly evolving. Treatment options include pharmaceuticals, orthotics, ambulatory assistive devices (walkers or crutches), intrathecal baclofen, botulinum
toxin injections, rhizotomy, or musculotendinous lengthening/transfers.

There is no current experience in the use of intrathecal baclofen in the treatment of
ambulatory problems due to rigidity. It is currently in use and under evaluation in the
management of severe rigidity in nonambulatory patients [26].

Botulinum toxin is being studied to determine its utility in the management of spasticity in the younger child [27]. It irreversibly binds to the acetylcholine receptors at the
neuromuscular junction. It temporarily diminishes spasticity until new receptors are generated. Because of dose limitations, it is currently used to manage spasticity in isolated
muscle groups (e.g., gastrocnemius, adductors, or hamstrings). Advantages over the use
of phenol or alcohol blocks are that the injection of botulinum toxin is painless, produces
no soft-tissue scarring, and diffusion throughout the muscle belly is rapid, eliminating the
need for injection precisely at the neuromuscular junction. Its effects are temporary.

Rhizotomy, on the other hand, permanently decreases tone. In appropriate patients,
rhizotomy can play an important role in the management of spasticity [28]. Hesitancy in
accepting rhizotomy as a treatment option is due to numerous concerns. Perhaps greatest
of these is that it is a destructive and irreversible procedure. Excessive weakness has also
been noted. Poor clinical results have been generally due to poor patient selection, the
nonuniform nature of cerebral palsy, excessive degree of rhizotomy, and incorrect selection
of nerve root levels. Patient selection is of utmost importance. When spasticity is felt to be
a significant impediment to walking, rhizotomy may be considered. Its distinct advantage
is that it provides a permanent reduction in spasticity. The following are characteristics of
the ideal patient:

1. Pure spasticity
2. Good trunk control
3. Antigravity strength and control
4. Good selective motor control
5. No fixed contractures
6. Good motivation, intelligence, and availability of therapy

Contraindications to rhizotomy include:

1. Weakness of antigravity muscles
2. Truncal hypotonia
3. Athetosis or ataxia
4. Hypertonicity due to rigidity rather than spasticity
5. Severe fixed contractures
6. Fixed spinal deformity

The rhizotomy must include all involved neurological levels (L1 to S1). Beginning
the division of rootlets at L2 or lower creates muscle imbalance at the hip with uncorrected
hip flexor and adductor spasticity [29]. Dynamic overactivity of these muscle groups per-
sists and might promote hip subluxation or dislocation. Bowel and bladder problems can
be avoided by preserving the S2, S3, and S4 nerve roots. Generally, division of no more
than 35 to 40 percent of the rootlets will avoid excessive weakness and adequately diminish

spasticity [30]. Correction of orthopaedic deformities (anteversion, midfoot break) is often necessary. The timing of these procedures remains debatable. In our experience, simultaneous orthopaedic and neurosurgical procedures hinders the rehabilitation from each. Heterotopic bone formation at the femoral osteotomy sites has occurred when these procedures have been performed during the same hospitalization. Staggering the two interventions seems to be more appropriate.

Rhizotomy leads to improved range of motion [31]. The arc of functional knee range of motion during walking is increased. Hip extension in terminal stance is also improved. Overall walking velocity and step-length are increased [31,32]. In addition, metabolic energy expenditure with walking is decreased to a greater extent than following orthopaedic surgery [33].

Psoas Contracture/Spasticity. Crouch gait (simultaneous increased hip, knee, and ankle flexion) and increased lumbar lordosis are the characteristic visible gait abnormalities when the psoas is contracted and/or spastic. Physical exam might reveal a hip flexion contracture (Thomas test) or hip flexor spasticity. Anterior pelvic tilt, "double bump" pelvis pattern, and decreased hip extension in terminal stance are commonly seen kinematic abnormalities [Figures 13-9 and 13-13(*a*)] that can be related to psoas overactivity. Kinetics reveal hip extensor moment dominance pattern and a delayed crossover point of the hip flexion-extension moment (Figure 13-10). If fine-wire electromyography (EMG) is done, spasticity is revealed (Figure 13-11).

The psoas is an essential power generator in normal walking; therefore, release is not advocated [34]. The author's preferred method of treatment is psoas lengthening over

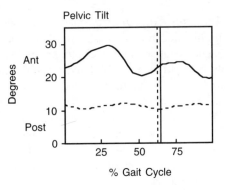

Figure 13-9. Comparison of normal pelvic tilt (dashed line) and anterior pelvic tilt with "double-bump" pattern (solid line); these changes have been related to psoas overactivity.

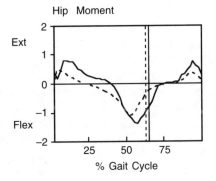

Figure 13-10. Comparison of normal hip moment (dashed line) and hip extensor moment dominance pattern (solid line). Hip extensor moment is increased in magnitude and prolonged in duration compared to normal; zero crossover point is delayed.

Psoas Fine-Wire EMG

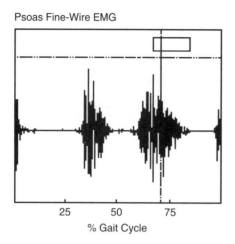

25   50   75

% Gait Cycle

Figure 13-11. Dynamic fine wire electromyographic (EMG)
pattern of psoas overac-
tivity. Toe-off line at approximately 70% of gait
cycle divides stance phase
(left) and swing phase
(right). Normal duration
of psoas activity depicted
by open bar near toe-off
line. EMG reveals nor-
mal appropriate activity at
toe-off and spastic burst of
activity as hip is extending
in midstance.

the brim of the pelvis. An oblique incision medial to the anterior superior iliac spine is
made (beware of the lateral femoral cutaneous nerve). The plane of deep dissection is
extraperiosteal on the inner table of the ilium and is *always lateral to the iliacus* (the muscle
protects the femoral neurovascular bundle). The psoas tendon is palpated intramuscularly
at the superior pubic ramus, and isolated with a right angle clamp. After tenotomizing the
tendon, one palpates for the adequacy of lengthening of the fascial structures. The muscle
fibers of the iliacus remain intact.

Adductor Contracture/Spasticity. Scissoring is the characteristic gait deviation
when the hip adductors are spastic or contracted. Physical exam might reveal the presence of
an adduction contracture or adductor spasticity. Kinematics might reveal pelvic obliquity
with the affected side elevated and a shift of the hip ad/abduction curve into adduction
(Figure 13-12). It should be noted that the combination of crouch gait and excessive
femoral anteversion can produce scissoring without adductor overactivity.

Treatment generally consists of an adductor longus tenotomy alone in ambulators,
followed by an appropriate postoperative positioning/stretching program. A transverse or
longitudinal groin incision can be used. The tendinous origin of the adductor longus is
bluntly isolated and transected near its origin on the pubis, allowing it to recess. Reattachment is not necessary.

Hamstring Contracture/Spasticity. Hamstring contracture or overactivity can
be another component of crouch gait. Physical examination reveals an increased popliteal
angle and decreased range of straight leg raising. Kinematics are characterized by excessive
knee flexion at initial contact, midstance, and terminal stance (Figure 13-13). A posterior
pelvic tilt and limited hip flexion in terminal swing might be present in severe cases. All of
these contribute to a shortened step length. Kinetics show constant knee extensor moment
in stance due to crouch, as in Figure 13-14(*a*). This moment is generated by quadriceps
activity. The moment is named by the net internal muscle moment. Since the GRF falls
inappropriately posterior to the knee joint center in crouch gait, a constant knee extensor
moment is necessary to maintain an upright position. The quadriceps should be inactive
during midstance. Figure 13-14(*b*) shows constant quadriceps activity in crouch gait.

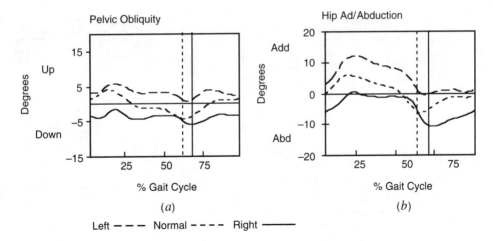

Figure 13-12. (*a*) Pelvic obliquity and (*b*) hip ad/abduction kinematics: effect of left hip adductor overactivity.

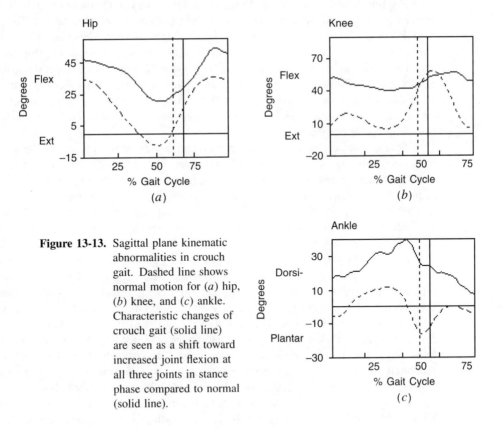

Figure 13-13. Sagittal plane kinematic abnormalities in crouch gait. Dashed line shows normal motion for (*a*) hip, (*b*) knee, and (*c*) ankle. Characteristic changes of crouch gait (solid line) are seen as a shift toward increased joint flexion at all three joints in stance phase compared to normal (solid line).

Treatment can include serial or dropout casting in the very young child if the standard program of stretching is unable to maintain adequate length of the musculotendinous unit. The stretching program can be supplemented by botulinum toxin injection.

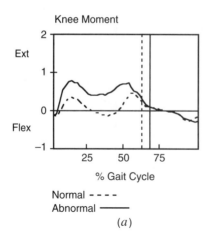
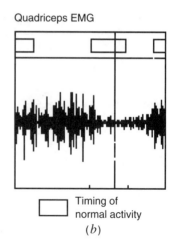

Figure 13-14. The consequence of crouch gait. (*a*) kinetics, (*b*) EMG.

Fractional medial hamstring lengthening is necessary in the older child to treat progressive musculotendinous contracture. Prone positioning in surgery is easiest. The goal is a 30-degree popliteal angle after lengthening. This generally requires medial lengthening only. Intramuscular lengthening of the gracilis and semimembranosis is performed. The semitendinosis can be lengthened intramuscularly or by Z-lengthening. Lateral lengthening is generally required only in more mature individuals with fixed knee flexion contracture, in which case postoperative dropout casting is often necessary to stretch posterior capsular tightness. In severe cases, posterior knee capsular release or distal femoral extension osteotomy might be required.

Semitendinosis transfer to the distal femur might be useful in preserving the important role of the hamstrings as hip extensors when both medial and lateral hamstring lengthening is necessary. This has not been proved, and disagreement exists regarding the role of this procedure. As originally described by G. W. N. Eggers [35], multiple hamstring tendons were divided from their insertions on the proximal tibia and transferred to the femoral condyles. Recently, transfer of the semitendinosus alone has been advocated. Experience with this procedure at Newington Children's Hospital has shown that the semitendinosus transfer might excessively shorten the step length by tethering the femur and decreasing hip flexion (unpublished). If the transfer is performed with excessive tension on the musculotendinous unit, and the length of the tendon is excessively shortened, its springlike properties are lost. Preserving tendon length and avoiding excessive tension might correct this limitation.

Recent research has directed attention away from hamstring shortening as the etiology for crouch gait for some patients. S. A. Hoffinger et al. [36] have found that in fact the hamstrings in the majority of their cases were longer than resting length! This work suggests that hip flexion deformity and anterior pelvic tilt displace the hamstring origin proximally, causing a secondary knee flexion deformity. J. R. Gage has dubbed this phenomenon "hamstring shift" [37]. If this is true, then more attention should be paid to correcting hip flexion deformity and anterior pelvic tilt than to lengthening hamstring tendons.

Rectus Femoris Contracture/Spasticity.   The classic "stiff knee gait" and positive Duncan-Ely are found during physical examination. Dynamic EMG reveals inappropriate swing phase rectus activity. Decreased swing phase knee flexion, delayed peak knee flexion, and/or diminished rate of progressive knee flexion [38] might be apparent kinematically (Figure 13-15). Kinetics might reveal an increased knee extensor moment and increased power absorption during preswing. The result is insufficient swing phase clearance leading to other compensations.

Figure 13-15. Diminished swing phase knee flex-ion due to rectus femoris spasticity. Maximum knee flexion normally oc-curs in the first third of swing phase and is approximately 60°. Patho-logical changes in this patient (solid line) compared to normal (dashed line) include decreased maximum knee flexion in swing and abnor-mal increased knee flexion in stance (crouch).

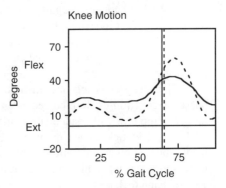

Distal rectus femoris transfer is the most popular treatment for this problem [39]. It can be transferred to the sartorius or the gracilis with equivalent results [40]. This author prefers the suture repair to the tendinous structure of the gracilis, as it is more satisfying.

Rectus femoris transfer can be simplified by exposure of the gracilis and creation of a medial intramuscular septum defect during hamstring lengthening. The intramuscular por-tion of the gracilis tendon is isolated two centimeters above the distal end of the muscle belly and is stripped out of the muscle dividing the tendon longitudinally down to its insertion. Two halves remain. One consists primarily of the contracted tendon. The other is the intact musculotendinous unit which is less contracted. If hamstring lengthening is not performed concurrently, preparation of the gracilis can be done from the anterior rectus femoris expo-sure. The contracted half is ultimately used for the transfer and is divided proximally once the rectus has been isolated. To do this, the interval between the rectus and the vasti is identi-fied proximally and developed. Next, an extension of the rectus tendon from within the con-fluence of the quadriceps tendon is dissected. The rectus tendon is divided near its insertion on the patella. A nonresorbable suture is placed in its substance. Further dissection is then completed proximally to allow the muscle to course in a straight line once it has been trans-ferred medially. Dissection is continued medially around the vastus medialis to the medial intramuscular septum, and a longitudinal defect is created in it (if not already done during hamstring lengthening). The contracted gracilis tendon is palpated and the knee is flexed to deliver the tendon into the wound. At that point, the gracilis is divided proximally and the transfer is completed using a side-to-side suture technique. Appropriate transfer length allows full knee extension but with tension on the repair when the knee is fully extended.

The rectus has now been changed from a hip flexor/knee extensor to a hip flexor/knee flexor. Inappropriate swing phase rectus activity will augment rather than hinder knee flexion. Some authors have advocated rectus femoris release rather than transfer. D. H. Sutherland et al. [38] have shown greater improvement with transfer. Release should not be done if knee range of motion is less than 80 percent of normal [41]. It should also be noted that hamstring lengthening without rectus femoris transfer results in skewing of the knee flexion/extension curve toward extension [39].

Equinus Contracture/Spasticity. Gastrocnemius overactivity or contracture can cause poor clearance in swing, inappropriate positioning for initial contact, and/or instability in stance. The soleus is very sensitive to lengthening [42] and usually is not contracted or spastic. Tendoachilles lengthening (TAL) is rarely necessary or indicated. TAL can produce excessive length and weakness of the gastrocsoleus musculotendinous unit postoperatively. TAL alone to treat toe walking frequently leads to crouch gait [43].

Visually, characteristic gait patterns include toe walking, early heel rise (limited second rocker), drop foot in swing phase, and/or footflat initial contact (absent first rocker) or on the toe (absent second rocker). It is important to note that toe walking might be the result of limited knee extension at initial contact and not a function of overactivity of the ankle plantarflexors.

Gait analysis is the best method to make this distinction. Kinematics in stance phase reveal equinus, limited second rocker, and/or abnormal PF/KE couple. In swing phase, a drop foot with inadequate swing phase clearance can result [Figures 13-16(*a*) and 13-17(*a*)]. Kinetic changes might include abnormal early plantarflexor moment generation, inappropriate power generation in midstance, diminished power generation at push-off, or increased knee flexor moment (abnormal PF/KE couple) [Figures 13-16(*b*) and (*c*) and 13-17(*b*) and (*c*)].

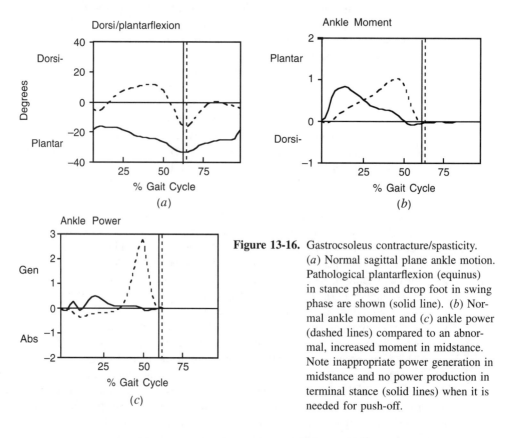

Figure 13-16. Gastrocsoleus contracture/spasticity. (*a*) Normal sagittal plane ankle motion. Pathological plantarflexion (equinus) in stance phase and drop foot in swing phase are shown (solid line). (*b*) Normal ankle moment and (*c*) ankle power (dashed lines) compared to an abnormal, increased moment in midstance. Note inappropriate power generation in midstance and no power production in terminal stance (solid lines) when it is needed for push-off.

Treatment options include the use of an ankle-foot orthosis. Serial casting can be useful if the child is less than 4 to 5 years of age. Botulinum toxin injections can augment the serial casting program. One must beware that a midfoot break is not created. Gastroc-

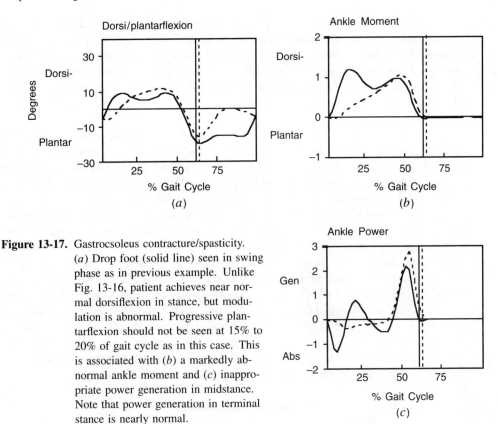

Figure 13-17. Gastrocsoleus contracture/spasticity. (a) Drop foot (solid line) seen in swing phase as in previous example. Unlike Fig. 13-16, patient achieves near normal dorsiflexion in stance, but modulation is abnormal. Progressive plantarflexion should not be seen at 15% to 20% of gait cycle as in this case. This is associated with (b) a markedly abnormal ankle moment and (c) inappropriate power generation in midstance. Note that power generation in terminal stance is nearly normal.

nemius lengthening (L. D. Baker [44] or L. Strayer [45]) is used in the older child. The Strayer technique is the one most commonly performed at Gillette Children's Hospital. It employs a posterior longitudinal midcalf incision at the musculotendinous junction of the gastrocnemius (isolate and protect the lesser saphenous vein and sural nerve). The fascial interval between the gastroc and soleus is developed just distal to the musculotendinous junction of the gastroc. The gastroc fascia is divided, leaving the soleus fascia intact underneath. The gastrocnemius tendon is allowed to retract about 2 cm and is sutured to the underlying soleus fascia using nonabsorbable suture. Gastrocnemius recession has been shown to improve ankle modulation while preserving the power-generating capabilities at the ankle [46].

13.4. SUMMARY

The above discussion is meant to portray the surgical decision-making process and surgical techniques that are currently in use at the author's institution (Gillette Children's Hospital). There is no "cookbook" correct answer for the many surgical decisions that are made. It is tempting to create a table with a listing of specific indications for each surgical procedure that, if followed, would lead to an optimal result. Unfortunately, the treatment of gait deviations due to cerebral palsy is not that straightforward.

Hopefully this chapter provides some insight into the numerous dilemmas in the management of the ambulatory cerebral palsy patient. Certainly it should be apparent that abnormalities at multiple levels must be evaluated and treated simultaneously to avoid the creation of other problems and the need for numerous treatments over the years of a child's life. As one can see, the decisions are based heavily on the results of dynamic gait analysis. This tool enables multiple simultaneous surgical procedures because abnormalities can be identified simultaneously at multiple levels.

Using this tool to evaluate the results of treatment is an ongoing process. In addition, gait-modeling techniques are rapidly gaining clinical application. Questions have been and will be answered about actual musculotendinous lengths during gait and the effects of surgery on their force-generating capability [37]. Similar techniques will provide essential information to improve decision making in order to maximize outcomes.

In the 1990s, outcomes analysis will demand more stringent evaluation of the individual's level of function in the community. This will require assessment of the pretreatment condition as well as the posttreatment outcome. The use of a functional assessment tool will be essential. At Gillette Children's Hospital, a functional mobility tool has been developed and is currently being implemented and tested for validity. Correlation between a functional assessment tool and an analysis of energy consumption will provide new insight into the importance of individual gait deviations and their costs in terms of energy expenditure and loss of function. The impact of surgical solutions on these increased costs will be assessed in an attempt to maximize outcomes. It is through the combination of gait analysis techniques, functional outcomes assessment, and gait modeling that further advances will be made in the treatment of ambulatory cerebral palsy.

Acknowledgments

The author would like to acknowledge Mary Trost and Joyce Phelps Trost, RPT, for their assistance with the preparation of this manuscript.

References

[1] Bleck EE. Orthopaedic Management in Cerebral Palsy. Stanford, Ca: MacKeith Press; 1987.

[2] Samilson RL. Current concepts of surgical management of deformities of the lower extremities in cerebral palsy. *Clin Orthop* 1981;158:99–107.

[3] Rang M. Cerebral Palsy. *Pediatric Orthopaedics* 3rd ed, vol 1. Philadelphia, Pa: J. B. Lippincott; 465–506.

[4] Gage JR. *Gait Analysis In Cerebral Palsy*. New York, NY: MacKeith Press, 1991.

[5] Perry J. *Gait Analysis: Normal and Pathological Function*. Thorofare, NJ: Slack Inc; 1992.

[6] Sutherland DH, Biden EN, Wyatt HP. The development of mature walking. *Clinics in Developmental Medicine, Nos 104/105* London: MacKeith Press with Philadelphia, Pa: Blackwell Scientific; 1988.

[7] Õunpuu S, Gage JR, Davis RB. Three-dimensional lower extremity joint kinetics in normal pediatric gait. *J Ped Orthop* 1991;11:341–349.

[8] DeLuca PA. Gait analysis in the treatment of the ambulatory child with cerebral palsy. *Clin Orthop* 1991;264:65–75.

[9] Õunpuu S, DeLuca PA, Davis RB, Gage JR. The application of joint kinetics in clinical gait analysis. *ICL American Academy of Cerebral Palsy and Developmental Medicine (AACPDM) Annual Meeting*, Nashville, Tenn; October, 1993.

[10] Rogers SP. A method for determining the angle of torsion of the neck of the femur. *J Bone Joint Surg Am* 1931;12:821–824.

[11] Ruwe PA, Gage JR, Ozonoff MB, DeLuca PA. Clinical determination of femoral anteversion. *J Bone Joint Surg Am* 1992;74A:820–830.

[12] Magilligan DJ. Calculation of the angle of anteversion by means of horizontal lateral roentgenography. *J Bone Joint Surg Am* 1956;38A:1231–1246.

[13] Hernandez RJ, Tachdjian MO, Poznanski AK, Dias LS. CT Determination of femoral torsion. *Am J Roentgenol* 1981;137:97–101.

[14] Root L, Siegal T. Osteotomy of the hip in children: Posterior approach. *J Bone Joint Surg Am* 1980;62A(4):571–575.

[15] Kidder SM, Harris GF, Johnson JE, Abuzzahab FS Jr. A kinematic model for clinical description of foot and ankle motion. (abstr), *Proc 8th Annual East Coast Clinical Gait Laboratory Conf* Rochester, Minn; May 5–8, 1993:111–114.

[16] Dennyson WG, Fulford R. Subtalar arthrodesis by cancellous grafts and metallic fixation. *J Bone Joint Surg Br* 1976;58B:507–510.

[17] Evans D. Calcaneo-valgus deformity. *J Bone Joint Surg Br* 1975;57B:270.

[18] Mosca VS. Calcaneal neck lengthening for severe abducto-valgus (flat) hindfoot deformity in children. *POSNA Meeting*, Newport, RI:May 6–9, 1992.

[19] Frost HM. Surgical treatment of spastic equinus in cerebral palsy. *Arch Phys Med Rehabil* 1971;52:270.

[20] Green NE. Split posterior tibial tendon transfer: The universal procedure. *The Diplegic Child*. Portland, Ore: American Academy of Orthopaedic Surgery, 1992;33:417–426.

[21] Dwyer FC. Osteotomy of the calcaneum for pes cavus. *J Bone Joint Surg Br* 1959;41B:80.

[22] Renshaw T, Sirkin R, Drennan J. The management of hallux valgus in cerebral palsy. *Dev Med Child Neurol* 1979;21:202–208.

[23] McKeever DC. Arthrodesis of the first metatarsophalangeal joint for hallux valgus, hallux rigidus, and metatarsus primus varus. *J Bone Joint Surg Am* 1952;34A:129–134.

[24] Ziv I, Blackburn N, Rang M, Koreska J. Muscle growth in normal and spastic mice. *Dev Med Child Neurol* 1984;26:94–99.

[25] Lance JW. Symposium synopsis. In: Feldman RG, Young RR, Koella WP eds. *Spasticity-disordered motor control*. Chicago, Ill: Yearbook Medical Publishers;1980:45.

[26] Albright AL, Cervi A, Singletary J. Intrathecal baclofen for spasticity in cerebral palsy. *JAMA* 1991;265(11):1418–1422.

[27] Koman LA, Mooney JF III, Smith B, Goodman A, Mulvaney T. Management of cerebral palsy with botulinum a toxin: Preliminary investigation. *J Ped Orthop* 1993;12:489–495.

[28] Peacock WJ, Staudt LA. Selective posterior rhizotomy: Evolution of theory and practice. *Pediatr Neurosurg* 1991-92;17:128–134.

[29] Dunn, MB, Stout JL, Gage JR, Krach L, Johnson L. Selective dorsal rhizotomy: The effect on gait in children with cerebral palsy. *Gillette Children's Hospital Rhizotomy Conference*; St Paul, Minn; April 29, 1994.

[30] Peacock WJ, Staudt LA. Selective dorsal rhizotomy for spastic cerebral palsy. *Gillette Children's Hospital Rhizotomy Conference*; St Paul, Minn; April 29, 1994.

[31] Boscarino LF, Õunpuu S, Davis RB III, Gage JR, DeLuca PA. Effects of selective dorsal rhizotomy on gait in children with cerebral palsy. *J Ped Orthop* 1993;13:174–179.

[32] Peacock WJ, Staudt LA. Functional outcomes following selective posterior rhizotomy in children with cerebral palsy. *J Neurosurg* 1991;74:380–385.

[33] Stout JL, Gage JR, Phelps JA, Koop S, Dunn MB. A comparison of metabolic energy expenditure after orthopaedic surgery or posterior selective rhizotomy (abstr), *Proc 8th Annual East Coast Clinical Gait Laboratory Conference*, Rochester, Minn; May 5–8, 1993:101.

[34] Bleck EE, Holstein A. Iliopsoas tenotomy for spastic hip flexion deformities in cerebral palsy. *Annual Meeting American Academy of Orthopaedic Surgery*, Miami Beach, Fla, January 20–25, 1963.

[35] Eggers GWN. Transplantation of hamstring tendons to femoral condyles in order to improve hip extension and to decrease knee flexion in cerebral spastic paralysis. *J Bone Joint Surg Am* 1952;34A:827–830.

[36] Hoffinger SA, Rab GT, Abou-Ghaida H. Hamstrings in cerebral palsy crouch gait. *J Ped Orthop* 1993;13(6):722–726.

[37] Gage JR. Personal correspondence, February 4, 1994.

[38] Sutherland DH, Santi M, Abel MF. Treatment of stiff-knee gait in cerebral palsy; A comparison by gait analysis of distal rectus femoris transfer versus proximal rectus release. *J Ped Orthop* 1990;10:433–442.

[39] Gage JR, Perry J, Hicks RR, Koop S, Werntz JR. Rectus femoris transfer as a means of improving knee function in cerebral palsy. *Dev Med Child Neurol* 1987;29:159–166.

[40] Õunpuu S, Muik E, Davis RB III, Gage JR, DeLuca PA. Rectus femoris surgery in children with cerebral palsy. Part I: The effect of rectus femoris transfer location on knee motion. *J Ped Orthop* 1993;13(3):325–330.

[41] Õunpuu S, Muik E, Davis RB III, Gage JR, DeLuca PA. Rectus femoris surgery in children with cerebral palsy. Part II: A comparison between the effect of transfer and release of the distal rectus femoris on knee motion. *J Ped Orthop* 1993;13(3):331–335.

[42] Delp SL, Zajac FE. Force- and moment-generating capacity of lower-extremity muscle before and after tendon lengthening. *Clin Orthop* 1992;284:247–259.

[43] Sutherland DH, Cooper L. The pathomechanics of progressive crouch gait in spastic diplegia. *Ortho Clinics of North America* 1978;9:142–154.

[44] Baker LD. A rational approach to the surgical needs of the cerebral palsy patient. *J Bone Joint Surg Am* 1956;38A:313–323.

[45] Strayer L. Recession of the gastrocnemius. *J Bone Joint Surg Am* 1950; 32A(3):671–676.

[46] Rose SA, DeLuca PA, Davis RB III, Õunpuu S, Gage JR. Kinematic and kinetic evaluation of the ankle after lengthening of the gastrocnemius fascia in children with cerebral palsy. *J Ped Orthop* 1993;13(6):727–732.

Chapter 14

Jacquelin Perry

The Role of EMG in Gait Analysis

14.1. INTRODUCTION

Walking and other ambulation skills are patterns of limb motion under muscular control. Dynamic electromyography (EMG) is the only means of defining the timing and relative intensity of specific muscle action. The electrical signals that activate the muscle fibers are captured, isolated from noise, and interpreted. Despite the need to know the contributions muscle activity makes to a particular gait, the role of EMG continues to be debated. Three factors encourage the use of circumventing procedures. These are the technical requirements for getting meaningful EMG, variability in muscle force production, and the limited voluntary control of spastic patients.

14.2. IMPLIED MUSCLE ACTION

Motion analysis identifies the action occurring at each joint, but it doesn't tell why. Moment and force calculations determine the effects of ground reactions, body segment weights, and inertias at each joint. The product of joint angular velocity and the moment represents the power at each joint. It's assumed that the resulting moments reflect active muscle control [1–3]. While a single-focus problem such as the quadriceps response to a torn anterior cruciate ligament (ACL) has given logical results [4], more complex pathology can lead to misinterpretations. One example is a recent study of unilateral below-knee (BK) amputees using different prosthetic feet. A major objective of the new energy-storing foot designs is to conserve energy [5]. Energy cost measurements of the traumatic BK amputees walking at a normal speed revealed an increased expenditure 40 percent above normal for both the "old" solid ankle cushion heel (SACH) foot as well as all of the new designs tested (Flex foot, Seattle, Carbon Copy II, Sten). The cause of this increased energy cost was sought by additional gait measurements. Motion analysis displayed reduced knee flexion during weight acceptance (Figure 14-1) [6]. Power calculations at the knee reported by A. Gitter et al. were also less than normal [7]. These data imply energy savings. Dynamic EMG of the quadriceps, however, demonstrated increased intensity and duration of muscle action (Figure 14-2) [6]. This was also true for the hip extensors (gluteus maximus and biceps femoris, long head). The source of the extra energy expenditure had been found. The reason for the additional effort lies in the hindfoot design of prostheses. While all have a cushion heel for shock absorption, they lack the plantarflexion mobility needed for early forefoot contact. The result is prolonged heel-only support, which is accompanied by continuing tibial instability. Intense and prolonged quadriceps stabilization of the knee is required. A slight forward lean also is used to reduce the quadriceps demand. This postural adaptation, by moving the weight line more anterior, is the basis of the reduced power calculations. The custom of interpreting the motion data by peak displacement also contributed to the misinterpretation by obscuring the abnormal prosthetic foot mobility. While 10 degrees plantarflexion equaled normal function, further analysis, which considered cycle time, identified a major delay in initial peak ankle plantarflexion following foot contact (20 percent gait cycle versus 5 percent gate cycle for normal). Hence, comprehensive motion analysis did reveal gait abnormalities, but the power calculations misread the knee control pattern. The true mode of knee control was identified only by dynamic EMG.

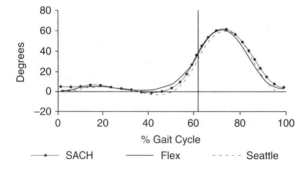

Figure 14-1. Knee motion of BK amputees (N=5) walking at their customary speed using three types of prosthetic feet (SACH, Flex, Seattle).

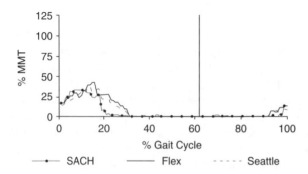

Figure 14-2. Quadriceps EMG during free speed gait of BK amputees using three types of prosthetic feet (SACH, Flex, Seattle).

14.3. EMG IN ANALYSIS OF PARALYTIC GAIT DYSFUNCTION

The most frequent indication for dynamic EMG is in the analysis of paralytic gait dysfunction. Generally, the purpose is to assist in surgical planning by identifying the patient's muscle control errors. Gait corrections are made by either surgical lengthening or transfer of specific muscles [8–10]. Hence, one must know the exact offenders. Normal and abnormal function must be differentiated.

14.3.1. Spastic Paralysis Gait

Spastic paralysis gait is particularly difficult to diagnose. The functional pathology resulting from cerebral palsy, stroke, brain injury, and so on, is a mixture of hyperactive stretch reflexes (spasticity), impaired selective control (weakness), emergence of primitive mass flexor and extensor synergies, limb and body postural reflexes (tone), and secondary contracture [11]. Inappropriate muscle action is the basic impairment of the patient's gait, but it is difficult to discern because the resulting walking pattern is a mixture of intrinsic error supplemented by voluntary substitutions within the limits of the patient's residual control.

Because the patient's gait patterns are so complex, laboratory gait analysis is being used with increasing frequency to identify the dysfunction. The standard clinical examination with the patient supine or sitting on a treatment table can offer only a limited diagnosis of the patient's dysfunction since the stimuli of floor impact, upright posture, and the mechanics of walking impose functional demands that cannot be reproduced manually. While the clinician can make estimates based on prior knowledge, each patient is a unique mixture of functional pathology [12]. Motion analysis, as described by D. H. Sutherland [13] is valuable in differentiating the contributions of pelvis, hip, knee, and ankle action to limb instability in stance and limb advancement in swing [14]. Moments and power are calculated in the hope that such information will facilitate the interpretation of muscle control [15]. Each joint, however, is controlled by groups of muscles, and the response to the pathological influences can differ among the individual muscles. Dynamic EMG is needed to differentiate normal from abnormal muscle action so the cause of the patient's gait dysfunction can be identified [14].

14.3.2. Varus Foot Example

The foot twisted into varus is a good example. Any of three strong invertor muscles—tibialis anterior, tibialis posterior, and soleus—can be the cause [16–19]. The long toe flexors (hallucis and common), also, are potential contributors [17]. There might be any combination of normal, premature, or prolonged action by the muscles within the inverting complex [14]. Motion analysis can differentiate swing and stance alignment of the foot and ankle. The severity of the equinus and varus is defined, but not their cause. Equinus induces varus by lifting the patient onto the obliquely aligned forefoot. The cause might be premature activity or contracture of the soleus, while the tibial muscles display normal function. Either EMG or blocking neural control by anesthesia is required to differentiate this situation. Varus, independent of ankle position, follows excessive timing and/or intensity of the tibialis anterior and posterior. The common assumption is that the tibialis posterior is the cause, but this muscle might be silent and the tibialis anterior continuously active

Part 2 Clinical Applications

through stance [Figure 14-3(*a*)]. Both tibialis anterior and posterior might show excessive activity in stance [Figure 14-3(*b*)] or the tibialis posterior might change its phasing to swing [Figure 14-3(*c*)]. Each situation is managed by a different surgical procedure. A review of inversion muscle patterns among 50 cerebral palsy children showed the tibialis posterior

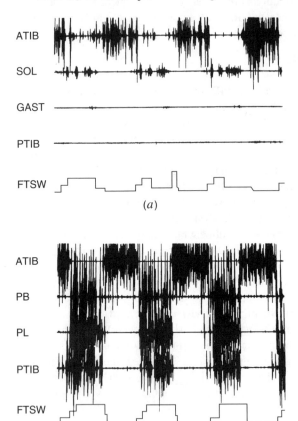

(*a*)

(*b*)

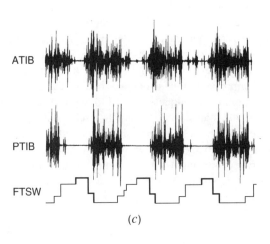

(*c*)

Figure 14-3. Varying EMG patterns of anterior and posterior muscle action seen in cerebral palsy varus foot during gait. (*a*) Nearly continuous activity of anterior tibialis (ATIB) with a silent posterior tibialis (PTIB). Soleus (SOL) with low activity and gastrocnemius (GAST) silent. (*b*) Both anterior (ATIB) and posterior (PTIB) tibialis muscles show excessive activity, as do peroneus brevis (PB) and peroneus longus (PL). (*c*) Posterior tibialis (PTIB) has changed to swing phase action similar to anterior tibialis (ATIB). FTSW stands for footswitch, baseline is swing, and elevated segment is stance.

was the primary cause in only 25 percent, though it was a contributor in 55 percent of the foot deformities [19]. The tibialis anterior was a more frequent cause (45 percent) and contributed to the deformity in 75 percent of the cases. In stroke and adult brain trauma patients, activity of the toe flexors is also significant [17]. For each of these clinical situations only dynamic EMG using wire electrodes can identify the offending muscles.

14.3.3. Spastic Stiff-Knee Gait Example

Similar unpredictability occurs with the spastic stiff-knee gait. Failure to adequately flex the knee in initial swing inhibits limb advancement and initiates a toe drag [14]. Substitutive efforts are always laborious and variably effective. The basic determinant for surgical improvement depends on which head(s) of the quadriceps are active in swing. This might be only the rectus femoris [Figure 14-4(*a*)], the addition of the vastus intermedius, or the nonexpendable medial and lateral vasti [Figure 14-4(*b*)] [20]. Prolongation of the vasti into late stance reduces the restoration of swing knee flexion [20]. Only wire EMG will delineate the swing phase action of the various heads of the quadriceps. Hamstring muscle activity in initial swing phase is another deterrent to adequate knee flexion as the contribution of rapid thigh advancement is lost [21].

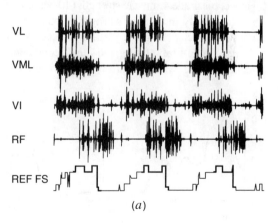

(*a*)

Figure 14-4. Variations in quadriceps swing-phase action as a cause of spastic stiff-legged gait of stroke patients. (*a*) Rectus femoris (RF) strongly active in swing, Vasti (VL, VML, VI) active only in stance. (*b*) Significant vastus lateralis (VL), vastus intermedius (VI), and vastus medialis longus (VML) action in swing as well as stance. No significant RF EMG. REF FS stands for reference footswitch. OPP FS stands for opposite foot switch.

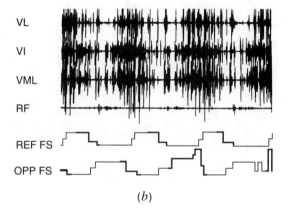

(*b*)

14.3.4. Use of EMG in Patients with Flaccid Paralysis

A recent extension of dynamic EMG is its use to determine the factors causing muscular symptoms (pain, fatigue, and new weakness) in patients impaired by flaccid paralysis. The postpolio patients have functioned well for thirty or more years and now are experiencing disabling symptoms [22,23]. Life-style assessments have identified neuromuscular overuse as the probable cause, but the mechanics are still unclear. Clinical examination only determines the patients muscle availability and strength, not how they are used.

Patients with normal proprioception and control spontaneously substitute to minimize the dysfunction. Muscle weakness allows uncontrolled motions, but these can be masked by postural adaptations, contractures of substitutive action of adjacent or remote muscles. Motion analysis reveals the resulting joint postures but not the mode of muscular control. For these patients, the clinical question involves the intensity of muscle action as well as the timing. An example is a former patient who was previously doing well.

The patient's motion analysis revealed excessive dorsiflexion in terminal stance (20 degrees versus normal 10 degrees) accompanied by mild (5 degrees) knee flexion. Was this sufficient to cause his symptoms? Dynamic EMG demonstrated excessive and prolonged quadriceps activity [Figure 14-5(a)] compared to the normal pattern [Figure 14-5(b)]. Hence, his grade 4 muscle strength (40 percent normal as quantified by W. C. Beasley [24]) exerted nearly maximum strength to control loading response knee flexion. This would not be suspected, as grade 4 strength accepts considerable examiner resistance [25]. Then during single-limb stance, the quadriceps continued to contract to resist the flexor moment imposed by the tibial instability of increased ankle dorsiflexion. Hence, there were

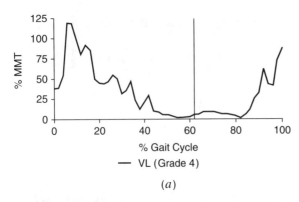

(*a*)

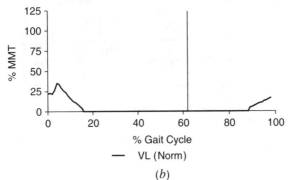

(*b*)

Figure 14-5. Quadriceps (VL) EMG activity during free velocity gait. (*a*) Postpoliomyelitis syndrome patient with grade 4 strength. (*b*) Normal function. %MMT stands for percent manual muscle test. Vertical bar (62% GC) designates transition from stance to swing.

two disabling mechanisms: (1) underestimated quadriceps weakness, and (2) the predicted substitution for calf muscle weakness.

14.3.5. Multiplicity of Muscle Control

Underlying all of these clinical situations is the multiplicity of muscle control. There are 28 major muscles in each lower extremity whose actions can be delineated by discriminating EMG [14]. By their dominant action, they fall into major functional groups such as hip extensors, flexors, abductors, and so on. Most muscles also have an eccentric or oblique alignment, so they contribute to more than one motion and thus belong to more than one functional group. For example, the gluteus maximus and adductor magnus are single joint hip extensors, but the upper gluteus maximus is also an abductor and contributes to external rotation, while, as the name implies, the adductor magnus has the opposite accessory actions of adduction and internal rotation. Some muscles cross two joints and thus have an even greater array of actions. The three hamstrings are an excellent example. In addition to providing hip extension and rotation, these muscles also contribute to knee flexion and rotation. In addition, the rotational effects of the medial and lateral hamstrings differ, while they have similar flexor and extensor actions. There is similar complexity among the hip flexors. All of the muscles controlling the ankle have varying rotator effects at the foot.

Thus, in summary, if the proposed treatment is focused on specific muscle action, dynamic EMG should be included in the gait analysis protocol. Dynamic EMG answers the questions "Why" and "How." Why do the motion errors occur? Why do patients have muscle fatigue? How is the person accommodating? Dynamic EMG also allows one to differentiate the actions of adjacent or potentially synergistic muscles. These questions can apply to any type of pathology. In the absence of specific answers to these questions, the surgeon must select a clinical model that appears similar to the patient. Pathology distorts gross assumptions by unpredictable neurocontrol errors or subtle substitutive actions.

The challenge is to obtain meaningful EMG data. Contaminated EMG is useless. Interpretations of the data also must be factual.

14.4. TECHNICAL REQUIREMENTS

Limiting the recorded signals to meaningful data involves two basic procedures, signal management and electrode selection. Signal management focuses on isolation of the functionally pertinent elements of the EMG spectrum. The electrical signals that are captured by the electrodes are a mixture of electronic noise and functional EMG. As both types of signals have a random waveform pattern, by eye, they look alike. Fortunately there are good criteria for filtering out the noise. Within the total EMG spectrum (10 to 10,000 Hz) [26], the low end (10 to 25 Hz) includes tissue motion artifact. To assure exclusion of this type of contamination, a 40-Hz cutoff is recommended. Environmental lights and power sources have a 60-Hz frequency. These are excluded with a 60-Hz notch filter. The high end of the theoretical spectrum exceeds the range of useful information. A maximum of 1000 Hz is sufficient.

Several factors determine the choice between surface and intramuscular wire electrodes. Surface electrodes are the most convenient, but they cannot restrict the signals to a specific muscle. These electrodes capture the signals that spread through the tissues from the active muscle to the body surface. As muscles rarely, if ever, function alone, the signals that reach the recording area represent the action of a synergistic group. In addition, signals from other muscles might be recorded when the primary group is silent [27]. This latter situation is called *cross talk*. Its presence erroneously extends the assumed phasing of primary muscles. C. J. De Luca determined that cross talk from remote or neighboring muscles could be as much as 16.6 percent of the peak values recorded [28]. This can be eliminated by raising the threshold. Surface EMG cross talk, however, cannot be eliminated if the active and quiescent muscles are separated only by a common fibrous septum, such as the ankle dorsiflexors and the peroneus longus (Bogey unpublished data). If pathology has changed the muscle's period of activity, the data might be totally wrong. Consequently, surface electrodes are of value only to identify muscle group action, and low levels of activity should be ignored as probable cross talk from one or more unidentified antagonists [14].

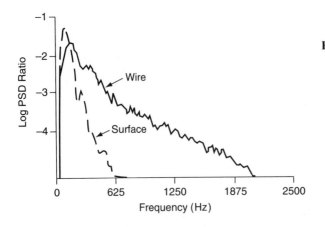

Figure 14-6. EMG power spectrum of surface and wire electrodes. Vertical axis is a logarithmic scale of EMG power spectral density ratio (Log[PSD(f)/PSD(total)]). Horizontal scale is signal frequency. [Adapted from Perry J, *Gait Analysis: Normal and Pathological Function*; Thorofare, NJ: Slack, Inc, 1992.]

Wire electrodes allow muscle isolation, but they require skin penetration. A pair of fine wires (50-micron diameter) are inserted into the designated muscle with a small hypodermic needle (25 gauge) [29]. There is still the potential for signal spread from adjacent muscles but it can be eliminated by selective filtering. Cross talk from synergists or antagonists is eliminated by excluding the spectrum below 150 Hz [14]. Basically, this eliminates the lower frequency components that spread through the tissues from the remote muscles. Exclusion of these signals is practical because the power spectrum of intramuscular signals is so much broader than the surface signals (Figure 14-6). This is comparable to removing the portion of the spectrum recorded by surface electrodes.

Hence, the functionally significant bandwidth for surface EMG is 40 to 300 Hz, with a 60-Hz notch filter and post recording exclusion of the low 15 percent. For some modern differential amplifiers with very high common mode rejection, the notch filter might not be necessary. The use of a 60-Hz notch filter, however, will eliminate the potential for 60-Hz noise regardless of how good the amplifier. For wire electrodes, the functional bandwidth should be 150 to 1000 Hz [14]. The bandpass filters should have a low frequency roll-off of 24 dB per octave (4-pole Butterworth). The high-frequency roll-off is not critical, as there is no energy in the EMG signal above 1000 Hz.

The choice of electrode (surface versus wire) depends on the purpose of the recording. Surface electrodes are appropriate if one merely wishes a display of muscle group action (such as the quadriceps) or the gross timing of a muscle (e.g., lateral hamstrings). The pattern of peak action will be accurate. Care must be taken, however, not to interpret the lowest amplitudes as continuing activity. It most likely represents cross talk. Intramuscular wire electrodes are indicated whenever the accurate phasing of particular muscles is required. Wire electrodes are also essential to differentiate the action of muscles that are in physical contact or are part of a synergy.

Normalization of the EMG is required whenever one wishes to compare the intensity of action among muscles or subjects. Basically, the electromyogram represents the action of an unknown number of motor units. Neither the exact relationship between the electrodes and the underlying muscles nor the precise muscle fiber pattern are known. To overcome this limitation, the data from each electrode are normalized; that is, a ratio is calculated between the functional EMG and that obtained during a standardizing test. While one can select any event as the standardizing test, the EMG obtained during the muscle's manual strength test is the common practice [30]. This procedure also indicates the relative intensity of muscle action compared to its capability.

Most spastic patients can produce an adequate muscle test response for EMG normalization. If the impaired patient lacks sufficient selective control to cooperate with a manual muscle test, an alternate normalization technique must be used. A useful sign of an invalid muscle test, in addition to the patient's behavior, is gait EMG values that are more than 2.5 times the mean MMT value. There are two options for alternate normalization. One practice is the use of the peak EMG obtained during the gait trials as the normalizing base [31]. While convenient, the differences in the relative effort among muscles are obscured by each muscle displaying a 100 percent level of activity. Another approach is to use a laboratory mean EMG value as the normalizing base. In our laboratory, the resulting values are expressed in microvolts to reflect the difference in the normalization base.

14.5. EMG INTENSITY: MUSCLE EFFORT VERSUS FORCE

The electromyogram is a record of the myoelectric signals activating the muscle fibers. In response to stimulation, each muscle fiber contracts completely; in other words, the "all or none" rule applies [32]. Muscle force is increased by activating more muscle fibers [33]. This might be through the addition of other muscle fibers (i.e., motor units) or by increasing the rate of stimulation of the same fibers [34,35]. Consequently, the magnitude of the EMG is proportional to the number of muscle fibers firing. If the functional EMG is normalized to a maximum effort (percent MMT), the relative effort used during that activity is identified. This is valuable clinical information about the degree of exertion required or the extent to which a pathologically active muscle is contributing to the dysfunction.

The quantified EMG also shows a linear correlation with the muscle force being produced, but the absolute muscle force varies with the functional situation. Muscle force capability is modified by three overlapping factors. These are joint position, rate of motion, and type of muscle contraction [14].

Joint position introduces two variables, muscle length and internal moment arm length. Each muscle fiber is a chain of force units called sarcomeres. The sarcomere's holding force varies with the overlap of its internal myofilaments (myosin and actin) [36]. Lengthening or shortening of the sarcomere from its optimum length (full myosin-actin bonding) reduces the myofilament overlap and, consequently, the force produced in response to stimulation. Functional strength of a muscle depends both on its force and mechanical advantage at the joint. The latter, called a moment arm, is the distance between the muscle's line of pull and the joint center [37]. This can increase or decrease as the joint is moved from its optimum position. The resulting muscle strength at any one joint position is therefore a balance between changes in the length of the sarcomere and the moment arm. Sensitivity to joint alignment varies among muscles. For example, relative muscle strength between 5 and 45 degrees flexion differs by 50 percent for the quadriceps, while the hamstrings register just a 10 percent change [38].

The modes of contraction are defined by the change in muscle length that occurs during an activity. The three motion patterns are lengthening (eccentric), no change (isometric), and shortening (concentric) [38]. For the same EMG intensity, the registered force can differ. An eccentric contraction occurs when the external demand force exceeds that produced by the resisting muscles. The rate or extent of motion is actively limited. Two factors are involved: a strong but yielding myosin-actin bond within the sarcomere [39], and passive tension of the fibrous tissue sheaths enveloping the muscle fibers. With an isometric contraction, the internal muscle force equals the external demand force, so no motion is allowed. The same two physiological factors are involved, but now the myosin-actin bond is static. A concentric contraction creates motion. Now the muscle force is greater than the external demand. As the joint moves, the controlling muscles shorten through continual realignment of the myofilaments within the sarcomeres. This requires repeated reattachment and release of the myosin-actin bonds. Also, the fibrous tissue would be slackened. As a result, the force registered for the same EMG is approximately 20 percent less during a concentric contraction than occurs with an isometric effort [38]. In the lower extremity (hamstring and quadriceps), the eccentric and isometric efforts produced equal force.

Speed of motion also reduces the force of concentric contractions. For example, knee extension at 150 degrees per second generated 38 percent less force than occurred during an isometric effort [40]. Theoretically, the force represented by the recorded EMG can be calculated. The muscle force (F) would equal the isometric value (I) modified by the type of contraction (C), rate of motion (V), and joint position (P): $F = I (C + V + P)$ [14]. None of these coefficients, however, have been established as yet.

14.6. CONCLUSION

In summary, EMG is the only means of identifying actual muscle action. Knowledge of muscle timing and relative intensity of effort is used to define normal function and the effects of various types of pathology, and to assist surgical planning, especially for spastic patients. Meaningful information, however, can only be gained with clean EMG. This means segments containing electrical system and environmental noise and tissue motion artifacts must be excluded. Electrodes must be chosen for the type of data they can accurately provide. Interpretations of individual muscle action and comparisons among muscles must consider the quality of the signals recorded.

References

[1] Hardt DE. Determining muscle forces in the leg during normal human walking: An application and evaluation of optimization methods. *J Biomed Eng* 1978;100:72–78.

[2] Morrison JB. Mechanics of muscle function in locomotion. *J Biomech* 1970;431–451.

[3] Winter DA. Energy generation and absorption at the ankle and knee during fast, natural, and slow cadences. *Clin Orthop* 1983;175:147–154.

[4] Berchuck M, Andriacchi TB, Bach BR, Reider B. Gait adaptations by patients who have a deficient anterior cruciate ligament. *J Bone Joint Surg Am* 1990;72A:871–877.

[5] Burgess EM, Hittenberger DA, Forsgren SM, Lindh DV. The Seattle prosthetic foot—A design for active sports: Preliminary studies. *Orthotics and Prosthetics* 1983;37(1):25–31.

[6] Torburn L, Perry J, Ayyappa E, Shanfield SL. Below-knee amputee gait with dynamic elastic response prosthetic feet: A pilot study. *J Rehabil Res Dev* 1990;27(4):369–384.

[7] Gitter A, Czerniecki JM, DeGroot DM. Biomechanical analysis of the influence of prosthetic feet on below-knee amputee walking. *Am J Phys Med Rehabil* 1991;70; 142–148.

[8] Gage J, Fabian D, Hicks R, Tashman S. Pre- and postoperative gait analysis in patients with spastic diplegia: A preliminary report. *J Ped Orthop* 1984;4:715–725.

[9] Sutherland DH, *Gait Disorders in Childhood and Adolescence.* Baltimore, Md: Williams and Wilkins Publishing Co; 1964:1–10.

[10] Sutherland DH, Santi M, Abel MF. Treatment of stiff-knee gait in cerebral palsy: A comparison by gait analysis of distal rectus femoris transfer versus proximal rectus release. *J Ped Orthop* 1990;10:433–441.

[11] Perry J. Determinants of muscle function in the spastic lower extremity. *Clin Orthop* 1993;288:10–26.

[12] Hoffer MM, Perry J. Pathodynamics of gait alterations in cerebral palsy and the significance of kinetic electromyography in evaluating foot and ankle problems. *Foot and Ankle* 1983;4(3):128–134.

[13] Sutherland DH, Hagy JL. Measurement of gait movements from motion picture film. *J Bone Joint Surg Am* 1972;54A:787–797.

[14] Perry J, *Gait Analysis, Normal and Pathological Function.* Thorofare, NJ: Slack, Inc; 1992.

[15] Olney SJ, Winter DA. Predictions of knee and ankle moments of force in walking from EMG and kinematic data. *J Biomech* 1985;18(1):9–20.

[16] Hoffer MM, Reiswig JA, Garrett AL Perry J. The split anterior tibial tendon transfer in the treatment of spastic varus hindfoot of childhood. *Orthop Clin North Am* 1974;5(1):31–38.

[17] Perry J, Waters RL, Perrin T. Electromyographic analysis of equinovarus following stroke. *Clin Orthop* 1978;131:47–53.

[18] Waters RL, Frazier J, Garland DE, Jordan C, Perry J. Electromyographic gait analysis before and after operative treatment for hemiplegic equinus and equinovarus deformity. *J Bone Joint Surg Am*, 1982;64A:284–288.

[19] Wills CA, Hoffer MM, Perry J. A comparison of foot-switch and EMG analysis of varus deformities of the feet of children with cerebral palsy. *Dev Med Child Neurol* 1988;30:227–231.

[20] Waters RL, Garland DE, Perry J, Habig T, Slabaugh P. Stiff-legged gait in hemiplegia: Surgical correction. *J Bone Joint Surg Am*, 1979;61A:927–934.

[21] Kerrigan DC, Gronley JK, Perry J. Stiff-legged gait in spastic paralysis: A study of quadriceps and hamstring activity. *Am J Phys Med Rehabil* 1991;70(6):294–300.

[22] Halstead LS, Rossi CD. New problems in old polio patients: Results of a survey of 539 polio survivors. *Orthopedics* 1985;8:845–850.

[23] Halstead LS, Rossi CD. Post-polio syndrome: Clinical experience with 132 consecutive outpatients. In: Halstead LS, Wiechers DO, eds. *Research and Clinical Aspects of the Late Effects of Poliomyelitis* White Plains, NY: March of Dimes Birth Defects Foundation; 1987:13–26.

[24] Beasley WC. Quantitative muscle testing: Principles and applications to research and clinical services. *Arch Phys Med Rehabil* 1961;42:398–425.

[25] Daniels L, Worthingham C. *Muscle Testing: Techniques of Manual Examination.* Philadelphia, Pa: WB Saunders Co;1980:3.

[26] Turker KS. Electromyography: Some methodological problems and issues. *Phys Ther* 1993;73(10):698–710.

[27] Hof AL, Van den Berg JW. Emg to force processing III: Estimation of model parameters for the human triceps surrae muscle and assessment of the accuracy by means of the torque plate. *J Biomech* 1981;14(11):771–785.

[28] De Luca CJ, Merletti R. Surface myoelectric signal cross-talk among muscles of the leg. *Electro Clin Neurophys* 1988;69:568–575.

[29] Basmajian JV, Stecko GA. A new bipolar indwelling electrode for electromyography. *J Appl Physiol* 1962;17:849.

[30] Lyons K, Perry J, Gronley J.K., Barnes L, Antonelli D. Timing and relative intensity of hip extensor and abductor muscle action during level and stair ambulation: An EMG study. *Phys Ther* 1983;63:1597–1605.

[31] Winter DA, *Biomechanics of Human Movement*. New York, NY: John Wiley and Sons, Inc; 1979.

[32] Milner-Brown HS, Stein RB, Yemm R. The contractile properties of human motor units during voluntary isometric contractions. *J Physiol* 1973;228:285–306.

[33] Parker PA, Scott RN. Statistics of the myoelectric signal from monopolar and bipolar electrodes. *Med Bio Eng Comp* 1973;11:591–596.

[34] Milner-Brown HS, Stein RB, Changes in firing rate of human motor units during linearly changing voluntary contractions. *J Physiol* 1973;230:371–390.

[35] Milner-Brown HS, Stein RB, Yemm R. The orderly recruitment of human motor units during voluntary isometric contractions. *J Physiol* 1973;230:359–370.

[36] Gordon AM, Huxley AF, Julian FJ. The variation in isometric tension with sarcomere length in vertebrate muscle fibres. *J Physiol* 1966;184:170–192.

[37] Williams M, Lissner HR. *Biomechanics of Human Motion*. Philadelphia, Pa: WB Saunders Co; 1962.

[38] Smidt GL. Biomechanical analysis of knee flexion and extension. *J Biomech* 1973;6:79–92.

[39] Lieber RL, Boakes JL. Sarcomere length and joint kinematics during torque production in frog hindlimb. *Am J Physiol* 1988;254:C759–C768.

[40] Osternig LR, Hamill J, Corcos DM, Lander J. Electromyographic patterns accompanying isokinetic exercise under varying speed and sequencing conditions. *Am J Phys Med* 1984;63(6):289–297.

Chapter 15

Sylvia Õunpuu | # Joint Kinetics

Interpretation and Clinical Decision Making for the Treatment of Gait Abnormalities in Children with Neuromuscular Disorders

15.1. INTRODUCTION

Although gait analysis, including joint kinematics, electromyography (EMG), and a clinical examination, are accepted tools in clinical decision making [1–6], the routine use of joint kinetics in the clinical decision-making process in children with neuromuscular disorders is very new. Joint kinetics can increase our understanding of the cause of movement abnormalities [7,8], and help us evaluate the effects of treatment, including surgery and orthoses. Although kinetics are not routinely used in the fitting and evaluation of prostheses at this time, kinetics are a very useful tool in the overall evaluation of these devices in a research setting [9]. Systematic study of the changes in joint kinetic patterns as a result of surgery will ultimately increase our understanding of their potential use in clinical decision making, especially in children with cerebral palsy (CP). The limited previous research using joint kinetics to evaluate orthotics [10,11] or surgical decisions [12,13] has provided interesting results that have improved our understanding of pathological gait and ultimately had a direct effect on clinical decision making. Clinical examples will be discussed in detail in Sections 15.6 and 15.7.

It is the purpose of this chapter to demonstrate how joint kinetics (joint moments and powers) provide additional information that may be used in the treatment decision-making process in patients with gait abnormalities. It is assumed that the reader has a basic knowledge of gait, including the interpretation of joint kinematics. In this chapter, the basics of methodology and interpretation, normal kinetic patterns, trouble shooting joint kinetic data, typical patterns in patients with CP, application in the evaluation of orthoses, and examination of preoperative versus postoperative joint kinetics will be covered. In the latter part of this chapter, I will use graphic presentation of joint kinetic data for illustration of specific points. All the normal and pathological data presented in this chapter were calculated in three dimensions [14] using Newtonian mechanics [15] and are described in more detail elsewhere in this book.

15.2. JOINT KINETICS: A BRIEF DESCRIPTION OF METHODS

In order to interpret joint kinetic data, the clinician must have an appreciation for how joint kinetics (joint moments and joint powers) are calculated as well as a knowledge of the conventions used for presentation of the data. To begin this discussion two basic terms need to be defined: joint kinematics and joint kinetics.

> **Joint kinematics**   Parameters used to describe the spatial movement of the body, not considering the forces that cause the movement; for example, linear and angular displacements, linear and angular velocities, and linear and angular accelerations. The angle definitions used for the data presented in this chapter have been previously published [16].
>
> **Joint kinetics**   Parameters used to describe the mechanisms that cause movement; for example, ground reaction forces, joint moments, and joint powers.

There are two methods generally used for the calculation of joint kinetics: the inverse dynamic method and the ground reaction force method. Although both these methods provide an estimate of the net joint moment and power, there are greater limitations to the ground reaction force method [17]. The information required for the calculation of joint moments using the inverse dynamics method includes the following:

1. The three-dimensional (3-D) locations (kinematics) of the ankle, knee, and hip joints, which are derived from data collected by a motion measurement system. These data are typically obtained through the application of reflective markers placed relative to bony landmarks.

2. The 3-D locations of the center of mass of the foot, shank, and thigh segments. This information is based on anthropometric relationships that define the point located between joint centers.

3. The 3-D linear and angular accelerations of the center of mass of the foot, shank, and thigh. This information is determined from the numerical differentiation of the center of mass locations.

4. The ground reaction forces, which include the three components of the force vector, the vertical torque, and the location of the point of application of the ground reaction force vector, referred to as the center of pressure. These data are obtained by using a force platform.

5. The segment weight (in Newtons) which is determined from anthropometric relationships expressed as a percentage of total body weight.

6. The mass moment of inertia (in kilograms-meters^2) is the resistance that the segment offers to being accelerated in rotation about a particular point or axis.

With the above information the net joint moment and power can be calculated. The calculations should be based on Newtonian mechanics (i.e., force = mass × acceleration) and on fully 3-D motion data combined with 3-D force platform data [14,18]. It is important to note that the joint kinematic and force information must be obtained simultaneously. The joint moments should be computed about joint center locations and not external markers placed on the skin in the vicinity of the joint. These calculations should include inertial and acceleration effects.

15.2.1. Joint Moment

A moment is produced when a force is applied to a body at a distance from the center of rotation. A moment (in Newton-meters) is the product of this force and the distance between the point of application of the force and the center of rotation.

$$\text{Moment} = \text{Force} \times \text{Distance} \tag{15-1}$$

Relating this concept to the body, the force is produced by the muscle and/or ligaments that act at a distance from the joint center. This results in a net internal or muscle moment that represents the body's response to an external load. The external load during walking includes the ground reaction force and the segment weight. Joint moments quantify the net moment of all muscles crossing a joint, typically indicate which muscle group is dominant, and are expressed as flexor or extensor.

15.2.2. Joint Power

Joint power (in watts) is the net rate of generating or absorbing energy by all muscles crossing a joint. The joint power is the product of the joint moment and the joint angular velocity.

$$\text{Joint Power} = (\text{Joint Moment}) \times (\text{Joint Angular Velocity}) \tag{15-2}$$

The joint power is also related to the type of contraction. A concentric contraction occurs when a contracting muscle shortens under tension and is associated with power generation. An eccentric contraction occurs when a contracting muscle lengthens under tension and is associated with power absorption.

15.3. NORMAL JOINT KINETICS

15.3.1. Selected Conventions

Unfortunately, one of the reasons that gait analysis has not been readily accepted by the medical community is the difficulty in communicating gait analysis data such as joint kinematics and kinetics. This problem is enhanced by the lack of standards between various gait laboratories in the presentation of these data. There is a significant amount of debate about the best way to present gait analysis data; for example, plotting internal or external moments. The conventions used in this chapter are by no means universal, but they have been used routinely over the past ten years in clinical decision making by clinicians that do or do not have a background in the field of gait analysis. For all the data presented in the remainder of this chapter the following conventions are used:

1. Moments plotted reflect the body's response to an external load; that is, they are the muscle or internal moments.
2. Moments plotted correspond with the dominant muscle group, and therefore EMG data correspond to the plotted moment data.
3. Extensor/plantarflexor and abductor moments are positive moments.
4. Flexor/dorsiflexor and adductor moments are negative moments.
5. Power generation is positive.
6. Power absorption is negative.

15.3.2. Sagittal Plane Kinetics for the Hip, Knee, and Ankle

The following is a description of the normal hip, knee, and ankle sagittal plane kinematics, moments, and powers (Figure 15-1). These variables will be defined in terms of the phases of the gait cycle [19], which include loading response (0 to 10 percent of the gait cycle), midstance (10 to 30 percent), terminal stance (30 to 50 percent), preswing (50 to 60 percent), initial swing (60 to 73 percent), midswing (73 to 87 percent), and terminal swing (87 to 100 percent). These data represent the average patterns for 32 normal children ranging in age from 5 to 18 years (mean 11 years). The data presented in this chapter differ slightly from previously reported data [8] because of differences in methods. As mentioned above, the following data were collected in 3-D using estimated joint center locations.

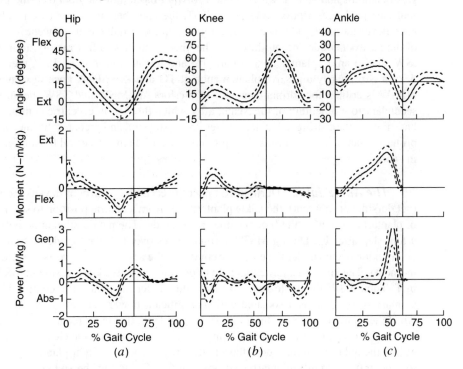

Figure 15-1. Normal sagittal plane joint kinematics (first row), moments (second row), and powers (third row) for (a) hip, (b) knee, and (c) ankle. Mean ±1 S.D. are presented.

The Hip Joint. During the first part of stance phase [loading response (LR) and midstance (MST)] the hip extends from about 35 degrees of flexion at initial contact (IC) to a few degrees of extension. This motion is a result of a net hip extensor moment and power generation, which helps bring the center of gravity to its highest position in single limb stance. Just before full extension there is a net hip flexor moment and associated power absorption as the hip extension is decelerated. In preswing (PSW) or the last 10 percent of stance phase, hip flexion occurs secondary in part to a net hip flexor moment (hip flexor activity) and associated power generation. The peak of the power generation burst is usually at toe-off (TO). This power generation continues through initial swing (ISW) and helps advance the swing limb. In midswing (MSW), full hip flexion is attained with a negligible moment and power. In terminal swing (TSW) the hip extends slightly in preparation for initial contact. There is a small hip extensor moment and associated power absorption as the hip extensors generate tension/force in preparation for IC. Therefore, the hip has two primary power generation periods: in the first half of stance and at TO.

The Knee Joint. At IC, the knee is generally slightly flexed and during LR continues to flex to approximately 15 degrees under the eccentric control of the quadriceps, resulting in a net knee extensor moment and power absorption. The power absorption contributes to shock absorption during weight acceptance. In MST, the knee extends under concentric control of the quadriceps and associated power generation. In the remainder of MST and terminal stance (TST), the knee almost fully extends under the control of the gastrocnemius and soleus, which control forward motion of the tibia over the plantigrade foot (see ankle description below). In TST, the knee begins to flex as a result of a net knee flexor moment and power generation due to the simultaneous concentric contraction of the gastrocnemius and hip flexors. The knee continues to flex rapidly until the end of ISW, due to ankle plantar flexion until TO and hip flexion through ISW, therefore knee flexion is primarily a passive phenomenon at TO and ISW. Peak knee flexion at the end of ISW is critical for normal clearance of the foot. In MSW and TSW the knee extends secondary to momentum of the shank, after which there is an eccentric contraction of the knee flexors (hamstrings) that decelerates knee extension and prepares the knee for IC. The primary function of the knee is absorption (Figure 15-1) in stance and flexion for clearance in swing.

The Ankle Joint. During LR, under the eccentric control of the ankle dorsiflexors (net dorsiflexor moment), the ankle plantarflexes from a neutral position to several degrees of plantarflexion, until the foot becomes plantigrade. The net dorsiflexor activity prevents a foot slap after IC. During MST the tibia moves over the plantigrade foot so that ankle dorsiflexion occurs under the eccentric control of the ankle plantarflexors (net plantarflexor moment). The ankle plantarflexors help to prevent excessive knee flexion in MST. Finally, in TST and PSW the ankle starts to plantarflex under the concentric control of the ankle plantarflexors. This is associated with a significant power generation in TST and PSW, which helps to advance the limb into swing. In ISW, the ankle plantarflexes slightly and then dorsiflexes under control of the ankle dorsiflexors, to provide clearance in swing. In MSW, the ankle is slightly dorsiflexed, after which there is slight plantarflexion in TSW to a neutral or slightly plantarflexed position for IC. During the swing phase, the ankle moments and powers are negligible. The primary functions of the ankle in stance are power absorption to restrict the forward movement of the shank and power generation to help advance the limb into swing.

15.3.3. Coronal Plane Kinetics for the Hip and Knee

The following is a description of the normal hip, knee, and ankle coronal plane kinematics, moments, and powers (Figure 15-2).

The Hip Joint. During LR, the hip adducts under eccentric control of the hip abductors. Therefore, there is a net hip abductor moment and associated power absorption. This controls the lowering of the opposite hemipelvis and prevents a pelvic drop on the swing-limb side. In the remainder of stance the hip abducts under the concentric control

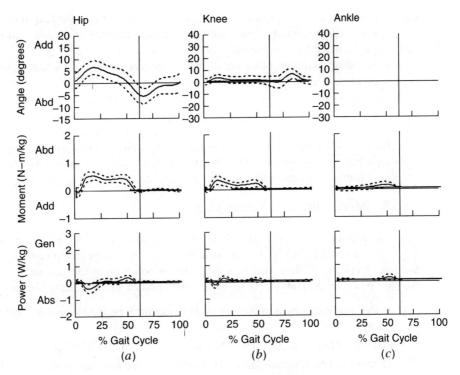

Figure 15-2. Normal coronal plane joint kinematics (first row), moments (second
row), and powers (third row) for (a) hip, (b) knee, and (c) ankle.
Mean ±1 S.D. are presented.

of the hip abductors. Therefore, there is a continued hip abductor moment and associated
power generation. This helps to elevate the contralateral hemipelvis to aid in clearance of the
contralateral swing limb. Hip joint kinetics in the coronal plane during swing are negligible.

   The Knee Joint.   During normal gait there is negligible movement of the knee in
the coronal plane.   There is, however, a net knee abductor moment throughout stance
that is created primarily by ligamentous forces. There is negligible power generation and
absorption in the stance phase and negligible moments and powers in the swing phase.

15.3.4. Stride-to-Stride Consistency

   Stride-to-stride consistency is generally good within a day and slightly reduced across
days in normal gait [20,21]. Fortunately, most children with CP spastic hemiplegia, diplegia,
and quadriplegia also show excellent stride-to-stride repeatability in joint kinematic and
kinetic data [22]. This is important for the utilization of this type of data in the clinical
setting, where the collection of a large number of trials might not be feasible. During data
interpretation, it is important to be aware of the stride-to-stride consistency for each variable.
Therefore, stride-to-stride consistency should be determined on a patient-by-patient basis
through the collection of multiple-stride data. Typically, three strides are recommended as
a minimum. This will help ensure that the data presented is reasonably representative of
a typical pattern of walking. If the clinician notices a variable gait pattern at the time of
the gait test, it is recommended that more trials be obtained. If stride-to-stride variability is

sufficient to result in different clinical decisions depending on the individual stride analyzed, treatment will tend to be more conservative. A child demonstrating a consistent deformity will tend to be treated less conservatively.

It is also necessary to be aware of other common sources of variability in joint kinetic patterns such as changes in walking velocity. A child with minimal experience with ambulation (less than a few years) generally shows greater stride-to-stride variability as ambulatory patterns might not yet be established. Ambulatory patients with athetosis can also exhibit stride-to-stride variability that appears very significant on observation of their gait. Review of the joint kinematics and kinetics in many of these patients, however, can show excellent stride-to-stride consistency in the lower extremity motion with the apparent variability primarily a function of variable arm movements.

15.3.5. Interpreting Joint Kinetic Data

Interpretation of the joint kinetic data typically involves the review of the data in plot form. The selected format for plot presentation should aid in the interpretation of the joint kinetics. A column of plots with the joint kinematic followed by the joint moment and then the joint power lends itself nicely to the interpretation checklist indicated below.

1. Select a specific phase in the gait cycle to evaluate the joint kinematic, moment, and power.
2. Determine the motion on the kinematic plot for the phase selected.
3. Determine which muscle group is dominant on the joint moment plot for the phase selected (if not confirmed on EMG movement, may be produced by other bony or soft tissue).
4. Conclude which type of contraction (concentric or eccentric) is occurring for the phase selected.
5. Confirm type of contraction on the power plot for the phase selected.

An example exercise for the ankle joint kinematics and kinetics in the stance phase is presented in Figure 15-3.

15.3.6. Troubleshooting Joint Kinetic Data

Joint kinetic data collected on normal persons results in typical patterns and easy interpretation based on the discussion above. Since most people without functional deficits walk in a similar manner, the joint kinetic patterns are easy to recognize and therefore reasonably easy to troubleshoot and search for potential problem data. This is not always the case in pathology as joint kinetic data can be very unpredictable in terms of "patterns" that indirectly reflect the complicated motion often exhibited in persons with abnormalities. Therefore, it is important to understand what potential problems might look like in terms of the data and to be aware of the potential problems in the collection of joint kinetics.

15.3.7. Important Points

There are two potential sources of error: (1) equipment errors such as force-plate and motion system malfunction or calibration problems, and (2) data collection errors such as incorrect foot positioning in relation to the force plate or poorly restrained joint markers.

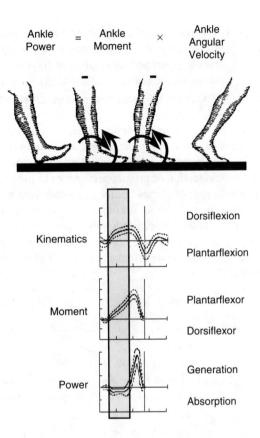

Figure 15-3. Normal (mean ±1 S.D.) sagittal plane joint kinetics for the ankle are plotted with the midstance highlighted. Three ankle rockers are drawn above plotted data with arrow pairs (left = moment, right = angular velocity) highlighting midstance. Evaluation of motion (top plot) indicates ankle is dorsiflexing over this phase in gait cycle. Net joint moment (middle plot) indicates ankle plantarflexors are dominant. If ankle is dorsiflexing when ankle plantarflexors are dominant, these muscles must be contracting eccentrically, or lengthening under tension, which is associated with a power absorption that can be confirmed on ankle power (bottom plot).

The following suggestions should help prevent the misinterpretation of problem data that might not be easily recognizable.

- Be aware of expected normal patterns and normal variability before interpreting pathological data.
- Be aware of connections between motion (kinematics) and kinetics in most circumstances (e.g., toe walking results in a net ankle plantarflexor moment).
- Be aware that ankle joint moments and powers should be negligible in the swing phase.
- Be careful to scale plots equally in all planes at all joints to prevent overinterpretation of relative differences in the data.
- Be suspicious if a curve extends beyond the preset graphing limits.
- Look for discontinuity in curves; that is, sharp and temporary changes in direction.

During the collection of data, the clinician should also look for potential problems. The simultaneous collection of video can also help confirm whether any problems occur that were not noticed during the data collection. Some typical problems include the following.

- Clearance problems of the opposite limb in the swing phase might contaminate force-plate data for the stance limb if the swing-limb foot comes into contact with the force plate.

- Clearance problems generally result in poor quality force-plate data; for example, onset of force-plate data might not be "initial contact" (if the foot slides to a stop on the plate) and termination of force-plate data might not be "toe-off" (if the foot drags on the plate in initial swing).
- Swing-limb foot comes into contact with the stance-limb foot or ankle.

If any of the above problems occur, the clinician can troubleshoot the data for potential problems by examining the force-plate data for inconsistencies in the ground reaction force plots. The center of pressure progression can also be evaluated for sudden excursions away from the direction of progression. An example of joint kinetic calculations made when the swing-limb foot comes briefly in contact with the force plate is given in Figure 15-4(a). Small spikes in the joint kinetic data are noticed at the hip and knee, with less obvious problems at the ankle. Further evaluation of the ground reaction force plots and the center of pressure path show abnormalities (discontinuities in the plots) indicating a problem in force data that are used in the calculation of the joint moments and powers [Figure 15-4(b) and (c)].

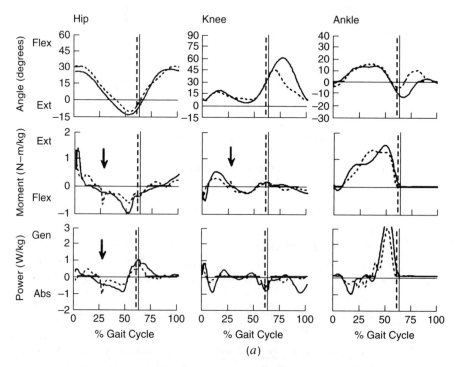

Figure 15-4. Illustration of a force-plate artifact due to minimal force-plate contact with swing-limb foot. (a) Inconsistencies are seen in the hip and knee moments and powers, with no noticeable problems at the ankle. Although the problem at the ankle is not "visible," it is still present as the problem force is used to calculate the ankle joint kinetics as well as the knee and hip. Inconsistencies are also seen in (b) the ground reaction force plots and (c) the center of pressure plot.

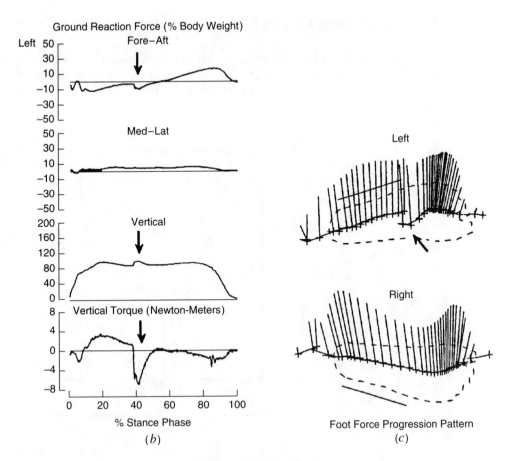

Figure 15-4. (*Continued*)

15.4. TYPICAL JOINT KINETIC PATTERNS

As mentioned in the previous section, it is wise to be aware of normal as well as typical expected patterns for certain deformities. This will help prevent misinterpretation of problem data and ultimately aid in the understanding of the mechanisms in pathological gait. In the future, patterning of gait analysis data might help direct treatment decision making for patients with gait abnormalities. Initial efforts in pattern recognition have been made for patients with CP [23]. Patterning will never remove the final clinician input into treatment decision making, but it may help improve consistency in treatment decision making as well as reduce the potential for interpretive errors.

The following is a brief discussion of some of the typical patterns seen in children with CP and myelomeningocele. The patterns are joint specific but are not meant to suggest that only one abnormal pattern occurs at a time. Generally, children with neuromuscular disorders exhibit patterns that involve problems at multiple levels on both lower limbs. At this time, the majority of these patterns do not suggest a specific type of treatment but help the clinician categorize the specific problems.

15.4.1. Double Bump Ankle Pattern

A double bump shape of the ankle moment and power usually occurs in those persons with spastic triceps surae as indicated by positive clonus on clinical exam, although there are some exceptions. This pattern typically occurs with simultaneous excessive knee flexion at initial contact. The following is a list of the typical characteristics of this pattern, which are also plotted in Figure 15-5.

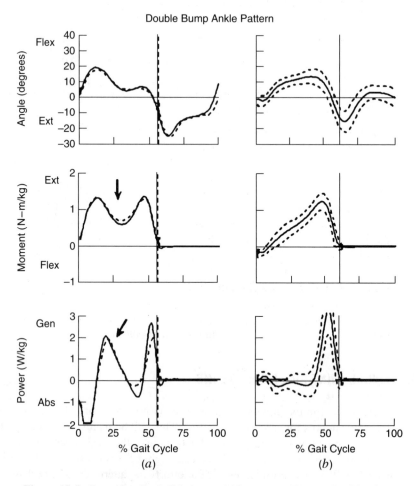

Figure 15-5. Example of a double bump ankle pattern. Repeated strides for a single side are plotted for ankle kinematic, moment, and power for (*a*) a child with cerebral palsy in comparison to (*b*) a normal reference.

Ankle joint kinematic

- Toe or foot-flat IC
- Neutral or excessive plantarflexion at IC
- Rapid dorsiflexion followed by premature plantarflexion in LR

- Rapid dorsiflexion followed by plantarflexion in the last half of stance
- Final plantarflexion might be nonfunctional (does not correspond with power generation)

Ankle joint moment

- Plantarflexor moment throughout 100 percent of stance (ankle plantarflexor dominance throughout stance)
- Premature excessive plantarflexor moment in early stance followed by rapid decrease, increase, and decrease in plantarflexor moment (double bump)

Ankle joint power

- Large power absorption in early stance (eccentric contraction of ankle plantarflexors as the ankle dorsiflexes)
- Premature power generation in MST (concentric contraction of ankle plantarflexors as the ankle plantarflexes)
- Inappropriate power generation in MST, driving body up not forward
- Second power absorption and generation (A_2)
- Second generation peak within normal limits or less than normal

A similar pattern can be seen in anyone who vaults to clear the opposite side for any reason. A double bump ankle pattern seen for a vault differs from a double bump pattern seen in an involved ankle by the dorsiflexor moment typically observed at the beginning of the stance phase on the vaulting side. Generally, there is a plantarflexor moment throughout the stance phase on the involved side.

15.4.2. Knee Extensor Moment Pattern

Knee extensor moment throughout the stance phase generally occurs in the more highly involved person with CP. Multiple associated problems also exist that contribute to the crouch, which include triceps surae, hip extensor weakness, and hamstring contracture. This pattern might or might not be associated with hip flexion contractures. Of interest, this pattern is a typical long-term result of isolated heel cord lengthening procedures in persons with more proximal involvement, which includes decreased knee extension at IC and lower extremity weakness (principally the hip extensors and ankle plantarflexors). The following is a list of the typical characteristics of this pattern, which are also plotted in Figure 15-6.

Joint kinematic

- Greater than normal knee flexion at initial contact and throughout the stance phase
- Minimal knee sagittal plane range of motion

Joint moment

- Knee extensor moment approximately equal to 100 percent of stance associated with dominant and continuous activity of the quadriceps throughout the stance phase
- Rapid extensor moment development during LR followed by a decrease in extensor moment
- Pattern of increasing and decreasing moment repeated (double bump pattern)

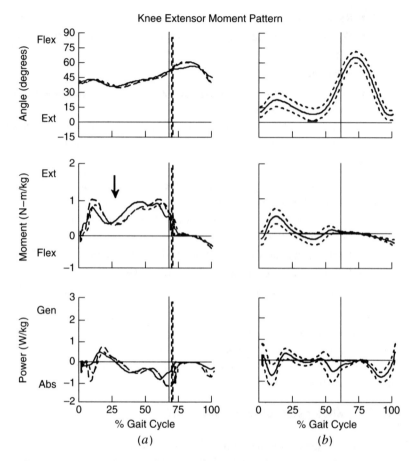

Figure 15-6. Example of a knee extensor moment pattern. Repeated strides for a single side are plotted for knee kinematic, moment, and power for (a) a child with cerebral palsy in comparison to (b) a normal reference.

Joint power

- Greater peak power generation and absorption
- Large power absorption in TST and PSW

15.4.3. Knee Flexor Moment Pattern

Knee flexor moment in the majority of stance phase typically occurs in a person with CP with heel cord tightness and/or spasticity and minimal hamstring contracture. This pattern is also common in persons with polio who exhibit a quadriceps avoidance gait. The following is a list of the typical characteristics of this pattern which are also plotted in Figure 15-7.

Joint kinematic

- Greater than normal knee flexion or full knee extension at IC
- Rapid knee extension after IC and hyperextension in MST
- Prolonged knee extension in TST

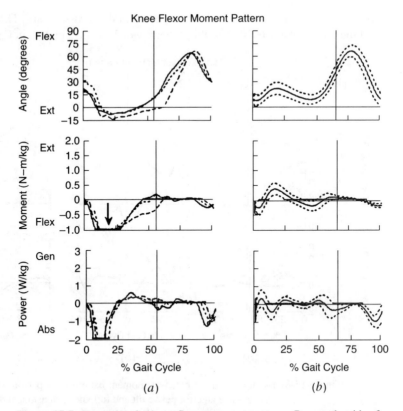

Figure 15-7. Example of a knee flexor moment pattern. Repeated strides for a single side are plotted for knee kinematic, moment, and power for (*a*) a child with cerebral palsy in comparison to (*b*) a normal reference.

Joint moment

- Rapid development and excessive peak knee flexor moment during the majority of stance (this might be hamstrings and gastrocnemius and/or ligamentous; EMG activity is required for confirmation of which muscles contribute to this moment)

Joint power

- Excessive power absorption in LR

15.4.4. Hip Extensor Moment Pattern

The hip extensor moment pattern is prolonged and generally greater than normal hip extensor moment in initial stance. This pattern is complex because it has many potential combinations of causes at the pelvis, hip, and knee. The most common associated problem in persons with CP is knee flexion (crouch) in stance. This can be a result of any one or a combination of conditions such as hip extensor and ankle plantarflexor weakness, hamstring tightness, or hip flexion contracture. A hip flexion contracture is usually associated with an excessive anterior pelvic tilt and can cause an excessive hip extensor moment pattern, which might or might not occur with excessive knee flexion. Finally, an excessive hip extensor moment pattern can be a result of a severe ankle equinus causing excessive knee and hip flexion as a compensation (this will be discussed in the next section). The following is a list of the typical characteristics of this pattern, which are also plotted in Figure 15-8.

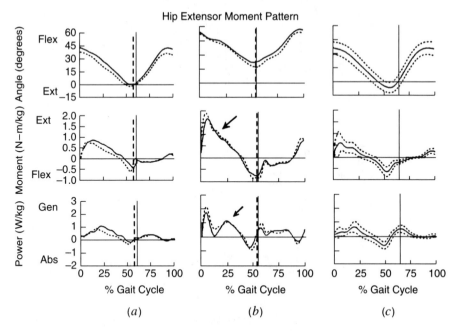

Figure 15-8. Example of a hip extensor moment pattern for a person with (*a*) an excessive anterior pelvic tilt and full knee extension, and (*b*) an excessive posterior pelvic tilt and knee flexion, in comparison to (*c*) a normal reference. Repeated strides for a single side are plotted for hip kinematic, moment, and power.

Joint kinematics
- Excessive hip flexion or delayed extension throughout the gait cycle, or
- Normal hip motion with excessive knee flexion with a posterior pelvic tilt

Joint moments
- Prolonged and greater than normal hip extensor moment from IC through TST, associated with
- Increased hip extensor activity

Joint powers
- Prolonged and greater than normal hip power generation from IC through TST

15.4.5. Hip Abductor Avoidance Pattern

Hip adductor moment throughout the stance phase typically occurs in patients with a functional or actual hip abductor weakness such as persons with myelomeningocele. This pattern is associated with excessive lateral lean of the trunk toward the stance side. This enables the resultant ground reaction force to pass lateral to the hip joint center so that the hip abductor musculature is not required. The following is a list of the typical characteristics of this pattern, which are also plotted in Figure 15-9.

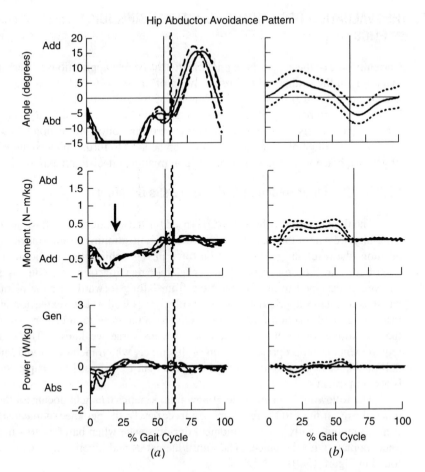

Figure 15-9. Example of a hip abductor avoidance pattern. Repeated strides for a single side are plotted for hip kinematic, moment, and power for (*a*) a child with myelomeningocele, and (*b*) a normal reference. Through lateral motion of the trunk toward the stance side a normal hip abductor moment is avoided.

Joint kinematic (hip)

- Hip abduction from MSW to MST
- Hip adduction from MST to MSW

Joint moment

- Hip adductor moment during 100 percent of stance, associated with
- Dominant hip adductor activity

Joint power

- Power absorption during LR, depicted as
- Eccentric contraction of the hip adductors
- Power generation during the remainder of stance

15.5. THE EVALUATION OF ORTHOTIC FUNCTION USING JOINT KINETICS

Currently, one of the areas where joint kinetics has direct applications to treatment decision making is in the evaluation and prescription of orthoses [6,10,11]. In those persons that already have fitted orthoses, the evaluation of the orthosis through gait analysis might indicate that another type of brace is more appropriate. This information can then be used for the next orthosis prescription. The purpose of the following section is to present some examples that illustrate how joint kinetics can be used to further understand the mechanics of gait and brace wear and ultimately help in treatment decision making.

15.5.1. The Floor Reaction Orthosis versus Barefoot

The floor reaction orthosis (FRO) is used for those patients who have significant lower extremity weakness that results in severe crouch positioning in the stance phase. In this position, the resultant ground reaction force passes behind the knee joint center, further contributing to the crouch problem. The floor reaction orthosis, with its strong ankle support, is designed to prevent the tibia from falling forward over the plantargrade foot and thus maintains appropriate ankle dorsiflexion as well as knee extension in stance. The resultant ground reaction force passes anterior to the knee joint center. The brace would then substitute for severe quadriceps and triceps surae weakness. There are minimum requirements for appropriate function of this brace, which include normal knee extension at IC and knee flexion contractures of no more than 15 degrees [24]. Hip extensor strength is also important.

The following is an example of how joint kinetics can help document the function of this orthosis. If the FRO is functioning appropriately, the net knee moment should change from a predominantly extensor moment during stance when barefoot to a more "normal" knee moment with the brace. The joint kinematics and kinetics for this example can be found in Figure 15-10.

Knee (barefoot walking): In this example, during barefoot walking the knee shows greater than normal flexion at IC and throughout the stance phase. This is associated with an excessive knee extensor moment pattern and abnormal power modulation.

Knee (FRO walking): With the FRO there is continued excessive flexion at IC and throughout the stance phase. This degree of knee flexion would usually suggest a toe IC despite the neutral position of the ankle held in the FRO. There is a continued knee extensor moment pattern throughout the stance phase, which indicates that the resultant ground reaction force never passes anterior to the knee. This would again indicate continuous quadriceps activity in the stance phase. Therefore, the FRO is not functioning as designed in this person. Also, the joint power shows greater peak generation and absorption during the FRO versus the barefoot condition.

15.5.2. Barefoot versus Orthoses in Patients with Myelomeningocele

Ambulatory problems in persons with myelomeningocele (ML) are generally treated using a combination of lower extremity surgery and orthoses. The type of orthoses applied varies between a simple ankle-foot orthosis (AFO) or knee-ankle-foot orthosis (KAFO) to complicated bracing systems including parawalkers and hip guidance orthoses [25]. By using joint kinematics and kinetics, gait analysis is an appropriate tool for the evaluation

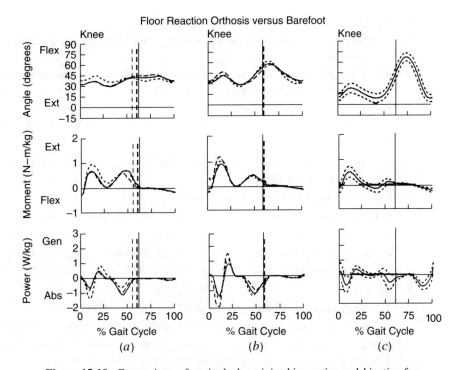

Figure 15-10. Comparison of sagittal plane joint kinematics and kinetics for the knee (multiple strides) during (*a*) barefoot walking, (*b*) floor reaction orthosis (FRO), and (*c*) normal walking for a selected limb in a boy with cerebral palsy spastic diplegia. FRO does not reduce crouch or knee extensor moment.

and prescription of brace wear in persons with ML, considering their very complex motion patterns. Systematic review of orthosis function in these persons shows that the appropriate application of a solid AFO results in changes in the sagittal gait patterns that approximate normal at the ankle, knee, and hip [10]. The data also suggest that the application of a KAFO does not provide any further benefit to the sagittal plane motion at the ankle, knee, or hip.

Treatment issues in this patient population, however, involve not only the sagittal plane but also medial knee instability, which can be addressed with evaluation of the coronal plane kinetics. The KAFO has been recommended for this problem to reduce the apparent knee "valgus thrust" during LR. In the following example, a child with ML is wearing KAFOs for protection of the knee against excessive valgus forces. Through the use of joint kinetics we can obtain an estimate of the knee coronal plane moments that will indicate the potential risk to the knee. The 3-D gait kinematics also help the clinician understand the reason for the visually apparent knee valgus thrust during LR.

Description of Kinematics.   Because of the complex motion patterns during barefoot walking in persons with ML, a brief discussion of the joint kinematics is necessary.

Trunk

• Excessive lateral motion towards stance side (to minimize hip abductor moment)

• Excessive transverse plane rotation in a pattern similar to the pelvis with internal rotation during LR and external rotation at TO

Pelvis

- Bilateral pelvic hike in swing and drop in stance in the coronal plane (hip abductor weakness)
- Excessive anterior pelvic tilt with double bump pattern of increasing lordosis twice during the gait cycle (hip extensor weakness)
- Excessive range of motion in the transverse plane with excessive internal rotation during LR and external rotation at TO (compensation for hip extensor weakness)

Hip

- Progressive adduction in MST through MSW (secondary to hip abductor weakness and pelvic hike in swing)
- Progressive abduction in TSW and LR
- Excessive abduction at IC (secondary to large internal pelvic rotation at IC)
- Sagittal plane motion within normal limits
- Progressive internal rotation during stance and external rotation during swing in the transverse plane (secondary to excessive pelvic motion in the transverse plane)

Knee

- Greater than normal knee flexion at IC
- Excessive knee flexion in stance (plantarflexor and hip extensor weakness)
- Knee flexion in swing (peak and timing) is within normal limits (possibly due to hip flexion and not ankle plantarflexion)
- Apparent "valgus thrust"* in the coronal plane of the knee during LR (visual effect as a result of simultaneous knee flexion, internal pelvic rotation, and external foot thigh angle)

Ankle

- Bilateral drop foot in swing (ankle dorsiflexor weakness) with associated absence of first rocker in LR
- Progressive dorsiflexion to excessive peak dorsiflexion in stance (ankle plantarflexor weakness)
- Excessive external foot progression in stance (pes planovalgus deformity and flail foot)
- Rapid external rotation of the foot in TSW (secondary to simultaneous rapid external rotation of the hip)

With the bilateral KAFOs, significant improvements in the joint kinematics were seen that are similar to those changes seen in the sagittal plane with the AFOs. For example, knee sagittal plane motion is within normal limits with full knee extension at IC attained (possibly due to the correction of the drop foot). Due to the ankle portion of the KAFO, an exaggerated flexion wave during LR occurs. Both ankles are held in approximately neutral position with some brace deflection into dorsiflexion during stance. Foot progression is corrected somewhat, with better forefoot alignment as a result of the brace. No changes in hip motion in all three planes were noted as the KAFO does not address any of the weakness problems at the hip joint. As a result, the compensations seen at the trunk for hip musculature weakness are the same in the AFO and KAFO. There is, however, an increase in

*Comment based on visual observation of coronal view.

the pelvic range of motion with a more exaggerated double bump pattern with the base-line pelvic tilt unchanged. No other changes in the coronal and transverse plane were noted.

Description of Joint Kinetics.   The following is a description of the joint kinetics in the same patient during barefoot walking [Figure 15-11(*a*)].

Hip

- Normal modulation in the sagittal plane
- Net adductor moment in the coronal plane, which is possible as a result of the trunk, pelvis, and hip position during LR (compensatory to reduce hip abductor muscle demand)

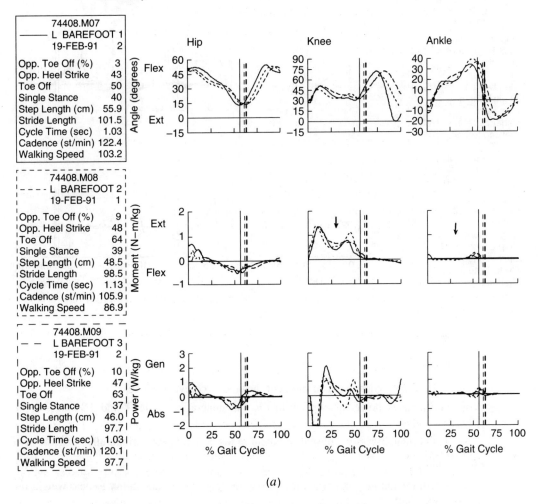

(*a*)

Figure 15-11. Comparison of sagittal plane joint kinematics and kinetics for hip, knee, and ankle in a patient walking (*a*) barefoot, and (*b*) with a knee-ankle-foot orthosis (KAFO). Multiple repeat trials for each condition are given. Application of KAFO results in improved knee and ankle joint kinematics and kinetics as indicated by arrows.

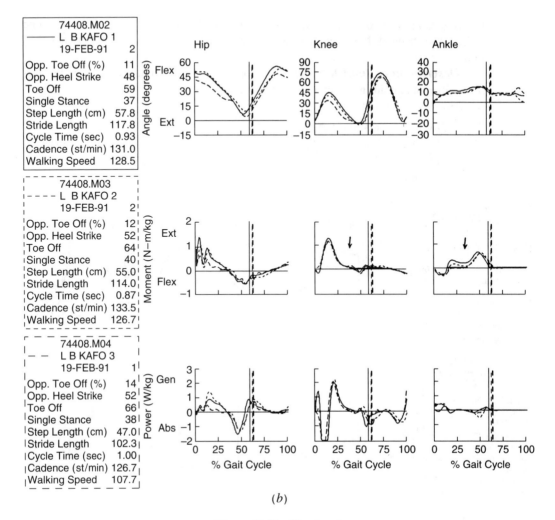

(b)

Figure 15-11. (*Continued*)

Knee

- Excessive knee extensor moment in stance to prevent collapse
- Excessive power absorption in LR and generation in MST and TST to prevent collapse
- Minimal abductor (muscle) moment in the coronal plane, bilaterally

Ankle

- Minimal ankle plantarflexor moment in stance (minimal ability to bear weight on the forefoot (see Figure 15-12)
- Negligible ankle power generation

The following is a list of comments about the changes in the sagittal plane joint kinetic patterns when wearing bilateral KAFOs. These changes are also illustrated in Figure

15-11(*a*) and (*b*). The changes noted are similar to those changes typically seen in the sagittal plane with the application of AFOs (not illustrated). With the KAFO, there is better ankle moment modulation in stance with a normal plantarflexor moment in TST. This is possible because of increased weight-bearing capabilities on the forefoot. Negligible power absorption/generation in stance as the KAFO minimizes ankle movement. At the knee, there is better moment modulation with a reduction of the extensor moment in MST and TST. There is a slightly greater than normal knee extensor moment in LR due to the knee flexion thrust with a reduction in the power absorption during LR and generation in TST. No changes in the coronal plane moments were noted. No changes in hip joint kinetics in the sagittal or coronal planes were noted.

A comparison of the center of pressure path and the resultant ground reaction force path for the barefoot and brace walk can help us appreciate the reason why the joint kinetics change with the application of the KAFOs (Figure 15-12). With the KAFOs, weight bearing on the distal aspect of the foot is possible. This, along with controlled forward motion of the tibia (also a function of the KAFO's solid ankle joint), reduces knee flexion and maintains the ground reaction force anterior to the knee joint center. This is confirmed by the reduced knee extensor moment in stance in the brace condition.

Center of Pressure Path

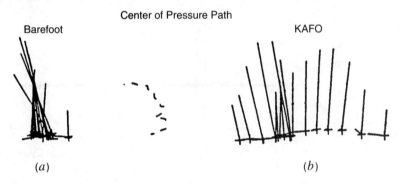

Figure 15-12. Comparison of center of pressure path and resultant ground reaction force path for (*a*) a barefoot, and (*b*) a KAFO walk. During barefoot walking, the majority of body weight is concentrated at the heel; with KAFO, weight bearing is possible on the distal aspect of the foot.

An evaluation of the knee valgus thrust can be completed using the coronal plane joint kinetics at the knee. If a knee valgus thrust is observed during LR, there should be an excessive knee (internal) adductor moment to protect the knee. In the child described above, there is a visual valgus thrust during LR that is not substantiated by the coronal plane joint kinetic data, which indicate that the knee has a net abductor moment (Figure 15-13). Therefore, the gait analysis data do not correspond with the visual interpretation of gait. Examining the complex motion patterns in this patient population suggests that a combination of excessive and continuing internal pelvic rotation, excessive and continuing knee flexion, and external rotation of the foot during LR results in an "apparent" knee valgus thrust. When this child with a knee valgus thrust was fitted with an appropriate AFO, which controlled the excessive knee flexion and improved the foot progression, the apparent knee valgus thrust was eliminated. Evaluation both in and out of the brace revealed normal knee kinetics in the coronal

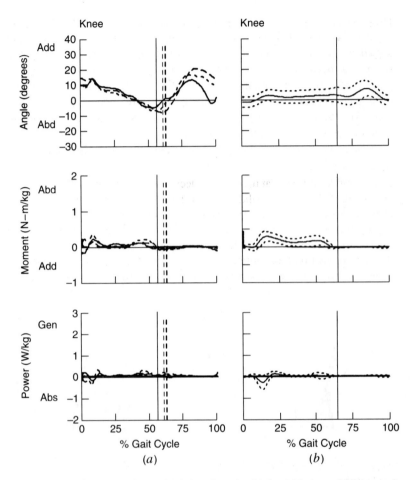

Figure 15-13. Comparison of (*a*) barefoot (multiple strides), and (*b*) normal
coronal plane knee joint kinematics and kinetics for a child with
myelomeningocele. Despite the apparent knee valgus thrust noted
on visual analysis of gait, normal knee moments were noted at the
knee during barefoot walking.

plane. This case result was similar to results found in a recent series of children tested at the
Newington Children's Hospital. Only 4 out of 20 who exhibited a visual knee valgus thrust
actually had net knee adductor moments [10]. These data do not indicate that all children will
not have an excessive adductor moment at the knee when visually they have a "valgus thrust,"
but it emphasizes the importance of a more objective documentation of gait through gait analysis before the higher bracing is prescribed for the specific problem of a knee valgus thrust.

15.5.3. Kinetic Analysis of Posterior Leaf Spring (PLS) Orthosis

The following information is based on a recent study to evaluate the function of the
posterior leaf spring (PLS) orthosis in ambulatory children with CP [11]. The PLS is
generally prescribed to eliminate drop foot or excessive plantarflexion in swing and thus

improve prepositioning of the foot and ankle for IC. Also, the supple ankle joint of this orthosis allows for progressive motion of the shank over the plantargrade foot, commonly referred to as *second rocker*. It is believed that the PLS augments push-off through a "spring-like action" of the brace, as suggested by the name. The truth of this can be evaluated with the application of joint kinetics or, more specifically, the effect of the PLS on the ankle joint powers. Therefore, the primary purpose of this study was to determine if the PLS actually increased the power-generating capability of the ankle in comparison to barefoot walking. Twenty-one children (24 limbs) with a diagnosis of CP were evaluated using gait analysis during barefoot and PLS gait. Force-plate data collection was completed for all trials in both conditions with the findings summarized in Table 15-1. The data indicates that the push-off power at the ankle is decreased on average with the application of the PLS as compared to barefoot walking. The total energy generated decreased and the total power absorbed increased. This data indicated that although the PLS allows power generation at the ankle during TST, the PLS does not augment this capability as the name suggests.

TABLE 15-1 COMPARISON OF SELECTED MEAN ($\pm$ 1 S.D.) JOINT KINETICS VALUES DURING BAREFOOT AND POSTERIOR LEAF SPRING WALKING

	Peak power generated (W/kg)	Total energy absorbed (J/kg)	Total energy generated (J/kg)
Barefoot	0.88 ± 0.30	-0.15 ± 0.07	0.11 ± 0.05
PLS	0.73 ± 0.27	-0.19 ± 0.07	0.07 ± 0.04
p level	< 0.01	< 0.05	< 0.0001

15.6. PREOPERATIVE VERSUS POSTOPERATIVE JOINT KINETICS

In this section, various comparisons of preoperative versus postoperative joint kinetic data from patients who have undergone surgical treatment of gait abnormalities will be presented. At this time, joint kinetics have a limited direct application to surgical decision making in children with CP. Although joint kinetics contribute to our knowledge of the cause of movement abnormalities, they will become a routine contributor to surgical decision making after systematic evaluation of the effects of surgery on joint kinetics has been completed.

15.6.1. Preoperative versus Postoperative Ankle Joint Kinetics

The following discussion is based on a recent study to evaluate the effects of the Baker-type heel cord lengthening on the ankle joint kinetics [13]. Twenty children (24 limbs) with a diagnosis of CP were included in the study. A gait analysis, including joint kinematics and kinetics, was completed just prior to and approximately one year after surgical intervention. All limbs underwent a gastrocnemius aponeurotic lengthening as well as simultaneous other procedures. The results showed increased static ankle range of motion and increased dorsiflexion in stance and swing after surgery. Joint kinetic results showed decreased MST power generation and increased TST power generation, both of which were statistically significant. These changes have also been characterized as changes in the modulation of the joint kinetic patterns. Also of note, increased knee extension in stance was noted in all cases.

A typical patient in this study is depicted in the following description and plots (Figure 15-14) as an example. The description refers directly to the preoperative and postoperative columns of plots. This patient underwent simultaneous Baker-type gastrocnemius aponeurotic lengthening, medial hamstring lengthening, distal rectus femoris release, and distal internal tibial derotation osteotomy. The comments will be limited to this example.

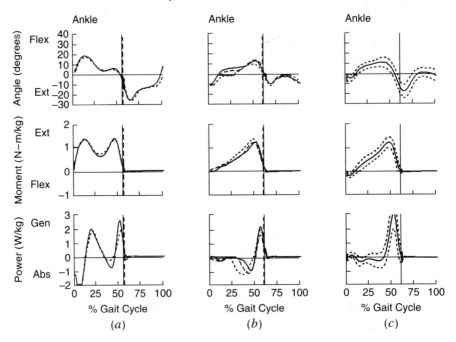

Figure 15-14. Comparison of sagittal plane joint kinematics and kinetics for ankle of involved limb (multiple strides) for a boy with cerebral palsy right spastic hemiplegia. (*a*) before surgery, (*b*) after surgery, and (*c*) normal. After Baker-type heel cord lengthening, the double-bump ankle kinetic pattern is eliminated with normal modulation noted and no decrease in ankle power-generating capabilities.

Preoperative ankle

- Ankle dorsiflexion (no first rocker) with plantarflexor moment and associated power absorption during LR
- Premature ankle plantarflexion with continued plantarflexor moment with power generation in MST
- Small period of ankle dorsiflexion with continued plantarflexor moment and associated power absorption in TST
- Second ankle plantarflexion with continued plantarflexor moment and associated power generation in PSW

Postoperative ankle

- Progressive ankle dorsiflexion in stance with progressive increase in ankle plantarflexor moment and associated minimal power absorption
- Ankle plantarflexion with peak plantarflexor moment and associated power generation in TST and PSW

Postoperative changes included more "normal" modulation, which is best appreciated by examination of the joint kinetic plots. The elimination of the inappropriate power generation and absorption during the first half of stance suggests improved efficiency postoperatively.

15.6.2. Preoperative versus Postoperative Tibial Derotation Osteotomy

The following child presented with a unilateral excessive external tibial torsion with resulting excessive external foot progression. Treatment for this deformity was a distal tibial internal rotational osteotomy. This surgical decision was not determined on the basis of the joint kinetic data but it is an interesting example of the effects of this surgery on the joint kinetics as described below and plotted in Figure 15-15. The effects of malrotations in the transverse plane on the sagittal plane motion and kinetics is little understood. In general, however, it is known that muscle function is further compromised in children with

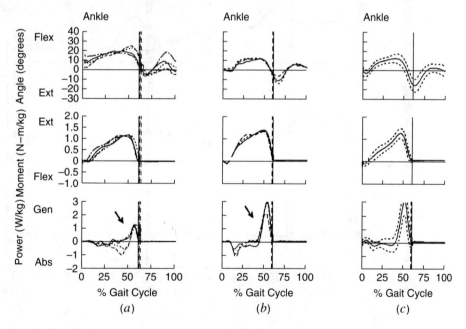

Figure 15-15. Comparison of sagittal plane joint kinematics and kinetics for ankle of involved limb (multiple strides) for a boy with external tibial torsion and no neuromuscular problems. (*a*) before surgery, (*b*) after surgery, and (*c*) normal. Surgery was a unique distal internal tibial and fibular osteotomy.

CP when the muscles are contracting with "reduced" moment arms or in a plane of motion not normal to their function. This concept has also been referred to as *lever arm deficiency* [26]. The preoperative ankle joint power shows reduced power generating capabilities in TST. Postoperatively, there is normal ankle kinematic and kinetic modulation in stance. As the tibial derotation was the only surgery performed in this case, one can state definitively that the osteotomy resulted in improved positioning of the foot with respect to the direction of progression, which increased ankle power-generating capabilities in TST.

15.6.3. Preoperative versus Postoperative Knee Joint Kinetics

The following child with CP spastic diplegia presented with a bilateral crouch gait pattern. Although the treatment of crouch gait is well defined in terms of joint kinematics [27–29], the effect on the joint kinetics is not well documented. The surgery performed included simultaneous bilateral medial hamstring lengthenings and distal rectus femoris transfers. The following is a description of the knee joint kinematic and kinetic changes before and after surgery (Figure 15-16).

Preoperative knee

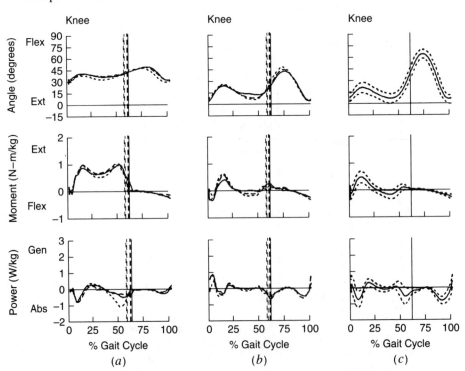

Figure 15-16. Comparison of sagittal plane joint kinematics and kinetics for knee (multiple strides) for a selected limb in a child with cerebral palsy spastic diplegia. (*a*) before surgery, (*b*) after surgery, and (*c*) normal. Surgery included medial hamstring lengthenings and rectus femoris transfers.

- Excessive knee flexion at IC and throughout the stance phase
- Limited and delayed peak knee flexion in swing
- Associated knee extensor moment through the stance phase
- Power absorption during mildly increasing knee flexion and knee extension moment during LR
- Power absorption during increasing knee flexion with continued knee extensor moment in PSW

Postoperative knee

- Normal knee kinematic and kinetic modulation in stance

The joint kinematics and kinetics demonstrate how a reduction in the crouch positioning also results in improved knee kinetics with a reduction in the knee extensor moment. This would indicate that postoperatively the child would have less demand on the knee extensors (quadriceps), suggesting a more energy-efficient gait. Also, the reduction in the excessive knee extensor moment in PSW might allow for improved knee flexion in the initial part of the swing phase.

15.6.4. Preoperative versus Postoperative Sagittal Plane Kinetics

The following child with CP spastic hemiplegia presented with unilateral problems. Surgical intervention included the following simultaneous procedures for the right side only: psoas recession over the brim of the pelvis, medial hamstring lengthening, distal rectus femoris transfer, Baker-type gastrocnemius lengthening, proximal femoral derotation osteotomy, and distal internal tibial derotation osteotomy. The changes in the sagittal plane joint kinematics and kinetics are described below and plotted in Figure 15-17(a) and (b). The postoperative evaluation was performed one year after surgery.

Preoperative Kinetics.

Ankle

- Dorsiflexion with a plantarflexor moment and associated power absorption during LR
- Premature plantarflexion with continued plantarflexor moment and associated power generation in MST
- Continued premature plantarflexion with continued plantarflexor moment and associated power generation in TST and PSW

Knee

- Excessive flexion at IC and during LR with associated exaggerated extensor moment and power absorption within normal limits
- Remainder of stance and swing kinematics and kinetics within normal limits

Hip

- Joint kinematics and kinetics within normal limits except for slightly reduced hip extension in TST [no hip flexion contracture on clinical exam and strength measured normal (5)]

Postoperative Kinetics.

- Improved modulation of the ankle kinematics and kinetics with increased power generating capabilities in TST
- Reduction of the flexion in stance and associated knee extensor moment
- Earlier and premature crossover of the hip extensor moment and power in stance
- No change in hip power generation burst timing at TO

Generally, there was an overall improvement of joint kinematics and kinetics in the sagittal plane. The only exceptions are the results at the hip in the early part of stance, with an early crossover of the hip moment and power from extensor to flexor and generation to absorption, respectively. The implications of this early crossover are unclear.

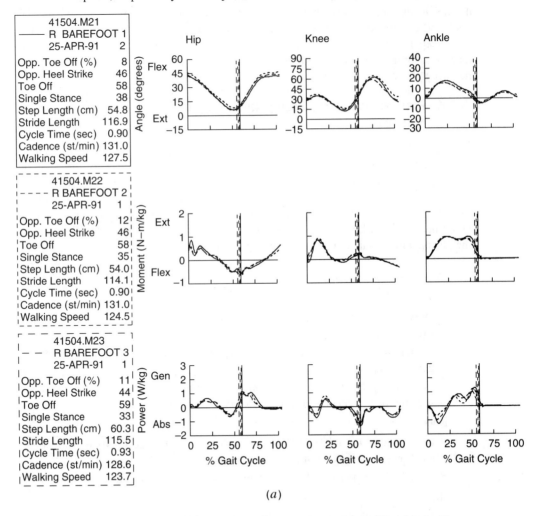

(a)

Figure 15-17. Example of sagittal plane joint kinematics and kinetics for hip, knee, and ankle for involved limb (multiple strides) (a) before surgery, and (b) after surgery in a teenage girl with cerebral palsy spastic hemiplegia. Surgery included a multiple-level approach for one side, including hip, knee, and ankle.

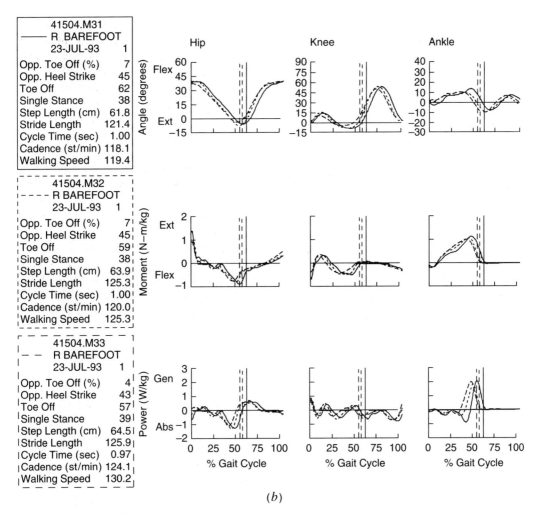

41504.M31	
R BAREFOOT	———
23-JUL-93	1
Opp. Toe Off (%)	7
Opp. Heel Strike	45
Toe Off	62
Single Stance	38
Step Length (cm)	61.8
Stride Length	121.4
Cycle Time (sec)	1.00
Cadence (st/min)	118.1
Walking Speed	119.4

41504.M32	
R BAREFOOT	- - - -
23-JUL-93	1
Opp. Toe Off (%)	7
Opp. Heel Strike	45
Toe Off	59
Single Stance	38
Step Length (cm)	63.9
Stride Length	125.3
Cycle Time (sec)	1.00
Cadence (st/min)	120.0
Walking Speed	125.3

41504.M33	
R BAREFOOT	— —
23-JUL-93	1
Opp. Toe Off (%)	4
Opp. Heel Strike	43
Toe Off	57
Single Stance	39
Step Length (cm)	64.5
Stride Length	125.9
Cycle Time (sec)	0.97
Cadence (st/min)	124.1
Walking Speed	130.2

(*b*)

Figure 15-17. (*Continued*)

15.6.5. Preoperative versus Postoperative Changes in Hip Kinetics

The following child with CP spastic hemiplegia presented with a problem of severe unilateral equinus and associated gait abnormalities. Evaluation of the preoperative versus postoperative sagittal plane joint kinematics and kinetics illustrates the effects of distal deformities on the more proximal joints. How one differentiates between a secondary and a primary problem is one of the greatest challenges in evaluating pathological gait. Further evaluation of the clinical examination might lead the clinician to conclude in this case that the dynamic involvement of the hip and knee is a function of the ankle alone and not pathology at the other joints. These conclusions are generally not so clear-cut. A description of the preoperative and postoperative findings are included below, along with the motion and kinetic data [Figure 15-18(*a*) and (*b*)]. This child underwent a right Baker-type gastrocnemius lengthening and posterior tibialis lengthening between the two gait tests.

Preoperative Sagittal Plane Kinetics.

Ankle

- Excessive ankle plantarflexion with associated plantarflexor moment through 100 percent of stance
- Degree of equinus resulting in a decreased ankle plantarflexor moment
- Power absorption/generation negligible

Knee

- Crouch with associated extensor moment in stance
- Negligible power generation/absorption

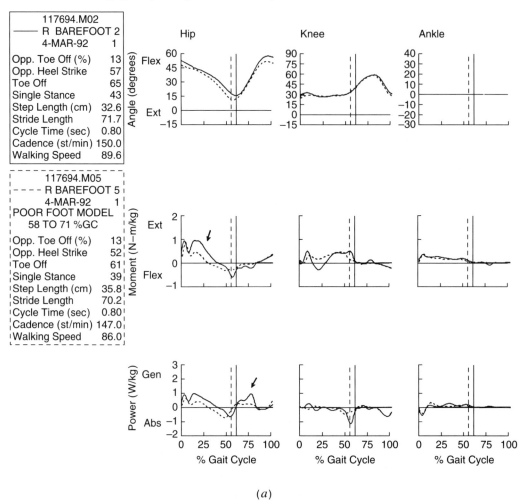

(*a*)

Figure 15-18. Example of sagittal plane joint kinematics and kinetics for hip, knee, and ankle for involved limb (multiple strides) (*a*) before surgery, and (*b*) after surgery in a boy with cerebral palsy spastic hemiplegia. Preoperative to postoperative changes were noted not only in ankle but in hip and knee joint kinematics and kinetics as well after surgery to ankle joint musculature alone.

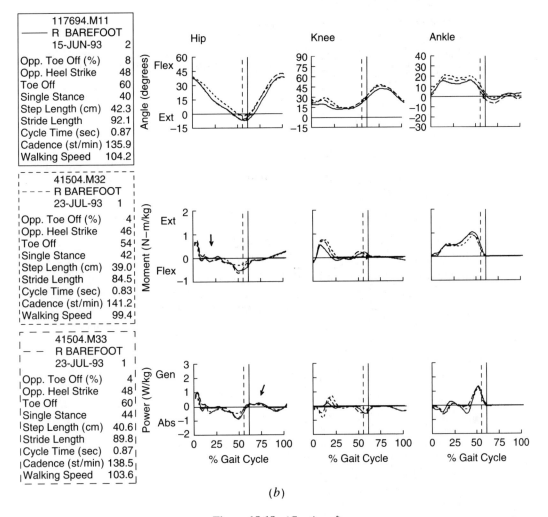

Figure 15-18. (*Continued*)

Hip

- Hip flexion-extension skewed toward flexion with limited extension in TST (no hip flexion contracture on clinical exam with normal strength)
- Prolonged hip extensor moment and power crossover with delay in power generation at TO

Postoperative Kinetics.

- Improved ankle kinetic modulation with power generation in TST
- Reduced knee flexion in stance and crouch pattern
- Premature hip moment and power crossover in stance; normalized power generation at TO

Examination of the joint kinematics and kinetics illustrates how changes at the knee and hip can be a direct function of the ankle surgery alone. This example illustrates how surgical decisions cannot be made on the evaluation of the joint kinematics or kinetics alone, as this can result in treatment of gait abnormalities that are compensations and not primary problems [12]. A normal clinical evaluation of the hip and knee and normal EMG, as in this case, would lead the clinician away from treating the abnormal hip and knee joint kinematics and kinetics.

15.7. CONCLUSIONS

Motion analysis has proved to be a very useful tool in the treatment of gait problems in children with neuromuscular conditions. Not only does it provide information about the specific joint abnormalities, it also documents the child's preoperative and postoperative status so that the clinician can accurately assess treatment. Because of this ability to scrutinize the results, the last ten years has been a time of rapid change as many traditional treatments have been discarded and new methods developed.

Initially, gait analysis included dynamic EMG, temporal and stride parameters, and joint kinematics. Electromyography allowed us to determine which muscles or muscle groups were active during gait. Temporal and stride characteristics quantified such measures as cadence, step and stride lengths, and walking velocity. Kinematics allowed us to see, for the first time, the 3-D joint angular motion. With kinetics, we can improve our understanding of the mechanisms underlying pathological gait and ultimately improve our understanding of the causes of gait abnormalities.

At the time of this writing, a systematic evaluation of the effects of surgery on joint kinetics will be required before joint kinetics become a routine part of the treatment decision-making process for children with neuromuscular disorders such as CP. Presently, however, joint kinetics can directly contribute to treatment decisions in the following ways:

1. Orthotic prescription evaluation with the use of joint kinetics provides valuable information for appropriate selection in patients with CP and other pathologies.
2. The presence of a power generation burst in MST at the ankle supports consideration for a Baker-type heel cord lengthening.
3. The transverse plane is better understood with the addition of kinetic information. Lever arm deficiency as a consequence of bony malrotation becomes a more quantifiable entity, and the correction of such malrotation is better evaluated by power data.
4. Surgical procedures involving single joints (i.e., the knee) can produce significant kinematic and kinetic changes at adjacent and even distant joints. The treatment decision tree might be substantially modified in the near future as more experience is accumulated relating to this issue.

Other areas of interpretation of joint kinetics, although not directly related to surgical treatment decisions at this point in time, might increase our understanding of the mechanisms of pathological gait. They include the following:

1. When there is a joint moment with minimal joint power and no EMG from the dominant muscles or muscle group, the joint stability is not being provided by active contraction. Comprehensive EMG data would be necessary to confirm the above.

2. Examination of the EMG data and joint moments can indicate whether the timing of the muscle or muscle group is appropriate to the net moment at the joint. A muscle group that is acting against a dominant moment might be an antagonist to the desired motion.

3. By overlaying the hip and knee power curves, we can show how energy is transferred between segments by the biarticular muscles. Further examination of normal versus pathological energy transfers might lead to further understanding of the effects of co-contraction on gait.

4. The concept of summing the hip, knee, and ankle joint moments into a single *support moment* has been used [30] to make some inferences about muscular control in the lower extremities. This technique, however, will not replace the potential decision-making utility of the individual joint moments at the hip, knee, and ankle.

5. A study of the relative contribution of power-generating capabilities at the hip, knee, and ankle in the sagittal plane before and after surgery will increase our understanding of the contributions of these joints to forward progression.

With the addition of joint kinetics to joint kinematics, dynamic EMG, and clinical examination, we can improve our ability to document and determine the causes of gait abnormalities. With this additional information and resulting new knowledge, we have already begun to make some significant improvements in treatment of the child with CP. With the broadening interest and understanding of pathological gait, the routine utilization of joint kinetics might be in the near future. The complex interactions of primary problems and compensations seen in all three planes of motion and at all joint levels only confirms the complexity of gait abnormalities in children with neuromuscular disorders and emphasizes the necessity of accurate objective documentation of gait for appropriate treatment decision making.

References

[1] Gage JR. Gait analysis for decision making in cerebral palsy. *Bull Hops Jt Dis Orthop Inst* 1993; 43:147–163.

[2] Perry J. Distal rectus femoris transfer. *Dev Med Child Neurol* 1987;29:153–158.

[3] Gage JR, Õunpuu S. Gait analysis in clinical practice. *Sem Orthop* 1989;4(2):72–87.

[4] Sutherland DH, Santi M, Abel, MD. Treatment of stiff-knee gait in cerebral palsy: A comparison by gait analysis of the distal rectus femoris transfer versus proximal rectus release. *J Ped Orthop* 1990;10:433–441.

[5] DeLuca PA. Gait analysis in the treatment of ambulatory child with cerebral palsy. *Clin Orthop* 1991;264:65–75.

[6] Rose SA, Õunpuu S, DeLuca, PA. Strategies for the assessment of gait in a clinical setting. *Phys Ther* 1991;71:961–980.

[7] Inman VT, Ralston HJ, Todd, F. *Human Walking*. Baltimore, Md: Williams & Wilkins Publishing Co;1981:Ch 4:78–88.

[8] Winter, DA. *Biomechanics and Motor Control of Human Movement 2nd ed.* Waterloo, Ontario: University of Waterloo Press;1990; Ch 1:9.

[9] Schneider K, Hart T, Zernicke RF, Setoguchi Y, Oppenheim W. Dynamics of below-knee child amputee gait: SACH foot versus Flex foot. *J Biomech* 1993;26(10):1191–1204.

[10] Õunpuu S, Davis RB, Banta JV, DeLuca PA. The effects of orthotics on gait in children with low level myelomeningocele. *Proc N Amer Congr on Biomech* 1992:323–324.

[11] Õunpuu S, Bell KJ, Davis RB, DeLuca PA, An evaluation of the posterior leaf spring orthosis using gait analysis. *Dev Med Child Neurol* 1993;35(9):8.

[12] Gage JR, Õunpuu S. In: Patla AE ed. *Adaptability of Human Gait* North-Holland: Elsevier Science Publishers BV;1991:359–385.

[13] Rose SA, DeLuca PA, Davis RB, Õunpuu S, Gage JR. Kinematic and kinetic evaluation of the ankle after lengthening of the gastrocnemius fascia in children with cerebral palsy. *J Ped Orthop* 1993;13:727–732.

[14] Davis RB, Õunpuu S, Tyburski DJ, DeLuca PA. A comparison of two-dimensional and three-dimensional techniques for the determination of joint rotation angles. *Proc Intl Symp on 3-D Anal of Human Mvmt* 1991:67–70.

[15] Davis RB, Õunpuu S, Tyburski DJ, Gage JR. A gait analysis data collection and reduction technique. *Hum Mvmt Sci* 1991;10(5):575–587.

[16] Õunpuu S, Gage JR, Davis RB. Three-dimensional lower extremity joint kinetics in normal pediatric gait. *J Ped Orthop* 1991;11:341–349.

[17] Wells RP. The projection of the ground reaction force as a predictor of internal joint moments. *Bull Prosthetic Res* 1981;18:15–19.

[18] Greenwood DT. *Principles of Dynamics.* Englewood Cliffs, NJ: Prentice-Hall Inc; 1965:362–366.

[19] Perry J. *Gait Analysis: Normal and Pathological Function.* Thorofare, NJ: Slack Inc; 1992:9–16.

[20] Winter DA. Kinematic and kinetic patterns in human gait: Variability and compensating effects. *Hum Mvmt Sci* 1984;3:51–76.

[21] Kadaba MP, Ramakrishnan HK, Wooten ME, Gainey J, Gorton G, Cochran GVB. Repeatability of kinematic, kinetic and electromyographic data in normal adult gait. *J Orthop Res* 1990;7:849–860.

[22] Õunpuu S, Davis RB, Bell KJ, Gage JR. The repeatability of joint kinematic and kinetic data in children with cerebral palsy spastic diplegia. *Proc Cdn Soc Biomech Conf* 1990:49–50.

[23] Kadaba MP, Ramakrishnan HK, Jacobs D, Chambers C, Scarborough N, Goode B, Gait pattern recognition in spastic diplegia. *Dev Med Child Neurol* 1991;33(9):28.

[24] Harrington ED, Lin RS, Gage JR. Use of the anterior floor reaction orthosis in patients with cerebral palsy. *Orth and Prosth J* 1984;37(4):34–42.

[25] Carroll N. The orthotic management of the spina bifida child. *Clin Orthop* 1974; 102:108–114.

[26] Gage JR. *Gait Analysis in Cerebral Palsy.* London: MacKeith Press;1991:106,163–165,189,198.

[27] Õunpuu S, Muik E, Davis RB, Gage JR, DeLuca PA. Part I: The effect of the rectus femoris transfer location on knee motion in children with cerebral palsy. *J Ped Orthop* 1993;13:325–330.

[28] Gage JR, Perry J, Hicks RR, Koop S, Werntz JR. Rectus femoris transfer to improve knee function of children with cerebral palsy. *Dev Med Child Neurol* 1987;29: 159–166.

[29] Sutherland DH, Cooper L. The pathomechanics of progressive crouch gait in spastic diplegia. *Orthop Clin North Am* 1978;9(1):143–154.

[30] Winter DA. Biomechanical motor patterns in normal walking. *J Mot Behav* 1983; 15:302–330.

Michael D. Aiona

Chapter 16

Human Motion Analysis

A Method of Outcome Assessment in Selective Dorsal Rhizotomy

16.1. INTRODUCTION

Gait analysis provides an objective method to review the abnormalities of gait in neuro-muscular patients. This chapter describes the clinical entity, cerebral palsy, and the role of selective dorsal rhizotomy in the treatment of this condition. A historical review of selective dorsal rhizotomy (SDR) and previous reports documenting gait changes after rhizotomy will be presented. Gait changes in a group of patients from the Shriners Hospital for Crippled Children, Portland Unit, who have undergone SDR will be reported. Some thoughts regarding the future role of gait analysis and long-term clinical concerns about SDR will conclude the chapter.

16.2. GAIT ANALYSIS

Inman et al. analyzed and quantified gait through their pioneering work in the field of gait analysis [1,2]. Joint motion during the gait cycle was described, as were gait parameters. With continued technical developments and engineering advancements, gait analysis is now a precise tool for the quantification of human locomotion. Many clinical labs across the country collect three-dimensional (3-D) joint kinematic and kinetic data in the evaluation of ambulation in various conditions, including cerebral palsy. The use of electromyography (EMG) details muscle activity during the gait cycle. This ability to provide objective analysis of gait assists the clinician in making surgical recommendations [3,4]. Objective analysis of the surgical result by documentation of the changes in gait provides a better understanding of the surgical effect and clinical outcome and can guide changes in treatment methodologies in the future.

16.3. CEREBRAL PALSY

Cerebral palsy is defined as a static encephalopathy manifested by a disorder of movement and posture [5]. It represents a group of nonprogressive neuromuscular conditions caused by injury to the immature central nervous system (CNS) in the perinatal period. Delayed or abnormal motor development is the hallmark of the condition. The incidence of cerebral palsy varies among published reports from 1.4/1000 in Denmark to 5.9/1000 in a New York study. K. B. Nelson and J. H. Ellenberg reported an incidence of 5.2/1000 in the National Institute of Neurological and Communicative Disorders and Stroke Collaborative Perinatal Project (NCPP) [6].

Cerebral palsy has many causes [6,7]. Perinatal infection can cause significant motor and cognitive delays. The birth history might reveal low birth weight and prematurity. The susceptibility of the CNS to injury in the premature infant predisposes it to the possibility of a resultant motor disorder. Periventricular and intraventricular hemorrhage are relatively common causes of cerebral palsy in these children. Anoxia and a variety of toxic agents are also frequent causes of CNS injury.

Though movement abnormalities are common to all children with cerebral palsy, other CNS–mediated functions can be affected. Mental retardation, visual perceptual abnormality, and speech and hearing impairment can all be present. Seizures occurred in 30 percent of these children in the NCPP population [6].

The anatomic location and severity of CNS injury determines the type and degree of involvement (Table 16-1). Hemiplegic involvement describes a child with one side affected, the arm more so than the leg. Gait patterns in this population have been subclassified by T. F. Winters et al. [8] using 3-D gait analysis. A diplegic child has equal involvement of the right and left side with relative sparing of the upper extremities in comparison to the lower limbs. Quadriplegia or total body involvement, refers to a child with all four limbs involved to a significant degree (Table 16-1). The two most common types of cerebral palsy are spastic diplegia (32 percent) and hemiplegia (29 percent) as noted by Nelson and Ellenberg [6].

TABLE 16-1 EXTREMITY INVOLVEMENT

Condition	Involvement
Hemiplegia	One side of body affected
Diplegia	Legs more than arms
Quadriplegia	All four limbs affected equally
Monoplegia	Single limb affected

The quality of motor movement abnormality varies from child to child (Table 16-2). Spasticity, defined as velocity-dependent tone, is the most common abnormality. Children with difficulties with balance and motor control are generally ataxic. Others have extrapyramidal involvement as evidenced by nonpurposeful movements. A small percentage of children might actually be hypotonic. Many of them have a mixed pattern of these motor dysfunctions. By combining the quality of movement disorder with the limb involvement, a descriptive classification of children such as spastic quadriplegia can subdivide this heterogeneous population. The spectrum of children range from those with only minor motor skills deficits to a totally dependent nonambulatory child.

TABLE 16-2 QUALITY OF MOTOR ABNORMALITY

Condition	Abnormality
Spastic	Velocity-dependent tone
Athetosis	Uncontrolled nonpurposeful motor movements
Ataxia	Motor incoordination manifested with balance abnormality
Hypotonic	Low muscle tone
Mixed	Combination of above

The initial treatment of the child with cerebral palsy relies on interventional physical and occupational therapy. The goals are to maximize motor development and translate these achievements to improve function. Presently, there are many theories of motor development. Behavior and learning theory is based heavily on the concept of maturational development [9]. Neurophysiological theorists emphasize a sensory integration approach to the development of motor pattern and skills [10]. The perceptual motor theorists emphasize that interpretation of sensory input occurs first, then accurate motor responses develop [11]. With differing philosophies regarding motor skill acquisition, each group has developed a unique therapy approach to emphasize specific functions to assist the children. Incorporated in some theories has been the use of appropriate orthotics and ambulatory aids. The goals of treatment are to maximize independent function and mobility through acquisition of skills in a guided sequence.

Ambulation is a complex function requiring the integration of the nervous system and the musculoskeletal system. The joints and muscles provide the structural base and power necessary to maintain erect posture. Adequate motion of the lower extremity joints in a functional position is a prerequisite to efficient walking. The muscles provide the power generation and absorption necessary for smooth, rhythmic motion of the limb segments. The muscles are under the control of the nervous system, which provides the appropriate timing for muscle contraction and relaxation. Any abnormality in these anatomic organ systems can cause abnormalities of gait.

Balance is a very important component of normal gait. In spite of normal muscle power and joint function, someone without balance cannot walk independently. This complex system relies on multiple levels of input to function properly [12]. Peripheral sensory input from the extremities (e.g., joint proprioception), along with central vestibular feedback, helps regulate balance. Visual input can significantly improve the balance reactions of individuals. This sensory input is continuous, providing feedback for regulation of motion instantaneously. Appropriate muscular response to this input is regulated at the spinal cord level and at higher central areas. All these sensory/proprioceptive feedback mechanisms are integrated by the nervous system to provide the appropriate signals for smooth acceleration and deceleration of joint motion.

In cerebral palsy, the central nervous system is the affected organ system. These children have varying degrees of balance, motor control, and integration deficits. Sensory input might be impaired as well as cognitive skills. The severity of the deficit determines the ultimate degree of functional impairment.

Muscle function can be divided into two major areas. Power generation and absorption are regulated by the nervous system ultimately through the alpha motor neuron. It innervates the large extrafusal fibers of skeletal muscles. Excitation of the nerve causes contraction of the muscle producing controlled movement of limb segments. Energy is produced with muscle shortening (concentric contraction). Energy absorption occurs through elongation of a contracted muscle (eccentric contraction). The loss of motor neurons can result in muscle weakness. Inappropriate timing or abnormal intensity of muscular contraction can result in functional weakness.

16.4. SPASTICITY

Muscle tone is regulated through a complex system of feedback loops, with additional inhibitory and facilitory modifications [13]. The muscle spindle (intrafusal fibers) is an anatomic structure scattered throughout the muscle. This sensory structure regulates muscle tone through direct feedback to the alpha motor neuron. As the spindle elongates with muscle stretch, activity of the sensory afferent neurons increases. The gamma afferent system transmits this activity to the alpha motor neuron through the posterior (dorsal) spinal rootlets at each spinal segmental level. This facilitory action stimulates the alpha motor neuron, causing muscular contraction to control the stretch of the muscle and secondarily the muscle spindle. Interneuronal connections from other spinal levels modify this direct spinal level regulation. Multiple higher levels of the central nervous system provide additional regulation of the system. The pioneering work of C. S. Sherrington elucidated this important central inhibition. By removal of central input to the spinal cord, he produced spasticity in experimental animals [14,15]. He demonstrated the importance of inhibitory input from the central nervous system in the regulation of the sensitivity of the muscle system; the stronger the central inhibitory input, the less the resistance to stretch of the muscle. Conversely, with diminished inhibition, the muscle becomes more resistive to stretch. If this muscle becomes too sensitive to stretch, spasticity occurs. In cerebral palsy, the regulation of this central inhibition is affected; the greater the loss of inhibition, the more spastic the muscles.

16.4.1. Nonsurgical Treatment Options

Most health care providers believe that spasticity inhibits the functional abilities of patients. The retention of primitive reflexes and increased tone make functional gains difficult. A variety of options are available to the clinician for the treatment of spasticity (Table 16-3).

TABLE 16-3   SPASTICITY TREATMENT

	Type	
Treatment	Systemic	Local
Medication	Valium	Baclofen Botulinum-A toxin Phenol
CNS stimulators	Cerebellar	
Orthotics	Tone reducing braces	
Surgery	Selective dorsal rhizotomy	

Medication has been utilized to decrease muscle spasm. Muscle relaxants (e.g., Valium) can be taken orally. They might reduce muscle tone through a central sedative effect—not through direct muscle relaxation. Local injection of medications (phenol, botulinum-A toxin) produce short-term reductions in muscle tone [16,17]. The time-limited effects of this medication can make them unsuitable for long-term control of spasticity. Their benefit for short-term treatment has yet to be established, nor are the long-term effects known. Medication (Baclofen) placed directly into the intrathecal sac in the spinal canal reduces spasticity [18]. Implantable pumps to regulate the quantity of medication delivered are a promising development, though a preliminary study revealed a high complication rate with this treatment.

Bracing and casting as an adjunct to physical therapy reduce spasticity [19]. By placing the joints and muscles in a stretched functional position, the reactivity of the muscles diminishes. This is most beneficial in the foot/ankle area but is less effective in more proximal joints. The effects are short-term in duration. Attempts at increasing the inhibitory input from the central nervous system have produced unpredictable, varying results. Implantable cerebellar and spinal cord stimulators inconsistently decrease tone in patients [20].

16.4.2. Selective Dorsal Rhizotomy

Selective dorsal rhizotomy is a neurosurgical procedure directed at the spinal cord level to reduce tone. It reduces the reactivity of the muscle to stretch by addressing the sensory input regulating muscle tone. The sensory posterior rootlets transmit information to many neurons in the spinal cord. They are part of the stretch reflex and gamma motor system. As stated previously, their facilitory action on the alpha motor neuron assists in muscle tone control. Transection of these rootlets reduces muscle tone and reactivity. Work by Sherrington in experimentally produced spasticity, provides the anatomical basis for this procedure. He reduced spasticity by transecting the posterior rootlets [14,15]. O. Foerster was one of the first surgeons to perform rhizotomy on patients [21]. Applying the knowledge gained by Sherrington's work, 159 patients had surgery for spasticity reduction. The spinal root levels were L_2-S_2 with sparing of L_4 to preserve quadriceps muscle function. He mentioned the use of electric current stimulation during surgery to distinguish anterior from posterior rootlets. Though scattered reports followed, a major advance occurred when V. A. Fasano et al. developed a technique to improve surgery by recording the electrical muscle activity during surgery [22,23]. They stimulated the nerve rootlets in the spinal cord during the surgical procedure. The normal EMG response is decremental with no spread to adjacent muscles. A variety of abnormal EMG responses were recorded when the posterior rootlets were stimulated in spastic patients. These responses included incremental responses, tonic-let-clonic response, and sustained activity. By electrically identifying the abnormal rootlets to be divided, the normal rootlets could be spared. With this selective approach, they produced a permanent reduction of hypertonia with no diffuse sensory deficits.

W. J. Peacock et al. popularized this surgical approach to spasticity in the United States. They modified the procedure by changing the anatomic location of the surgery to the cauda equina region, though the principles of rootlet selection for division remain the same. Their numerous articles about the surgical approach and functional end results have encouraged many other centers to perform this procedure [24–27].

Patient selection determines to a large extent the functional outcome of the procedure. Many factors, other than spasticity, affect gait efficiency. Evaluation of muscle strength and control, trunk stability, and the presence of extrapyramidal signs help determine the suitability of patients for rhizotomy. Good balance, voluntary isolated motor control, and muscle strength are good prognostic factors for a satisfactory outcome in an ambulatory patient. The greater the contribution of spasticity to the gait abnormality, the greater the benefit from rhizotomy.

Surgical Procedure. The patient is brought to the operating room and placed in the prone position after routine anesthetic induction. Specific medications or anesthetic agents that might interfere with EMG activity are avoided. Surface electrodes are placed on the major muscle groups of the lower extremities to record the EMG generated by stimulation of each rootlet. The patient is draped to allow adjustment of the electrodes and observation of muscular activity during the surgical procedure. The dorsal rootlets are identified at levels L_2-S_1. The S_2 rootlet is spared to preserve bowel/bladder function. A variable number of rootlets, usually four to eight, are present at each level and side. Each rootlet is stimulated to determine a threshold response. Then a stimulus of one second duration at 50 Hz is applied. The EMG and muscular activity observed are recorded. If this response is abnormal, the dorsal root is sectioned. Each rootlet at each level undergoes the same sequence of evaluation. The percentage of rootlets divided varies from 25 to 60 percent. By preservation of some rootlets, sensory deficit and muscle weakness can be avoided.

Once the patient has recovered from the surgery, approximately the fifth day after surgery, the patient enters into a progressive goal-oriented physical and occupational therapy program. The initial goal is an upright posture and lower extremity weight bearing. Bracing, usually ankle-foot orthoses (AFOs), might be required at this early stage as patients are initially weak. Assistive devices such as walkers are usually necessary early in the postoperative period. The focus of treatment is regaining strength in the leg muscles and improving the gait pattern. Range of motion and stretching exercises are an integral part of the program. This program is recommended for one year postoperatively. Evaluations at three-month intervals monitor the patient's progress.

Early complications are uncommon. Hyperesthesias might be present early but usually resolve rapidly. Structural abnormalities including scoliosis or lordosis have been reported, though the incidence appears very low [28]. Rapid hip subluxation after surgery has also been reported [29]. Awareness of these possible orthopaedic deformities allows early identification and treatment when necessary.

Literature Review. A review of the literature reveals three studies utilizing a reflective marker system for gait analysis in selective dorsal rhizotomy. L. D. Cahan et al. noted changes in joint kinematics, stride characteristics, and EMG activity in their 14 patients with an average of eight months' follow-up [30]. With the use of a two-dimensional (2-D) gait analysis system to record sagittal motion, significant improvements in ankle motion and position were recorded. The amount of ankle dorsiflexion after selective dorsal rhizotomy was significantly improved. Changes at the knee were noted with improved extension during stance phase. At the hip, extension at terminal stance improved. EMG activity remained unchanged in the majority of patients, though the intensity diminished significantly in the hamstrings, quadriceps, and calf muscles. Two stride characteristics, velocity and stride length, improved with no change in cadence. They concluded that the profound improvement in gait mobility after spasticity reduction was related to the decelerating capability of the limb's extensor muscles during stance.

C. L. Vaughan et al. published their data on 14 patients with three-year follow-up. Two-dimensional gait analysis along with stride characteristics were obtained preoperatively and, one and three years postrhizotomy to determine temporal relationship of changes [31]. Stride length improved significantly at one and three years follow-up, with average speed increasing at the three-year follow-up. It is not known whether the controls used were age matched, as the three-year data actually showed speed and stride length to be greater than the given norm. Utilizing angle/angle diagrams, thigh range exceeded normal at one and three years. Knee motion range reached near normal at three years, with the midpoint showing a decrease (less knee flexion during stance), though it was actually increased at the one-year follow-up (excessive flexed position). This initial flexed posture was postulated as secondary to initial weakness that improved at the three-year follow-up. According to the authors, these findings suggest patients can increase their strength and muscular control following SDR with physical therapy playing an important role in the functional improvement.

L. F. Boscarino et al. presented gait changes in 11 independent and 8 dependent ambulatory children after SDR [32]. This report utilized 3-D gait analysis and EMG data along with static measurements. The dynamic changes during gait were confined to the sagittal plane. The independent ambulators showed a significant increase in hip/knee range of motion and stance phase ankle dorsiflexion. The dependent ambulators significantly improved their maximum knee flexion in swing and mean foot progression angles. This group also improved knee range of motion and ankle dorsiflexion during gait. Significant increases in stride length occurred, though velocity remained the same. No consistent phasic changes in EMG were noted, though 12 of 19 developed a more distinguishable phasic pattern. All patients had muscle tone reduction after selective dorsal rhizotomy. They concluded that SDR produced certain positive changes in gait, though the relationship of these improvements to functional changes in a person's ability to ambulate were not easy to define.

16.5. MATERIALS AND METHODS

For four years, the Shriners Hospital for Crippled Children, Portland Unit has been involved in an ongoing rhizotomy program. Patients are evaluated by a team of health professionals including physicians, therapists, nurses, and a social worker. Patient selection is based on the previously outlined criteria. Patients and families are fully informed of the treatment options and expected outcomes.

16.5.1. Patient Population

Thirty-six patients have undergone the surgical procedure. Three nonambulatory patients with cerebral palsy, 3 with myelodysplasia, 1 patient with hereditary spastic paraplegia, and 5 patients with less than one year follow-up were excluded from this review. Twenty-four ambulatory spastic diplegic patients underwent SDR with preoperative and one-year postoperative 3-D gait analysis. The data presented is a summation of the one-year postoperative evaluations. Eleven patients were independent walkers, 13 patients required ambulatory aids. The average age of the patient was 6.25 years with a range of $3 + 8$ to $10 + 2$ years. There were 10 females and 14 males; only 1 patient had a previous orthopaedic procedure (bilateral heel cord lengthenings). The surgical procedure divided the L_2-S_1 posterior rootlets in all patients except 1 (the S_1 rootlet was spared in the 1 patient with a previous heel cord lengthening). The percentage of rootlets divided varied from patient to patient, level to level and side to side. The range was a minimum of 24 percent to a maximum of 61 percent. All patients received twice daily inpatient therapy immediately postsurgery for at least one month. Postoperative outpatient therapy was recommended three to four times per week for one year in all patients.

16.5.2. Clinical Assessment

Clinical examination included passive range of motion measurements and manual muscle test [33]. Standard range of motion measurements include hip flexion/extension, abduction/adduction, knee flexion/extension, ankle dorsiflexion/plantarflexion, popliteal angle, and Ely test [34].

16.5.3. Testing Protocol

A 3-D Vicon system (Oxford Metrics Ltd., Oxford, England) assessed joint kinematics at the pelvis, hip, knee, and ankle. Retro-reflective markers were aligned to bony landmarks on the pelvis, thigh, shank, and foot bilaterally [35]. Five Pulnix charge-coupled device (CCD) cameras collected data at 50 Hz from the retroreflective markers as the child walked. Foot switches placed on the plantar surface of the foot on the toe, heel, and first and fifth metatarsal heads determined temporal parameters for each trial. Two Advanced Mechanical Technology Inc. (AMTI) force plates (Newton, Massachusetts) collected kinetic data at 500 Hz during independent walking trials. Joint kinematics of the lower extremities were determined from the 3-D coordinates of the markers [35]. The children walked at their own self-selected walking speeds. Patients performed a minimum of three trials. Children who walked independently performed successive trials until the child achieved two left and two right trials with clean force plate assessments. A step was considered clean if only one foot hit the force plate at a time. Children who walked with assistive devices such as walkers or crutches utilized them during the gait analysis. Motion and EMG data were collected both barefoot and in orthoses. Only the trials in the barefoot condition were analyzed for this report. Multiple trials plotted against each other determined consistency. From these trials, one representative trial was selected for analysis based on the stride length, cadence, velocity, and single-limb stance times.

16.5.4. Electromyography

Electromyography was performed separately. Ten preamplified surface electrodes (Motion Control, Inc., Salt Lake City, Utah) were placed over the muscle belly according to the *Anatomic Guide for the Electromyographer* [36]. A 10-channel MA100 system (Motion Lab Systems, Tampa, Florida) recorded the activity of the rectus femoris, medial hamstring, tibialis anterior, gastrocnemius, and adductors bilaterally. Data was sampled at 500 Hz for 10 seconds. Data was passed through a low-pass filter at 300 Hz and a high-pass filter of 40 Hz. All data was normalized for 100 percent of the cycle, and on/off activity was determined.

16.6. RESULTS

Data were analyzed statistically employing the paired t-test. Patients acted as their own controls and the limbs were divided into right and left sides due to asymmetry. A p value of < 0.05 was chosen as significant. The data presented are cumulative for all the patients. Representative individual gait data are shown to illustrate specific points.

The modified Ashworth Bohannon scale, a standard measure of spasticity, was utilized to evaluate changes in extremity tone (Table 16-4) [37]. As some patients might have subtle asymmetric involvement, the extremities were separated into dominant and nondominant categories based on handedness. The goal of surgery, which was spasticity reduction, was achieved in all patients. The data did not reveal side-to-side differences; rather, in all muscles tested a global reduction in tone occurred (Table 16-5).

TABLE 16-4 MODIFIED ASHWORTH BOHANNON SCALE

Score	Modifier	Description
5	Extreme	Affected part rigid in flexion or extension
4	Severe	Considerable increase in tone, passive movement difficult
3	Moderate	More marked increase in tone through most of range of motion but affected part is easily moved
2	Mild	Slight increase in tone "catch" in limb movement or mild resistance to movement through less than half of the range
1	Normal	No increase in muscle tone
0	Hypotonic	Less than normal muscle tone, floppy

TABLE 16-5 RESULTS FROM SPASTICITY MEASUREMENT

Parameter	Preoperative	Postoperative	P value
Adductor dominant	3 (1)	1 (1)	0.0001
Adductor nondominant	3 (1)	2 (1)	0.0001
Hamstrings dominant	3 (1)	1 (0.4)	0.0001
Hamstrings nondominant	3 (1)	1 (0.5)	0.0001
Quadriceps dominant	2 (0.5)	1 (0.3)	0.0001
Quadriceps nondominant	2 (0.5)	1 (0.3)	0.0001
Gastrocnemius dominant	3 (1)	2 (0.5)	0.0001
Gastrocnemius nondominant	3 (1)	2 (0.6)	0.0001

This reduction in spasticity translated into significant gait changes. Kinematic data analysis revealed significant changes in sagittal motion in all three-lower limb joints. Maximum hip extension during stance phase improved significantly (Table 16-6, Figure 16-1). As maximum hip flexion in stance did not change, the improvement in hip position was indicative of a more upright posture while retaining adequate range of motion. No change in pelvic tilt was noted. Anterior pelvic tilt was 17 degrees preoperatively and postoperative average pelvic tilt was 18 degrees. The pelvic arc of motion remained unchanged.

Sagittal plane knee motion improved in both stance and swing phase (Table 16-7, Figure 16-2). The ability of the patients to straighten the knee during stance improved the crouch position during gait, though some knee flexion remained. The reduction in velocity-

TABLE 16-6   HIP MOTION

Hip motion–right	Mean	S.D.	P value
Extension stance—preoperative	5.63	9.7	0.0018
Extension stance—postoperative	−0.33	8.4	
Flexion stance—preoperative	53.1	10.2	N.S.
Flexion stance—postoperative	55.7	11.7	

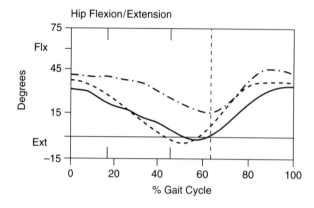

Figure 16-1. Representation of hip motion during the gait cycle (individual patient).

TABLE 16-7   KNEE MOTION

Knee motion—right	Mean	S.D.	P value
Extension stance—preoperative	21.6	14.7	0.0006
Extension stance—postoperative	9.7	11.8	
Flexion swing—preoperative	64.3	10.6	N.S.
Flexion swing—postoperative	61.1	10.2	
Extension swing—preoperative	43.0	9.7	0.0001
Extension swing—postoperative	28.5	11.9	

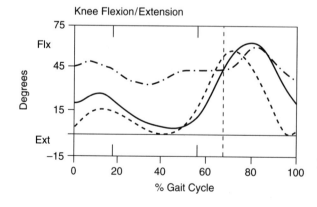

Figure 16-2. Representation of knee motion during the gait cycle (individual patient).

dependent tone allowed better knee extension in swing phase, which improved the stride length in the patients. Of equal importance, peak swing phase knee flexion maintained its normal value from preoperative to postoperative status. By maintaining knee flexion, the total knee arc of motion improved. By reducing spasticity on both sides of a joint, SDR can allow freer joint motion.

Many patients' initial contact improved from a toe-toe gait pattern to a more normal foot-flat or heel-contact position. Maximum ankle dorsiflexion in stance phase improved significantly (Table 16-8, Figure 16-3). Total ankle range of motion did not improve but was translated toward the dorsiflexion direction, approaching a near normal position. Though some improvement in swing phase dorsiflexion occurred, the persistent drop foot was indicative of abnormal tibialis anterior function due to either decreased strength or abnormal timing of contraction.

TABLE 16-8 ANKLE MOTION

Ankle motion—right	Mean	S.D.	P value
Dorsiflexion—preoperative	−8.54	27.0	0.002
Dorsiflexion—postoperative	8.25	10.9	
Plantarflexion—preoperative	−36.0	34.4	N.S.
Plantarflexion—postoperative	−26.5	16.8	

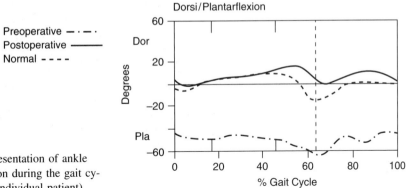

Preoperative — · — ·
Postoperative ———
Normal - - - -

Figure 16-3. Representation of ankle motion during the gait cycle (individual patient).

Significant coronal plane motion changes were not seen. No significant increase in hip motion or tendency toward increased adduction was noted. Rotational changes were not consistent and were insignificant in amount. The majority of patients have increased femoral anteversion, which accounts for the majority of rotational deformity during gait.

Gait parameter changes included a significant increase in stride length (Table 16-9). This was felt to be secondary to the changes in the sagittal plane motion, allowing greater knee and hip extension. Statistically insignificant changes were seen in velocity, with cadence unchanged when compared to age-matched controls.

EMG data were evaluated qualitatively by examining the timing of muscle activity during the gait cycle. Twenty-five percent of the muscles reviewed (56/260) showed some

TABLE 16-9 GAIT PARAMETERS

Gait parameters	Mean	S.D.	P value
Velocity—preoperative	60.5	20.6	0.1086
Velocity—postoperative	67.2	26.9	
Stride—preoperative	68.8	15.3	0.0283
Stride—postoperative	77.8	22.0	
Cadence—preoperative	83.5	19.9	0.9098
Cadence—postoperative	83.1	23.1	

pattern change. Of these 56 muscles, 41 (73 percent) showed an "improvement" toward the pattern of muscle activity seen in normal gait (closer to a normal phasic pattern). Muscles showing increased activity from their preoperative pattern numbered 15 (27 percent). Muscles showing a consistent pattern change with statistical significance could not be found in this group. This is consistent with previously published studies regarding muscle activity after selective dorsal rhizotomy; L. F. Boscarino et al. describe similar findings of EMG improvement in their patients [32].

16.7. SUMMARY

Selective dorsal rhizotomy has been recently touted as the treatment of spasticity in a wide variety of patients [38–42]. Our evaluation of patients undergoing SDR with the use of 3-D gait analysis confirms the findings of the previous articles in the literature. Significant sagittal plane kinematic changes can occur after spasticity reduction in a selected group of ambulatory patients with cerebral palsy. Although tone is significantly reduced, abnormal gait patterns persist even after rhizotomy. SDR "unmasks" other elements of the neuromuscular disorder present in these children. Abnormalities of muscle strength, muscular control, and inappropriate sequential timing of muscle activity are still present in these patients and are not addressed by SDR.

Force-plate data were collected on only 11 patients as 13 patients were dependent on ambulatory aids at the time of surgery. The small number of patients with sufficient kinetic data does not allow any specific trends or observations to be made at the time of this publication.

Continued investigation into the kinetic aspects of human gait will provide further insight into the pathomechanics of cerebral palsy patients' gait abnormalities in this population. The calculation of moments and powers with appropriate software will continue in those patients. These kinetic data will shed light onto the differences between active pathologic processes and compensatory mechanisms. By determining the primary gait abnormality, treatment intervention including surgery can be made more specific.

Energy consumption studies have recently been utilized to determine gait efficiency in this select group of patients [43]. As gait analysis methods and interpretation advance, the challenge will be to determine which quantitative kinematic/kinetic variables are the primary determinants of gait efficiency. In some instances, gait efficiency as measured per unit distance traveled might be most important. Someone might walk slowly, but do so relatively efficiently with the minimum oxygen consumption. At other times, they might find that velocity is the most important functional element. Gait is inefficient as measured by oxygen consumption at this speed, yet might be one important functional outcome to be achieved.

This leads to a most important aspect of future development in this area: how to measure directly and improve the patient's *functional* outcome. The reduction in spasticity might translate to gait "improvements," but this must positively impact the functional daily activities important to self-care independence in this patient population.

We have found significant improvements in toileting and dressing skills after SDR, important gains needed for independent function. A comprehensive standardized functional assessment will determine whether the observed changes after SDR are associated with improvements in functional outcome [44]. More importantly, the natural history of functional and motor development in children with cerebral palsy must be elucidated or at least inferred to provide controls to truly determine the effect of any intervention. Comparisons to alternative treatments other than SDR, such as orthopaedic surgery, will determine the role of each in the treatment of these children.

Gait analysis provides an objective measure of walking abilities in this population. This valuable information can document the outcome of surgical intervention. As the quality of gait analysis techniques continues to improve with better standardization, improved software programs, and further refinements in data collection and analysis, the pathophysiology of gait in children with cerebral palsy will be understood. The continued cooperative effort between engineering and medical colleagues to provide objective measures of treatment outcomes will benefit both the patient and society.

Acknowledgments

I would like to express my gratitude and appreciation to Lily Nigo and Susan Sienko Thomas for their assistance in preparing this manuscript.

References

[1] Saunder JB, Inman VT, Eberhart HD, The major determinants in normal and pathologic gait. *J Bone Joint Surg Am* 1953;35A:543.

[2] Inman VT, Ralston HJ, Todd FL. *Human Walking*. Baltimore, Md: William & Wilkins Publishing Co;1981.

[3] Perry J, Hoffer M. Preoperative and postoperative dynamic EMG as an aid in planning tendon transfers in children with cerebral palsy. *J Bone Joint Surg Am* 1977;59A:531.

[4] Gage JR, Fabian O, Hicks R, Tashman S. Preoperative and postoperative gait analysis in patients with spastic diplegia: A preliminary report. *J Ped Orthop* 1984;4:715.

[5] Bax MCO, Terminology and classification of cerebral palsy. *Dev Med Child Neurol* 1964;6:295.

[6] Nelson KB, Ellenberg JH. Epidemiology of cerebral palsy. In: Schoenberg BS ed. *Advances in Neurology* New York, NY: Raven Press, 1978;19:421–435.

[7] Bleck EE. *Orthopaedic Management in Cerebral Palsy* London: MacKeith Press; 1987.

[8] Winters TF, Gage JR, Hicks R. Gait patterns in spastic hemiplegia in children and young adults. *J Bone Joint Surg Am* 1987;69A:437–441.

[9] Drowatzky JN. *Motor Learning Principles and Practices*. Minneapolis, Minn: Burgess Publishing Co; 1975.

[10] Crowe WC, Auxter D, Pyfer J. *Adapted Physical Education and Recreation* 4th ed. St Louis, Mo: CV Mosby Company; 1981.

[11] Ayres AJ, Improving academic skills through sensory integration. *J Learning Disabilities* 1972;5:336–343.

[12] Shumway-Cook A, Woollacot M. The growth of stability: Postural control from a developmental perspective. *J Mot Behav* 1985;17:131–147.

[13] Bishop B. Spasticity: Its physiology and management. Parts I-IV. *Phys Ther* 1977;57:371–401.

[14] Sherrington CS. On reciprocal innervation of antagonistic muscles. *Proceedings of the Royal Society*, 1896;60:414–417.

[15] Sherrington CS. Decerbrate rigidity, and reflex coordination of movements. *J Physiol (Lond)* 1898;22:319–337.

[16] Koman LA, Mooney JF, Smith B, Goodman A, Mulvaney T. Management of cerebral palsy with Botulinum-A toxin: Preliminary investigation. *J Ped Orthop* 1993;13:489.

[17] Halpren D, Meelhuysen FE. Phenol motor point block in the management of muscular hypertonia. *Arch Phys Med Rehab* 1966;47:528.

[18] Albright AL, Cervi A, Singletary J. Intrathecal Baclofen for spasticity in cerebral palsy. *JAMA* 1991;265:1418–1422.

[19] Sussman MD, Cusick B. The role of short-leg, tone reducing casts as an adjunct to physical therapy of patients with cerebral palsy. *Johns Hopkins Med J*, 1979;145:112.

[20] Ivan LP, Ventureyra ECG, Wiley J, Doyle D, Pressman E, Knights R, Guzman C, Ultley D. Chronic cerebellar stimulation in cerebral palsy. *Surg Neurol* 1981;15:81–84.

[21] Foerster O. On the indications and results of the excision of posterior spinal nerve roots in men. *Surg Gynecol Obstet* 1913;16:463–464.

[22] Fasano VA, Broggi G, Barolat-Romana G, Squazzi A. Surgical treatment of spasticity in cerebral palsy. *Child's Brain* 1978;4:289–305.

[23] Fasano VA, Barolat-Romana G, Zeme S, Sguazzi A. Electrophysiological assessment of spinal circuits in spasticity by direct dorsal root stimulation. *Neurosurgery* 1979;4:146–151.

[24] Peacock WJ, Arens LJ. Selective posterior rhizotomy for the relief of spasticity in cerebral palsy. *S Afr Med J* 1982;62:119–124.

[25] Peacock WJ, Arens LJ, Berman B. Cerebral palsy spasticity: Selective posterior rhizotomy. *Ped Neurosci* 1987;13:61–68.

[26] Berman B, Vaughan CL, Peacock WJ. The effect of rhizotomy on movement in patients with cerebral palsy. *Am J Occ Ther* 1990;44:511–516.

[27] Peacock WJ, Staudt LA. Spasticity in cerebral palsy and the selective posterior rhizotomy procedure. *J Child Neurol* 1990;5:179–185.

[28] Hall JH, Millis MB. Progressing lumbar hyperlordosis following selective posterior rhizotomy for spastic quadriplegia. *Proc Pediatric Orthopaedic Society of North America* Dallas, Tex, 1991.

[29] Greene W, Dietz F, Goldberg MJ, Gross RH, Miller F, Sussman MD. Rapid progressive hip subluxation in cerebral palsy after selective posterior rhizotomy. *J Ped Orthop* 1991;4:494–497.

[30] Cahan LD, Adams JM, Perry J, Beeler LM. Instrumented gait analysis after selective dorsal rhizotomy. *Dev Med Child Neurol* 1990;32:1037–1043.

[31] Vaughan CL, Berman B, Peacock WJ. Cerebral palsy and rhizotomy: A three-year follow-up evaluation with gait analysis. *J Neurosurg* 1991;74:178–184.

[32] Boscarino LF, Õunpuu S, Davis RB III, Gage JR, Deluca PA. Effects of selective dorsal rhizotomy on gait in children with cerebral palsy. *J Ped Orthop* 1993;13:174–179.

[33] Daniels L, Worthingham C. *Muscle Testing-Techniques of Manual Examination.* Philadelphia, Pa: WB Saunders Co; 1980.

[34] Esch D, Lepley M. *Evaluation of Joint Motion Methods of Measurement and Recording.* Minneapolis, Minn: University of Minnesota Press, 1974.

[35] Kadaba MP, Ramakrishnan HK, Wootten ME. Measurement of lower extremity kinematics during level walking. *J Orthop Res* 1990;8:383–392.

[36] Delagi EF, Perotto A, Anatomic Guide for the Electromyographer, Springfield, Ill: Charles C Thomas Publisher, 1981.

[37] Bohannon RW, Smith MB. Interrater reliability of a modified Ashworth scale of muscle spasticity. *Phys Ther* 1987;67:206–207.

[38] Abbott R, Forem SL, Johann M. Selective posterior rhizotomy for the treatment of spasticity: A review. *Child's Nerv Syst* 1989;5:337–346.

[39] Laitinen LV, Nilsson S, Fugl-Meyer AR. Selective posterior rhizotomy for treatment of spasticity. *J Neurosurg* 1983;58:895–899.

[40] Marty G, Dias LS. Selective Dorsal Rhizotomy. presented at American Academy of Orthopaedic Surgery/Shrine/Symposium on Treatment of Spastic Diplegia, 1991, Charlottesville, Va; 1991.

[41] Oppenheim WL, Peacock WJ, Staudt LA, Gage JR. Selective dorsal rhizotomy for cerebral palsy. Symposium on Rhizotomy Issues and Answers, presented at American Academy of Cerebral Palsy and Developmental Medicine Meeting, San Francisco, Calif, October 1989.

[42] Oppenheim WL. Selective posterior rhizotomy for spastic cerebral palsy. *Clin Orthop* 1990;253:20–29.

[43] Rose J, Medeiros JM, Parker R. Energy cost index as an estimate of energy expenditure of cerebral palsy children during assisted ambulation. *Dev Med Child Neurol* 1985;27:485.

[44] Haley SM, Coster WJ, Ludlow LH, Haltiwanger JT, Andrellos PJ. Pediatric Evaluation of Disability Inventory. New England Medical Center Hospital, Boston, Mass; 1992.

Chapter 17

Ronald J. Triolo
Rudi Kobetic
Randal R. Betz

Standing and Walking with Functional Neuromuscular Stimulation

Technical and Clinical Challenges

Functional neuromuscular stimulation (FNS) refers to the activation and coordination of paralyzed muscles via the excitation of intact peripheral nerves with small electrical currents to produce useful, purposeful movements. Standing and stepping motions have been reproduced in well-selected and highly motivated individuals with paraplegia at various research centers. Although FNS offers many potential therapeutic and functional benefits, complications following spinal cord injury such as hip subluxation, disuse osteoporosis, and peripheral denervation, as well as social and economic factors can limit its applicability. Similarly, many technical considerations associated with FNS systems themselves, as well as the quality of the motions they provide, might compromise their acceptance. Excessive energy costs, reliance on a walker, variability of stimulated responses, and inadequate swing limb clearance or hip extension moment limit the functionality of FNS devices. Conventional human motion analysis might not be adequate to assess or refine FNS gait, and new evaluation methods might need to be developed. This chapter outlines the potential benefits, recent advances, technical and clinical limitations, and direction of future research in the field.

17.1. INTRODUCTION

Electrical stimulation has been used since 1840 to reduce spasticity associated with spinal cord injuries and to reverse disuse atrophy [1,2]. In addition to therapeutic applications, the activation of paralyzed muscles with intact lower motor neurons (LMNs) can be used to augment or replace external braces [3–7]. To distinguish it from exercise or other therapeutic use, excitation of the peripheral nerves resulting in controlled and coordinated movements designed to accomplish or assist a specific, goal-oriented task is referred to as functional neuromuscular stimulation, or FNS [8,9].

318

FNS can have significant impact on the lives of many individuals with disabilities. It has been applied to people with complete and incomplete spinal cord lesions, as well as stroke, head trauma, and other neuromuscular dysfunctions such as cerebral palsy and myelomeningocele. It has also been used to assist with bowel or bladder function, respiration, or to provide active grasp or other upper extremity function to individuals with cervical level lesions.

Since 1986, researchers at the Philadelphia Unit of Shriners Hospitals, together with Case Western Reserve University (CWRU) and the Department of Veterans Affairs Medical Center in Cleveland, Ohio, have been investigating the application of FNS to children, teenagers, and young adults paralyzed by spinal cord injuries for the purposes of providing standing, walking, and other lower extremity functions. What follows is a summary of the experience gained by applying FNS in the clinical setting of Shriners Hospitals, and the technical experience of synthesizing ambulatory motions at the Department of Veterans Affairs Medical Center. This discussion will focus on the clinical and technical challenges to providing standing and walking function to individuals with complete paralysis resulting from spinal cord injury.

17.2. BACKGROUND AND HISTORICAL REVIEW

To fully appreciate the progress made in providing lower extremity movements to individuals with paralysis, as well as the challenges remaining to be addressed, it is necessary to understand the characteristics of spinal cord injury and the fundamentals of FNS.

17.2.1. Fundamentals of Spinal Cord Injury (SCI)

Conservative estimates place the current SCI population of the United States between 177,000 and 195,000, with an incidence of between 30 and 40 new cases per million people per year [10–12]. Males are at greater risk of SCI and outnumber females in the population by almost 4 to 1. Spinal cord injuries occur most frequently in persons between 15 and 20 years of age, and approximately 65 percent of all people with SCI were below the age of 30 at the time of injury [10–16]. Motor vehicle accidents (MVAs) are responsible for between 40 and 50 percent of all lesions in this age group. More neurologically complete lesions are observed in children and young adults than in older segments of the population.

Prior to World War II, people sustaining spinal cord injuries usually died within weeks of the trauma due to neurologic shock and kidney infection. With the advent of antibiotics and better treatment, individuals with spinal cord injuries can now expect to live a normal life span of close to 75 years. Patients between the ages of 10 and 19 have the highest 10-year survival rates of all individuals sustaining a traumatic injury, followed closely by patients 0 to 9 years of age [11]. The chances of survival and life expectancies of individuals injured at 20 years of age have been shown to be significantly higher than those who are 40 or 60 at the time of injury [12]. More than half of all persons with SCI alive today were injured before 1980 and the average patient has been injured for over 14 years, indicating a dramatic improvement in survival and medical management over the past decade [10].

The physical problems encountered by individuals with SCI include rapid and dramatic muscle atrophy, which results in an increased incidence of pressure sores and poor wound healing. These individuals also become severely osteoporotic, which can result in a heightened risk of fracture. In addition, the heart and cardiovascular systems become deconditioned, resulting in symptomatic hypotension and decreased endurance for the activities of daily living. There are several possible therapeutic and physiological reasons why standing might be beneficial for a paralyzed individual [17]. These include prevention of lower extremity contractions, reversal of osteoporosis in the long bones, assistance with bowel and bladder function, reduction of pressure sores, improvement in blood flow and cardiovascular responses, and reduction in spasticity. The psychological benefits can include an improvement in self-esteem resulting from an increase in the functional ability to reach while standing, although the functional benefits of standing have not been quantified completely or widely reported.

While it is possible to stimulate muscle tissue directly, most FNS applications rely on activating the peripheral nerve, which is much more excitable. One study of 24 individuals with injuries between C5 and L3 reported denervation in over 45 percent of those patients with thoracolumbar (T12-L3) lesions and over 7 percent of those patients with thoracic (T1-T11) lesions.

Although spinal cord regeneration is under investigation and offers much promise, it is a field still very much in its infancy. It is unlikely that such efforts will result in a practical treatment methodology until well into the next century. For individuals who have had their spinal cords destroyed by gunshot wounds, infections, or tumors, the probability of regeneration is far more remote. Wheelchairs, conventional long leg braces, and FNS might be the only options available to increase independent functional mobility for individuals with paraplegia in the short term.

17.2.2. Functional Neuromuscular Stimulation for Standing and Walking

Many investigators have pursued lower extremity applications of FNS to restore or improve standing and walking ability in adults with complete or partial lesions [17–28]. FNS systems for these applications have ranged from single-channel devices to reduce or eliminate foot drop, to complex multichannel microprocessor-controlled devices [8,9,29]. Control of stimulation for functional tasks has been provided by timers [20,22], finger, foot, or crutch-tip switches [24,28], preprogrammed computers [21], and EMG-triggered devices [26]. Stimulation in such systems has been delivered to the nerve transcutaneously from electrodes placed on the surface of the skin [19–21,24,26–28], intramuscularly via percutaneous wires [22,25,30], or by electrodes sutured directly to the epimysium or cuffs surrounding the motor nerve [9]. Completely implantable systems have also been developed for neuromuscular applications [9,23].

Standing has been achieved with relatively simple systems consisting of two to four channels of surface stimulation [20]. Electrodes are most often applied only to the anterior thigh to excite the quadriceps. Infrequently, additional surface channels have been used simultaneously to activate the hip extensors [21,31]. Subjects standing with surface stimulation are trained to adopt a "C posture," hyperextending the hips and gaining stability from the anterior ligaments. Although standing times in excess of 30 minutes have been reported after considerable practice with such systems, fatigue is often an obstacle to prolonged use. Erect posture has been maintained by switching between stimulation sequences, which put the body segments into different alignments to minimize the fatigue that any single muscle group might experience [7,32]. Still other systems have combined FNS with varying degrees of external bracing to constrain the motions generated by the stimulated muscles, simplify control, reduce the number of stimulation channels, or provide mechanical support [24,33].

Stepping with surface stimulation has been demonstrated in individuals with complete paraplegia by applying additional channels to one of several sites on the lower extremity that elicit a flexion withdraw reflex. The reflex tends to vary with time and activation history, however. Some paralyzed subjects have been reported to walk at speeds approaching one quarter of normal, and ascend a curb or step with surface stimulation [21]. As the number of surface channels increases to eight and beyond, the systems become impractical. Surface systems are complicated by the need to doff and don multiple surface electrodes and the poor repeatability resulting from daily variation in electrode placement. They also suffer from poor selectivity and often cause skin irritation [34].

More complex systems for lower extremity function have been designed and tested for use with percutaneous intramuscular electrodes [22,25]. Up to 48 channels of stimulation have been applied to individual muscles controlling the trunk, hip, knee, and ankle to achieve standing, locomotion, stair climbing, side and back stepping, and other activities in individuals with SCI, head trauma, or stroke [35,36]. Subjects have been reported to walk at speeds close to two-thirds of normal and are able to perform one-handed reaching tasks. Percutaneous electrodes are reported to provide selective and repeatable muscle activation and have been proven safe and effective in humans [37]. Their tendency to move or break can necessitate reimplantation, so such systems are not totally acceptable for widespread clinical application, but are useful for development and simulation of completely implantable devices [30].

Currently, standing and walking with any form of FNS is not possible without the use of assistive devices such as crutches or a rolling walker for balance. Methods of closed-loop control of single joints during standing and walking are being investigated to minimize the necessity of upper extremity support to maintain posture and balance [38,39]. Systems for continuous closed-loop control are still confined to the laboratory and have not yet been incorporated into the designs of portable stimulators or completely implantable devices. Open-loop stimulation might have immediate clinical application for standing for short periods of time and walking short distances.

17.2.3. Central Responses to FNS in the SCI Population

Impaired or inappropriate cardiovascular responses can limit the application of FNS in the SCI population. Loss of venous return with SCI restricts the central blood volume and leads to a reduced cardiac performance. Although no significant differences have been observed between maximal heart rates of able-bodied and wheelchair-bound adults during maximal or submaximal exercise [40], maximal oxygen uptake is severely compromised with SCI. In spite of the restrictions that SCI places on the ability to cope with the stress of exercise, aerobic training effects have been observed with FNS, as evidenced by heart rate and blood pressure responses [41].

The energy costs of ambulation in paraplegics with long leg braces have been documented in adults by several investigators [42,43]. The energy cost of FNS walking has been reported to be approximately 76 percent of the maximal aerobic power as determined by an arm ergometry graded exercise test plus FNS to the lower extremities [44].

17.2.4. Contractile Properties of Stimulated Muscle

The strength and endurance of a stimulated contraction are key determinants to the quality of the standing or walking motions achievable with FNS. Muscles atrophied from disuse can be restrengthened with electrical stimulation, but the rate of strength increase and final strength of the muscle might be extremely dependent on the initial strength and endurance of the individual [45].

An electrical stimulus will recruit fast, fatiguable motor units first because of the low threshold of large, myelinated nerve fibers [34,46]. This is the opposite of what typically occurs during a voluntary contraction. Surface stimulation will recruit superficial muscle fibers that tend to be part of large, rapidly fatiguing motor units. Although it might be possible to recruit more fatigue-resistant fibers by stimulating deeply in the muscle via implanted rather than surface electrodes, fatigue induced by motor unit recruitment patterns during electrical stimulation is largely unavoidable with methods that are currently available. Natural recruitment order has been demonstrated with various novel stimulation techniques in animal preparations.

Evidence indicates that the metabolic properties of muscle fibers can be altered under the influence of electrical stimulation, thereby increasing fatigue resistance. The most effective exercise program to maximize both strength and endurance has not been determined, and optimal protocols in preparation for standing and walking still require further refinement.

Predictions from computer simulations of FNS gait indicate that a minimum of seven muscle groups are necessary bilaterally to produce a step: soleus, gastrocnemius, ankle dorsiflexors, vasti, gluteus medius/minimus, hamstrings, and iliopsoas [47]. After exercise with stimulation, individuals with paraplegia are able to produce joint moments at or above the levels predicted by the computer model for these muscles, confirming that sufficient muscle strength to achieve stepping is possible with FNS. Other factors might compromise the ability to achieve stimulated ambulation, however. Several of the muscle groups included in the model are inaccessible with surface stimulation, but can be activated with percutaneous or implantable intramuscular electrodes. Although it is possible to obtain an isolated contraction of the target muscle with intramuscular stimulation, additional muscles or reflex activity might be recruited simultaneously and unintentionally by a single electrode. The selectivity of the stimulated responses, as well as the absence of reflex activity, are simplifying assumptions of computer models that might not always be achievable in reality.

Since a number of paralyzed muscles need to be activated in a coordinated manner in order to produce a smooth and useful movement, the delays, rise times, and relaxation times associated with a stimulated contraction need to be taken into account. The rise times of stimulated force are typically between 100 and 300 ms. Relaxation times can vary from 40 to 240 ms for fast twitch and slow twitch fibers, respectively. Because of the complicated interaction of a large number of stimulated muscles required to produce a dynamic movement, a change of as little as 20 ms in the activation timing of one muscle can produce significant changes in the quality of the resulting motion.

17.3. THE LOWER EXTREMITY FNS PROGRAM AT SHRINERS HOSPITALS

Figure 17-1 depicts the stages of the standing and walking program at the Philadelphia Unit of Shriners Hospitals from 1986 to 1993. The Shriners program represented a staged approach to implementing lower extremity FNS in a clinical setting. Phases of the program included: screening to identify potential FNS users, conditioning to reestablish strength and endurance, laboratory-based standing, ad lib standing in the home and community, and supervised walking in the laboratory. The program was also structured to permit the controlled study of the physiological and functional effects of exercise and weight bearing with stimulation. In addition to the tests specific to each stage of the program, baseline tests of bone mineral density and joint integrity (MRIs, arthrometry, standing X-rays, and ranges of motion) were repeated at regular intervals in an attempt to characterize completely the beneficial or deleterious effects of FNS.

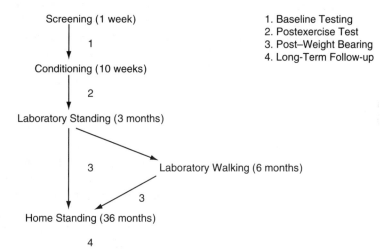

Figure 17-1. Phases of Lower Extremity FNS Program at Philadelphia Unit of Shriners Hospitals.

17.3.1. Screening and Candidate Selection

This phase of the program was designed to identify potential recipients of lower extremity FNS systems for standing and walking and to gain insight into the characteristics of the SCI population. During the course of a one-week screening admission, candidates were examined by the clinical and research staff to determine their medical, psychosocial, and rehabilitation status. Although no assessment tools have been validated expressly for the psychological screening of FNS candidates, coping skills, the ability to tolerate uncertainty, and the ability to provide informed consent have been identified as key elements in the emotional makeup of successful participants in FNS research programs [48]. Medical tests at this stage included formal screening for peripheral denervation of the major muscles of the lower extremity, dual photon absorptiometry to determine bone mineral density, and MRIs, radiographs, and clinical examinations of the knees and ankles.

More than 70 children and young adults with thoracic and lumbar level spinal cord injuries were examined for inclusion in the experimental program of standing and walking. The inclusion criteria for the research program are:

1. Age up to 20 years
2. Motor complete spinal cord injury below T1
3. No LMN involvement of the quadriceps, gluteal, or hamstring muscles
4. Functional independence in ADLs, wheelchair management, and transfers
5. Range of motion within functional limits for standing and walking with KAFOs (hip and knee flexion contractures less than 20 degrees)
6. Ability to stand and ambulate in braces
7. No outstanding orthopaedic involvement (such as scoliosis, history of spontaneous fracture, etc.)
8. No outstanding medical problems (such as uncontrolled spasticity, skin involvement, etc.)
9. No outstanding psychosocial involvement that would negatively influence research participation

Over 60 percent of the individuals examined were found to be medically fit for the FNS program according to these guidelines. As illustrated in Figure 17-2, few instances of psychosocial involvement severe enough to limit participation were observed, and close to 95 percent of the physically appropriate candidates were also well suited psychosocially. This suggests that over 55 percent of all individuals examined with thoracic or lumbar level injuries would be able to take advantage of lower extremity FNS in the research setting. These findings are in contrast to earlier reports implying that between 10 and 16 percent of all adults with paraplegia would be potential users of a stimulation system for standing and walking [17,27,49].

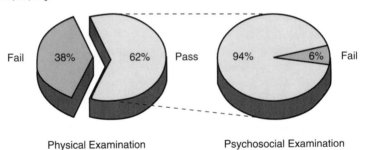

Physical Examination   Psychosocial Examination

Figure 17-2. Screening results for candidacy for research applications of lower extremity FNS at Shriners Hospitals.

A summary of the physical impediments to participation in the lower extremity FNS programs is given in Figure 17-3. Of the individuals categorized as physically inappropriate, almost 70 percent showed denervation of the antigravity muscles of the legs. An interaction between injury level and peripheral denervation was observed. Over half of the individuals with injuries below T12 exhibited some peripheral denervation in the lower extremities because of the proximity to the cauda equina [50]. Orthopaedic problems included joint subluxation, recurrent skin problems, and adverse sensation.

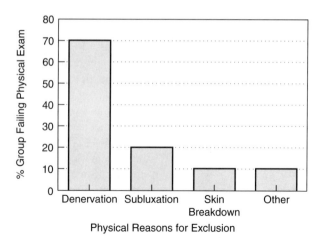

Figure 17-3. Physical contraindications to lower extremity FNS.

Individuals who met the inclusion criteria for the research program were extended an invitation to participate. Candidates who chose to participate were scheduled for readmission for the conditioning phase of the program. For those individuals who did not meet the physical or psychosocial inclusion criteria, treatment programs or other clinical interventions were identified to better prepare them for FNS.

The results of the screening phase of the program indicated that the bone mineral densities of children with SCI were significantly less than those of their able-bodied peers. Values for the SCI population averaged approximately 60 percent of published data from age- and sex-matched controls. Unlike their able-bodied counterparts, females with SCI exhibited higher trochanteric and femoral densities than males (by almost 10 percent). Factors such as age at injury, injury level, time postinjury, and flaccid or spastic paralysis had no significant effect. Individuals with histories of multiple spontaneous fractures exhibited bone densities that were significantly less than children without fractures. Values for the fracture group averaged approximately 50 percent of normal, while the nonfracture group exhibited values closer to 68 percent. Because of the natural variability of the data, it was impossible to determine a threshold of bone density for increased risk of fracture. As a general rule in the clinical setting, FNS was not offered to children exhibiting bone densities less than 60 percent of normal. Half the knees examined showed evidence of effusion on MRI, indicating that the immobilization resulting from SCI might be injurious to the joints. No abnormalities were observed upon clinical or radiographic examination, although one child showed evidence of hip instability.

17.3.2. Conditioning and Preparatory Exercise

Applicants passing the screening battery who chose to participate in the FNS program underwent a rigorously controlled period of exercise designed to reverse the effects of disuse atrophy. The conditioning phase consisted of one week of baseline testing followed by eight weeks of exercise and a final week of postexercise testing. Percutaneous intramuscular electrodes were implanted close to the femoral nerve to recruit all four heads of the quadriceps. Throughout this and all the phases of the program a constant current (20 mA) balanced biphasic stimulus of variable pulse duration was employed. Stimulation frequency was set at 20 Hz for the duration of the exercise period. Recruitment curves were generated to ascertain maximal stimulus parameters and pre-exercise measurements of strength, endurance and other contractile properties were obtained during the baseline period.

The exercise prescription included progressive resistance strength training consisting of three sets of 10 knee extension contractions five days per week. Resistance was increased weekly to a level at which 30 repetitions could be completed without loss of full extension range of motion. Endurance training consisted of either one or two hours of unresisted knee extension at a 4:1 duty cycle five days per week. The on:off ratio was chosen to coincide with that observed for the quadriceps muscle during walking with FNS. Strength and endurance were measured biweekly with the knee in 20 degrees of flexion. Isometric strength was defined as the average joint moment over the last second of a two-second contraction with the knee in 20 degrees of flexion. Cyclic stimulation for 30 minutes at the 4:1 duty cycle was used to characterize endurance. Peak isokinetic strength was also measured.

Preliminary results indicate that isometric strength plateaus after four weeks of exercise. The most dramatic gains in endurance also occur within the first four weeks of training. Preliminary data also suggest that endurance gains for children undergoing one hour of endurance training were comparable to those in the two-hour exercise group. These initial findings indicate that static activities such as quiet standing might be possible after short preparatory conditioning programs (four weeks) consisting of short training sessions (one hour). Gains in isokinetic strength were observed throughout the eight-week period, suggesting that dynamic activities, such as walking, might require extended training programs.

Significant decreases in fusion frequencies were observed after the eight-week conditioning program. However, exercise appears to have had little effect on other contractile properties of the stimulated muscle such as the twitch delay, rise, and relaxation times. Along with the strength and endurance data, these results offer some indirect evidence that suggests a possible conversion of fast, fatiguable muscle fibers (Type IIb—fast glycolytic) to a mixed type (fast oxidative/glycolytic—Type I).

Bone density and MRIs were repeated during the postexercise interval. Exercise produced a modest, but statistically significant, increase in bone mineral density on the order of 10 percent at the femoral neck, Ward's triangle, and distal femur. Exercise with FNS might be more useful in preventing the rapid mineral loss characteristic of the first six weeks of immobilization, rather than at restoring bone minerals at a much later time. Upon reexamination with MRI, half as many knees exhibited evidence of effusions as before the exercise period. No abnormalities were observed clinically or radiographically, indicating that remobilization with FNS might be beneficial to the status of the paralyzed joints.

17.3.3. Laboratory Standing

After completing the conditioning phase, appropriate candidates were given the option of standing in the laboratory. This stage of the program lasted approximately three months and consisted of continued implantation of percutaneous intramuscular electrodes, exercise, coordination of functional stimulation patterns, standing training, and functional testing.

In addition to the electrodes for conditioning, the hip extensors (gluteus maximus and hamstrings), hip abductors (gluteus medius), hip adductors (posterior portion of the adductor magnus) and individual heads of the quadriceps (vastus lateralis, medialis, and intermedius) were implanted. The vasti were implanted to provide knee extension without the hip flexion component present in the rectus femoris. Due to the extent of preserved sensation, paraspinals were also implanted in individuals with lesions above T7. Subjects often received these electrodes during the 10-week conditioning phase, and the new muscles were added to their exercise programs as they were installed. The response of each electrode (in terms of a crude recruitment curve consisting of the threshold and maximal pulse durations, manual muscle grade, and electrode impedance) was characterized completely on a biweekly basis, and this information was used to update the stimulation patterns for standing function.

After implantation of the required electrodes, a one- to two-week period was dedicated to generating the patterns of stimulation necessary to rise from the wheelchair, maintain upright standing posture, and return to the seated position. Specification of these activation patterns involved an iterative process of trial and error to customize the stimulation to the individual. After sliding forward in the wheelchair and leaning forward to position the head and trunk over the feet, the volunteer initiated standing by pressing a switch mounted on the stimulator enclosure or on a command ring worn on the index finger. A delay between the switch depression and stimulation was often programmed into the system to allow the user to reposition the hands and upper body in preparation for standing. In general, standing was achieved by first slowly increasing the stimulation to all four heads of the quadriceps. Later in the coordination pattern, stimulation to the gluteals, hamstrings, or posterior adductors increased as the rectus femoris was deactivated. This assisted the patient in achieving a stable C posture, with the hips extended in the absence of the active flexion provided by the rectus. When the vasti were not accessible, certain individuals were able to stand upright with stimulation to the rectus femoris. Most volunteers were unable to achieve adequate hip extension under these circumstances. Once upright, the hip abductors and adductors were adjusted to align the trunk and pelvis and provide mediolateral stability. Proper balance and alignment were assessed visually and by requesting the participant to release one hand from the parallel bars or walker.

The remainder of the laboratory standing phase was divided into six stages, each lasting approximately two weeks, to train individuals in uses of the system during activities of daily living. The stages were: (1) rising and sitting, (2) balance and duration, (3) one-handed reaching, (4) standing transfers, (5) mobility, and (6) advanced tasks. The first stage concentrated on practicing the basic tasks of standing up and sitting down as users learned to interact with the system. During the second stage, users worked on improving elapsed standing times, assuming stable postures, and balancing with two hands. Volunteers were often ready to move out of the parallel bars and into a rolling walker at the completion of this period. The third stage emphasized one-handed tasks, including reaching from the standing position and working in kitchen, bathroom, or other real-world environments. Stimulation patterns were fine-tuned throughout the first three stages as standing skill improved or new electrodes were added to the system. The fourth and fifth stages focused on skills related to using the FNS system to move in or out of the wheelchair or negotiating inaccessible locations. Transfers from one seated position to another, such as from wheelchair to car, and mobility-related tasks such as entry or exit through narrow doorways or ascending and descending stairs, were practiced during these stages. Finally, recreational or user-identified standing activities were attempted during stage six, if time permitted.

The ability to stand and complete one-handed reaching tasks was assessed quantitatively during the last two weeks of the laboratory standing phase. An evaluation, called the *functional standing test* (FST), was developed based on the assumption that truly functional standing implies the ability to free one hand to manipulate the environment [51,52]. The FST consisted of 20 tasks requiring fine coordination, pushing, pulling, and reaching in the standing position that represent extensions of a standardized test of hand function usually applied while seated. Inter-rater reliability of the assessment has been established, and the test has been shown to be insensitive to age, although differences in the performances of boys and girls were found to be statistically significant. Results while standing were significantly different than those reported for identical tasks performed in the seated position, suggesting that an aspect of posture and balance that is absent while sitting is being detected by the test. The test has been repeated on seven individuals with SCI under two conditions: (1) standing with FNS, and (2) standing with knee-ankle-foot orthoses (KAFOs). Although preliminary results are extremely variable and patient dependent, performance with FNS appears to be as good or better than performance in braces. Differences might be due to stimulation of the hip and trunk muscles, which tend to stabilize the unbraced pelvis and torso. Application of the FST during standing with FNS is pictured in Figure 17-4.

The laboratory standing phase was designed not only to study FNS and brace standing, but to prepare an individual for discharge with an FNS system or to continue to walk in the laboratory. At the completion of the laboratory standing phase, individuals qualifying for discharge with a standing system underwent another series of medical tests. Dual photon absorptiometry, MRIs of the knees and ankles, arthrometry, knee and ankle ranges of motion, and standing X-rays were repeated as new baselines for a longitudinal study of the effects of long-term weight bearing with FNS.

17.3.4. Home Standing

After successful completion of the laboratory standing phase, qualified individuals were given the option of walking with FNS in the laboratory, or enrolling in a three-year program of standing in the home and community. The home standing phase was designed to assess the costs and benefits of FNS technology in nonlaboratory environments, determine if it is perceived as useful, and establish the long-term medical consequences of standing with stimulation.

The fundamental design criteria for lower extremity FNS systems identified by J. Stallard and R. E. Major [53] included: independence (in donning, doffing, and function), minimal energy costs, cosmesis, system reliability, and system cost. Figures 17-5 and 17-6 show the stimulator system resulting from the application of these criteria to a home-bound system for standing. A small, lightweight, and rechargeable device capable of delivering 16 independent channels of stimulation was designed and fabricated (Figure 17-5). Doffing, donning, and daily wear were facilitated by a battery life in excess of eight hours per charge and a molded cable that was polarized to ensure easy and proper connection to up to eight muscles per leg. Independence was further encouraged by providing the users with a portable suction handle that could be easily carried in a seat backpack and used on smooth surfaces such as countertops in unadapted environments (Figure 17-6). A rolling walker was also provided to allow swing-to gait with the knees and hips extended with FNS. Cosmesis was addressed by prescribing low-profile UCBL (University of California Biomechanics Laboratories) orthoses, which are hidden in high-top sneakers and stabilize the structures of the foot and ankle inconspicuously. Reliability was achieved by using printed circuit boards in the electronic design and utilizing components that met medical and military specifications. Connectors without pins that would bend or break were also

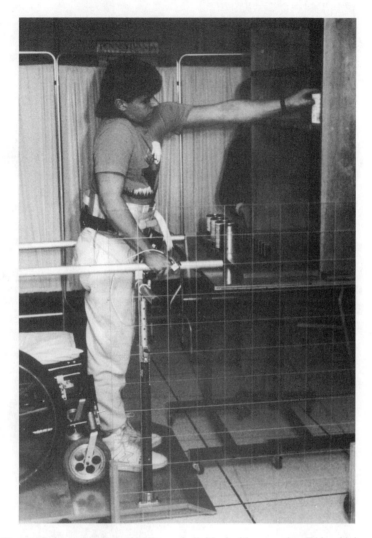

Figure 17-4. Application of FST to an individual with a complete T4 level injury
standing with FNS.

chosen. Although the percutaneous intramuscular electrodes made doffing and donning the
system much more convenient than multichannel surface systems, they exhibited a tendency
to break at the connector site. For this reason, volunteers were provided with the proper
crimping tools and training to effect the necessary repairs on their own, thereby minimizing
loss of function (Figure 17-6).

A home visit to identify potential uses of the standing system was intended to precede
discharge. The first six months of nonlaboratory use was designated as a "homework"
period. Weekly telephone contact was used to identify and follow up on assignments for
exercise or functional use. A structured questionnaire was administered to ascertain the
perceived costs and benefits of using the FNS system. Readmissions to the laboratory
for continued training, reimplantation, maintenance, and testing were scheduled for three

Figure 17-5. Sixteen-channel stimulator, stimulation cable, and charger for home standing phase of the Shriners FNS program.

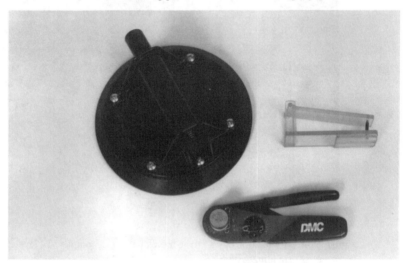

Figure 17-6. Home standing accessories—portable suction handhold, crimp tool, and insertion tool for electrode connectors.

and six months postdischarge. The six-month homework period was followed by a period of "ad lib" use in which subjects were free to experiment with the system on their own. Although no formal expectations on system usage were imposed during this time, subjects were encouraged to incorporate homework tasks previously identified as useful into their routine. Phone contact was continued on a biweekly basis, and a follow-up admission was scheduled at the end of the ad lib period. The remaining two years consisted of continued biweekly contact and semiannual readmissions. Medical tests (including bone density, MRI, and X-rays) were repeated at each six-month follow-up interval. To date, 5 volunteers have been discharged with percutaneous FNS systems for standing function out of a target group of 12 users.

Preliminary data indicate that standing to reach inaccessible items in the kitchen, bathroom, school, or workplace might be only one of many possible uses of the system. Subjects tend to use the system to exercise or increase their mobility. Future research will concentrate on FNS systems to provide simple motions, such as sidestepping and curb climbing, that would enhance mobility by providing options for gaining access to places that a wheelchair cannot.

17.3.5. Laboratory Walking

A minimum commitment of six months was required to participate in the reciprocal walking phase of the program. Walking necessitated the implantation, exercise, and coordination of muscles in addition to those for standing. During this phase, the hip flexors (iliopsoas, sartorius, gracilis, and tensor fascia lata), knee flexors (short head of the biceps femoris), and ankle plantarflexors and dorsiflexors (gastrocnemius, soleus, and tibialis anterior) were implanted. Several of these muscles, such as the iliopsoas, were difficult or impossible to isolate with surface stimulation. In this case, the psoas was most often activated by implanting electrodes at the L1-L2 spinal roots. Although isolated contraction of the iliopsoas was possible, overflow to the quadriceps was commonly observed.

The laboratory walking phase consisted of weekly sessions to update or fine-tune the patterns of stimulation for reciprocal ambulation. This was complemented by daily sessions of walking practice. By the end of the laboratory walking phase, subjects were routinely able to complete 10 repetitions of approximately 20 meters each at speeds approaching 20 percent of normal during these sessions. Maximum distances and velocities for volunteers in the Shriners program are listed in Table 17-1. The mechanics of walking with FNS and common problems and gait deviations are discussed in the following section.

TABLE 17-1 MAXIMAL SPEEDS AND DISTANCES OF WALKING SUBJECTS IN THE SHRINERS FNS PROGRAM

Subject	Age* (years)	Injury level	Month post SCI*	Time from admission (months) Stand	Time from admission (months) Walk	Max. walk (m)	Max. speed (m/min)
JC	16	T5	24	7	10	11.2	4.8
RH	17	T7	14	6	7	81.0	10.8
MM	16	T4	28	4	8	225.6	15.0
LC	13	T12	60	4	5	166.0	6.0
TS	18	T11	24	5	10	141.1	6.0
KB	17	T4	24	4	6	804.8	3.5
MR	14	T8	78	3	6	12.2	10.6
BK	17	T5	29	3	6	99.9	11.3

* At time of admission

Bone mineral density measurements and assessments of the status of the knee and ankle joints were repeated upon completion of the six-month laboratory walking phase and combined with the data from the laboratory standing phase. A statistically significant increase in bone density in excess of 30 percent was observed at the distal femur, which happens to be the most metabolically active region of the bone. Clinical and radiographic evaluation of the joints again demonstrated no abnormalities of any structure of the knees or ankles. One volunteer with a preexisting hip instability and history of adduction and flexion spasms experienced a hip subluxation that might have been aggravated by standing and walking with FNS. The subluxation was repaired surgically.

17.4. THE MECHANICS OF WALKING WITH FNS

The requirements for ambulation with FNS are similar to those of the intact central nervous system for controlling normal gait [53,54]. They are: (1) support body weight against gravity to prevent collapse, (2) maintain balance in anterior-posterior and medial-lateral directions, and (3) inject propulsive forces. For reciprocal walking, several additional requirements must be met, such as: (4) control foot trajectory for swing limb clearance and gentle landing, (5) forward progression of the swing limb, and (6) forward progression of the trunk over the stance limb. While the intact control system is highly developed at achieving these tasks efficiently and in the presence of many disturbances, reciprocal walking with FNS remains much more difficult. The best FNS systems to date have been most successful in advancing the swing limb through stimulation of the hip flexors and knee extensors, preventing collapse with stimulation to the knee and hip extensors, and injecting propulsive forces through stimulation of the hip extensors and ankle plantarflexors. FNS has been less successful at achieving the other requirements for smooth, unencumbered, and energy-efficient ambulation. Foot trajectory is difficult to control because stimulated responses and their resulting joint motions vary from step to step with fatigue, stimulation history, the position of the previous step, and the activity of the upper body. Forward progression of the trunk is still difficult, and weight transfer from the trailing to the leading limb usually requires significant upper extremity exertion. The most obvious deficit is the inability to provide automatic postural corrections. Balance is still maintained by voluntary motions of trunk and upper extremities.

In spite of these difficulties, the best walking with open-loop stimulation has been approaching normal speed and appearance. The kinematics, kinetics, and control problems associated with walking with FNS are summarized below.

17.4.1. Kinematics

The kinematics of electrically stimulated walking depend on the availability, strength, and endurance of paralyzed muscles, the ability of the therapist or engineer to specify patterns of stimulation for ambulation, and the subject's experience with the FNS system. Some well-trained subjects can walk 300 m repeatedly at 0.5 m/s, while others struggle at lower speeds and shorter distances. By triggering the steps with insole pressure sensors, walking speed was increased to 0.73 m/s with a cadence of 65 steps/min in one subject. Double support was 12 to 16 percent of the gait cycle, while swing averaged close to the nominal value of 40 percent. The effects of fatigue were evident in one subject whose velocity and stride length decreased by over 25 percent after walking 300 m at a constant cadence.

The differences in joint angles of the hip, knee, and ankle during walking with FNS as compared to normal [55,56] are illustrated in Figure 17-7. The average joint angle

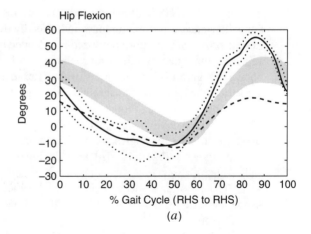

(a)

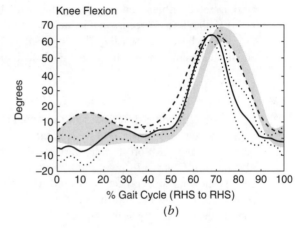

(b)

Figure 17-7. Kinematics of walking with FNS normalized to gait cycle. Solid lines indicate average joint trajectories of FNS walking. Dashed lines represent normal walking at a comfortable speed, and shaded area represents range for faster cadences. (a) Hip angle, (b) knee angle, (c) ankle angle.

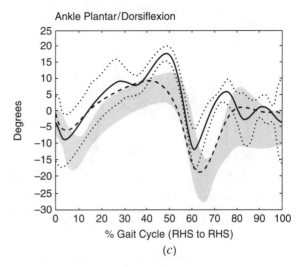

(c)

trajectories for FNS walking are indicated by the solid lines in Figure 17-7(*a*), (*b*), and (*c*), with standard-deviation ranges indicated by dotted lines. For comparison, an average normal profile at a comfortable speed is indicated by the dashed lines, and the shaded areas represent the range of values for walking at a faster cadence (85 to 102 steps/min). As shown in Figure 17-7(*a*), the hip is slightly flexed at initial contact when the trunk is carried forward as the foot strikes the ground. Hip angle tends to lag normal during stance, possibly because pulling on the rolling walker to propel the body forward might overextend the hips. Conversely, hip flexion is exaggerated during swing to facilitate ground clearance and more closely resembles the angles observed at faster cadences.

As shown in Figure 17-7(*b*), knee flexion is absent during early stance after heel-strike, indicating an absence of a loading response and the necessity to vault over the extended knee. There is often inadequate preswing as evinced by delayed flexion of the knee. During swing the knee extends prematurely, although peak angular excursion coincides with the normal profile.

At the ankle, plantarflexion is slightly accelerated at initial contact, probably due to weakness in the tibialis anterior and loading with the knee extended. As illustrated in Figure 17-7(*c*), dorsiflexion occurs late in stance, and the absence of a rocker action contributes to minimal heel rise, possibly due to weak gastrocnemius-soleus. In swing, the ankle dorsiflexes prematurely to help ensure adequate limb clearance.

17.4.2. Kinetics

There are some differences in the ground reaction forces produced in normal and FNS-generated gait. Instead of the normal two-peak vertical force associated with weight acceptance and push-off, a more variable three-peak force is observed during stance, as illustrated in Figure 17-8. An initial peak occurs early in stance phase (6 percent of the cycle) following foot contact, with a dip at the end of double support and a delayed weight acceptance peak at the end of midstance. Weight acceptance is abnormal, and the arms contribute significantly to the support.

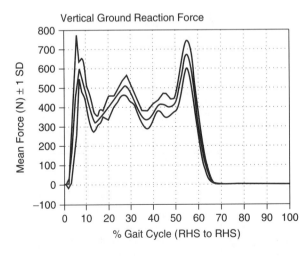

Figure 17-8. Average (±1 SD) vertical ground reaction force during FNS walking, normalized to gait cycle.

The role of the upper extremities in walking with FNS is to provide corrective forces through a walking aid. Upper extremity forces on an instrumented walker are shown in Figure 17-9. The critical times for arm support are at initial contact on the right arm [Figure 17-9(*a*)] and during late stance on the left arm [Figure 17-9(*b*)]. The mean peak resultant force can exceed 20 percent of body weight. These forces increased to 40 percent on each arm as hip and trunk muscles fatigued. While the walker provides good support in both frontal and transverse planes, it impedes smooth progression by exerting horizontal forces against the body. Good propulsive forces can be achieved with crutches; but crutch walking requires better transverse and frontal plane stability than is currently available with FNS.

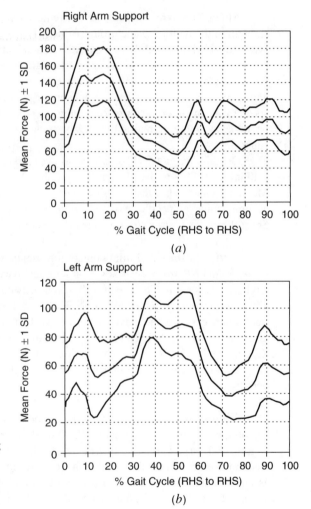

Figure 17-9. Average (±1 SD) upper extremity vertical reaction forces during FNS walking as measured by an instrumented rolling walker. (*a*) Right arm support, (*b*) left arm support.

17.4.3. Energy Expenditure

The metabolic energy currently required is still too high to make walking with FNS a practical alternative to the wheelchair for long distance transportation over level surfaces. Average maximum aerobic capacity of untrained females and males with thoracic SCI was determined to be 16 and 25 ml O_2/kg/min respectively, while conditioned males averaged 28 ml O_2/kg/min [57]. Currently, walking with FNS at 0.5 m/s requires an average close to this maximal value, as opposed to normal walking which requires only 8 ml O_2/kg/min. When applied to a paralyzed subject supine on a mat, the stimulation pattern for walking consumes 20 ml O_2/kg/min. Therefore, 8 ml O_2/kg/min are used by the voluntarily controlled arm and trunk muscles.

17.4.4. Control of Walking with FNS

Although maximal forces are not required during normal gait [58], reduced muscle strength in the major muscle groups of the trunk and lower extremities will reduce speed, symmetry [59], and stability of gait and increase the energy cost [60]. The muscles acting at the hip and ankle joints are particularly sensitive to strength reductions, and the forces at these joints had a significant correlation to walking speed. In FNS-generated gait, elimination of hip or trunk extensors or plantarflexors significantly reduced walking speed by as much as one half. Removing the posterior adductor caused a wide stance with lateral sway, and eliminating the erector spinae reduced speed and required increased arm support.

Quantitative gait analysis with a passive marker system has been performed on subjects walking with FNS at the Motion Study Laboratory at the Department of Veterans Affairs Medical Center in Cleveland, Ohio. The gait cycle can be divided into eight phases, each accomplishing a specific task and highlighting specific control problems for FNS [61]. Several of these phases are illustrated in Figure 17-10(*a*) through (*e*).

Initial Contact.   Initial contact represents the start of the stance phase of the gait cycle. With FNS, the heel strikes the floor after an exaggerated swing phase with the foot in slight plantarflexion. The knee is fully extended and the hip can be flexed up to 50 degrees. The neutral position in the ankle is difficult to achieve in some individuals with paraplegia due to heel cord tightness even with maximal activity of the pretibial muscles. The knee is extended by the activity of the quadriceps in the late swing phase. Extensors of the knee move the leg into excessive hip flexion before heel contact, but the hip angle at initial contact is somewhat controlled by hamstring, gluteus maximus, and posterior adductor activity.

Weight Acceptance.   This is the period of double-limb support in which the leading leg progresses from initial heel-strike to total foot contact with the floor, as illustrated in Figure 17-10(*a*). The ankle moves into further plantarflexion even though restrained by maximum pretibial muscle stimulation. In some individuals, maximum pretibial stimulation is undesirable since it may cause a withdrawal reflex resulting in knee and hip flexion. During the loading phase, the knee tends into slight hyperextension instead of flexion even though the quadriceps are deactivated just before heel strike. In the early part of this phase, the ground reaction vector (GRV) passes behind the ankle joint and in front of the knee and hip, indicating moments tending to plantarflex the foot and extend the knee. Knee extension is partly due to the hip extensors, which produce posterior rotation of the thigh. Weight acceptance on the leading leg is not completed until halfway into midstance. With the body

(a)

Figure 17-10. Selected phases of gait cycle when walking with FNS: (a) Weight
acceptance, (b) midstance, (c) terminal stance (showing contralateral swing), (d) midswing, (e) terminal swing.

weight still behind the leading foot and excessive forward lean on the trunk, the hip flexes,
resulting in loss of forward momentum and hampering leading leg weight transfer. At
contralateral toe-off, the GRV passes in front of the ankle and remains in front of the knee
and hip. This indicates a dorsiflexion moment at the ankle and a flexion moment at the
hip. The knee remains in forced extension. Weight transfer to the stance leg is delayed and
brief forces that can exceed 20 percent of body weight are exerted on each arm through the
walking aid.

(*b*)

Figure 17-10. (*Continued*)

Midstance.   Midstance represents the initiation of single-limb support with the foot in total contact with the floor. The beginning of this phase is illustrated in Figure 17-10(*b*). In FNS-generated gait, a substantial amount of weight is still being accepted on the supporting leg. The GRV remains in front of the ankle, knee, and hip throughout this phase, indicating that the ankle is passively forced into dorsiflexion throughout midstance without pretibial stimulation. The ankle reaches plantigrade when the heel begins to rise. As the heel rises, the ankle dorsiflexes up to about 10 degrees. Knee extension during midstance causes excessive vertical fluctuation of the center of mass, requiring extra hip and trunk

(*c*)

Figure 17-10. (*Continued*)

extensor force to bring the body forward over the stance leg. As a result, much metabolic energy is wasted. The knee remains locked in extension primarily by the hip extensors, which produce a posterior rotation of the thigh. Quadriceps activity is reinitiated during midstance, and the hip extensors are relaxed before their second burst of activity during terminal stance. When hip extensor stimulation is removed, a slight knee flexion occurs. The GRV remains behind the knee for the rest of the stance.

In subjects with weak hip and trunk extensors, the hip flexes rather than extends, interfering with the body's forward momentum. Increased hip flexion effectively lengthens

(d)

Figure 17-10. (*Continued*)

the swing leg and interferes with toe clearance, shortening step length and making weight transfer difficult. Much of the body weight must be absorbed through the arms to prevent falling. The GRV passes lateral to the subtalar joint and medial to the knee and hip joint in the frontal plane. This indicates that an eversion moment is occurring at the ankle and an adduction moment at the hip. In this phase, stimulation of the posterior portion of the adductor magnus produced hip extension and quadratus lumborum, erector spinae, and gluteus medius produced hip abduction. Weak abductors result in a drop of the pelvis, which can cause the swing-limb foot to catch the stance limb or to cross midline.

Terminal Stance. This is the single-limb support phase that begins with heel rise, and terminates with double-limb support, as illustrated in Figure 17-10(*c*). The activity

(e)

Figure 17-10. (*Continued*)

of the plantarflexors is initiated to generate the push-off force and to prevent excessive dorsiflexion due to the passive moment created by the GRV positioned in front of the ankle. This is a very critical part of the gait. If the plantarflexors act too soon, they tend to raise the body instead of propelling it. This effectively shortens the swing leg and prevents proper swing-foot contact. In addition, activity of the swing-leg extensors will rotate the leg backward, reducing its effective step length and interfering with weight transfer. A push-off delayed into double stance is less effective in weight transfer. A poor transfer will result in collapse of the support knee as swing is attempted. With the body weight far posterior and with loss of momentum, the hip of the weight-accepting leg will tend to flex, and again much of the body weight must be supported by the arms.

A second burst of stimulation is delivered to the hip and trunk extensors. It helps to stabilize the hip and trunk, especially at the opposite heel-strike. The GRV is now behind the hip helping the active hip extensors. The knee remains in slight flexion with the GRV behind it. Knee collapse is prevented by active knee and hip extensors. The short head of biceps femoris is activated when needed to initiate knee flexion for the swing.

Preswing. Regulation of the knee and ankle is critical for weight transfer to the other leg and for initiation of swing. A stiff knee during stance can effectively shorten the swing leg, making transfer more difficult. Similarly, if the body weight has not progressed far enough forward, the stance knee will collapse and interrupt weight transfer. Proper control of knee flexion is difficult with preprogrammed stimulation and depends on the relaxation properties of the extensor muscles and the contraction properties of the knee flexors. Knee flexion is achieved by stimulation of the sartorius, gracilis, and biceps short head. Knee flexion magnitude is less than normal and varies between 30 and 40 degrees. Even though the GRV is far behind the knee, the relaxation time of the quadriceps resists flexion. An observable improvement in forward progression is achieved with some preswing knee flexion versus a stiff knee. The ankle continues to plantarflex and reaches 10 degrees before toe-off. Plantarflexor stimulation is discontinued half way into this phase, but the relaxation moment continues to create further plantarflexion for the next 100 ms. Early deactivation of hip extensors results in internal leg rotation and foot inversion. Hip flexion is initiated by the sartorius, gracilis, tensor fascia latae, and iliopsoas. Neutral is reached prior to toe-off.

Initial Swing. Initial swing begins at the time of toe-off. Knee flexion is produced by contraction of the sartorius, gracilis, and biceps femoris short head and is often initially inadequate, resulting in toe drag and poor swing. Since the gracilis also strongly adducts, balance from the tensor fascia latae and the gluteus minimus or medius is needed to clear the swing leg. The tensor fascia latae medial thigh rotation also balances the sartorius external rotation. Stimulation of the contralateral abductors and the ipsilateral quadratus lumborum will give additional toe and leg clearance.

Midswing. Midswing is illustrated in Figure 17-10(*d*). Maximum knee flexion in FNS-generated gait is nearly normal. At peak knee flexion, hip flexion is normal and continues to overshoot to 60 degrees. This exaggerated flexion is due to acceleration of the leg resulting from stimulation of the quadriceps while hip flexors are deactivated. Energy is wasted since muscle action is used to overcome gravity for an unnecessary motion, but a benefit is that a vigorous leg swing provides needed progressional force during terminal stance of the opposite leg.

Terminal Swing. An overly flexed hip is extended by gravitational forces of the leg and activity of the hamstrings to control step length in preparation for foot contact. The start of this phase of the cycle is illustrated in Figure 17-10(*e*).

17.5. CLINICAL ISSUES RELATED TO LOWER EXTREMITY FNS

Because of their expense, complexity, unknown functional benefits, and high level of maintenance, FNS systems have been primarily experimental in nature and restricted to use in clinical research programs, making their clinical impact difficult to predict. Due to the possible presence of orthopaedic complications, peripheral denervation, and social or economic constraints, not all individuals with SCI might be well suited for FNS. However, several precautions can be taken to prevent these interfering complications from developing. Other clinical interventions can be identified to address preexisting medical contraindications in preparation for standing or walking with FNS.

17.5.1. Prophylactic Measures and Preparatory Interventions

Several medical conditions need to be identified early when screening potential candidates for lower extremity FNS programs. The major physical barriers to application of FNS, possible interventions, and corresponding precautions are summarized in Table 17-2. Attention to these clinical issues can maximize the ability of a patient to utilize FNS technology.

TABLE 17-2 CLINICAL CONTRAINDICATIONS TO FNS AND POSSIBLE PREPARATORY INTERVENTIONS

Physical impediment	Clinical intervention	Precaution
Soft tissue contractions	Stretching Splinting Surgical release	Avoid overlengthening. Preserve innervation.
Spasticity	Medication (Lioresal/Valium) Baclofen pump Selective rhizotomies	Can adversely affect stimulated contractions. Rhizotomies unexplored.

Pressure sores	Conservative treatment
	   (pressure relief)
	Surgical repair (muscle flaps)
		Preserve hip extensors and
		   abductors.
		Use tensor fascia lata only if
		   other hip flexors are intact.
		Avoid latissimus dorsi.

Joint instability	Abduction splint Bony augmentation Prophylactic bracing at the knee	Monitor regularly. Avoid stimulating hip flexors and adductors while sitting. Augment acetabulum posteriorly.
Spinal deformities	Thoracic bracing Spinal fusion	Modify brace for standing. Preserve L4-L5 if possible. Monitor for long-term effects.
Peripheral denervation	Tendon transfers Neurotization	Unexplored options in the lower extremities.

Soft Tissue Contractions.   Contractions are a common orthopaedic problem encountered at the joints of individuals with long-term paralysis. They can best be controlled with medication for spasticity and good daily stretching regimens. In the lower extremity, all three joints (hips, knees, and ankles) are commonly affected. The hips develop flexion contractures, which can be prevented most effectively by sleeping in a prone position with the hips in maximum stretch. The knees develop flexion contractures and the ankles equinus contractures. Stretching is the mainstay of treatment, although when severe spasticity or equinus deformities are involved, night splinting should be prescribed. When stretching fails, early surgical release before bony deformity becomes a problem (especially in the growing child) is essential. If releases are performed, it is important that they be done so as not to overlengthen muscles that might be utilized for function with electrical stimulation in the future.

Spasticity.   Excessive spasticity can be troublesome for the patient trying to stand and walk with FNS. Exercise with FNS appears to result in less frequent, although significantly stronger, involuntary spasms. Medication is recommended as the first option for controlling spasticity that might interfere with function. Lioresal can be prescribed up to the maximal dosage where the side-effect of drowsiness becomes intolerable. The addition of Valium twice a day can be of help. The preliminary results of the baclofen pump appear to be most promising if medication should fail. Pharmacological treatment should not include neuromuscular blocking agents that might adversely affect the excitability of the peripheral nerve or contractile ability of the muscle and hence result in weak, nonfunctional responses to stimulation. Thermal rhizotomies of isolated spastic muscles appear appropriate in theory, although there have been no reports of their use with FNS in the SCI population.

Pressure Sores.   Decubitus ulcers have prevented several individuals from participating in the FNS research programs. Prevention of these is essential for numerous reasons related to the general health and well-being of any individual with spinal cord injury, but unforeseen circumstances, accidents, or other problems often result in pressure sores from Grade 1 through 4. Grades 1 and 2 can be treated effectively by removing the pressure through a prolonged change in the patient's posture. Surgery might be indicated for the recalcitrant Grade 3 and 4 ulcers, however. The plastic surgeon should consult with the clinical research or therapy team to confirm the plans for the particular patient to use FNS as an option in the future. Certain muscles that might be utilized for standard surgical repairs might be critical for standing or walking with FNS. Their sacrifice as muscle flaps to repair the decubiti might ruin the patient's chances for using FNS technology. For example, gluteus medius and maximus flaps, commonly used for buttock and sacral sores, are essential for standing and walking, and their neurovascular supply and anatomic positioning should be preserved or minimally altered. It would be preferable to use the tensor fascia latae for this procedure, but only if the iliopsoas and sartorius are innervated and available to provide stimulated hip flexion. One of the hamstrings, since several of them are redundant in function, might be a good muscle to donate for a flap. The latissimus dorsi free flap is not a good option, as the patient needs all aspects of upper extremity strength and function for support, balance, and propulsion with current FNS systems.

Joint Instability.   Lack of joint stability appears to be a common problem at the hip. The incidence of hip subluxation might be as high as 28 percent in the pediatric SCI population [62]. Acetabular coverage of the femoral head is at a minimum with the hips flexed, so stimulated exercise of the hip adductors and flexors in preparation for walking with FNS should be performed in prone or supine positions, rather than while sitting. Soft-tissue stretching of the adductors and flexors, control of spasticity, and prophylactic abduction bracing will help prevent the contractions and deforming forces that can contribute to subluxation. Bracing will not treat an established instability, however. Should subluxation occur, surgical procedures such as soft-tissue releases and bony supplementation are possible. Early surgical interventions are strongly recommended for established instabilities. Since hips dislocate posteriorly, the bony coverage needs to be augmented in the posterior region of the acetabulum. This procedure has been performed on two participants with hip dislocations who went on to stand with FNS after surgery and rehabilitation.

Preliminary experience suggests that FNS does not appear to accentuate the knee hyperextension commonly seen in females. The hyperextension also does not appear to interfere with function, although prophylactic bracing for ligamentous instability in the knee should be considered. The mediolateral instability associated with cruciate ligamentous tears observed in one patient has not compromised her standing performance. The long-term effects of stimulation, and the additional demands of ambulation, on the insensate joints have yet to be determined. Ankle instability is easily braced and cosmetically acceptable with several standard options ranging from a UCBL orthosis to an AFO.

Spinal Deformities. Curvature of the spine occurs in 98 percent of patients with spinal cord injury, with 67 percent requiring surgery [62]. In lower extremity applications, spinal curves compromise standing posture and result in excessive use of the arms for support. Balance and reaching tasks become difficult if not impossible. Early prophylactic bracing should be considered for FNS candidates before the curves begin to interfere with function. Lower extremity FNS systems can be implemented in the presence of prophylactic bracing, although modifications to either the system or brace might be required. For example, a brace designed to correct sitting posture might need to be customized to allow a patient to adopt a stable C posture.

Once the curve progresses past 40 degrees, a spinal fusion is indicated [62]. Stabilization of the spine with instrumentation down into the sacrum can be utilized with the FNS system provided that normal sagittal alignment is maintained. In fact, five individuals who were found to be appropriate for FNS at Shriners Hospitals had undergone surgery to correct spinal curvatures prior to their screening examinations. All of these individuals were able to stand and step with FNS successfully. If the curve does not extend to L5, it is preferable to stop the instrumentation at L4-L5 to maintain some flexibility in the lumbosacral spine. Caution is advised, however, since long-term use of FNS for standing and walking might put extra deleterious demands on the lumbosacral spine and precipitate additional surgery, such as that for a Charcot spine.

Peripheral Denervation. The most frequently observed impediment to the application of FNS is the presence of peripheral nerve damage. Without an intact and excitable peripheral nerve, high stimulating currents or long-duration stimulating pulses are required to activate the muscle tissue directly. Techniques for activating denervated muscle are generally impractical for functional applications requiring the coordination of many muscles, and might even be dangerous as the chance of an electrical or chemical burn increases. Without the input from reflex arcs and spasms, denervated muscle is also frequently replaced by unexcitable connective tissue. In the lower extremity, the highest incidence of denervation was observed in individuals with T12-L3 level injuries. Although this suggests that FNS systems for ambulation or standing might be more applicable to individual lesions above T11, tendon transfers or neurotization are options with much potential that have yet to be explored in the lower extremities.

17.6. CONCLUSIONS

Lower extremity applications of FNS for standing and walking present many technical and clinical challenges to rehabilitation professionals and engineers alike. The medical and psychological aspects of spinal cord injury cannot be ignored in the design and application of systems for standing and walking. Physical problems that might at first contraindicate FNS can often be obviated by suitable preparatory treatment. Preliminary results indicate that exercise and weight bearing with FNS at the doses provided are not injurious to the bones and joints of paralyzed individuals. Preexisting joint abnormalities of the articular surfaces might be improved with mobilization through FNS. However, preexisting joint instabilities might be aggravated by stimulation.

Walking with FNS is still inefficient, cumbersome, and impractical for long distances. Stepping short distances in the vicinity of the wheelchair, ascending or descending a curb, or sidestepping at a counter are simpler activities that can complement quiet standing and increase the independence of individuals with spinal cord injuries by providing them with options for gaining access to inaccessible places.

Human motion analysis is becoming an important tool for the identification and rectification of deviations observed in FNS-generated walking. However, kinematic and kinetic analyses of ambulation with FNS are much more complicated than traditional gait analyses. The step-to-step variability of FNS walking appears to be appreciable, even with the application of identical stimulus patterns. The rapid rate of fatigue of stimulated muscles also compromises repeatability. The quality of walking will vary with the strength of the stimulated responses of the muscles and the procedure used to produce the step, the talent and experience of the clinician or engineer designing the stimulation patterns, and the motivation and training of the volunteer. Assistive devices are still required that often interfere with the data collection apparatus or marker systems. Models of the musculoskeletal system also need to incorporate more detailed knowledge about the mechanics of the arms, torso, and hips for more accurate predictions of the moments produced while walking with stimulation. Addressing these technical challenges will help further the application of objective and quantitative techniques to the issues that currently keep FNS from being a practical clinical alternative for providing ambulatory function to individuals with complete spinal cord injuries.

Acknowledgments

The authors would like to acknowledge the financial support of both the Department of Veteran Affairs Rehabilitation Research and Development Service, and Shriners Hospitals for Crippled Children. The contributions of the clinical and research staff at the Philadelphia Unit of Shriners Hospitals and the Department of Veterans Affairs Medical Center in Cleveland, Ohio, are also worthy of note. In particular, the efforts of Elizabeth Gardner, Joy Cohn, Cecilia Mullin, Megan Moynahan, Carolyn Barbieri, and Kathy Goodstein are greatly appreciated.

References

[1] Sunderland S. *Nerves and Nerve Injuries*. Baltimore, Md: Williams and Wilkins Publishing Co;1968.

[2] Guttman L. *Spinal Cord Injuries: Comprehensive Management and Research* 2nd ed. Oxford, England: Blackwell Scientific Publications;1976.

[3] Vodovnik L, Crochetiere WJ, Reswick JB. Control of a skeletal joint by electrical stimulation of antagonists. *Med Biol Engr* 1967;5:97–109.

[4] Stanic U, Trnkoczy, A. Closed-loop positioning of hemiplegic patient's joints by means of functional electrical stimulation. *IEEE Trans Biomed Engr* 1974;21:365–370.

[5] Stanic U, Acimovic-Janezic R, Gros N, Trnkoczy A, Bajd T, Kljajic M. Multi-channel electrical stimulation for correction of hemiplegic gait. *Scan J Rehab Med* 1977;10:175–192.

[6] Brindley GS, Polkey CE, Rushton DN. Electrical splinting of the knee in paraplegia. *Paraplegia* 1978;16:428–435.

[7] Jaeger R. Design and simulation of closed-loop electrical stimulation orthoses for restoration of quiet standing in paraplegics. *J Biomech* 1986;19:825–835.

[8] Cybulski GR, Penn RD, Jaeger R. Lower extremity functional neuromuscular stimulation in cases of spinal cord injury. *Neurosurg* 1985;15:132–146.

[9] Peckham PH. Functional electrical stimulation: Current status and future prospects of applications to the neuromuscular system in spinal cord injury. *Paraplegia* 1987;25:279–285.

[10] Harvey C, Rothschild R, Asmann A, Stripling T. New estimates of traumatic SCI prevalence: A survey-based approach. *Paraplegia* 1990;28:537–544.

[11] Stover SL, Fine PR. *Spinal Cord Injury: The Facts and Figures*. Birmingham:University of Alabama at Birmingham; 1986.

[12] Stover SL, Fine PR. The epidemiology and economics of spinal cord injury. *Paraplegia* 1987;25:225–228.

[13] DeVivo MJ, Fine PR, Maetz HM, Stover SL. Prevalence of spinal cord injury: A re-estimation employing life table techniques. *Arch Neurol* 1980;37:707–708.

[14] Fine PR, Kuhlemeier KV, DeVivo MJ, Stover SL. Spinal cord injury: An epidemiologic perspective. *Paraplegia* 1979–1980;17:237–250.

[15] Bracken MB, Freeman DH, Hellenbrand K. Incidence of acute traumatic hospitalized spinal cord injury in the United States. *Am J Epidemiology* 1981;113:615–622.

[16] Ergas Z. Spinal cord injury in the United States: A statistical update. *Nervous Sys Trauma* 1985;2:19–30.

[17] Kralj A, Bajd T. *Functional Electrical Stimulation: Standing and Walking after Spinal Cord Injury*. Boca Raton, Fla:CRC Press;1989.

[18] McNeal D, Reswick J. Control of skeletal muscle by electrical stimulation. *Adv Biomed Eng* 1976;6:209–256.

[19] Bajd T, Kralj A, Turk R. Standing-up of a healthy subject and a paraplegic patient. *J Biomech* 1982;15(1)1–10.

[20] Bajd T, Kralj A, Turk R, Benko H, Sega J. The use of a four-channel electrical stimulator as an ambulatory aid for paraplegic patients. *Phys Ther* 1983;63:11–16.

[21] Kralj A, Bajd T, Turk R, Benko H. Gait restoration in paraplegic patients: A feasibility demonstration using multichannel surface electrode FES. *J Rehabil Res Dev* 1983;20:3–20.

[22] Marsolais E, Kobetic R. Functional walking in paralyzed patients by means of electrical stimulation. *Clin Orthop* 1983;175:30–36.

[23] Holle J, Frey M, Gruber H, Kern H, Stohr H, Thoma H. Functional electro-stimulation of paraplegics. *Orthopedics* 1984;1145–1155.

[24] Andrews B, Baxendale R. A hybrid orthosis incorporating artificial reflexes for spinal cord damaged patients. *J Physiol* 1988;198:380.

[25] Marsolais EB, Kobetic R. Functional electrical stimulation for walking in paraplegia. *J Bone Joint Surg Am* 1987;69A:728–733.

[26] Graupe D. EMG pattern analysis for patient-responsive control of FES in paraplegics for walker-supported walking. *IEEE Trans Biomed Eng* 1989;36:711–719.

[27] Jaeger R, Yarkony G, Smith R. Standing the spinal cord injured patient by electrical stimulation: Refinement of a protocol for clinical use. *IEEE Trans Biomed Eng* 1989;36:720–728.

[28] Yarkony GM, Jaeger R, Roth E, Kral A, Quintern J. Functional neuromuscular stimulation for standing after spinal cord injury. *Arch Phys Med Rehab* 1990;70: 201–206.

[29] Vance F, Kobetic R, Marsolais EB, Chizeck HJ. Portable microprocessor-controlled stimulation for activation of paralyzed muscles. In: Proceedings 23rd International Symposium on Mini- and Microcomputers and Their Applications. Hamza M ed. *Mini and Microcomputers and Their Applications.* San Antonio, Tex: ACTA Press;1983.

[30] Marsolais EB, Kobetic R. Implantation techniques and experience with percutaneous intramuscular electrodes in the lower extremities. *J Rehabil Res Dev* 1986;23:1–8.

[31] Isakov E, Mizrahi J, Majenson T. Biomechanical and physiological evaluation of FES-activated paraplegic patients. *J Rehabil Res Dev* 1986;23:9–19.

[32] Kralj A, Jaeger RJ. Posture switching enables prolonged standing in paraplegic patients functionally electrically stimulated. *Proc. 5th Conf on Rehab Engr* Houston, Tex;1982:60.

[33] Solomonow M, Baratta RV, Hirokawa S, Rightor N, Walker W, Beaudette P, Shoji H, D'Ambrosia R. The RGO generation II: Muscle stimulation powered orthosis as a practical walking system for paraplegics. *Orthopedics* 1989;12:1309–1315.

[34] Benton LA, Baker LL, Bowman BR, Waters RL. *Functional Electrical Stimulation: A Practical Clinical Guide* 2nd ed. Downey, Calif: Professional Staff Association of Rancho Los Amigos Medical Center; 1981.

[35] Kobetic R, Carroll SG, Marsolais EB. Paraplegic stair climbing assisted by electrical stimulation. *Proc 39th Alliance Conference in Engineering, Medicine & Biology* 1986: 265.

[36] Kobetic R, Pereira JM, Marsolais EB. Electromyographic study of the side step for development of electrical stimulation patterns. *Proc 9th Rehabilitation Engineering Society of North America Conf* 1986:372–374.

[37] Mortimer JT, Kaufman D, Roessman U. Intramuscular electrical stimulation: Tissue damage. *Ann Biomed Engr* 1980;8:235–244.

[38] Chizeck HJ, Kobetic R, Marsolais EB, Abbas JJ, Donner IH, Simon E. Control of functional neuromuscular stimulation systems for standing and locomotion in paraplegics. *Proc of the IEEE* 1988;76(9)1155–1165.

[39] Abbas JJ, Chizeck HJ. Feedback control of coronal plane hip angle using functional neuromuscular stimulation. *IEEE Trans Biomed Eng* 1991;38:687–698.

[40] Zwiren L, Bar-Or O. Responses to exercise of paraplegics who differ in conditioning level. *Med Sci Sports* 1975;7:94–98.

[41] Ragnarsson KT, Pollack S, O'Daniel W, Edgar R, Petrofsky J, Nash M. Clinical evaluation of computerized functional electrical stimulation (FES) in spinal cord injury: A pilot multicenter study. *Arch Phys Med Rehab* 1988;69:672–677.

[42] Cerny K, Waters RL, Hislop HJ, Perry J, Antonelli D, and the staff of Pathokinesiology Lab., Ranchos Los Amigos Hospital, Downey, Calif. Energetics: Application to the study and management of locomotor disabilities. *Orthop Clin North Am* 1978;9: 351–375.

[43] Clinkingbeard JR, Gersten JW, Hoehn D. Energy cost of ambulation and cardiopulmonary responses for electrically induced and voluntary exercise. *Am J Phys Med Rehabil* 1964;43:157–165.

[44] Edwards BG, Lew RD, Marsolais EB. Relative energy costs of long-leg brace and FNS ambulation. *Proc 9th Rehabilitation Engineering Society of North America Conf* 1986:322–324.

[45] Gruner JA, Glaser RM, Feinberg SD, Collins SR, Nussbaum NS. A system for evaluation and exercise conditioning of paralyzed leg muscles. *J Rehab Res Dev* 1983;20: 21–30.

[46] Guyton AC. *Textbook of Medical Physiology* Philadelphia, Pa: WB Saunders Co;1981: 118,132–135, 140.

[47] Yamaguchi GT, Zajac FE. Restoring unassisted natural gait to paraplegics via functional neuromuscular stimulation: A computer simulation study. *IEEE Trans Biomed Eng* 1990;37:886–902.

[48] Heinemann AW. Evaluating the special needs of functional neuromuscular stimulation in research candidates. *J Med Eng Tech* 1985;9:167–173.

[49] Jaeger RJ, Yarkony GM, Roth EJ, Lovell L. Estimating the user population of a simple electrical stimulation system for standing. *Paraplegia* 1990;28:505–511.

[50] Campbell J, Meadows P. Therapeutic FES: From rehabilitation to neural prosthetics. *Assistive Tech* 1992;4.1:4–18.

[51] Triolo RJ, Reilley B, Freedman W. Development and standardization of a clinical evaluation of standing function. *IEEE Trans Rehab Engr* 1993;1:18–25

[52] Triolo RJ, Reilley B, Freedman W, Betz R. The functional standing test. *IEEE Eng in Med Biol Magazine* 1992;11:32–34.

[53] Stallard J, Major RE. A review of the fundamental design problems of providing ambulation for paraplegic patients. *Paraplegia* 1989;27:70–75.

[54] Winter D. CNS strategies in human gait: Implications for FES control. *Automedica* 1989;11:163–174.

[55] Inman VT, Ralston HJ, Todd F. *Human Walking*. Baltimore, Md: Williams & Wilkins Publishing Co;1981:45–46.

[56] Winter DA. *Biomechanics and Motor Control of Human Movement* 2nd ed. New York, NY: John Wiley & Sons Inc;1990.

[57] Edwards BG, Marsolais EB. Metabolic responses to arm ergometry and functional neuromuscular stimulation. *J Rehab Res Dev* 1990;27:107–114.

[58] Ericson MO, Nisell R, Ekholm J. Quantified electromyography of lower limb muscles during level walking. *Scan J Rehab Med* 1986;18:159–163.

[59] Murray MP, Guten GN, Sepic SB, Gardner GM, Baldwin JM. Function of triceps surae during gait. *J Bone Joint Surg Am* 1978;60A:473–475.

[60] Saunders JB, Inman VT, Eberhart HD. The major determinants in normal and pathologic gait. *J Bone Joint Surg Am* 1953;35A:543–558.

[61] Perry J. Normal and pathologic gait. In: *Atlas of Orthotics* 2nd ed. American Academy of Orthopaedic Surgeons. Bunch WH et al., eds., St. Louis, Mo: CV Mosby Company;1985:76–111.

[62] Dearolf WW, Betz RR, Vogel LC, Levin J, Clancy, M Steel H. Scoliosis in spinal cord injured patients. *J Ped Orthop* 1990;10:214–218.

Chapter 18

Jeffrey E. Johnson
Steven M. Kidder
Faruk S. Abuzzahab, Jr.
Gerald F. Harris

Three-Dimensional Motion Analysis of the Adult Foot and Ankle

18.1. INTRODUCTION

Human locomotion requires the stability and function of all body segments, although those most directly involved and routinely analyzed are the pelvis and two lower limbs. While all the articulations of the lower limb are directly involved in ambulation, 11 of them (lumbosacral, bilateral: hip, knee, ankle, subtalar, and metatarsophalangeal joints) are most frequently cited [1].

The foot and ankle represent the final and distal link in the human locomotor chain. Whole-body gait has been studied extensively in both children and adults, but little information has been gathered regarding the complex motions of the foot and ankle during ambulation. Past observations on dynamic foot and ankle motion have been obtained by instrumentation of cadaver specimens [2–6], interrupted (stroboscopic) light photography [7,8], electrogoniometers [8–10], roentgen stereophotogrammetric techniques [11–14], computed tomographic methods [15], and the analysis of cine film high-speed photography [16–21] of normal subjects during walking and running. More recently, modern computer-aided digitization of whole-body video images have objectively measured foot and ankle motion [22–30]. These studies have greatly enhanced our understanding of foot and ankle kinematics and provided the basis of our current models for dynamic foot and ankle motion. However, there are limitations to every method of measurement of foot kinematics.

The cadaver studies are limited in that they are either not loaded or are manually loaded in a constrained system without active muscle contraction. Studies of instrumented whole-body gait in human subjects during walking or running are limited because the foot and ankle complex is represented by a single rigid body, lacking individual segments and reporting only sagittal and transverse plane stance components. It is not possible to isolate which segments or joints of the foot are contributing to the motion seen. Other systems designed to focus on the complexities of foot and ankle motion have been limited to study of ankle and hindfoot motion only and do not include swing phase data [19,23,28]. S. H. Scott and D. A. Winter developed an eight-segment model of the foot and ankle and measured kinematics and kinetics during stance phase of walking in three young adult subjects [31]. The model used in this study was felt by the authors to be too complex for most direct dynamical human models. However, the quantitative results of their study substantiate the qualitative description of foot function during locomotion and provide important information for further development of foot models and systems for studying the dynamics of the foot and ankle.

Earlier reports of a system for measuring three-dimensional motion of the foot and ankle during stance phase of gait were provided by I. J. Alexander et al. [32] and G. S. DeLozier et al. [33], utilizing a four-segment model of the foot and ankle complex. Preliminary clinical data with this system has been reported by S. D. D'Andrea and co-workers [34] . Although this system has significant advantages over previous attempts to measure dynamic foot and ankle motion, it does not include a swing phase analysis of gait.

In order to optimize the clinical relevance and practicality of system implementation, several enhancements to previously described systems are necessary. The system should be:

- Noninvasive
- Capable of capturing both swing and stance phase data
- Implemented with a reasonable accuracy using standard video technology offering suitable rates of analog-to-digital conversion
- Able to produce output displayed in a clinically relevant format

A new system is described in this chapter that utilizes a slightly different four-segment model from that previously described by Alexander and DeLozier [32,33]. This system utilizes Vicon motion analysis technology (Oxford, England) to quantify three-dimensional (3-D) foot and ankle motion during both stance and swing phases of gait. The clinical results of the application of this system to five normal healthy volunteers are also reported.

18.2. MCW THREE-DIMENSIONAL FOOT AND ANKLE MOTION ANALYSIS SYSTEM

A system and kinematic model for three-dimensional foot and ankle motion analysis has been developed at the Orthopaedic Human Motion Laboratory at the Medical College of Wisconsin (MCW) for clinical application [35–38]. The system consists of five Vicon (Oxford, England) video cameras calibrated to acquire data from a capture volume (Figure 18-1) tailored to the dimensions of the leg, foot, and ankle structures measuring 2.4 m (length) by 0.9 m (width) by 0.62 m (height) to allow full definition of the segment markers throughout one complete gait cycle (stance and swing phases). The cameras are outfitted with infrared strobes that are synchronized to the camera shutter and used to illuminate the retro-reflective markers. The system includes a Micro-VAX 3100 workstation (DEC, Maynard, Massachusetts), an Advanced Mechanical Technology, Inc. (AMTI) force plate (Newton, Massachusetts), a 10-channel electromyography (EMG) system (Oxford, England) and two footswitch channels (heel and toe placement).

A calibration frame was constructed to outline the capture volume with an overall system accuracy measured at 98.9 percent with an overall resolution of 0.86 ± 0.13 mm.

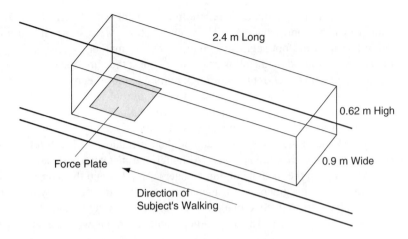

Figure 18-1. Lab data capture volume tailored to dimensions of adult tibia, ankle, and foot during both swing and stance phase.

During testing, a single footswitch was attached with adhesive tape to the plantar surface of the hallux of the instrumented foot to indicate toe-off. The force plate was monitored to determine heel-strike. The video colection rate of the Vicon system was 60 frames per second, while analog data collection was accomplished at 600 Hz. Camera calibration, camera placement, lab temperature, linearization, and frequency of calibration were found to be critical factors in maintaining the accuracy and resolution of the system on a daily basis [39].

A marker set was developed for placement on anatomic landmarks about the foot and ankle. It was composed of twelve 15.9-mm diameter nylon spheres, each carefully coated with reflective tape, each attached to a metal washer. A lightweight triad structure was developed for attachment of markers to the hallux.

A four-segment biomechanical model was developed for description of foot and ankle kinematics (Figure 18-2). The model segments consisted of (1) tibia/fibula, (2) hindfoot,

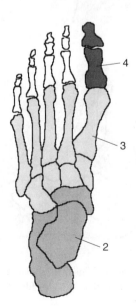

Figure 18-2. Four-segment rigid-body model: (1) tibia/fibula (not shown); (2) hindfoot (calcaneus, talus, navicular); (3) midfoot/forefoot (cuneiforms, cuboid, metatarsals); (4) hallux.

(3) forefoot, and (4) hallux. The hindfoot segment was described as consisting of the talus, calcaneus, and navicular. These designations were somewhat arbitrary, since the entire hindfoot/midfoot segment is represented by markers solely on the calcaneus. No markers were placed on the talus or midfoot bones; thus, motion of these segments cannot be identified with the current system. All motion of these segments was not monitored. All motion of the forefoot segment relative to the hindfoot segment was "composite" motion, and included the effects of the intervening articulations.

The original forefoot segment was also modified slightly. Previously, the forefoot segment included the cuneiforms, cuboid, and metatarsals. The forefoot model included only the first and fifth metatarsals. Although the metatarsals demonstrate some relative motion (between the medial column metatarsals 1, 2, 3 and the lateral column metatarsals 4, 5), the forefoot segment is considered to act as a single rigid body in the model.

Twelve retro-reflective markers were placed on bony landmarks to identify the four motion segments (Figure 18-3). A radiographic technique was also developed to index the

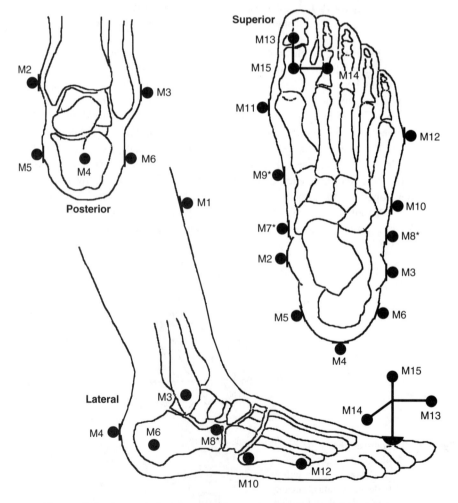

Figure 18-3. Anatomic location of 12 foot and ankle markers. Extra markers (*) are positioned to provide redundancy to reduce dropout effects.

motion data with reference to bony landmarks. An anteroposterior, lateral, and modified coronal hindfoot alignment view of the foot and ankle were used to provide these indexing measurements [40].

18.3. NORMAL SUBJECT KINEMATIC DATA

Averaged results from clinical trials of five normal adult subjects were computed. The subjects were between 20 and 30 years of age and were tested during a minimum of two trials per side. Figure 18-4 summarizes these results, which include sagittal, coronal, and transverse plane motions of the four modeled segments yielding 12 sets of data curves. The mean motion is bracketed by one standard deviation in these graphs. The plots show data presented in the sequence in which they were captured. The convention of heel-strike representing 0 percent of the gait cycle, however, is maintained. The abscissa on the plots is indexed at 0 percent at heel-strike.

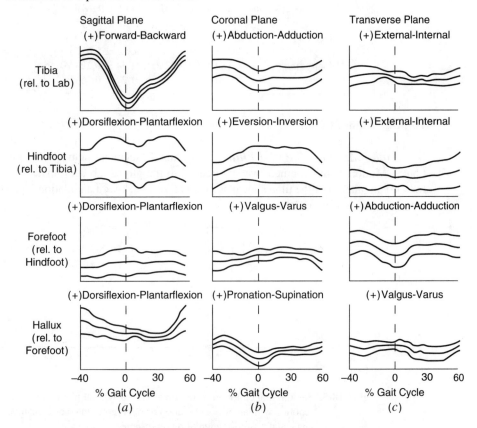

Figure 18-4. Twelve data sets representing motion of four modeled segments in three planes: (*a*) sagittal, (*b*) coronal, and (*c*) transverse. Mean curve bracketed by one standard deviation. *Note:* Swing phase precedes stance.

Tibia motion is reported with respect to the fixed (global) lab coordinate system. Motion of the other segments is reported as relative motion of the distal segment with respect to the next most proximal segment.

18.3.1. Temporal Parameters

The temporal and distance parameters of stride length, cadence, stance percent, swing percent, and speed are presented in Table 18-1. These parameters compare well with other reported studies [24]. Cadence values are somewhat higher than those in other studies, probably because of the relatively young age of the subjects tested. The standard deviation values are also somewhat high, reflective of the smaller sample size of this population.

TABLE 18-1 TEMPORAL PARAMETERS AS COMPARED TO KADABA STUDY [24]

Parameter	Present study	Kadaba et al. [24]
Stride Length (m)	1.301 ± 0.099	1.41 ± 0.14 (M)
		1.30 ± 0.10 (F)
Cadence (steps/min)	138.46 ± 24.811	112 ± 9 (M)
		115 ± 9 (F)
Stance (%)	58.393 ± 3.417	61.0 ± 2.1 (M)
		60.7 ± 2.6 (F)
Velocity (m/s)	1.501 ± 0.693	1.34 ± 0.22 (M)
		1.27 ± 0.16 (F)

18.3.2. Tibial Motion

Tibial Motion—Sagittal Plane. The "tibial" segment included the tibia and the fibula. Motion of this segment was referenced to the global lab coordinate system, with forward angulation of the tibia shown as positive, and backward angulation represented as a negative angle (Figure 18-5).

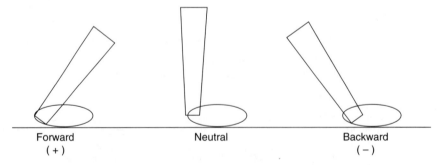

Forward   Neutral   Backward
(+)   (−)

Figure 18-5. Sagittal plane motion of the tibia. Tibial sagittal plane motion is reported with anterior angulation of tibia represented as a positive angle and posterior angulation represented as negative.

Tibial motion during gait (Figure 18-6) in the sagittal plane demonstrates a positive angle at toe-off (i.e., the knee forward of the ankle) as the body moves over the stationary foot. This angle then becomes negative during swing phase (knee posterior to ankle) in preparation for heel-strike. The angle then increases steadily through stance phase to its position at toe-off.

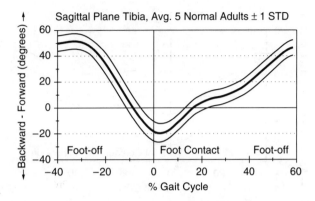

Figure 18-6. Sagittal plane tibia motion.

Although hip and knee motion are not measured by this system, some comparison to previous work might be inferred since these are normal subjects with assumed normal hip and knee motion. The range of motion of knee flexion of 55 to 70 degrees reported in previous work [5,24] is similar to the change in tibial angle from toe-off to heel-strike of approximately 75 degrees (+55 to −20 degrees).

   Tibial Motion—Coronal Plane. Coronal plane motion of the tibia is represented as abduction (+) when the knee is closer to the midline of the body than the ankle (i.e., the leg leans toward a vertical line placed between the legs). Adduction (−) is defined as the motion when the knee is farther from the midline of the body than the ankle (i.e., the leg leans away from a vertical line placed between the legs) (Figure 18-7).

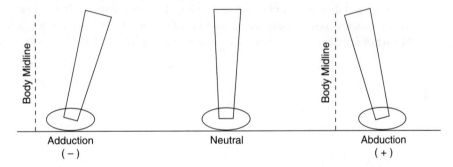

Figure 18-7. Coronal plane motion of the tibia. Coronal plane motion of tibia is represented as abduction (+) when knee is closer to body midline than ankle and adduction (−) when knee is farther from body midline than ankle.

   The coronal plane motion of the tibia (Figure 18-8) demonstrates an increase in adduction during swing phase. At heel-strike, the tibia is in a position of adduction (relative to the lab coordinates) that progresses toward abduction throughout stance phase. This is followed by a return to an adduction position in the latter half of swing phase.

   Direct comparison to other work is difficult because whole-body gait measurements of coronal plane tibial motion report this angle relative to the knee. This system describes tibial motion relative to the lab coordinate system, which might explain why the motions seen are different from the motion that is expected based on the current understanding of

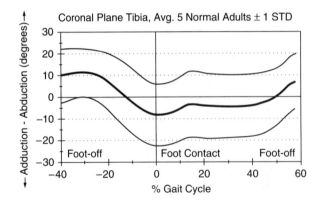

Figure 18-8. Coronal plane tibia motion.

the events of the gait cycle [1]. The abduction seen from early swing to heel-strike might be associated with leg motion for purposes of better foot clearance around the opposite leg during preparation for heel-strike. The tibial adduction during stance phase as measured by whole-body gait systems might be secondary to the known adduction vector occurring at the hip, due to the alignment of the center of the foot with the midpoint of the pelvis throughout mid- and late-stance phase [1]. This tibial adduction motion is not seen during stance phase in the averaged data from the five normals presented, which might occur because the tibia is not adducted (knee farther from body midline than the ankle) relative to the lab coordinates even though there might be "adduction" of the tibia at the knee.

Tibial Motion—Transverse Plane. Transverse plane motion of the tibia relative to the lab coordinate system is defined such that external rotation (rotation away from the line of progression) is assigned a positive value, and internal rotation (rotation toward the line of progression) is assigned a negative value (Figure 18-9).

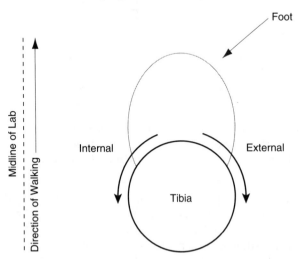

Figure 18-9. Transverse plane motion of the tibia. Rotation of hindfoot away from midline with respect to tibia (external rotation) is considered positive, and rotation toward midline is considered negative (internal rotation).

Transverse plane motion of the tibia (Figure 18-10) demonstrates an increase in external rotation throughout swing phase. The leg rotates internally from late swing phase to heel-strike during approximately 15 percent of the gait cycle. During midstance, the leg rotates externally and continues through midswing before internally rotating in preparation for heel-strike. The tibia maintains absolute external rotation throughout the gait cycle although directions of rotation change. The tibia does not reach a neutral position even during early stance phase.

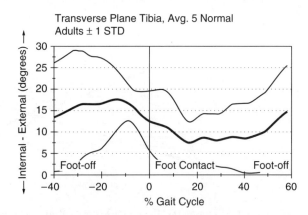

Figure 18-10. Transverse plane tibia motion.

The tibial rotation patterns agree with previously reported motion with internal rotation of the tibia beginning at toe-off and continuing through the loading response [1]. The tibia has also been shown to have an accelerated internal rotation during the loading response of early stance phase [17].

18.3.3. Hindfoot Motion

Hindfoot Motion—Sagittal Plane. Sagittal plane hindfoot position is described as the angular relationship of the hindfoot segment (calcaneus) relative to the tibial segment. Dorsiflexion is defined as positive and plantarflexion as negative. A radiographic measurement was made from the standing lateral X-ray (Figure 18-11, Angle A) and used to index motion to the anatomic alignment between these two segments. Angle A is the relationship between the tibial segment (represented by the midaxial line along the tibial shaft) and the hindfoot segment (represented by a line along the plantar surface of the calcaneus). The Angle A was measured between a line 90 degrees to the tibial segment and the line representing the hindfoot segment. This angle determines the "dorsiflexion offset" of the hindfoot relative to the tibia.

The indexed position of a normal adult foot is approximately 20 to 30 degrees of dorsiflexion when in a neutral standing position. Accurate interpretation of the sagittal plane hindfoot motion requires the knowledge of a noticeable dorsiflexion shift to the motion pattern due to the bony alignment. The motion described is that of the calcaneus relative to the longitudinal axis of the tibia.

The sagittal plane hindfoot motion pattern (Figure 18-12) indicates an increase in dorsiflexion (+) throughout swing phase as the foot prepares for heel-strike. The hindfoot begins to plantarflex during late swing and continues through heel-strike. At the beginning of midstance, the hindfoot motion reverses and begins to dorsiflex until late stance, when the hindfoot plantarflexes during toe-off.

In absolute terms, sagittal plane motion of the hindfoot remains in dorsiflexion throughout the gait cycle due to the indexing procedure. Many previous researchers have studied

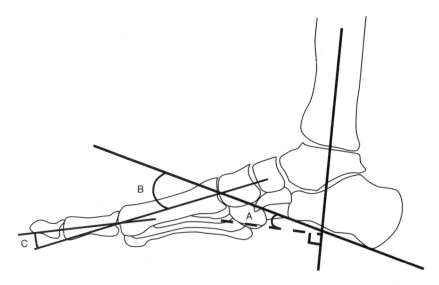

Figure 18-11. Lateral X-ray measurements: *Angle A*: Relationship between tibial segment (represented by midaxial line along tibial shaft) and
hindfoot segment (represented by line along plantar surface of
calcaneus). *Angle B*: Relationship between hindfoot segment and
forefoot segment (represented by line down midaxial line of first
metatarsal). *Angle C*: Relationship between forefoot segment and
hallux segment (represented by midaxial line of proximal phalanx
of hallux).

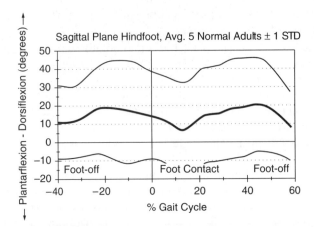

Figure 18-12. Sagittal plane hindfoot
motion.

hindfoot motion with respect to the tibia. Most of these studies consider the remainder
of the foot to be a single rigid body. The patterns and ranges of motion obtained for the
sagittal plane in this study agree with previous work [9,20,22,24,26,33,41]. D'Andrea et
al. also used a similar four-segment model of the foot and reported similar motion patterns
and ranges of motion [34].

Hindfoot Motion—Coronal Plane. Motion of the hindfoot in the coronal plane (Figure 18-13) is defined as eversion when the hindfoot externally rotates with respect to the tibia (positive value) and inversion when the hindfoot moves in an internal rotation direction (negative value). The recorded motion pattern demonstrates an increase in hindfoot inversion at toe-off, which moves to a neutral to slight eversion shortly before heel-strike. Through most of stance phase, a relatively neutral position is maintained, with a movement back into inversion prior to toe-off.

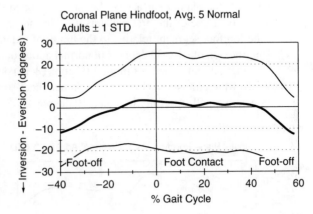

Figure 18-13. Coronal plane hindfoot motion.

Coronal plane hindfoot motion has been studied by many previous investigators. The data presented here demonstrate overall patterns and ranges of motion which agree with other reports [9,22,33,34].

Hindfoot Motion—Transverse Plane. Rotation of the hindfoot away from the midline of the tibia (external rotation) is termed a positive direction and internal rotation is termed a negative direction.

Transverse plane hindfoot motion (Figure 18-14) shows steady internal rotation throughout swing phase until the beginning of midstance. At midstance the hindfoot begins to rotate externally, which continues through toe-off.

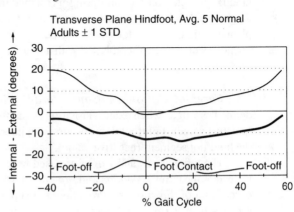

Figure 18-14. Transverse plane hindfoot motion.

18.3.4. Forefoot Motion

Forefoot Motion—Sagittal Plane.   Dorsiflexion motion of the forefoot in the sagittal plane with respect to the hindfoot segment is assigned a positive value and plantarflexion is assigned a negative value. Figure 18-11 (Angle B) illustrates the radiographic measurement to describe the angular relationship between the forefoot and the hindfoot segments. Angle B is the relationship between the hindfoot segment (represented by a line along the plantar surface of the calcaneus) and the forefoot segment (represented by the midaxial line of the first metatarsal). This angle represents the "plantarflexion offset" of the forefoot segment relative to the hindfoot. Measurement of this angle demonstrates plantarflexion of over 30 degrees in normal adults during quiet standing.

Sagittal plane forefoot motion (Figure 18-15) demonstrates relative plantarflexion at toe-off, which transitions to dorsiflexion near heel-strike. The total range of motion of this segment is small (typically less than 10 degrees).

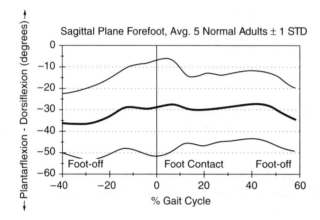

Figure 18-15. Sagittal plane forefoot motion.

Few previous studies have reported data for this motion segment. D'Andrea et al. reported similar motion patterns but with significantly greater ranges of motion [34]. The gradual dorsiflexion motion during midstance might represent a gradual flattening of the longitudinal arch as the body progresses over the stance foot. The sharp increase in forefoot plantarflexion prior to toe-off might be due to tightening of the plantar fascia from the "windlass mechanism" combined with activity in the tibialis posterior and peroneus longus muscles.

Forefoot Motion—Coronal Plane.   Motion of the forefoot in the coronal plane is defined as valgus when external rotation of the forefoot occurs with respect to the hindfoot (positive value). Forefoot varus occurs with internal rotation of the forefoot with respect to the hindfoot segment (negative value).

The terms *varus* and *valgus* are used here to describe coronal plane forefoot motion instead of the terms *pronation* and *supination*, which have been used by some in the clinical description of this motion. Pronation and supination are not used because they are open kinetic-chain terms, and motions of the foot during normal stance phase of gait are a closed kinetic-chain activity. Pronation and supination have generally been used to describe a complex triplanar motion of the entire foot around an oblique axis [42]. Open kinetic-chain supination consists of plantarflexion, adduction, and inversion. Open kinetic-chain pronation consists of dorsiflexion, abduction, and eversion.

Coronal plane forefoot motion (Figure 18-16) shows forefoot varus at toe-off with rotation toward a forefoot valgus at midstance. A sudden increase in forefoot varus rotation occurs at toe-off.

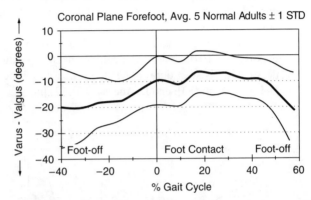

Figure 18-16. Coronal plane forefoot motion.

Forefoot Motion—Transverse Plane. Motion of the forefoot in the transverse plane is defined as abduction when the forefoot externally rotates away from the midline with respect to the hindfoot segment (positive) and adduction when the forefoot rotates internally toward the midline with respect to the hindfoot segment (negative).

Transverse plane forefoot motion (Figure 18-17) demonstrates a near neutral position at toe-off with an abduction motion occurring in early swing followed by adduction that increases through heel-strike. During the load response period of early stance phase, forefoot adduction changes to abduction that continues through toe-off.

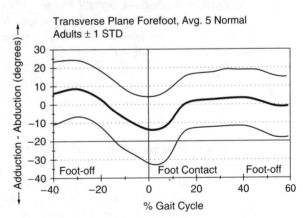

Figure 18-17. Transverse plane forefoot motion.

18.3.5. Hallux Motion

Hallux Motion—Sagittal Plane. Motion of the hallux in the sagittal plane is defined as dorsiflexion (positive) and plantarflexion (negative). The radiographic measurement from the lateral standing X-ray (Figure 18-11, Angle C) indexes the relationship between the forefoot segment (represented by the midaxial line of the first metatarsal) and the hallux segment (represented by the midaxial line of the proximal phalanx of hallux). Angle C shows the hallux in a dorsiflexed position of approximately 15 degrees relative to the first metatarsal. The five normal adult subjects demonstrated a range between 8 to 23 degrees of dorsiflexion offset of the hallux relative to the first metatarsal. When interpreting this data, it is important to note that the radiographic indexing procedure demonstrates this large "dorsiflexion offset" of the hallux segment relative to the forefoot segment.

Sagittal plane hallux motion (Figure 18-18) shows dorsiflexion at toe-off with progressive plantarflexion movement to a neutral position at midstance. Rapid transition to dorsiflexion is seen during late stance phase and toe-off. These data correlate well with DeLozier et al. [33], and D'Andrea et al. [34].

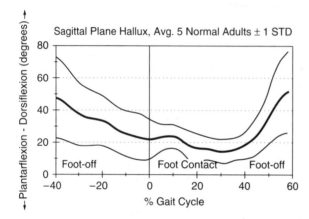

Figure 18-18. Sagittal plane hallux motion.

Hallux Motion—Coronal Plane. Motion of the hallux in the coronal plane away from the midline (external rotation) with respect to the forefoot segment is termed pronation (positive). Rotation toward the midline (internal rotation) is defined as supination and assigned a negative value (Figure 18-19).

Coronal plane hallux motion (Figure 18-20) shows that from midswing to heel-strike there is an increase in hallux supination. At heel-strike the motion changes to pronation that increases gradually throughout stance phase. Hallux pronation increases more rapidly at toe-off until midswing, when it returns to a supination motion.

Hallux Motion—Transverse Plane. Motion of the hallux in the transverse plane with respect to the forefoot segment that is away from the midline is defined as valgus (positive). Hallux motion toward the midline is termed varus (negative).

The hallux demonstrates motion in a varus direction from shortly after heel-strike through midstance phase with rapid movement to valgus at toe-off (Figure 18-21). The hallux remains in a relative valgus position throughout swing phase.

Preliminary data reported by D'Andrea et al. [34], is significantly different from the hallux rotation observed in this system. The data of D'Andrea and co-workers describes the hallux as moving in an abduction direction (i.e., valgus direction by convention of the present study) from heel-strike to midstance followed by adduction through toe-off. The curves are almost inverse of one another, which opens the possibility that differences in terminology or data display for the hallux motion in the transverse plane might be responsible for these variations.

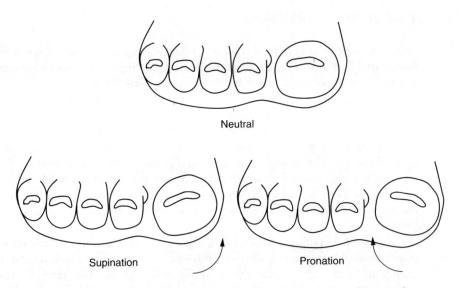

Figure 18-19. Coronal plane motion conventions for the hallux with pronation (+) and supination (−).

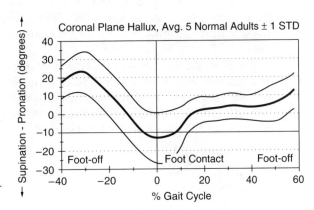

Figure 18-20. Coronal plane hallux motion.

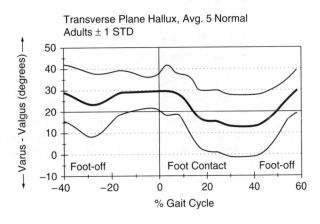

Figure 18-21. Transverse plane hallux motion.

18.4. SUMMARY AND CONCLUSIONS

There has been little published regarding systems designed for measuring complex 3-D foot and ankle motion. Four-segment models representing normal foot kinematics are only reported in our studies and two other preliminary reports [33–38].

There are several potential sources of error, which include marker location uncertainty, marker dropout, soft tissue movement, and radiographic measurement error. The four-segment rigid-body model of the foot and ankle estimates the complex motion patterns. Motion that occurs within the defined rigid-body model segments might introduce additional error. The averaged data presented in this study were determined from analysis of motion patterns in five normal adult subjects and should be considered preliminary. However, despite the lack of previous work that can be directly compared to this study, the patterns described by this system appear to follow those generally accepted from other studies.

Interpretation of these clinical data require an understanding of the specific assumptions and model conventions used with this system. The motions described in this model are reported with respect to the next most proximal segment. The curve offsets are determined from radiographic parameters and might vary considerably among subjects, making direct comparison of the motion angles difficult. However, the shape or patterns of the motion curves seem quite consistent regardless of the magnitude of the curve offset. Thus the curve patterns and total ranges of motion are features that might be of the greatest value. As in whole-body gait studies, curve pattern analysis might represent a quantitative method for discriminating between normal and pathological motions.

Despite the limitations of the system, attempts to describe 3-D motion patterns of the complex articulations of the foot and ankle might advance our understanding of human foot and ankle motion. A larger sample size is needed to increase confidence in describing "normal" kinematics of the foot and ankle. Pathological conditions that might eventually benefit from 3-D motion analysis include:

- Amputations
- Diabetic neuropathy
- Charcot foot deformities
- Posterior tibial tendon pathology
- Physiologic pes planus
- Pes cavus
- Talipes equinovarus (club foot)
- Post foot fracture
- Rheumatoid arthritis
- Hallux valgus

There are also a number of pediatric conditions that might benefit from appropriate technical advancement of the system. As clinical experience with these systems evolves, refinements will undoubtedly allow a more complete understanding of the kinematics and perhaps kinetics of the foot and ankle.

References

[1] Perry J. *Gait Analysis Normal and Pathological Function*. Thorofare, NJ: Slack Inc;1992.

[2] Chen J, Siegler S, Schneck CD. The three-dimensional kinematics and flexibility characteristics of the human ankle and subtalar joints—Part II: Flexibility characteristics. *J Biomech Eng*; 1988;110(4):374–385.

[3] Gellman H, Lenihan M, Halikis N, Botte MJ, Giordani M, Perry J. Selective tarsal arthrodesis: An in vitro analysis of the effect on foot motion. *Foot and Ankle* 1987;8(3):127–133.

[4] Ortloff S, Harris GF, Wynarsky G, Smith J, Shereff M. Noninvasive biomechanical analysis of joint motion. *Proc IEEE Eng Med Bio Soc* Oct 31–Nov 3, 1991;1962–1963.

[5] Ouzounian TJ, Shereff MJ. In Vitro Determination of Midfoot Motion. *Foot and Ankle* 1989;10(3):140–146.

[6] Siegler S, Chen J, Schneck CD. The three-dimensional kinematics and flexibility characteristics of the human ankle and subtalar joints—Part I: Kinematics. *J Biomech Eng* 1988;110(4):364–373.

[7] Murray MP, Drought AB, Kory RC. Walking patterns of normal men. *J Bone Joint Surg Am* 1964;46A(2):335–360.

[8] Saunders JB, Inman VT, Eberhart HD. The major determinants in normal and pathological gait. *J Bone Joint Surg Am* 1953;35A(3):543–558.

[9] Buck P, Morrey BF, Chao EYS. The optimum position of arthrodesis of the ankle: A gait study of the knee and ankle. *J Bone Joint Surg Am* 1987;69A(7):1052–1062.

[10] Wright DG, Henderson WH. Action of the subtalar and ankle-joint complex during the stance phase of walking. *J Bone Joint Surg Am* 1964;46A(2):361–464.

[11] Lundberg A. Kinematics of the ankle and foot: In vivo roentgen stereophotogrammetry. *Acta Orthop Scand* 1989;60(233):1–24.

[12] Lundberg A, Goldi I, Kalin B, Selvik G. Kinematics of the ankle/foot complex: Plantarflexion and dorsiflexion. *Foot and Ankle* 1989;9(4):194–200.

[13] Lundberg A, Svensson O, Bylund C, Goldie I, Selvik G. Kinematics of the ankle/foot complex—Part 2: Pronation and supination. *Foot and Ankle* 1989;9(5):248–253.

[14] Lundberg A, Svensson O, Bylund C, Selvik G. Kinematics of the ankle/foot complex—Part 3: Influence of leg rotation. *Foot and Ankle* 1989;9(6):304–309.

[15] Jend HH, Ney R, Heller M. Evaluation of tibiofibular motion under load conditions by computed tomography. *J Orthop Res* 1985;3(4):418–423.

[16] Close JR, Inman VT, Poor PM, Todd FN. The function of the subtalar joint. *Clin Orthop* 1967;50:159–179.

[17] Levens AS, Inman VT, Blosser JA. Transverse rotation of the segments of the lower extremity in locomotion. *J Bone Joint Surg Am* 1948;30A:859–872.

[18] Procter P. Ankle joint biomechanics. *J Biomech* 1982;15(9):627–634.

[19] Soutas-Little RW, Beavis GC, Verstraete MC, Markus TL. Analysis of foot motion during running using a joint coordinate system. *Med and Sci in Sports and Exercise* 1987;19(3):285–293.

[20] Stauffer RN, Chao EYS, Brewster RC. Force and motion analysis of the normal, diseased, and prosthetic ankle joint. *Clin Orthop* 1977;127:189–196.

[21] Sutherland DH, Hagy JL. Measurement of gait movements from motion picture film. *J Bone Joint Surg Am* 1972;54A(4):787–797.

[22] Apkarian J, Naumann S, Carins B. A three-dimensional kinematic model of the lower limb. *J Biomech* 1989;22:143–155.

[23] Engsberg JR, Andrews JG. Kinematic analysis of the talocalcaneal/talocrural joint during running support. *Med Sci Sports* 1987;19(3):275–283.

[24] Kadaba MP, Ramakrishnan HK, Wootten ME, Measurement of lower extremity kinematics during level walking. *J Orthop Res* 1990;8:383–392.

[25] Kadaba MP, Ramakrishnan HK, Wootten ME, Gainey J, Gorton G, Cochran GVB. Repeatability of kinematic, kinetic, and electromyographic data in normal adult gait. *J Orthop Res* 1989;7(6):849–860.

[26] Mazur JM, Schwartz E, Simon SR. Ankle arthrodesis: Long-term follow-up with gait analysis. *J Bone Joint Surg Am* 1979;61A(7):964–975.

[27] Nissan M, Whittle MW. Initiation of gait in normal subjects: A preliminary study. *J Biomed Eng* 1990;12(2):165–171.

[28] Scott SH, Winter DA. Talocrural and talocalcaneal joint kinematics and kinetics during the stance phase of walking. *J Biomech* 1991;24(8):743–752.

[29] Sutherland DH, Cooper J, Daniel D. The role of the ankle plantar flexors in normal walking. *J Bone Joint Surg Am* 1980;62A(3):354–363.

[30] Sutherland DH, Olshen R, Cooper L, Woo SLY. The development of mature gait. *J Bone Joint Surg Am* 1980;62A(3):336–353.

[31] Scott SH, Winter DA. Biomechanical model of the human foot: Kinematics and kinetics during the stance phase of walking. *J Biomech* 1993;26:1091–1104.

[32] Alexander IJ, Campbell KR, Dynamic assessment of foot mechanics as an adjunct to orthotic prescription. In: Donatelli R, Wolf SL eds. *The Biomechanics of the Foot and Ankle*. Philadelphia, Pa: FA Davis Company, 1990; Ch6(App)148–152.

[33] DeLozier GS, Alexander IJ, Narayanaswamy R. A method for measurement of integrated foot kinematics. *Proc 1st Intl Symp on 3-D Anal Human Mvmt*; Montreal, Canada, July, 1991.

[34] D'Andrea SD, Tylkowski C, Losito J, Arquedas W, Bushman T, Howell V. Three-dimensional kinematics of the foot. *Proc 8th Ann East Coast Gait Conf*; Rochester, Minn, May 5–8, 1993:109–110.

[35] Abuzzahab FS Jr, Harris GF, Kidder SM, Johnson JE. A system for foot and ankle motion analysis during gait. *Proc 8th Ann East Coast Gait Conf* Rochester, Minn, May 5–8, 1993:137–138.

[36] Abuzzahab FS Jr, Harris GF, Kidder SM, Johnson JE, Alexander IJ, DeLozier GS. Development of a system for dynamic 3-D analysis of foot and ankle motion. *Proc IEEE Eng Med Bio Soc*, Paris, France; Oct 29–Nov 1, 1992:110–111.

[37] Kidder SM, Harris GF, Johnson JE, Abuzzahab FS Jr. A kinematic model for clinical description of foot and ankle motion. *Proc 8th Ann East Coast Gait Conf*, Rochester, Minn, May 5–8, 1993:111–112.

[38] Kidder SM, Harris GF, Johnson JE, Alexander IJ, DeLozier GS, Abuzzahab F Jr. A four segment kinematic model for clinical description of foot and ankle motion. *Proc IEEE Eng Med Bio Soc*, Paris, France; Oct 29–Nov 1, 1992:52–53.

[39] Whittle MW. Calibration and performance of a 3-dimensional television system for kinematic analysis. *Biomech* 1982;15(3):185–196.

[40] Cobey JC. Posterior roentgenogram of the foot. *Clin Orthop* 1976;118:202–207.

[41] Inman VT, Ralston HJ, Todd F. *Human Walking*, Baltimore, Md: Williams & Wilkins Publishing Co, 1981.

[42] Donatelli R. Normal anatomy and biomechanics. In: Donatelli R., Wolf SL eds. *The Biomechanics of the Foot and Ankle*, Philadelphia, Pa: FA Davis Co; 1990:Ch1:3–31.

Chapter 19

Peter A. Smith
Gerald F. Harris
Ziad O. Abu-Faraj

Biomechanical Evaluation of the Planovalgus Foot in Cerebral Palsy

19.1. INTRODUCTION

Gait analysis outlines ambulatory patterns of children with cerebral palsy. It is currently used to help make surgical decisions and measure surgical outcome at the hips, knees, and ankles [1–3]. However, the clinical analysis of foot disorders with quantifiable parameters of gait is less common [4]. Recent technological advances in this area enable gait analysis to be more useful clinically [5–8]. This chapter details a recent project designed to use advances in technology for the analysis of gait and plantar pressure patterns in children with cerebral palsy who have planovalgus foot deformity. We chose a commonly performed procedure, subtalar stabilization, as the intervention that was investigated in the study. We used currently available technology, including a Vicon motion analysis system (Oxford, England), and developed a portable microprocessor-based system to quantitatively measure plantar pressures at discrete insole locations.

This chapter reviews the planovalgus foot disorder in cerebral palsy and presents the technology available for study of the foot. Results from tests of a few patients who have undergone evaluation are also presented. The purpose is to show what can be measured currently in terms of clinical utility.

19.2. PLANOVALGUS DEFORMITY

Planovalgus foot deformity is common in children with diplegic and quadriplegic cerebral palsy [1,9]. Unlike the idiopathic flatfoot, this deformity is progressive and can be debilitating [10,11]. The deformity is characterized by valgus of the hindfoot and a

370

pronated posture of the midfoot with a flattened longitudinal arch (Figure 19-1). Hindfoot valgus reflects a divergence of the longitudinal axis of the talus and the calcaneus in both the transverse and sagittal planes. The distal talus lies medial to the substance of the calcaneus. In the midfoot, the navicular slides laterally in relation to the talar head, with a corresponding shift of the calcaneal cuboid joint. The talar head becomes prominent both medially and plantarly because the talus plantarflexes after losing the support of the plantar ligaments. The prominence is commonly an uncomfortable area during shoe wear and callouses can arise. Difficulties occurring include poor stance phase stability, shoe wear problems and impaired push-off power during walking [1]. The deformity is also commonly associated with hallux valgus at the metatarsal phalangeal joint [12].

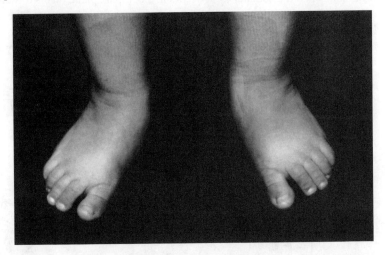

Figure 19-1. The planovalgus feet in a child with cerebral palsy. The medial longitudinal arch is absent, and the forefoot is pronated and deviates laterally. The medial midfoot is prominent.

19.3. ETIOLOGY

The etiology of the planovalgus deformity is multifactorial and variable among patients [9,13]. In the normal situation, many muscles function to control foot motion during gait [14]. Patients with cerebral palsy, however, have poor selective motor control. Considering this lack of control, the presence of a foot deformity is not surprising given the large number of musculotendinous units that cross the ankle and subtalar joints. Several studies have shown that peroneals can be spastic with a weak or inactive tibialis posterior muscle [9,10,15]. In addition, the presence of a tight heel cord can exacerbate the deformity, with ligamentous laxity contributing to the deformity. Weakness of the posterior tibial tendon alone might cause a flatfoot deformity due to gravity collapse of the subtalar joint into valgus. However, this weakness does not explain why lengthening of the peroneal brevis, or subtalar arthroereisis, might cause the foot of some cerebral palsy patients to drift into varus over time. Thus the deformity seems to result from an imbalance in the evertors and invertors of the foot.

19.4. ANATOMY

The anatomy of the subtalar joint has been described by V. T. Inman [16]. There are three facets at the articulation between the talus and calcaneus. At the posterior facet, the calcaneus provides a platform for the talus to glide upon. At the middle and anterior facets, the calcaneus rotates around the talus. The spring ligament spans from the calcaneus to the navicular and provides a support for the talar head [17]. The overall alignment of the talocalcaneal joint is oblique, with the anterior facet being more medial and superior than the posterior facet. The joint axis is oblique and directed at a 42-degree axis to the horizontal. It is also directed medially from the midline at approximately 23 degrees (Figure 19-2). Motion through the subtalar joint occurs in a complex plane that is difficult to evaluate and describe clinically. Some studies suggest that a simple model for the joint is a mitered hinge (Figure 19-3). Functionally the joint acts as a torque converter, converting forces around the longitudinal axis of the foot to internal and external rotatory forces at the tibia and fibula.

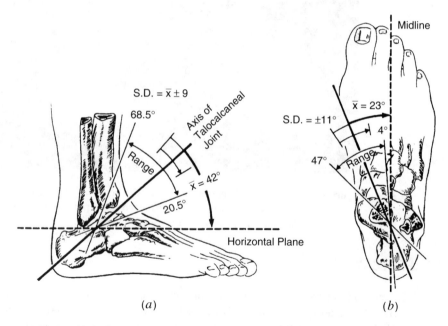

(a)   (b)

Figure 19-2. The axis of the subtalar joint is demonstrated in the (a) sagittal and
(b) transverse planes. (From Inman VT, *Joints of the Ankle*. 2nd
ed. Baltimore, Md: Williams & Wilkins Publishing Co, 1991.)

Subtalar motion is therefore reflected in the clinical measurements of plantarflexion and dorsiflexion, inversion and eversion, and adduction and abduction. Motion of the foot and ankle in the sagittal plane, clinically described as plantarflexion and dorsiflexion, thus involves both the ankle and subtalar joints. The two joints act in conjunction and are clinically indistinguishable in the sagittal plane. Along its oblique axis, the extent of subtalar motion was determined to be 18 degrees ± 6 degrees by Inman in a study of cadavers. H. Gellman et al. demonstrated a significant amount of dorsiflexion and plantarflexion after tibiotalar arthrodesis, supplied by motion in the subtalar joint and in the joints of the midfoot

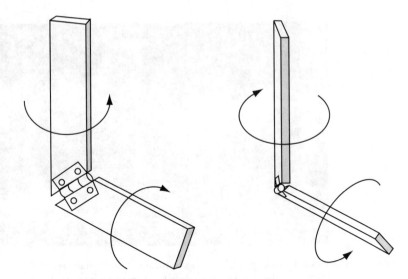

Figure 19-3. The oblique axis of the subtalar joint is simply modeled as a mitered hinge, which converts the rotatory forces of foot pronation and supination to internal and external rotatory forces at the shank. (From Inman VT, *Joints of the Ankle.* 2nd ed. Baltimore, Md: Williams & Wilkins Publishing Co, 1991)

[18]. More detail on the contribution of the subtalar joint to such complex patterns has been provided by J. R. Engsberg and S. Siegler et al. [19,20]. Inman recognized the combined contribution of the ankle and subtalar joints and referred to such motion as that of the "joints of the ankle" [16].

19.5. SURGICAL TREATMENT

Surgical treatment for the planovalgus foot in cerebral palsy provides stabilization of the subtalar joint to prevent excessive valgus of the hindfoot [10,11,21]. This can be accomplished with arthroereisis or arthrodesis techniques. The options include limiting joint motion with a staple [22], polyethylene insert [23], fusion of the subtalar joint [24–28], or osteotomy of the calcaneus [29]. In this study we performed a subtalar arthrodesis using a screw that coursed from the talar neck into the calcaneus (Figure 19-4) [24]. Iliac crest bone graft supplemented the fusion. The goal of the procedure was to position the distal talus over the calcaneus in a neutral position and to prevent eversion. Fusing the subtalar joint stabilizes midfoot alignment between the talus and navicular and prevents excessive pronation of the forefoot. This technique has yielded successful results in improving the foot position and function of children with cerebral palsy [30].

In most published studies, results of subtalar fusion are based upon subjective criteria with results ranging from 60 to 90 percent "good" to "excellent" [24,30]. These studies rely solely on reports of physical examination supplemented by radiographic analysis. The accuracy of the studies is limited by clinical assessment, and relies on such vague criteria as "regular shoe wear" and "plantigrade foot." There is no definition of what constitutes a "satisfactory" foot, and certainly there are no quantitative indices that have been used to

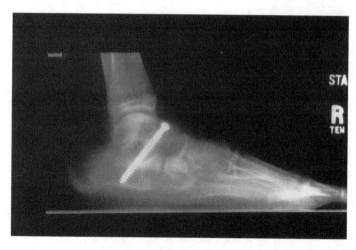

Figure 19-4. Radiograph of a subtalar fusion. A screw transfixes the talus to the calcaneus in a neutral position, and bone graft is placed to fuse the subtalar joint.

describe results in a clinical series. There is also a paucity of information on the effects of subtalar fusion on foot biomechanics.

19.6. INSTRUMENTATION

With the technical ability to perform many different measurements on subjects while walking, it has now become possible to quantify foot motion, as well as plantar foot pressures [8]. The resulting analyses yield millions of bits of data that need to be analyzed in a meaningful and reasonable fashion. Early studies of foot pressures date back to the work of M. Marey and G. Carlet in 1870 with a special shoe-mounted measurement system [31,32]. An air chamber was placed in the sole of the shoe and rubber hoses were attached to recording devices that were carried by the subject. A device mounted on the head measured the vertical and horizontal oscillations during gait and the subject pushed a rubber ball to mark each step (Figure 19-5).

Since then, the study of foot contact pressures has advanced to visual techniques and more sophisticated electronic sensing devices. Current technology has led to the availability of instrumented shoes, in-shoe sensors, and floor-mounted plates as different options for measurement [31, 33–37]. Pressures are measured electrically by utilizing various modes of transduction including capacitance and resistance. For example, padlike pressure-sensitive transducers can be either capacitance transducers or conductive transducers. These transducers can be mounted in a shoe. In 1947, R. P. Schwartz and A. L. Heath described foot contact pressures with a complicated transducer system that relied on a mechanical oscillograph, light from reflected prisms, and a moving roll of photographic paper [38]. Since then transducers have gone through several generations of refinement so that they are now smaller and more reliable. In our own laboratory we are using pressure sensors (Interlink Electronics, Santa Barbara, California) which are 1.1 cm in diameter, 0.5 mm thick and relatively inexpensive (about $4). The sensor consists of a conductive polymer film and metal bands assembled together with an O-ring spacer. The response of the sensor to pressure

Figure 19-5. An early device to study human locomotion. (From Marey M. De la locomotion terreste. *Journal de l'Anatomie et de la Physiologie de l'Homme et des Animaux* 1873:9.)

is logarithmic. The hysteresis, nonrepeatability, and temperature drift are known and are within acceptable ranges [7,39].

19.7. PRELIMINARY STUDIES

The results obtained from walking children with cerebral palsy across a floor-mounted plate show dramatic differences in plantar pressures between clinically satisfactory and unsatisfactory feet following subtalar stabilization (Figure 19-6). The metrics most sensitive to these differences are peak pressures at different areas of the foot, contact durations, and pressure-time integrals. Floor-mounted plates also demonstrate the instantaneous center-of-pressure location and its migration during stance. These differences are apparent in both floor-mounted plate systems (F-Scan and AMTI) and in the in-shoe system (EMED).

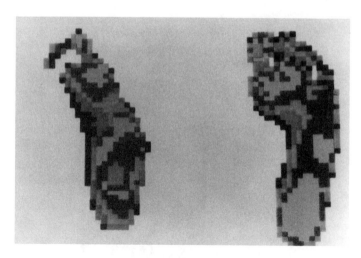

Figure 19-6. The plantar pressure pattern of a child with cerebral palsy, as measured with a floor-mounted plate system (EMED, Minneapolis, Minnesota). The right foot has had a successful subtalar arthroereisis; the left foot has a severe planovalgus deformity. Each grid is color-coded according to peak pressure.

19.8. PORTABLE INSOLE SYSTEM

There are several limitations of single-step systems. The assumption that one footstep accurately predicts pressure patterns during gait might not be correct, particularly with children who have control problems and immature gait patterns. Floor-mounted systems have the added disadvantage of subjects "targeting" the plate with possible deviations from natural motion patterns. Moreover, testing of the materials used in sensors has shown that quantification of measurements can be difficult. For example, materials might be sensitive to heat or repeated use and might be difficult to calibrate accurately.

Since 1990, experience with testing FSRs (force-sensing resistors) in insole systems shows that they can be dynamically calibrated to provide quantitative pressure data. Moreover, a portable insole system can be used in a natural setting outside the gait lab by using a backpack. The system measures hundreds of steps. The sole drawback is the diminished number of discrete plantar locations from which data are recorded.

The pediatric insole system consists of a Dallas semiconductor DS5001-16 microprocessor with a built-in down-loading control program. The device contains 32 K of static RAM, and 4 Mb of storage for recording up to two hours of pressure samples per subject. The force-sensing resistors are placed in custom insoles. The insoles are constructed of Plastazote (BXL Plastics, Ltd., United Kingdom) and placed in low-top tennis shoes (Figure 19-7).

The placement of FSRs within the custom-made insole for each child depends on preoperative footprint analysis. The sensors are placed in areas of relatively high loading at each of six locations at the hindfoot, medial midfoot, lateral midfoot, first metatarsal head, lateral metatarsal head, and hallux.

All walking trials are conducted with three runs per subject, and between 700 and 1000 total steps are sampled (Figure 19-8). The cadence is self-selected by patients, and the test duration ranges from 15 to 30 minutes. Data are sampled at 40 samples per second.

Figure 19-7. Force-sensing resistors placed in an insole to measure plantar pressures.

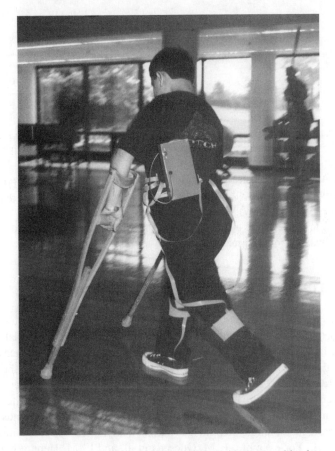

Figure 19-8. A child with cerebral palsy walking with the portable plantar pressure measurement system. The backpack contains a microprocessor that stores data up to two hours.

19.9. ANALYSIS METHODS

Prospectively, patients with cerebral palsy and a planovalgus foot deformity underwent three-dimensional gait analysis with the five-camera Vicon system. Kinetics were obtained on all patients who walked without assistive devices.

Portable plantar pressure analysis was accomplished, and then subtalar stabilization was performed following the methods of W. G. Dennyson and R. Fulford [24]. Table 19-1 lists the four patients who were tested at least six months following surgery. There are three males and one female. Two patients had procedures performed on both feet.

TABLE 19-1   STUDY PATIENTS

Patient	Diagnosis/ date of operation	Age	Sex	Feet	Other procedures	Results	Follow-up
M.A.	C.P. 11/10/92	16	M	B	0	Good	7 months
J.M.	C.P. 9/2/92	17	M	R	R-HS R-rectus R-MP fusion R-Vulpius	Good	1 year
K.C.	C.P. 10/21/92	15	M	R	0	Good	6 months
N.O.	C.P. 9/8/92	15	F	B	B-HS B-rectus trans.	Good	8 months

An analysis of the study results demonstrates which metrics might be useful. The sensitivity of the system is such that changes in the foot pressure patterns (preoperatively versus postoperatively) were measurable.

The true clinical utility of the system will be determined with continued study of the larger patient population.

19.10. RESULTS OF FOOT PRESSURE MEASUREMENTS

Single-step analysis shows that the planovalgus foot demonstrates greater than normal contact duration and peak pressure at the medial midfoot. In normal walking, the velocity of the center of pressure decelerates initially after heel-strike, but then accelerates to rapidly cross the midfoot. However, in the patients studied prior to surgery, the center of progression of force followed a line medial to the anatomic midline of the foot. The progression of the center of pressure lingered at the midfoot area. Similar patterns and high midfoot pressures were also seen in older patients and in those with pes planus [8]. The quantitative interpretation of single-step images has been attempted by several investigators for normal feet [40]. For example, P. M. Quesada et al. and E. M. Hennig have shown differences between adult and children's feet, with an increased midfoot break corresponding to a more lax longitudinal arch in children [41]. The extension of these studies to pathologic feet has not been performed but might provide useful information about preoperative deformity and surgical outcome.

19.10.1. Case Example

J. M., a 17-year-old boy with diplegic cerebral palsy, had significant planovalgus deformity of the right foot, crouch gait, and hallux valgus. After gait analysis, he underwent right hamstring lengthening, transfer of the rectus femoris to the sartorius, lengthening of the gastrocnemius, subtalar fusion, and metatarsophalangeal fusion. His preoperative foot pressure measurements showed high loading of the midfoot, first metatarsal head, and hallux. Postoperatively, the pattern of loading showed less force at the medial midfoot and hallux (Figure 19-9).

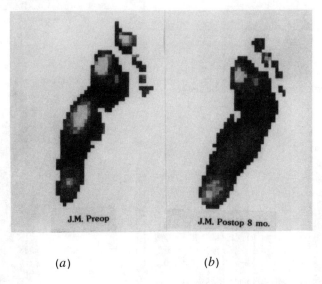

(*a*)   (*b*)

Figure 19-9. Plantar pressure pattern from a floor-mounted plate (AMTI, Newton, Massachusetts) (*a*) preoperatively and (*b*) eight months following subtalar fusion. Note the area of high midfoot loading
preoperatively, which is not seen postoperatively.

19.11. PORTABLE INSOLE SYSTEM

A comparison of preoperative and postoperative status shows that the insole system is successful in showing quantifiable differences in loading of the foot after surgery. These differences were consistent with the changes noted on the single-step analyses; that is, at the midfoot, the peak pressures, contact durations, and pressure-time integrals were diminished medially and increased laterally. The same three metrics were also diminished at the first metatarsal head, with increases at the more lateral metatarsal heads. Interestingly, loading of the hallux was unchanged and occasionally increased. These findings have been consistent among the several patients tested (Figure 19-10).

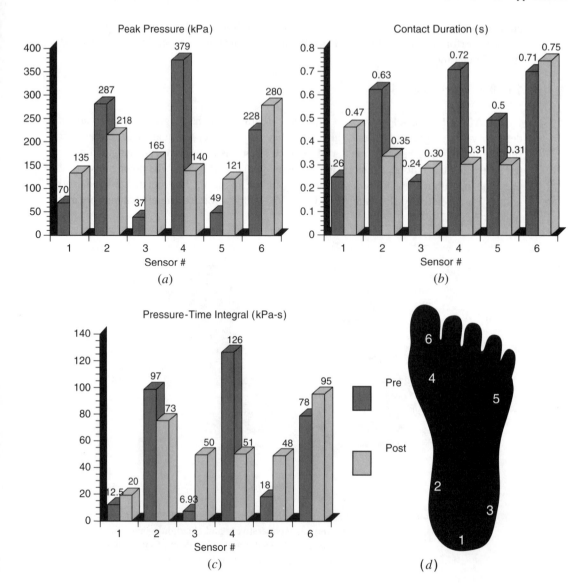

Figure 19-10. Averaged data from the portable insole system for the four patients tested (six feet). (*a*) Peak pressure, (*b*) contact duration,
(*c*) pressure-time integral, and (*d*) numbered sensor locations on
stylized foot.

19.11.1. Case Example

K. C., a 15-year-old boy with diplegic cerebral palsy had problems with shoe wear
and planovalgus feet. He underwent a subtalar fusion. Seven hundred steps were analyzed
before and six months after subtalar stabilization surgery with the portable insole system.
Preoperative versus postoperative changes showed less contact duration at the medial midfoot area during walking (Figure 19-11). Maximum pressures were generally diminished

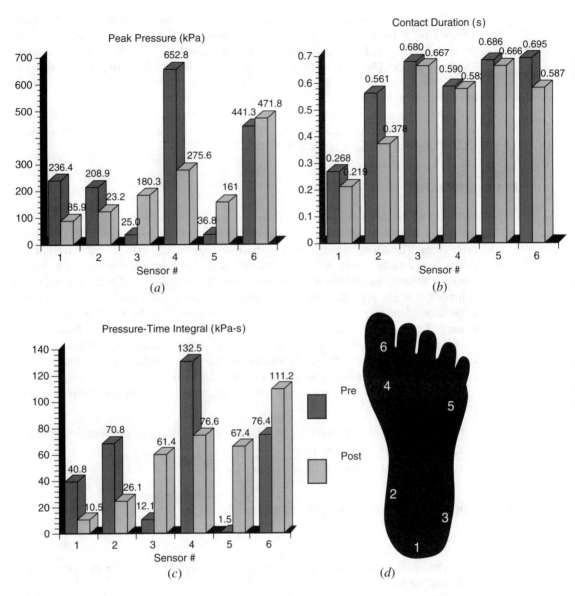

Figure 19-11. Data from the portable insole system for K.C., a 15-year-old boy with diplegia: (*a*) Peak pressures, (*b*) contact duration, (*c*) pressure-time integral, and (*d*) numbered sensor locations on stylized foot.

at the heel and medial midfoot and increased at the lateral midfoot. The greatest change in pressure postoperatively seemed to occur at the first metatarsal head, with a 42 percent reduction of peak pressure. Loading of the second metatarsal head was increased to a level 60 percent that of the first metatarsal head after surgery. Pressure-time integrals again diminished at the first metatarsal head and increased in the more lateral metatarsal head area. Interestingly, the hallux pressure-time integral was actually increased. The comparison of these data with the AMTI floor-mounted plate showed similar findings, and helped validate the pattern of postoperative change. Moreover, the floor-mounted plate provided many more sensors, so a better visualization of the change was possible. With the use of these electronic footprints in combination with known pressures over multiple footsteps, it should be possible to objectively examine the results of surgery. These types of measurements will undoubtedly be used in preoperative and postoperative gait analysis of children with neuromuscular disorders and will be used along with the clinical exam to make decisions about which type of surgery to perform and the expected outcome. These measurements will provide a more realistic record of the results than the clinical exam, which is inexact in measurement of the foot [42].

19.12. KINEMATICS

Kinematics provides a description of body segment motion in three dimensions based on the analysis of 3-cm diameter retro-reflective markers in standard positions on the lower extremities. The information obtained has become standardized to the extent that clinicians can exchange data to make decisions. Because of the large capture volume of the system, it is most accurate for evaluations of the pelvis, hip, knee, and ankle. Evaluation of the foot is limited. For example, the ankle/foot complex is modeled as a single joint with its axis at the level of the lateral malleolus. The foot axis is determined by a marker placed at the dorsum of the second metatarsal head and by a temporary marker placed at the calcaneus (this is used during calibration but removed during testing because it tends to overlap the lateral malleolus marker). Therefore, motion accuracy through the subtalar joint, midfoot, and forefoot is not measured as separate from the ankle motion by the current Vicon system.

The use of whole-body gait analysis in the evaluation of the subtalar fusion and other foot surgeries is useful for:

1. Evaluation of how changes occurring at the foot impact more proximal joint motion
2. Evaluation of the foot progression angle
3. Evaluation of compensation at the other joints

19.13. KINEMATIC RESULTS (FIGURE 19-12)

19.13.1. Ankle

The sagittal plane motion of the ankle was compared in the six preoperative and postoperative feet.

The general patterns of second and third rockers during stance were preserved, but postoperatively the ankles ranged into less dorsiflexion during stance. The amount of diminished dorsiflexion possibly represented the limitation in sagittal plane motion achieved by subtalar fusion.

19.13.2. Knee

The knee showed marked improvement in stance phase extension and improvement in sagittal plane motion. These changes were likely due to the simultaneous performance of hamstring lengthening and rectus transfer procedures on some of the study patients.

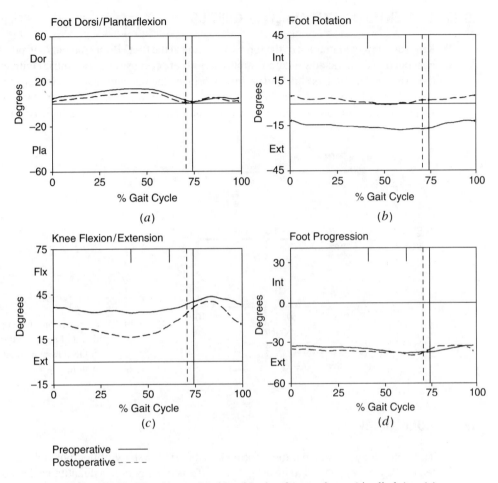

Preoperative ————
Postoperative – – – –

Figure 19-12. The kinematic data for the four patients (six limbs): (*a*) foot dorsiflexion/plantarflexion, (*b*) foot rotation, (*c*) knee flexion/extension, and (*d*) foot progression.

19.14. TRANSVERSE PLANE

Postoperatively, the foot progression angle of all patients was external. Foot progression angle did not change after subtalar fusion and remained external for all patients. However, the foot rotation relative to the axis of the tibia moved internally following subtalar fusion. Therefore, the patients seem to compensate for a change in foot rotation by turning outward at the hip and knee to maintain a constant foot progression angle. Performing a subtalar fusion, therefore, did not significantly change the foot progression angle in patients who had developed a mature pattern of walking. Rotational osteotomy of the tibia or femur was more likely to accomplish this.

Most patients showed more evidence of circumduction in their gait following their surgeries. The hip showed increased abduction and external rotation following subtalar fusion.

19.15. CONVENTIONAL GAIT ANALYSIS KINETICS

Kinetics allow examination of the forces occurring at the foot. Both moments and powers are generated. The ankle power demonstrates periods of eccentric and concentric contraction of the gastrocsoleus and its ability to perform work. As the talocalcaneal relationship becomes fixed, the foot becomes a more efficient lever for generation of push-off power. After subtalar fusion, power generation is greater near the end of stance, representing increased push-off power (Figure 19-13).

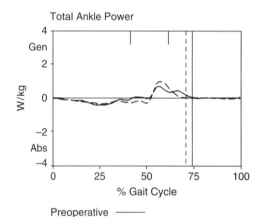

Figure 19-13. Comparison of preoperative and postoperative total ankle power with subtalar fusion.

19.16. CONCLUSION

The technology is available to perform gait analysis for study of the foot and ankle. This technology has been used to investigate the effects of surgery in a quantitative fashion. We developed an accurate and portable insole-mounted system to study the effects of subtalar fusion on the planovalgus foot in cerebral palsy. Three-dimensional gait analysis showed that ankle power was slightly improved in the subjects tested. Foot progression angle was unchanged. However, there were dramatic changes in foot pressures. Pressures were shifted from the medial midfoot and first metatarsal to more lateral positions postoperatively. Application of this technology should prove useful in future studies of foot and ankle motion and treatment.

References

[1] Gage JR. *Gait Analysis in Cerebral Palsy*, Clinics in Developmental Medicine, No. 121, London: MacKeith Press with New York, NY: Cambridge University Press, 1991.

[2] Perry J. Normal and pathological gait. In *Atlas of Orthotics* 2nd ed, Bunch WH ed. St Louis: CV Mosby;1985;76–111.

[3] Winter DA. *Biomechanics and Motor Control of Human Movement*, New York, NY: John Wiley & Sons Inc;1990.

[4] Sutherland DH. Varus foot in cerebral palsy: An overview. In *American Academy of Orthopaedic Surgery Instruction Course Lectures*, 1993:539.

[5] Katoh Y, Chao EYS, Laughman RK, Schneider E, Morrey, BF. Biomechanical analysis of foot function during gait and clinical applications. *Clin Orthop* 1983;177:23.

[6] Nigg BW. Gait analysis and sports shoe construction. In Asmussen E, Jorgansen K eds. *Biomechanics VI-A*, Baltimore: University Park Press;1978:303–309.

[7] Zhu H, Maalej N, Webster JG, Tompkins WJ, Bach-y-Rita P, Wertsch JJ. An umbilical data-acquisition system for measuring pressures between the foot and shoe. *IEEE Trans Biomed Eng* 1990;37(9):908–911.

[8] Alexander I, Chao EYS, Johnson KA. The assessment of dynamic foot to ground contact forces and plantar pressure distribution: A review of the evolution of current techniques and clinical applications. *Foot and Ankle* 1990;11:152.

[9] Bonnett G, Rang M, Jones D. Varus and valgus deformities of the foot in cerebral palsy. *Dev Med Child Neurol* 1982;24:499–503.

[10] Bleck EE. *Orthopaedic Management in Cerebral Palsy*. Oxford, England: MacKeith Press;1987:282.

[11] Fulford GE. Surgical management of ankle and foot deformities in cerebral palsy. *Clin Orthop* 1990;253–255.

[12] Renshaw TS, Sivker KB, Drennan JC. The management of hallux valgus in cerebral palsy. *Dev Med Child Neurol* 1970;21:202–208.

[13] Kreuger MP, Gage JR. Stance phase foot rocker problems in spastic diplegia. *Dev Med Child Neurol* 1986;28(Suppl 53, 4):3.

[14] Mann RA. Biomechanics of foot and ankle. In: Mann RA ed. *Surgery of the Foot*. St Louis, Mo: CV Mosby;1986:1–30.

[15] Skinner SR, Lester DK. Dynamic EMG findings in valgus hindfoot deformity in spastic cerebral palsy. *Orthop Trans* 1985;9:91.

[16] Inman VT. *The Joints of the Ankle*. Baltimore, Md: Williams & Wilkins Publishing Co, 1976.

[17] Perry J. Anatomy and biomechanics of the hindfoot. *Clin Orthop* 1983;177:9–16.

[18] Gellman H, Lenihan M, Halikis N, Botte J, Giordani M, Perry J. Selective tarsal arthrodesis: An in vitro analysis of the effect on foot motion. *Foot and Ankle* 1987;8:127.

[19] Engsberg JR. A biomechanical analysis of the talocalcaneal joint—in vitro. *J Biomech* 1987;20:429–442.

[20] Siegler S, Chen J, Schneck CD. The three-dimensional kinematics and flexibility characteristics of human ankle and subtalar joints—part I: Kinematics. *J Biomech Eng* 1988;110:364–373.

[21] Green WT, Grice DS. The surgical correction of the paralytic foot. Instruction course lecture at American Academy of Orthopaedic Surgeons, 1953;10:343.

[22] Crawford AH, Kucharzyk D, Roy DR, Bilbo J. Subtalar stabilization of the planovalgus foot by staple arthrodesis in young children who have neuromuscular problems. *J Bone Joint Surg Am* 1990;72A:840.

[23] Smith SD, Millar EA. Arthroriesis by means of a subtalar polyethylene peg implant for correction of hindfoot pronation in children. *Clin Orthop* 1983;181:15–23.

[24] Dennyson WG, Fulford R, Subtalar arthrodesis by cancellous grafts and metallic fixation. *J Bone Joint Surg Br* 1976;58B:507.

[25] Grice DS. An extraarticular arthrodesis of the subastragular joint for correction of paralytic feet in children. *J Bone Joint Surg Am* 1952;34A:927.

[26] Grice DS. Further experience with extraarticular arthrodesis of the subtalar joint. *J Bone Joint Surg Am* 1955;37A:246.

[27] Seymour N, Evans DK. A modification of the Grice subtalar arthrodesis. *J Bone Joint Surg Br* 1968;50B(no 2):372.

[28] Smith JB, Westin GW. Subtalar extraarticular arthrodesis. *J Bone Joint Surg Am* 1968;50A:1027.

[29] Armstrong G. Evans elongation of lateral column of the foot for valgus deformity. *J Bone Joint Surg Br* 1975;57B:530.

[30] Barrasso JA, Wile PB, Gage JR. Extraarticular subtalar arthrodesis with internal fixation. *J Ped Orthop* 1984;4:555.

[31] Bauman JH, Brand PW. Measurement of pressure between foot and shoe. *Lancet* 1963;1:629–632.

[32] Marey M. De la locomotion terrestre, Chez les bibider et les quadrupedes. *Journal de l'Anatomie et de la Physiologie* 1873;9:42.

[33] Collis WJMF, Jayson MIV. Measurement of pedal pressures. *Ann Rheum Dis* 1972;31:215.

[34] Frost RB. Cass CA. A load cell and sole assembly for dynamic pointwise vertical force measurement in walking. *Eng in Med* 1981;10:45–50.

[35] Gross TS, Bunch RP. Measurement of discrete vertical in-shoe stress with piezoelectric transducers. *J Biomed Eng* 1988;10:261–265.

[36] Hughes J, Pratt L, Linge K, Clark P, Klenerman L. Reliability of pressure measurements: The EMED system. *Clin Biomech* 1991;6:14–18.

[37] Soames RW, Blake CD, Scott JRR, Goodbody A, Brewerton DA. Measurement of pressure under the foot during function. *Med Bio Eng Comp* 1982;20:489–495.

[38] Schwartz RP, Heath AL. The definition of human locomotion on the basis of measurement with descriptions of oscillographic network. *J Bone Joint Surg* 1947;29:203–214.

[39] Zhu H, Wertsch JJ, Harris G, Loftsgaarden J, Price M. Foot pressure distribution during walking and shuffling. *Arch Phys Med Rehab* 1991;72:390–397.

[40] Hennig EM, Cavanagh PR, Albert HT, Macmillan NH. A piezoelectric method of measuring the vertical contact stress beneath the human foot. *J Biomed Eng* 1982;4:213–222.

[41] Quesada PM, Simon SR, Piciotta JY, Leurgans SS. Dynamic foot pressures in the early months of walking. In: *Proc 8th Annual East Coast Clinical Gait Laboratory Conf* Rochester, Minn, 1993:123.

[42] Finkenberg J, Watts HG. Reproducibility of clinical measurements in clubfeet. In: *Proc Ped Orthop Soc N Am* 1991:32.

Chapter 20

Ziad O. Abu-Faraj
Gerald F. Harris
An-Hsiung Chang
Michael J. Shereff
Joseph Nery

Quantitative Evaluation of Plantar Pressure Alterations with Metatarsal and Scaphoid Pads

20.1. METATARSAL PADS

20.1.1. Synopsis

Metatarsal pads (MPs) are often used to relieve the pain of metatarsalgia and minor symptoms of Morton's neuroma. They have been reported effective in relieving pressures under the metatarsal prominences of the foot. This work was designed to quantify changes in plantar pressures with MP usage. Part I of this chapter addresses results obtained from previous studies of a group of 10 normal adult male subjects [1]. Subjects tested were free from orthopaedic, neurological, or systemic complaint and were evaluated during a set of 400-step trials. Data were gathered from eight plantar locations at the right hindfoot, midfoot, and forefoot regions. A portable, microprocessor-based data-acquisition system was used to electronically record the ambulatory pressure history. Statistically significant alterations in the recorded metrics (peak pressures, contact durations, and pressure-time integrals) were noted at the metatarsal shaft region with MP use ($p \leq 0.05$). Increases were seen in peak pressures from 12 to 139 kPa. Contact durations were noted to increase from 82 to 450 ms. Pressure-time integrals increased from 2 to 40 kPa-s. Metric values did not change significantly at the other plantar locations. Metatarsal pad use did result in mild decreases in mean peak pressures at the first and second metatarsal heads. Decreases in contact durations were seen at all metatarsal head locations. Pressure-time integrals decreased at all metatarsal heads except 5M. Metatarsal pad and foot geometry might have an effect upon ultimate pressure redistribution with pad (MP) use. This information might allow more effective control of pad geometry and placement.

20.1.2. Introduction

The foot provides weight-bearing support, propulsive forces for locomotion, and shock absorption for distribution of impact loads [2]. The foot transmits the forces of stance-phase support during locomotion to the surrounding environment. The foot must adapt to variations in terrain, while providing both stability and load distribution [3]. S. R. Menkveld et al. characterize stance phase foot function in terms of four specific tasks. These tasks are: acceptance of impact load at heel-strike, terrain accommodation during weight acceptance, stability and load distribution during foot-flat, and propulsion for forward progression during push-off [4]. Variations in plantar load distribution are seen with changes in functional foot biomechanics secondary to pathology and injury. Areas of elevated pressure can present that might ultimately alter the structural stability and cause discomfort or pain.

Metatarsal pads are used to treat patients with metatarsalgia and minor symptoms of Morton's neuroma with the goal of relieving pain through plantar pressure redistribution [5–8]. Metatarsal pads are among the most frequently prescribed pedorthics for nonoperative treatment of foot and ankle disorders [6–8]. Use of MPs, however, requires great care in order to control the pressure redistribution and prevent excessive loading of adjacent plantar areas of the foot [5,9,10]. Quantitative, multistep studies of MP use and subsequent load redistribution are not cited in recent literature. Several investigators have studied ground reaction forces and plantar pressure distribution during various tasks [4,5,7,10–29]. Few studies, however, investigated the characteristics of multistep, in-shoe foot pressure distribution [15,16,22–29]. Effective pressure transducers should not alter the natural gait of the subject, and should be thin, flexible, durable, and capable of enduring repetitive gait cycles [22].

P. S. Schaff and P. R. Cavanagh (1990) utilized the EMED (Novel Electronics, Minneapolis, Minnesota) pressure-measuring insole system to assess the effects of rocker bottom shoe modifications on plantar pressures [10]. They noted that some regions of the foot could not be monitored. There were regions in the midfoot area, lateral aspects of the forefoot and toes, and medial aspects of the heel and hallux that were not fully covered by the sensors. Integration of residual noise in lightly loaded elements also resulted in some inaccuracies in estimated force values. G. B. Holmes and L. Timmerman (1990) evaluated metatarsal pad use and resulting plantar pressures in 10 volunteer subjects [7]. They acquired single-step data with a pedobarograph during 15 trials of each subject. The barefoot subjects had MPs affixed to their feet proximal to the metatarsal pressure areas (subjects were unshod). During normal application, metatarsal pads are usually fixed to the insole, which does not restrict forefoot motion during stance or swing phases of gait [30]. J. Guirini et al. in 1992 reported on the use of felted-foam dressings for treatment of diabetic foot ulcerations [14]. The dressings were reported effective in lowering pressures even though ulcer location varied. An F-Scan (Tekscan, Boston, Massachusetts) system was used for the study. It consisted of a thin sheet of 960 resistive insole sensors tethered to an umbilical. The F-Scan insole is usage-limited, and methods for calibration that compensate for nonlinearity, bending, wear, and temperature drift are not described [22,25].

In this study, Force Sensing Resistors (FSRs, Interlink Electronics, Santa Barbara, California) were used with a portable, microprocessor-based in-shoe data acquisition system to acquire multistep pressure data. There are several reports in which this system has been employed in studies of walking and shuffling gait, plantar asymmetry, cadence, and assistive device use [16,22–29].

20.1.3. Materials and Methods

A portable, in-shoe, microprocessor-based data-acquisition system was used in this study to monitor pressure data from eight plantar locations [16,22–29]. The system provided long-term recording capability (up to two hours at 40 Hz) from up to 14 discrete sensor locations. It utilized an 8-bit microprocessor (DS5001FP-16, Dallas, Texas) and was battery operated and weighed under 350 g. Subjects carried the unit in a beltpack during unrestricted gait. Upon test completion, recorded pressure data were uploaded into a 486 PC for further processing, analysis, and display.

We used Interlink circular FSRs (18-mm outer diameter, 15-mm active sensing diameter, 0.4-mm overall thickness), which offered the advantages of flexibility, durability, reliability, overload tolerance, electronic simplicity, and low cost (less than $4 each) [15,21–28,30]. The sensor is depicted in Figure 20-1. The conductive polymer sensors provide a logarithmic resistance drop with increasing load, which is converted into a pressure metric with the use of dynamic sensor calibration lookup tables. Dynamic and static sensor characteristics (hysteresis, nonrepeatability, nonlinearity, sensitivity, and temperature drift, etc.) have been reported by our group elsewhere [22,25,26,29,31].

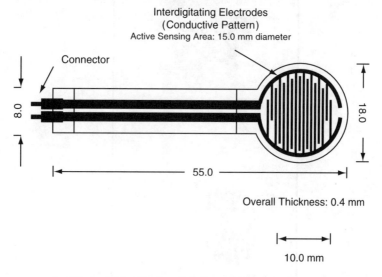

Figure 20-1. The Interlink Force Sensing Resistor.

A compression lever, 440 N load cell, and preamplifier were used to dynamically calibrate the FSRs. The calibration scheme provided time-varying loads with durations modeling those of stance phase foot contact. Resulting calibration data were subsequently transferred to the PC, where lookup tables were generated for each sensor. An 18-mm diameter (0.6 mm thin) stainless steel disc was mounted to the back of each sensor to keep it flat and prevent excessive hysteresis due to bending.

Sensors were mounted within the insole material. The upper Plastazote (BXL Plastics Ltd., United Kingdom) insole layer (3.2 mm thick) was sculpted to accept the sensors and thin metal backings which were flush mounted with the upper insole surface [22,24,29]. The 3.2-mm-thick lower insole layer was made of cork. Clinical examination and recorded foot impressions from an Apex foot imprinter (South Hackensack, New Jersey) during three successive barefoot trials were used to determine sensor locations. An Apex foot imprint of a typical test subject is shown in Figure 20-2. Because the hallux frequently extended medially beyond the insole margin, the hallux sensor (Hx) was positioned by rotating the recorded contact point laterally about an arc centered at the first metatarsophalangeal joint. This simulated hallux compression by the inner medial wall of the shoe. A medial longitudinal arch sensor (MLA) was placed medially near the edge of the insole and longitudinally at the center of the arch. A sensor was located between the third and fourth metatarsal heads (3&4M) in order to accommodate variations in proximity and size [7]. Other sensors were located beneath the calcaneal tuberosity (H), at the midpoint of the metatarsal shaft region corresponding with the apex of the metatarsal pad (MSR), at the head of the first metatarsal (1M), at the head of the second metatarsal (2M), and at the head of the fifth metatarsal (5M), Figure 20-3.

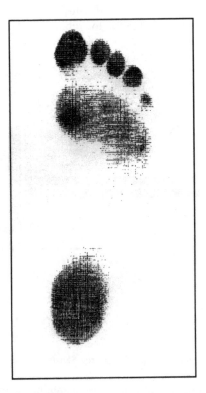

Figure 20-2. An Apex foot imprint of one of the test subjects.

The MPs were constructed of a rubber material with dimensions of 60 mm (length) × 50 mm (width) × 8 mm (thickness). An adhesive backing was applied to each pad to facilitate attachment and restrict motion during the subject testing. The pads were affixed to the base of the insoles such that the longitudinal (length) axis overlapped that of the heel oval as outlined by the foot imprint. The distal pad margins were separated by at least 5 mm from the metatarsal heads. An insole and pad without sensors was simultaneously used on the contralateral foot to provide a balanced gait pattern during subject testing. Each subject's instrumented insoles and metatarsal pads were inserted in a pair of P.W.

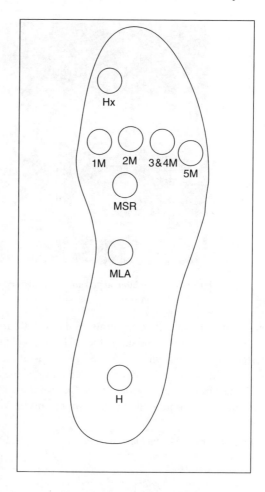

Figure 20-3. The eight discrete pressure sensor locations: calcaneus (H), medial longitudinal arch (MLA), metatarsal shaft region (MSR), first metatarsal head (1M), second metatarsal head (2M), third and fourth metatarsal heads (3&4M), fifth metatarsal head (5M), and hallux (Hx).

Minor Extra Depth Easy Sport athletic shoes (Batavia, New York). A metatarsal pad and an instrumented insole are illustrated in Figure 20-4.

Male rearfoot strikers, as determined by measurement of stresses beneath the calcaneus and other plantar surfaces with the insole system, were selected for the study [12,13]. Ten subjects ranging in age from 25 to 38 years (mean = 29.9, ± 4.2 years) with a mean height of 180.2 cm (± 6.6 cm) and mean weight of 80.2 kg (± 13.2 kg) were tested. The mean shoe size of the adult males tested was U.S. men's size 9 ½ (±1). The subjects were free from any orthopaedic, neurological, or systemic complaint and did not suffer from foot disorders or gross abnormality.

The subjects were asked to walk at a freely selected cadence on an 80 m concrete walkway [17]. Acclimation to the experimental shoes and establishment of a constant temperature (shoe) environment was provided during a 30-minute pretest period [12,13,22]. Two (400-step) data gathering sessions were then conducted. In the first session, subjects did not use the metatarsal pads. After a 10-minute rest period, a second test session was conducted, during which the pads were used. Steps around the ends of the walkway were excluded to eliminate any altered gait patterns during the turn maneuver. Peak plantar

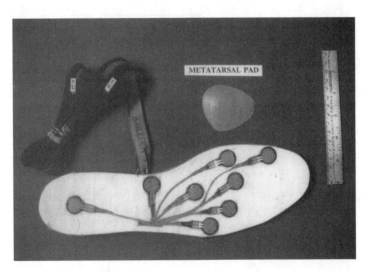

Figure 20-4. Metatarsal pad and instrumented insole with eight discrete pressure
sensors.

pressures, pressure-time integrals, and contact durations were determined for each of the
insole sensors during the multistep trials. Typical plantar pressure distribution for a subject
tested without and with the use of a metatarsal pad are illustrated in Figure 20-5. In this
subject, the MSR sensor demonstrated elevated loading with the use of the MP. Without the
pad, the MSR sensor registered zero pressure values. The MLA sensor demonstrated zero
pressure values both without and with use of the MP.

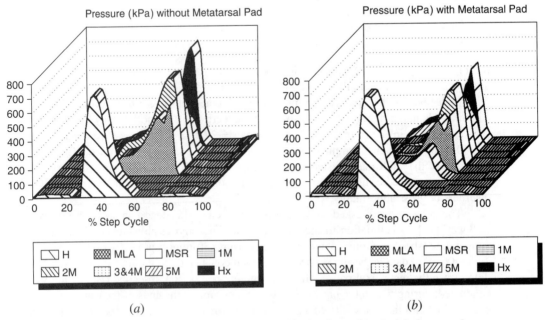

(a)   (b)

Figure 20-5. Typical plantar pressure distribution for a subject's right foot tested
without (a) and with (b) use of a metatarsal pad.

20.1.4. Results

Subjects were tested at a freely selected walking speed averaging 1.6 m/s ($\pm$ 0.1 m/s) both without and with metatarsal pad use. Mean stride length was 1.7 m ($\pm$ 0.1 m) and the mean number of steps per trial was 369 steps ($\pm$ 17 steps). Subjects did not report discomfort or fatigue during the test trials.

Results for the total subject population are illustrated in Table 20-1 (without MP use) and in Table 20-2 (with MP use). Mean, standard deviation, and coefficient of variation values for peak pressures (kPa), contact durations (ms), and pressure-time integrals (kPa-s) are provided in each table by sensor location. Without pad use, the lowest mean values for all metrics were seen at the MLA and MSR sensors. The highest mean values were noted at the H and Hx sensors for peak pressures, at the 3&4M and 5M sensors for contact durations, and at the H and 1M sensors for pressure-time integrals. With pad use, the lowest mean metric values occurred at the medial longitudinal arch (MLA) region. The greatest mean values were seen at the H and Hx sensors for peak pressures, at the 3&4M and 5M sensors for contact durations, and at the H and 1M sensors for pressure-time integrals.

TABLE 20-1   PLANTAR PRESSURE DISTRIBUTION WITHOUT PAD USE—
INSOLE ONLY

Sensor location	Peak pressure (kPa)			Contact duration (ms)			Pressure-time integral (kPa-s)		
	Mean	S.D.	Coef. var.	Mean	S.D.	Coef. var.	Mean	S.D.	Coef. var.
H	567.6	182.5	0.322	412.0	65.0	0.158	127.6	42.9	0.336
MLA	0.6	4.9	8.167	6.0	49.0	8.167	0.1	0.9	9.000
MSR	11.7	23.5	2.009	82.0	169.0	2.061	2.4	4.8	2.000
1M	527.1	210.3	0.399	506.0	76.0	0.150	132.3	53.1	0.401
2M	469.3	129.5	0.276	513.0	72.0	0.140	120.8	44.1	0.365
3&4M	392.2	113.2	0.289	592.0	62.0	0.105	112.9	26.5	0.235
5M	271.6	101.3	0.373	617.0	113.0	0.183	92.4	33.3	0.360
Hx	606.6	218.3	0.360	430.0	102.0	0.237	110.9	46.6	0.420

TABLE 20-2   PLANTAR PRESSURE DISTRIBUTION WITH PAD USE—
METATARSAL PAD

Sensor location	Peak pressure (kPa)			Contact duration (ms)			Pressure-time integral (kPa-s)		
	Mean	S.D.	Coef. var.	Mean	S.D.	Coef. var.	Mean	S.D.	Coef. var.
H	614.3	192.4	0.313	397.0	70.0	0.176	134.7	48.3	0.359
MLA	0.0	0.7		0.0	5.8		0.0	0.1	
MSR	138.7	93.6	0.675	450.0	169.0	0.376	40.1	29.3	0.731
1M	504.6	197.0	0.390	502.0	91.0	0.181	124.9	49.9	0.400
2M	455.9	110.5	0.242	496.0	98.0	0.198	112.4	41.7	0.371
3&4M	404.4	138.2	0.342	584.0	72.0	0.123	109.5	30.4	0.278
5M	281.3	109.8	0.390	608.0	94.0	0.155	94.7	36.2	0.382
Hx	559.4	162.0	0.290	433.0	118.0	0.273	102.7	39.1	0.381

The MLA sensor was positioned to detect increases in plantar pressure under the medial longitudinal arch, but none was seen. Normally arched feet should not bear vertical load under the medial longitudinal arch during walking.

The coefficient of variation (CV) describes the ratio of the standard deviation to the mean and offers a measure of consistency Tables 20-1 and 20-2 and Figure 20-6. The greatest consistencies in peak pressures were noted at H, 1M, and 5M. Contact duration consistencies were most noticeable at H. Consistencies in pressure-time integrals were seen most prominently at H, 1M, 2M, 5M, and Hx. Metric values for the population tested without and with metatarsal pads are graphically depicted in Figure 20-7.

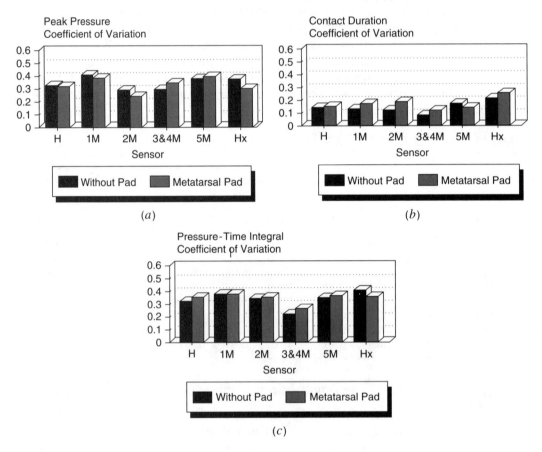

Figure 20-6. Coefficient of variation by sensor for the test group without and with the use of a metatarsal pad: (a) peak pressure, (b) contact duration, and (c) pressure-time integral.

For the subject population, the increases in peak pressure, contact duration, and pressure-time integral values following application of the metatarsal pad were statistically significant ($p \leq 0.05$). Peak pressures increased from 12 to 139 kPa, contact durations increased from 82 to 450 ms, and pressure-time integrals increased from 2 to 40 kPa-s. Statistically significant changes in metric values were not seen at the other plantar locations, although metatarsal pad use resulted in mild decreases in mean peak pressures at the first and

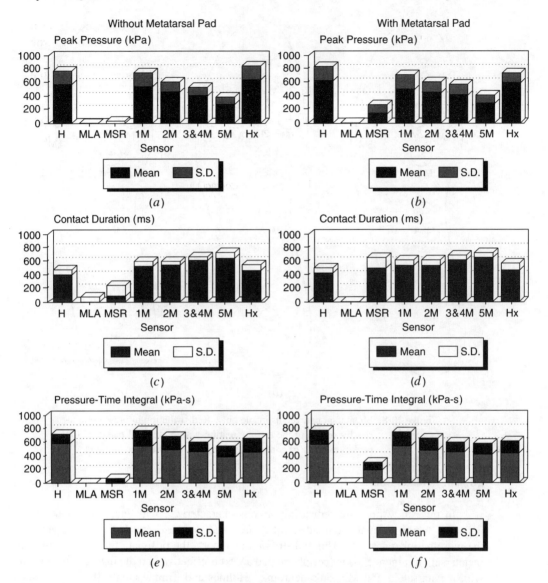

Figure 20-7. Alterations in metric values by sensor for the test group: (*a*) peak pressure without metatarsal pad, (*b*) peak pressure with metatarsal pad, (*c*) contact duration without metatarsal pad, (*d*) contact duration with metatarsal pad, (*e*) pressure-time integral without metatarsal pad, and (*f*) pressure-time integral with metatarsal pad.

second metatarsal heads and slight increases in lateral areas. Contact durations decreased at all metatarsal head locations while pressure-time integrals decreased at the first, second, third, and fourth metatarsal heads. A slight increase in pressure-time integrals was seen at the fifth metatarsal head. A summary of pressure changes noted in the test population with MP usage is presented in Figure 20-8.

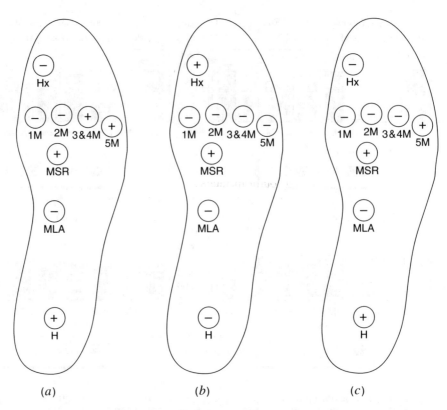

Figure 20-8. Metatarsal pad versus insole only. Redistribution in pressure metrics by sensor in the test population with metatarsal pad use: (*a*) peak pressure, (*b*) contact duration, (*c*) pressure-time integral.

20.1.5. Discussion

In this study pressure redistribution was characterized with increased peak loads delivered to the normally unloaded MSR area and decreased peak loads delivered to the more peripheral areas. This redistribution supports the postulate that decreasing the metatarsal prominence loads (peripheral pad areas) is effective in reducing pain associated with metatarsalgia and Morton's neuroma. Holmes and Timmerman (1990) noted that metatarsal pads have been considered when other mechanical alterations are suspected of causing metatarsal pain [7].

Although metatarsal pad use resulted in mild decreases in mean peak pressures at the first and second metatarsal heads and at the hallux, and slight increases laterally and at the calcaneus, these changes were not statistically significant. For average peak plantar pressures, increases were noted at H (8 percent), 3&4M (3 percent) and 5M (4 percent), while decreases were noted at 1M (−4 percent), 2M (−3 percent), and Hx (−8 percent). For contact durations, increases were only seen at Hx (<1 percent), while decreases occurred at H (−4 percent), 1M (−1 percent), 2M (−3 percent), 3&4M (−1 percent), and 5M (−2 percent). For pressure-time integrals, increases were noted at H (6 percent) and 5M (3 percent), while decreases were observed at 1M (−6 percent), 2M (−7 percent), 3&4M

(-3 percent), and Hx (-7 percent). The changes in peak pressures are consistent with the findings of Holmes and Timmerman in which subjects demonstrated differing outcomes with metatarsal pad use [7].

The results from this study tend to indicate that a metatarsal pad should be positioned near the center of the central rays, just proximal to the metatarsal heads. The optimal location appears to be within the margins defined by the medial border of the second metatarsal shaft and the lateral confines of the fourth metatarsal shaft.

In this study, metatarsal pad use resulted in mild decreases in mean peak pressures at the first and second metatarsal heads and slight increases laterally. Contact durations decreased at all metatarsal head locations, while pressure-time integrals decreased at the first, second, third, and fourth metatarsal heads. This redistribution in pressure metrics came at a cost of a significant increase in pressure in the metatarsal shaft region ($p \leq 0.05$).

20.2. SCAPHOID PADS

20.2.1. Synopsis

Scaphoid or longitudinal arch pads are frequently prescribed pedorthics for foot and ankle disorders. They are reported to be effective in mechanically supporting the medial longitudinal arch while also reducing plantar and medial soft tissue strain. Part II of this chapter addresses results from previous studies of a group of normal adults [32]. The objective of the study was to measure alterations in plantar pressure metrics with the application of scaphoid pads. Normal adult male subjects ($n = 10$) were evaluated during multiple trials. A microprocessor-based (DS5001FP-16 Dallas, Texas) portable, in-shoe, plantar pressure data-acquisition system was used to record sensor data. Recorded data were subsequently uploaded into a microcomputer for further display and analysis. Statistically significant ($p \leq 0.05$) increases in peak pressures, contact durations, and pressure-time integrals were seen in the medial longitudinal arch area with scaphoid pad use. Increases were seen in peak pressures from near zero to over 100 kPa. Contact durations were seen to increase from near zero to over 400 ms. Pressure-time integrals increased from near zero to over 25 kPa-s. Metric values did not change significantly at other insole regions, but scaphoid pad use did result in increased lateral side peak loads and decreased medial side and calcaneal peak loads.

20.2.2. Introduction

Scaphoid pads (SPs) are prescribed for treatment of posterior tibial tendon dysfunction, plantar fascitis, and other disorders of the foot resulting from medial soft tissue strain [8]. These pads are frequently prescribed for nonsurgical treatment of the foot and ankle [8,9]. The scaphoid pad structurally supports the arch while shifting the forefoot into varus. Collapse of the arch is prevented, reducing soft tissue strain and altering the foot load patterns. Although altered, the patterns of load redistribution are not well described. The pressure alterations resulting from SP usage at eight plantar locations were studied in 10 adult subjects. The multistep characteristics of dynamic load alteration during gait were assessed. Metrics chosen for characterization were based on data from previous studies [24].

The metrics were: peak pressure (kPa), pressure-time integral (kPa-s) and contact duration (ms). Interventions resulting in plantar pressure alterations that have been examined with the system include rehabilitative, therapeutic, surgical, and nonsurgical treatment [16,22–29].

20.2.3. Materials and Methods

Ten adult male subjects with a normal heel-strike [12,13] were selected for the study based upon measurement of pressures beneath the os-calcis and other plantar surfaces as determined with an Apex foot imprint mat (South Hackensack, New Jersey). The mat was evenly inked and covered with paper to record the footprints during stance-phase contact. Higher-pressure load areas appeared darker. The mean age of the subjects was 29.9 years (±4.2 years; range: 25 to 38 years). The mean height was 180.2 cm (±6.6 cm) and the mean weight was 80 kg (±13.2 kg). The shoe size of the tested subjects was an average size 9 ½ (± 1 U.S. size). Subjects did not exhibit foot disorders or other abnormalities. Insoles were 6.4 mm in thickness and consisted of two equally thick layers (the upper was Plastazote, the lower, cork). The Plastazote layer was hollowed to receive sensors and metal backings, which were mounted flush with the top surface [26,27]. Subjects could not perceive the presence of the sensors in the insole while walking. Sensors were placed on the basis of clinical exam and foot-imprint data. In several subjects the hallux extended medially beyond the insole margin. Consequently, positioning of the hallux sensor (Hx) was accomplished by rotating the hallux contact point laterally through an arc about the first metatarsophalangeal joint. This procedure simulated compression of the hallux by the shoe upper. A medial longitudinal arch sensor (MLA) was placed longitudinally at the center of the arch hollow and medially near the edge of the insole. One sensor was also positioned between the third and fourth metatarsal heads (3&4M) in a fashion similar to that prescribed by Holmes and Timmerman [7]. The remaining sensor locations were: calcaneal tuberosity (H), central metatarsal shaft region (MSR), first metatarsal head (1M), second metatarsal head (2M), and fifth metatarsal head (5M) (Figure 20-3).

The scaphoid pads were 11.5 cm long and 5.5 cm wide (maximum) with a thickness of 1.5 cm (maximum). The pads were located beneath the insoles and centrally mounted below the medial arch hollow, which was defined by foot imprint data. The contralateral foot was fitted with an insole and pad (without sensors). This supported a symmetrical gait pattern during subject testing. A scaphoid pad (longitudinal arch pad) and an instrumented insole are illustrated in Figure 20-9. Subjects were asked to walk at a freely selected pace on an 80-m walkway [17]. A constant temperature within the shoe was provided by allowing the subjects to wear the shoes during a pretest period of 30 minutes [12,13,22]. Two 400-step data gathering sessions were then conducted. Subjects were first tested without the use of scaphoid pads. A 10-minute rest period followed with a subsequent session in which the pads were applied. Steps during turn maneuvers (at the end of the walkway) and during standing were not included in the analysis. The metrics investigated in the study were peak plantar pressure, pressure-time integral, and contact duration as determined for each sensor during the 400-step trials. These metrics have proven useful in prior clinical studies [23–25,29].

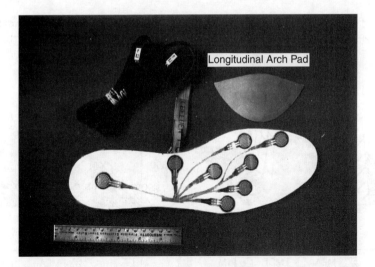

Figure 20-9. A scaphoid pad (also known as longitudinal arch pad) and an instrumented insole with eight discrete pressure sensors.

20.2.4. Results

Subjects did not report any discomfort or fatigue during the multiple 400-step trials. Mean walking speed was 1.6 m/s ($\pm$ 0.1 m/s) both without and with the SP. Stride lengths averaged 1.7 m ($\pm$ 0.1 m) while the mean number of steps (per trial) was 369 ($\pm$ 17), both without and with the SP.

Typical plantar pressure distribution for a subject tested without and with the use of a scaphoid pad are shown in Figure 20-10. In this subject, MLA and MSR sensors demonstrated significant loading with the use of a scaphoid pad. Without the scaphoid pad, MLA and MSR sensors registered zero pressure values. Scaphoid pad use resulted in increased peak loads on the lateral side of the foot and decreased peak loads on the medial and calcaneal regions of the foot.

Subject population results without and with pad use are illustrated in Tables 20-3 and 20-4, respectively. The means, standard deviations, and coefficients of variation for each metric are provided in the tables by sensor location. The coefficient of variation describes the ratio of the standard deviation to the mean and offers a measure of consistency (Tables 20-3 and 20-4 and Figure 20-11). Consistencies in peak pressures were seen prominently at H, 2M, 3&4M, and Hx. Contact duration consistencies were mostly manifested at H, 3&4M, and Hx. Pressure-time integral consistencies were most noticeable at H, 3&4M, 5M, and Hx.

Lower metric values were frequently seen without pad use at the MLA sensor. The H and Hx sensors demonstrated the largest peak pressures. Sensors 3&4M and 5M showed the highest contact durations, while sensors H and 1M exhibited the greatest pressure-time integrals. With the scaphoid pad, lower metric values occurred at the metatarsal shaft region (MSR). The highest values remained at H and Hx for peak pressures, at 3&4M and 5M for contact durations, and at H for pressure-time integrals.

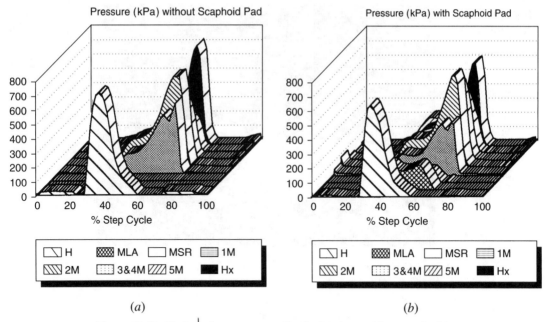

Figure 20-10. Typical plantar pressure distribution for a subject tested without (*a*) and with (*b*) the use of a scaphoid pad.

TABLE 20-3   PLANTAR PRESSURE DISTRIBUTION WITHOUT PAD USE—INSOLE ONLY

Sensor location	Peak pressure (kPa)			Contact duration (ms)			Pressure-time integral (kPa-s)		
	Mean	S.D.	Coef. var.	Mean	S.D.	Coef. var.	Mean	S.D.	Coef. var.
H	567.6	182.5	0.322	412.0	65.0	0.158	127.6	42.9	0.336
MLA	0.6	4.9	8.167	6.0	49.0	8.167	0.1	0.9	9.000
MSR	11.7	23.5	2.009	82.0	169.0	2.061	2.4	4.8	2.000
1M	527.1	210.3	0.399	506.0	76.0	0.150	132.3	53.1	0.401
2M	469.3	129.5	0.276	513.0	72.0	0.140	120.8	44.1	0.365
3&4M	392.2	113.2	0.289	592.0	62.0	0.105	112.9	26.5	0.235
5M	271.6	101.3	0.373	617.0	113.0	0.183	92.4	33.3	0.360
Hx	594.5	211.2	0.355	426.0	99.0	0.232	107.9	45.2	0.419

Results for the test population at all sensor locations are depicted in Figure 20-12. Application of the SP resulted in statistically significant increases in all metric values at the MLA region ($p \leq 0.05$). Peak pressures increased from near zero to 115 kPa, while contact durations increased from near zero to 438 ms and pressure-time integrals increased from near zero to 33 kPa-s. Although SP use frequently resulted in higher peak loads on the lateral side of the foot (with decreased peak loads at the medial and calcaneal regions) significant changes in metric values were not seen at the other plantar locations. Figure 20-13 depicts qualitative changes in pressure by sensor location with SP usage.

TABLE 20-4 PLANTAR PRESSURE DISTRIBUTION WITH PAD USE—
SCAPHOID PAD

Sensor location	Peak pressure (kPa)			Contact duration (ms)			Pressure-time integral (kPa-s)		
	Mean	S.D.	Coef. var.	Mean	S.D.	Coef. var.	Mean	S.D.	Coef. var.
H	540.9	165.3	0.306	389.0	65.0	0.167	115.6	38.2	0.330
MLA	115.3	52.6	0.456	438.0	151.0	0.345	33.4	18.1	0.542
MSR	30.4	46.7	1.536	166.0	230.0	1.386	7.0	10.3	1.471
1M	457.6	217.7	0.476	471.0	124.0	0.263	107.3	51.2	0.477
2M	474.3	139.2	0.293	469.0	96.0	0.205	106.9	46.6	0.436
3&4M	442.6	131.9	0.298	578.0	61.0	0.106	115.0	28.0	0.243
5M	314.1	133.0	0.423	593.0	76.0	0.128	98.9	38.2	0.386
Hx	488.1	169.0	0.346	431.0	107.0	0.248	90.5	40.7	0.450

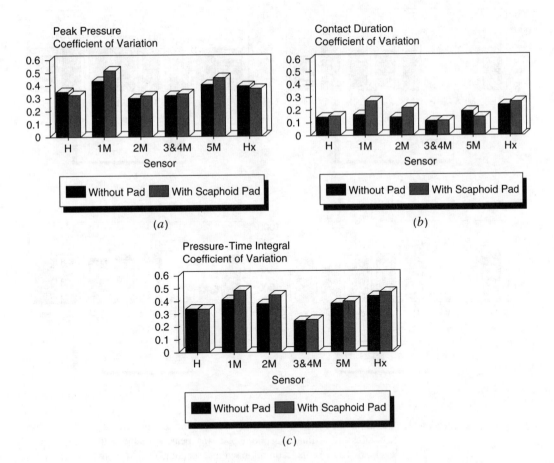

Figure 20-11. Coefficient of variation by sensor for the test group without and with the use of a scaphoid pad: (*a*) peak pressure, (*b*) contact duration, and (*c*) pressure-time integral.

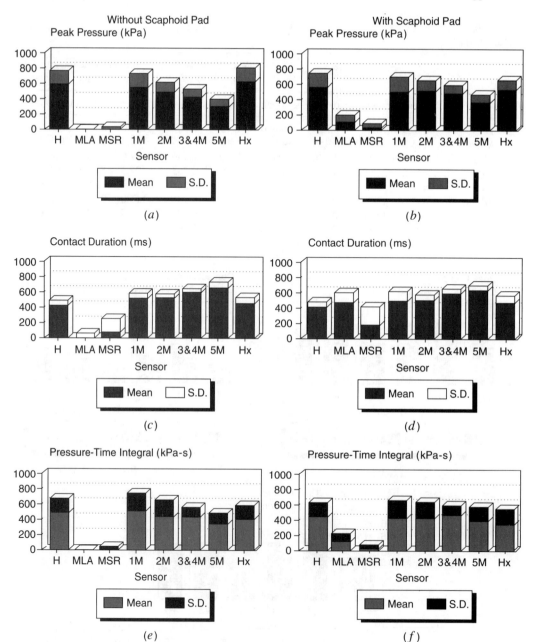

Figure 20-12. Alterations in metric values by sensor for the test group: (*a*) peak pressure without scaphoid pad, (*b*) peak pressure with scaphoid pad, (*c*) contact duration without scaphoid pad, (*d*) contact duration with scaphoid pad, (*e*) pressure-time integral without scaphoid pad, and (*f*) pressure-time integral with scaphoid pad.

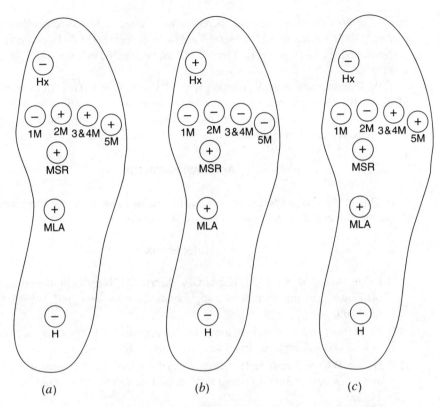

Figure 20-13. Scaphoid pad versus insole only. Redistribution in pressure metrics by sensor in the test population with scaphoid pad use: (*a*) peak pressures, (*b*) contact durations, (*c*) pressure-time integrals.

20.2.5. Discussion

Statistically significant increases in peak pressures, contact durations, and pressure-time integrals occurred in the medial longitudinal arch (MLA) area of the insole with scaphoid pad use ($p \leq 0.05$). Dynamic examination of the foot with the Apex foot imprinter revealed a medial noncontact area indicative of a normal anatomical arch. Thus, no ground support is provided during floor contact, but rather through the internal arch complex. Scaphoid pad usage results in stance phase arch contact with resulting load transfer and pressure redistribution.

Metric values were not significantly altered at the other plantar locations, though SP use did result in peak load increases at the lateral regions of the foot, and peak load decreases at the medial and calcaneal regions of the foot. For average peak plantar pressures, increases were noted at 2M (1 percent), 3&4M (13 percent), and 5M (16 percent), while decreases were noted at H (−5 percent), 1M (−13 percent), and Hx (−18 percent). For contact durations, increases were only seen at Hx (1 percent), while decreases occurred at H (−6 percent), 1M (−7 percent), 2M (−9 percent), 3&4M (−2 percent), and 5M (−4 percent). For pressure-time integrals, increases were noted at 3&4M (2 percent) and 5M (7 percent), while decreases were observed at H (−9 percent), 1M (−19 percent), 2M (−12 percent), and Hx (−16 percent). Overall, SP usage resulted in a general lateral tilt of the foot.

A slight increase in peak pressures with SP use was seen in four of the subjects at the MSR sensor. These increases were observed in subjects with smaller foot sizes.

In conclusion, the study results indicate that the SP elevates the medial rays of the foot. Measurements from the study show that this results in load transfer to the lateral foot.

Acknowledgments

This study was supported in part by intramural funds from the Department of Orthopaedic Surgery at the Medical College of Wisconsin.

References

[1] Chang AH, Abu-Faraj ZU, Harris GF, Shereff MJ, Nery J. Multistep measurement of plantar pressure alterations using metatarsal pads. *Foot and Ankle* 1994;15(12): 654–660.

[2] Klenerman L. Functional anatomy. In: Klenerman L ed. *The Foot and its Disorders* 3rd ed. Oxford England: Blackwell Scientific Publications; 1991:1:1–9.

[3] Hutton WC, Stokes IAF. The mechanics of the foot. In: Klenerman L ed. *The Foot and its Disorders* 3rd ed. Oxford England: Blackwell Scientific Publications; 1991:2: 11–25.

[4] Menkveld SR, Knipstein EA, Quinn JR. Analysis of gait patterns in normal school-aged children. *J Ped Orthop* 1988;8(3):263–267.

[5] Derbyshire B, Platts RGS. A shapeable foot-pressure measuring device. *J Biomed Eng* 1989;11:258–264.

[6] Fixsen JA. The foot in childhood. In: Klenerman L ed. *The Foot and its Disorders* 3rd ed. Oxford England: Blackwell Scientific Publications; 1991:4:33–55.

[7] Holmes GB, Timmerman L. A quantitative assessment of the effect of metatarsal pads on plantar pressures. *Foot and Ankle* 1990;11(3):141–145.

[8] Klenerman L, Nissen KI. Common causes of pain. In: Klenerman L ed. *The Foot and its Disorders* 3rd ed. Oxford England: Blackwell Scientific Publications; 1991:6: 93–111.

[9] Lockard MA. Foot orthoses. *Phys Ther* 1988;68(12):1866–1873.

[10] Schaff PS, Cavanagh PR. Shoes for the insensitive foot: The effect of a "rocker bottom" shoe modification on plantar pressure distribution. *Foot and Ankle* 1990;11(3): 129–140.

[11] Alexander IJ, Chao EYS, Johnson KA. The assessment of dynamic foot-to-ground contact forces and plantar pressure distribution: A review of the evolution of current techniques and clinical applications. *Foot and Ankle* 1990;11(3):152–167.

[12] Gross TS, Bunch RP. Measurement of discrete vertical in-shoe stress with piezoelectric transducers. *J Biomed Eng* 1988;10:261–265.

[13] Gross TS, Bunch RP. Discrete normal plantar stress variations with running speed. *J Biomech* 1989;22(6/7):699–703.

[14] Guirini J, Barry D, Chrzan J, Habershaw G, Lawrence M, Rosenblum B. A preliminary analysis of the felted-foam dressing for the management of diabetic foot ulcerations using F-Scan technology. *Abstract: III. EMED User Meeting*, Flagstaff, Arizona;1992:29–30.

[15] Harris G, Riedel S, Weber R. Validation, evaluation, and preliminary study of the AAMRL/BBD portable force dosimeter. *Proc Instrument Society of America*, 1988;34:391–396.

[16] Harris GF, Smith PA, Abler J, Abu-Faraj Z, Millar EA. Biomechanical evaluation of the planovalgus foot in cerebral palsy: A microprocessor-based insole system. *Proc 8th Annual East Coast Clinical Gait Laboratories Conf* 1993;125–126.

[17] Hennig EM, Rosenbaum D. Pressure distribution patterns under the feet of children in comparison with adults. *Foot and Ankle* 1991;11(5):306–311.

[18] Holmes GB, Timmerman L. Practical considerations for the use of the pedobarograph. *Foot and Ankle* 1991;12(2):105–108.

[19] Miyazaki S, Ishida A. Capacitive transducer for continuous measurement of vertical foot force. *Med Bio Eng Comp* 1984;22:309–316.

[20] Sheriff MJ, Bregman AM, Kummer FJ. The effect of immobilization devices on the load distribution under the foot. *Clin Orthop* 1985;192:260–267.

[21] Toyoshima E, Mano Y, Ando K, Ishihara T, Miyazaki S, Yamashita Y, Mayer RF. Recording and analysis of gait foot-forces using telemetric force-transducers in patients with Duchenne Muscular Dystrophy. Serial assessment of the pathological gait. *Electro Clin Neurophy* 1987;27:355-361.

[22] Wertsch JJ, Webster JG, Tompkins WJ. A portable insole plantar pressure measurement system. *J Rehabil Res Dev* 1992;29(1):13–18.

[23] Wertsch JJ, Loftsgaarden JD, Harris GF, Zhu H, Harris JL. Plantar pressures with contralateral versus ipsilateral cane usage. *Arch. Phys. Med. Rehab.* 1990;71:772.

[24] Zhu H, Wertsch JJ, Harris GF, Loftsgaarden JD, Price MB. Foot pressure distribution during walking and shuffling. *Arch Phys Med Rehab* 1991;72:390–397.

[25] Zhu H, Harris GF, Wertsch JJ, Tompkins WJ, Webster JG. A microprocessor-based data-acquisition system for measuring plantar pressures from ambulatory subjects. *IEEE Trans Biomed Eng* 1991;38(7):710–714.

[26] Zhu H, Maalej N, Webster JG, Tompkins WJ, Bach-y-Rita P, Wertsch JJ. An umbilical data-acquisition system for measuring pressures between the foot and shoe. *IEEE Trans Biomed Eng* 1990;37(9):908–911.

[27] Zhu H, Harris GF, Alba HM, Wertsch JJ. Effect of walking cadence on plantar pressures. *Arch Phys Med Rehab* 1991;72:834.

[28] Zhu H, Wertsch JJ, Harris GF. Asymmetry of plantar pressure during normal walking. *Arch Phys Med Rehab* 1990;71:808.

[29] Zhu H, Wertsch JJ, Harris GF, Alba HM, Price MB. Sensate and insensate in-shoe plantar pressures. *Arch Phys Med Rehab* 1993;74:1362–1368.

[30] Sheriff MJ, DiGiovanni L, Bejjani FJ, Hersh A, Kummer FJ. A comparison of non-weight-bearing and weight-bearing radiographs of the foot. *Foot and Ankle* 1990;10(6):306–311.

[31] Maalej N, Bhat S, Zhu H, Webster JG, Tompkins WJ, Wertsch JJ, Bach-y-Rita P. A conductive polymer pressure sensor. *Proc IEEE Eng Med Bio Soc* 1988;2:770–771.

[32] Abu-Faraj ZU. Quantitative evaluation of plantar pressure alterations with longitudinal arch pads. Shriners Workshop on Human Motion Analysis, 15th Annual International Conference IEEE Engineering in Medicine and Biology Society, San Diego, California, 1995.

Sheldon R. Simon
Philip J. Smith
Jack W. Smith
Jean C. Nippa
Kathy A. Johnson
Lawrence S. Stern
M. G. Sriram

Chapter 21

Applications of Intelligent Multimedia Technology in Human Motion Analysis

21.1. INTRODUCTION

Research on gait analysis has shown that there are many types of information that can aid in the diagnosis and treatment of walking disorders. These include the standard performance parameters of velocity, cadence, and stride length as well as angles and motions of joints, pressure plate information, and muscle activity. Gait analysis data take the form of text, numerical files from several sources, and video. Some prescreening of the data has been shown to be useful, such as the creation of stick figures showing the angulation of each joint at a particular time. In order to make the most use of the information available, it is desirable to develop a system that will aid in the analysis of data and generation of reports.

Our goal is to create a system that can aid in all aspects of gait analysis. The system should aid report generation by decreasing the time necessary to generate the report and providing formatting to make the report easy to read. It should help a lab clinician to interpret case data and understand a case report generated by an expert as well as provide a facility for consultation with an expert about the report. The system should provide an expert with relevant information about the case and inform the expert about new methods for interpreting findings or new treatment techniques. Finally, the system should provide a rich environment for training students to perform gait analysis. Due to the various types of information that can be put into the system as well as the interactive nature of the tools to access the information, it is beneficial to base the system on a multimedia database. Figure 21-1 shows an overview of the envisioned system.

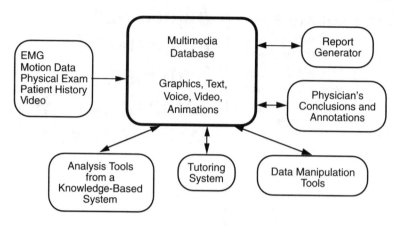

Figure 21-1. GAIT system overview.

21.2. GAIT ANALYSIS

Normal gait is efficient, adaptable, pain free, and requires no ancillary devices. Normally the neurological system controls the muscles through coordinated commands to rotate limbs at every joint, providing body propulsion and stability for walking in a repeatable fashion [1–3]. The summation of these muscle activities can be considered in the joint angles that are produced as well as the overall performance parameters of velocity, cadence, and stride length. It is appropriate to examine the gait cycle not only in terms of the overall performance parameters and the motions produced at each joint, but also to consider such motions as they are produced by particular muscles and their interaction with body weight and momentum at different times during the gait cycle.

Gait analysis laboratories can provide standardized, accurate, and objective data of the various parameters of a patient's gait related to measurements of the patient's time/distance parameters, motion data of limb segments and joints, activity of muscle groups via electromyography (EMG), and ground reaction force data (force-plate data). These laboratories can also provide derived kinetic and kinematic features of gait such as torque and muscle work and effort. These data, in combination with the patient's history and physical examination, provide extensive information for evaluating patients and selecting treatments.

Over the past decade, research efforts have been developing tools to objectively assess human gait performance. This has resulted in the establishment of gait analysis laboratories that are currently proving to be of significant clinical value. However, the analysis of information derived from such laboratories is left to the clinician and currently has become the major obstacle to the widespread clinical use of such systems. The analysis of pathologic gait is especially difficult for the large population of patients with central neurological diseases such as cerebral palsy, which typically give rise to a variety of gait dysfunctions.

The interpretation of data derived from gait laboratories is performed by a clinician. While many individuals are trained and experienced in the interpretation of physical examination and historical data, interpretation of gait laboratory data is less commonly understood, difficult to learn, and time-consuming. To assist clinicians, computational methods in analyzing gait could ensure a standardized, high-quality level of analysis, decrease the time involved in doing an analysis, and be part of a tool for instruction regarding gait analysis.

21.2.1. Gait Analysis Data

For a better understanding of the data available for gait analysis, we describe the collection and form of actual clinical data collected at the Ohio State University (OSU) Gait Analysis Laboratory. Patients are referred to the Gait Lab when they are experiencing difficulty in walking. Examples of such patients are those recovering from a stroke, children with cerebral palsy, automobile accident victims, people with arthritis, and amputees. Gait studies are often performed to determine if surgical intervention would improve the person's gait. At other times, it is found that fitting an orthotic device would help the patient. Gait analysis provides information about a person's gait that is not clearly diagnosed by simply watching the person walk.

A typical gait study involves many steps. First, a physical examination of the lower extremities is performed by a physical therapist. Next, reflective markers, which are used to identify the joint motion during a gait cycle, are taped to the patient's legs around each joint (pelvis, hip, knee, and ankle). The referring doctor specifies the muscles for which electromyographic data are to be collected. Electrodes are then taped over the prescribed muscles. When necessary, wire electrodes are inserted via needle into muscles that are difficult to read using surface electrodes.

During the gait study, the patient is asked to walk in a straight path across the Gait Lab. On the floor are force plates that record heel-strikes during the patient's gait cycle. This information is later provided in the gait report. The reflective markers move with the patient, and their paths are recorded by six charge-coupled device (CCD) cameras placed at different locations around the lab. Each camera is capable of recording the two-dimensional (2-D) path of each marker that it can trace. Later, the data from these six cameras are combined and sorted to provide three-dimensional (3-D) dynamic joint angles. The EMG data at the muscles are also recorded throughout each gait cycle and later correlated with the force-plate data to provide information on which muscles were active during the various phases of the gait cycle. A video of the patient walking is also recorded during the gait session.

21.2.2. Gait Analysis Report

The gait analysis report generated at OSU is currently on paper. It includes all the data collected by the laboratory in a standard form. Patient history is listed on the first page, followed by graphs showing the motion of all the joints in the sagittal and frontal planes. Next are a succession of stick figures showing joint angles and general posture at discrete time intervals. Following these are graphs generated by EMGs for each muscle tested. Finally, the conclusions from the gait analysis expert are included. The drawbacks of such a report include the following:

- Only static information is possible; sometimes animations or video provide additional information.
- Relevant data are mixed with irrelevant data, making it difficult to read the report.
- Multiple relations between data items are difficult to represent. For example, it would be useful to show the relation between the angle of the knee joint and the EMGs of the muscles around the knee at times when the knee is not performing as expected.
- No additional explanation of the data or interpretation is available.

21.2.3. Multimedia Report

Our objective is to provide a gait analysis interpretation tool (GAIT) that can be used to computerize patient reports of gait laboratory analysis as well as to provide training in gait analysis. A paper report would still be possible, but providing an electronic multimedia report would allow:

- Inclusion of video and animations as well as graphics and text
- Voice annotation of the report by the gait analysis technician
- Organized display of data according to relevance and relationship to other data
- Interactive browsing of the report
- Explanations of data items and their meaning as well as explanations of causal processes

Furthermore, elements of the gait analysis interpretation tool should be generalizable in order to provide a similar tool for orthopaedics and medicine in general.

There are many aspects of the gait analysis interpretation tool to consider. First, GAIT should automatically store the patient data from gait laboratory analysis. This includes text such as the medical history and time-distance parameters; graphics such as joint angle graphs and EMGs; and video of the patient walking. Including all these types of data in the report means that storage becomes an issue. A report with text, graphics, and some audio annotation currently requires 10 to 15 megabytes (Mb) of space. Adding video and more audio will increase the size of the record at a rate of about 10 Mb per view (i.e., sagittal or frontal). Delivery of the report would require many floppies, but one CD-ROM would provide enough space.

GAIT's interface for report generation should allow the analyst to view the data, annotate the data by voice or text, easily group relevant data, and accomplish all this in an efficient manner. Many of these functions can be achieved by a multimedia database. In addition, artificial intelligence (AI) techniques can be used to highlight and group relevant data. There are four subtasks of gait analysis that could be aided by AI programming: (1) determine which data indicate abnormalities, (2) determine possible causes of the abnormal data, (3) determine the explanatory coverage of a particular cause, and (4) determine the explanatory coverage of combinations of causes. General knowledge used by the AI program may also be available for tutoring. Before distribution of GAIT as a system, it should be analyzed for correctness, ease of report generation, time savings for report generation, and understandability of the report.

Complementing report generation, GAIT should provide an interface for report viewing and interpretation. It should provide an interface to view the data, to view the analyst's summary (including conclusions and treatment recommendations), and to listen to discussions of the data and summary while viewing pertinent data. Provision for interactive consultation with the analyst is also a possibility. Both the analyst and the person receiving the report have a copy of the report, so a computer interface over phone lines or the Internet would not need to carry too much data.

Finally, GAIT should provide an environment for learning about gait analysis. Many levels of explanation should be supported, ranging from a case-specific explanation of a data item or interpretation to a full tutoring session for a novice at gait analysis. This would entail incorporating explanations at various levels of detail as well as enabling a person to quickly and easily access the information wanted at the right level of detail.

21.3. EXISTING SYSTEM MODULES

Our efforts to produce a gait analysis interpretation tool have resulted in two modules so far. One is a knowledge-based system for performing gait analysis called QUAWDS (qualitative analysis of walking disorders) [4–6]. It contains program pieces that can be used to aid report generation and to provide explanation during training. The other module is a multimedia system for tutoring gait analysis called GAIT [7]. It will be augmented by modules from QUAWDS and additional programming to become the full gait analysis interpretation tool.

21.3.1. QUAWDS as a Cognitive Model of Gait Analysis Expertise[*]

QUAWDS is a computer system that was designed and developed for performing gait interpretation on patients with pathologic gaits resulting from diseases affecting neuromuscular control. QUAWDS was constructed using artificial intelligence techniques and expert system tools. These tools are based on the theory of generic tasks [4,8–10] as well as a qualitative physical model of gait [11,12]. QUAWDS performs its analysis by decomposing the problem of gait interpretation into a series of subtasks: *Determine Findings, Generate Muscle Faults, Rate Muscle Faults, Determine Explanatory Coverage of Faults,* and *Generate Interpretation.* Each subtask in QUAWDS solves a part of the gait interpretation problem through the coordination of the subtasks by an abductive hypothesis assembly method. The interpretation of the patient's gait is synthesized using the outputs of the subtasks. QUAWDS forms an interpretation by first identifying those gait motions that should be considered abnormal. QUAWDS then identifies all the possible causes for the motion deviations. Because of the large number of causes that can be proposed, QUAWDS identifies which causes are most likely. QUAWDS then computes the explanatory coverage for each plausible muscle fault; in other words, identifies the set of abnormalities that each muscle fault can explain. Considering the most likely causes before less likely ones, QUAWDS then builds a complete interpretation of the patient's motions.

Figure 21-2 shows the components of QUAWDS architecture. The rightmost column of boxes enclosed within a dashed rectangle illustrate the type of domain knowledge used by QUAWDS, which include the raw data from the gait analysis lab and the qualitative physical model of gait in QUAWDS. QUAWDS also uses domain knowledge consisting of the anatomy, physiology, and pathophysiology of the lower limb. The leftmost dashed rectangle in the figure contains the subtasks that QUAWDS performs in analyzing a gait. The subtask *Generate Interpretation* is the control module that iterates over the other subtasks. The first subtask, *Determine Findings,* identifies the abnormalities in the gait cycle that needs to be explained. QUAWDS uses the heuristic that any rotational motion differing by more than 10 degrees from normal needs to be accounted for, which typically translates to motion

[*]This section draws from the work in [4–6].

deviations of more then two standard deviations from normal. The importance of a motion deviation depends on the size and duration of the deviation.

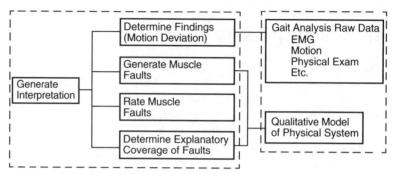

Figure 21-2. QUAWDS system overview.

The second subtask, *Generate Muscle Faults,* finds a set of muscle faults that potentially account for each abnormal observation identified. This set is determined by the qualitative model of lower limb movement. Because of the potentially large number of faults that can explain an abnormality in the gait cycle, QUAWDS only returns a set of muscle faults that directly explain the abnormality. Here the qualitative model, simply by its structure, can determine which components or processes are involved in an abnormality. For example, the qualitative model identifies the anterior tibialis, gastroc soleus, and other factors (e.g., knee flexion/extension) as possible causes of excess plantarflexion of the ankle. Both the anterior tibialis and the gastroc soleus are considered direct causes of ankle motion, while other muscles affecting knee motions are considered indirect.

The third subtask, *Rate Muscle Faults,* involves the evaluation of the plausibility of a fault. In QUAWDS, a classification hierarchy [13] and hypothesis matchers [14] rate faults. The different categories in the hierarchy are the potential muscle faults that can be present in the gait analysis domain. For each fault hypothesis there is knowledge to evaluate its presence or absence in particular cases. As is typical in expert systems using associations, domain experts can provide rules associating the abnormalities observed with muscle faults typically causing them. For example, the fault "underactive anterior tibialis" would be considered plausible if excessive plantarflexion of the foot is observed during the swing phase of the gait cycle.

The fourth subtask, *Determine Explanatory Coverage of Faults,* determines which observations a single or multiple fault can account for. This is accomplished using the qualitative model. The qualitative model in QUAWDS computes the direction of each joint rotation from a combination of the torque-producing forces—muscles, joints, and other forces—acting upon it. QUAWDS is also able to trace an abnormal angular joint position to abnormal angular acceleration, which can be accounted for by some muscle or joint producing an abnormal torque. For example, the fault hypothesis "overactive gastrocsoleus" would account for excessive plantarflexion of the foot, provided the muscle is not weak.

The fifth subtask, *Generate Interpretation,* is done by hypothesis assembly (i.e., the abductive assembler) [15]. The assembler produces a diagnosis by looping over these subtasks until all the abnormal observations are explained. After a diagnosis has been constructed, the assembler removes hypotheses that add little or no explanatory power. The interpretation generated by QUAWDS corresponds to the first page of the written report. The remaining pages of the report are the standard textual data, graphs, and EMG readings.

Example Using QUAWDS. To clarify the operation of QUAWDS, we will present a brief example. Figure 21-3 shows the patient data for a gait analysis case. These data are entered on-screen. An interpretation of the activity of the muscles must also be entered, as it is beyond the scope of this program to analyze the typically noisy signal values in muscle EMGs (see Figure 21-4). QUAWDS graphs and displays data about the angles of the joints in three planes of motion based on numerical data collected by the gait lab (the sagittal plane graphs are shown in Figure 21-5).

Patient Information					
Date: 18-May-1990					
Name: Jane Doe			Medication: None		
Height: DK	Weight:	DK	Diagnosis: Cerebral Palsy		
GAIT Study#: 378			Extremity Involvement: Diplegia		
Muscle Testing:			Passive Range of Motion		
HIP	Right	Left	HIP		
Flexors	4	4	Flexion flexed/straight	DK/45	DK/45
Extensors	4+	4+	Extension	30	30
Abductors	4	4	Abduction	45	45
Adductors	4	4	Adduction	10	10
Int. Rotation	DK	DK	Int. Rotation	70	70
Ext. Rotation	DK	DK	Ext. Rotation	35	35
KNEE			KNEE		
Flexors	4	4	Extension	-10	-10
Extensors	4+	4+	Flexion	120/120	120/120
ANKLE			ANKLE		
Dorsiflexors	DK	DK	Dorsiflexion	0/20	0/20
Plantarflexors	DK	DK	Plantarflexion	DK	DK
Eversion	DK	DK	Subtalar Inversion	DK	DK
Inversion	DK	DK	Subtalar Eversion	DK	DK
			Forefoot Adduction	DK	DK
			Forefoot Abduction	DK	DK

Figure 21-3. QUAWDS patient data (DK stands for *Don't Know*).

QUAWDS begins by determining the motions that are significantly different from normal. The left-hand column of Figure 21-6 shows the motion findings that QUAWDS identified for this case. A motion finding describes the change from normal of a particular joint in one plane of motion for a duration of part of the gait cycle. For example, the first finding is a decrease in the sagittal plane motion for the left hip from the beginning of the swing phase until one quarter of single limb stance.

For each motion finding, QUAWDS analyzes the accelerations involved and determines the likely causes for changes in acceleration within the duration of the finding. For example, QUAWDS identifies that the period from 50 to 100 percent of weight release shows decreased acceleration and that this can be explained by a number of different mus-

Right Side	WA	SLS1	SLS2	WR	Swing1	Swing2
Quadriceps	on	on	on	off	off	on
Hamstrings	on	on	off	on	off	on
Iliopsoas	DK	DK	DK	DK	DK	DK
Rectus	on	off	on	on	on	on
Gluteus Maximus	DK	DK	DK	DK	DK	DK
Gluteus Medius	DK	DK	DK	DK	DK	DK
Adductors	DK	DK	DK	DK	DK	DK
Ant. Tibialis	on	on	on	off	on	on
Gastroc Nemius	DK	DK	DK	DK	DK	DK
Soleus	DK	DK	DK	DK	DK	DK
Peroneals	DK	DK	DK	DK	DK	DK
Post. Tibialis	on	on	on	on	off	off
Left Side						
Quadriceps	on	on	on	off	off	on
Hamstrings	on	on	on	on	off	on
Iliopsoas	DK	DK	DK	DK	DK	DK
Rectus	DK	DK	DK	DK	DK	DK
Gluteus Maximus	DK	DK	DK	DK	DK	DK
Gluteus Medius	DK	DK	DK	DK	DK	DK
Adductors	DK	DK	DK	DK	DK	DK
Ant. Tibialis	on	on	on	on	on	on
Gastroc Nemius	on	on	on	on	off	on
Soleus	DK	DK	DK	DK	DK	DK
Peroneals	DK	DK	DK	DK	DK	DK
Post. Tibialis	on	on	on	on	off	off

Figure 21-4. EMG data (DK stands for *Don't Know*).

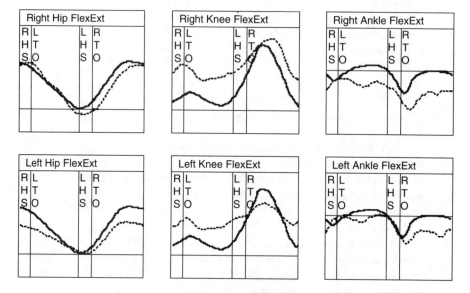

Figure 21-5. Joint angle graphs for the sagittal plane (solid line is normal).

Motion finding	Explanation
Decreased flexion/extension of the left hip from 0% of swing to 25% of single limb stance.	Overactive left hamstrings
Decreased internal/external rotation of the left ankle from 0% of weight acceptance to 100% of swing.	Weak left posterior tibialis Overactive left peroneals
Increased flexion/extension of the right knee from 50% of swing to 100% of weight release.	Overactive right hamstrings
Increased flexion/extension of the left knee from 75% of swing to 50% of weight release.	Overactive left gastroc soleus Overactive left hamstrings
Decreased flexion/extension of the right ankle from 0% of swing to 100% of swing.	Underactive right anterior tibialis
Decreased flexion/extension of the right ankle from 25% of single limb stance to 50% of weight release.	Overactive right gastroc soleus
Decreased flexion/extension of the left ankle from 25% of swing to 100% of swing.	Overactive left gastroc soleus
Decreased flexion/extension of the left knee from 0% of swing to 50% of swing.	Overactive left rectus femoris
Decreased adduction/abduction of the right hip from 0% of weight release to 25% of swing.	Weak right adductors Overactive right gluteus medius
Decreased flexion/extension of the right hip from 0% of swing to 50% of swing.	Overactive right hamstrings
Decreased adduction/abduction of the right hip from 75% of swing to 100% of swing.	Overactive right gluteus medius
Increased anterior/posterior tilt of the pelvis from 75% of single limb stance to 25% of swing.	No explanations found

Figure 21-6. QUAWDS findings and explanation.

cle faults (see Figure 21-7). The faults are rated, and the most likely fault is added to the current hypothesis about the causes of the patient's abnormal motion. Once all the motion findings have been analyzed in this way, the fault hypothesis becomes the combination of all the explanations (the right-hand column of Figure 21-6). Continuing with the abductive assembly process [15], the multicausal fault is checked for superfluous parts (explanations that are not needed because another explanation can explain the same finding). These extra explanations are removed. The hypothesis is also checked for incompatible parts, such as a muscle being both underactive and overactive. The hypothesis is analyzed to ensure that all the findings are still explained, and if not, the process can return to fault generation to add new hypotheses. The result of the entire process is a set of faults believed to be present (see Figure 21-8). A more detailed example can be found in [4].

Performance of QUAWDS. QUAWDS was analyzed on 32 gait studies of ambulatory patients with CP [16]. The abnormalities and muscle faults that QUAWDS detected were compared to reports generated by an expert. QUAWDS was able to detect 90 percent of abnormal gait motions and it identified 80 percent of muscle faults. In addition, it was able to detect significant abnormalities that were missed by the expert. Table 21-1 summarizes

Focusing on acceleration:
(Left hip FlexExt 50 WR 100 WR decreased -1)
   Faults being considered are:
    +3: Overactive left hamstrings
    +2: Overactive left gluteus maximus
    +2: Weak left rectus femoris
    +2: Weak left iliopsoas
    +1: Underactive left rectus femoris
    +1: Underactive left iliopsoas
Adding overactive left hamstrings
Overactive left hamstrings is the highest rated cause, so it is added to the current hypothesis about the cause of abnormal motion.

Figure 21-7. Potential explanations and their ratings for one acceleration portion of the first finding.

Set of faults after parsimony are:
   Overactive right gluteus medius
   Overactive right gastroc soleus
   Overactive left gastroc soleus
   Overactive right hamstrings
   Overactive left peroneals
   Overactive left hamstrings

Figure 21-8. Final set of muscle faults hypothesized to be causing the patient's abnormal motion.

QUAWDS performance on abnormality detection. Differences between the percentages for the nonsagittal versus the sagittal plane can be partially attributed to QUAWDS using the same criteria for abnormality for both planes (i.e., a finding is determined when a data item is more than 10 degrees different from normal). Nonsagittal plane motions are abnormal when there is a smaller deviation from the normal.

TABLE 21-1 QUAWDS PERFORMANCE

Plane	Significant abnormalities missed by		Insignificant abnormalities missed by	
	QUAWDS	Report	QUAWDS	Report
Sagittal	5.5%	4.0%	9.0%	1.6%
Nonsagittal	22.4%	4.9%	11.8%	10.0%

21.3.2. GAIT: Gait Analysis Instructional Tool*

The GAIT tutoring system is a multimedia tutoring system that provides students (orthopaedists and physical therapists) with access to explanations and feedback as they analyze patients with a variety of gait disorders [17]. GAIT provides students with access

*This section draws extensively from [7].

to gait analysis data for individual patients, and provides explanations for each piece of data, as well as an overall description of the primary and secondary problems and compensatory mechanisms contributing to a patient's gait disorder.

GAIT is rich with information but does not burden the more advanced student by forcing upon him something that is already known. For the less advanced student, definitions, descriptions, interpretations, and explanations are available for each piece of gait data simply by clicking the mouse on the item of interest. GAIT provides the student with information through the use of video, sound, graphical displays, pictures, and text. GAIT also gives the student the opportunity to complete a diagnostic gait report on the patient before viewing the expert's final answer for the particular case.

Design of GAIT. GAIT was designed to teach gait analysis to students such as orthopaedic residents, physical therapists, and biomedical engineers. To successfully diagnose a pathological gait case, one must have knowledge of anatomy (including muscles and their functions) and biomechanics. However, such knowledge is not the only key to successful gait analysis. Problem-solving skills are essential in analyzing a clinical gait case. One must first view the available data, choosing to focus on relevant information early on in the problem-solving process. Data that are insignificant to the particular clinical case should be noted as such. Next, abnormalities must be identified and a determination must be made as to whether these are normal variations or true abnormalities that might indicate a certain aspect of the patient's pathology. Finally, it is necessary to identify which abnormalities indicate the primary disorder of the patient, which contribute to the disorder but to a lesser degree (or are a secondary effect of the primary disorder), and which are compensatory. GAIT was designed to encourage the development of these problem-solving skills [18–46].

The tutoring system has been designed with the intention of fulfilling specific teaching goals. One goal is to use real clinical data to provide the student with a real patient in a simulated clinical environment [26,33,47–58]. The aim is to allow the student to access the patient's data as if reading a medical chart when seeking pertinent information about the patient. In a typical tutoring session using this system, the student collects patient data, makes a diagnosis, and finally completes a gait report in a format similar to a medical report.

Another goal is that the system support exploration by the student, allowing him the opportunity to follow any desired path, even if the path is incorrect. To guide the student, however, the system gives the student goals with every piece of data accessed and provides additional, context-sensitive help upon request.

A further aim of the system is to provide the student with feedback on his performance in preparing a medical report on his diagnosis of the case. The intent of this test is to enhance learning, not to be frustrating. Therefore, another system goal is to be helpful and provide clues for completing the test, and to allow the student to rework a hypothesis in the middle of the test by allowing the student to reaccess the data at any time and return to the test when ready. When the student indicates he is done, he is given the opportunity to compare his medical report with an expert's (available from the computer). The student's teacher could also supplement this feedback based on his reading of the student's medical report.

Implementation of GAIT. GAIT currently runs on a Macintosh computer. It has four pull-down menu categories: File, Load Case, View Data, and I'm Done. The File menu contains the Quit function, which exits the program. The Load Case menu lists by case number the available clinical cases that the student may choose to solve. The student chooses only one case for each tutoring session.

The View Data menu lists all available clinical data for the particular clinical case. All available data are shown in bold font, while unavailable data are listed in a faint gray color and cannot be highlighted by the mouse passing over it as the user makes a selection from the menu. The types of data found in this menu include: medical history, physical exam, video, sagittal plane stick figures, frontal plane stick figures, transverse plane stick figures, time-distance parameters, sagittal plane joint angle graphs, frontal plane joint angle graphs, transverse plane joint angle graphs, force-plate data, and EMG data. When the user makes a data selection, the data will appear on the screen for viewing (Figure 21-9). Whenever the student is viewing data, help is available. Every piece of data is a help button. Therefore, the student need only click the mouse on a piece of data to have the option of receiving general help (with audio explanations and descriptive pictures) or case-specific help (usually an audio explanation only) (Figure 21-10).

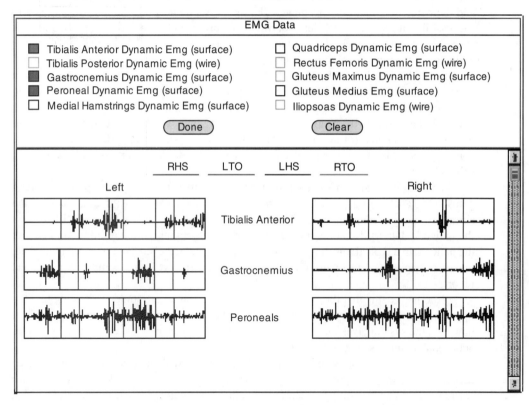

Figure 21-9. Sample data screen (EMG data).

The I'm Done menu should be accessed by the student either when the student feels that enough information has been gathered from the data to try solving the case or when the student is lost and would like to get the "answers" about the current clinical case. The I'm Done menu therefore provides two options: "Let me solve the case," and " I can't tell.

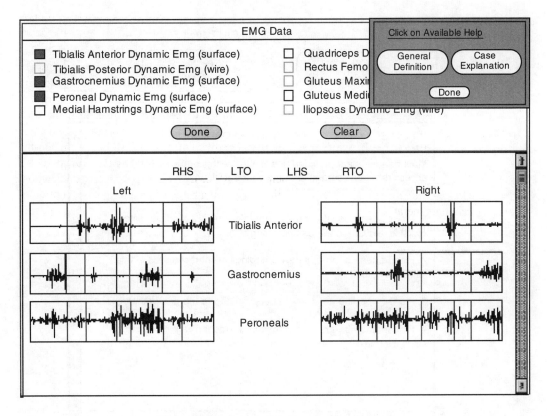

Figure 21-10. Sample data screen with help panel.

Help!" If the student chooses "Let me solve the case," the system prompts the student to enter his or her name. Next, a template for a short gait report is displayed on the screen, with two buttons appearing in a dialogue window above (Figure 21-11). The student is instructed to complete the gait report. The gait report window is a text editor. Therefore, the student is able to type in the window and save the report by clicking the Save Report button, which is the left button at the top of the screen. At all times during this part of the tutorial, the student is able to access data screens to aid in the completion of the report. If the student would like to receive a hint on any of the four sections of the gait report (medical history, primary pathological gait characteristics, lesser effects, or compensation mechanisms), the right button at the top of the screen should be clicked. This will bring up four Hint Buttons, one for each gait report category, which offer an audio message to direct the student to a place in the data where information can be found about that category (Figure 21-12).

After the student has clicked the Save Report button, a slide show is launched. This slide show contains an expert's message about the clinical case that was just solved. The slides show text, pictures, and graphs to illustrate the major points of the clinical case. The expert's voice is also heard with an audio explanation of the slide. If the student had chosen the "I can't tell. Help!" option from the I'm Done menu, the slide show would be launched immediately, and the gait report lesson would be skipped (Figure 21-13).

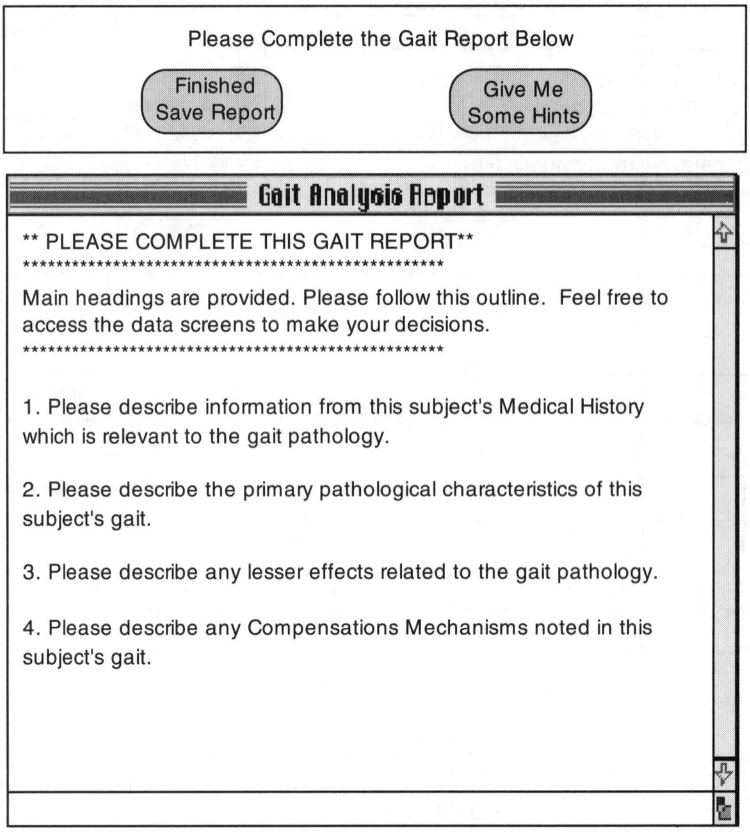

Please Complete the Gait Report Below

Finished
Save Report

Give Me
Some Hints

Gait Analysis Report

** PLEASE COMPLETE THIS GAIT REPORT**
****
Main headings are provided. Please follow this outline. Feel free to
access the data screens to make your decisions.
****

1. Please describe information from this subject's Medical History
which is relevant to the gait pathology.

2. Please describe the primary pathological characteristics of this
subject's gait.

3. Please describe any lesser effects related to the gait pathology.

4. Please describe any Compensations Mechanisms noted in this
subject's gait.

Figure 21-11. Gait report template.

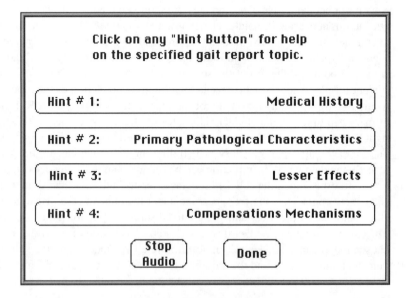

Click on any "Hint Button" for help
on the specified gait report topic.

Hint # 1:   Medical History

Hint # 2:   Primary Pathological Characteristics

Hint # 3:   Lesser Effects

Hint # 4:   Compensations Mechanisms

Stop
Audio

Done

Figure 21-12. Hint panel.

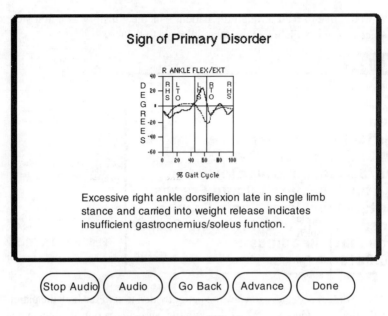

Sign of Primary Disorder

Excessive right ankle dorsiflexion late in single limb
stance and carried into weight release indicates
insufficient gastrocnemius/soleus function.

(Stop Audio)   (Audio)   (Go Back)   (Advance)   (Done)

Figure 21-13. Slide show.

Sequence of a Sample Tutoring Session.   The tutoring system was broadly described in the previous section. The system's design is intended to encourage the exploration
of clinical gait data. The pull-down menus from left to right (File, Load Case, View Data,
I'm Done) indicate the order of events intended for a typical tutoring session for a sample
student. We will now proceed through a sample tutoring session for a hypothetical student,
Student A, who just graduated from physical therapy school. While in school, Student
A had the opportunity to observe three gait studies in the gait lab and discuss the results
with the gait lab's physical therapist. However, this is his first attempt to interpret gait
data.

     When Student A begins the tutoring session, all items in the View Data and I'm Done
menus are dimmed and inaccessible. Therefore, selections can only be made from the File
and Load Case menus. Student A does not wish to quit, so nothing should be chosen from
the File menu. The only other available event is to load a clinical case for the tutoring
session. He therefore chooses clinical case number 1 from the Load Case menu (Figure
21-14). Upon executing this menu command, Student A is notified by the system that this
loading will take some time. During the loading process, the system initializes windows
and buttons that are created for the clinical data specific to the chosen case.

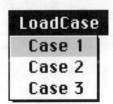

LoadCase
Case 1
Case 2
Case 3

Figure 21-14. The Load Case menu.

     When a case has been loaded, the View Data and I'm Done menus become active.
Student A decides which data to view first by looking at the data available (Figure 21-15).
In this case the View Data menu shows that medical history data is not available. Student

A would like to read through the patient's medical history as a first step, but realizes that since it is not available, other data will have to suffice.

View Data

Medical History
Physical Examination
Video
Sagittal Plane Stick Figures
Frontal Plane Stick Figures
Time/Distance Parameters
Sagittal Plane Joint Angle Graphs
Frontal Plane Joint Angle Graphs
Transverse Plane Joint Angle Graphs
Force Plate Readings
EMG Data

Figure 21-15. The View Data menu (available data is shown in bold font).

Student A decides to view the patient video first to see how the patient's gait looks. By selecting the video option, a video window and video control panel appear (Figure 21-16). When Student A clicks the Play button, a video of the patient begins in the video window. The video lasts approximately 7 seconds, and shows the patient walking first toward the viewer and then away from the viewer. Student A notes that this subject's gait appears fairly normal on the video and that there must be something going on that novice eyes do not immediately detect.

Figure 21-16. Video of patient walking.

Student A then sees in the View Data menu that sagittal plane stick figures are available. Upon choosing this option, a familiar movie window and control panel appear (Figure 21-17). Student A clicks the Play button, and an animated movie shows the patient's stick figures advancing across the movie window. This view is different from the video, which gave a frontal plane view. From this sagittal view of the stick figures, Student A notes that the patient's posture appears tilted back at the end of the gait cycle. This is interesting, but Student A has no idea why this postural adjustment occurs.

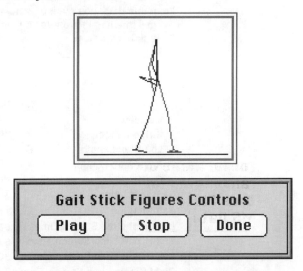

Figure 21-17. Animated stick figures.

Student A decides to look at the time-distance parameters. Upon selecting this option, a screen appears displaying the patient's time-distance data (Figure 21-18). Student A notices at the top of the screen a highlighted block with two questions. The first one asks "How much is this person's functional walking ability impaired?" Student A thinks the answer to that question is very clear, not from the time-distance data, but from seeing the video. The patient appeared to be walking at a normal pace with a fairly normal looking gait. Therefore, Student A does not believe the patient's walking is significantly impaired. The second question asks, "Which leg or legs are likely to have the underlying pathology?" Student A is stumped by this and begins to look at the data. Since the goal is to determine which leg is affected, he decides to scrutinize only the data dealing with right or left sides.

Noticing that the left step length is much shorter than the right, Student A clicks Left Step Length. A help window appears in the upper right corner of the screen (Figure 21-19). This window contains three help buttons labeled General Definition, Case Explanation, and Done. Student A clicks the General Definition button, and a picture and control panel appear (Figure 21-20). The following verbal message is played: "Left step length is the distance from the location of the right heel to that of the left heel at left heel-strike. Left step length is determined by the left side swing motion pattern and the right side stance motion pattern as well as pelvic rotation. The picture on your screen is an illustration of how left step length is measured during the gait cycle." Student A listens to this definition, but already knew what left step length was. Next, he clicks the Case Explanation button. The control panel appears in the upper right corner, and the following verbal message begins: "The left step length for this subject is shorter than the right. Step length is affected by the position of the limb at the end of stance on one side and the position of the opposite limb at the end of swing on the other side. A decrease in step length can be caused by the decrease in motion during stance at the hip, knee, and ankle or a decrease of the motion in swing at the hip and the knee. Therefore, for this subject, the shortness in left step length is related to an abnormality of the left leg completing stance or the right leg in swing." Student A then decides to look at the motion data to determine the side of the pathology.

Time Distance Parameters			
From this data, you should be able to answer the following questions: 1. How much is this person's functional walking ability impaired? 2. Which leg or legs are likely to have the underlying pathology?			
	Patient		**Normal**
	% of Normal	Raw	Raw
Velocity	73%	1.05 m/sec	1.45 m/sec
Stride Length	76%	1.19 m	1.57 m
Left Step Length	67%	0.53 m	0.78 m
Right Step Length	85%	0.66 m	0.78 m
Cadence	95%	105 step/min	111 step/min
Step Width	165%	0.132 m	0.08 m
Gait Phases:	% of Cycle	Raw	% of Cycle
Left Total Limb Stance Time	68%	0.77 sec	62%
Right Total Limb Stance Time	63%	0.71 sec	62%
Left Single Limb Stance Time	38%	0.43 sec	38%
Right Single Limb Stance Time	32%	0.37 sec	38%
Left Double Limb Stance Time	16%	0.18 sec	12%
Right Double Limb Stance Time	14%	0.16 sec	12%

Figure 21-18. Time distance parameter data screen.

Time Distance Parameters		Click on Available Help	
		General Definition Case Explanation	
From this data, you should be able to answer 1. How much is this person's functional walk 2. Which leg or legs are likely to have the ur		Done	
	Patient		**Normal**
	% of Normal	Raw	Raw
Velocity	73%	1.05m/sec	1.45 m/sec
Stride Length	76%	1.19 m	1.57 m
Left Step Length	67%	0.53 m	0.78 m
Right Step Length	85%	0.66 m	0.78 m
Cadence	95%	105 step/min	111step/min
Step Width	165%	0.132 m	0.08 m
Gait Phases:	% of Cycle	Raw	% of Cycle
Left Total Limb Stance Time	68%	0.77 sec	62%
Right Total Limb Stance Time	63%	0.71 sec	62%
Left Single Limb Stance Time	38%	0.43 sec	38%
Right Single Limb Stance Time	32%	0.37 sec	38%
Left Double Limb Stance Time	16%	0.18 sec	12%
Right Double Limb StanceTime	14%	0.16 sec	12%

Figure 21-19. Time distance data screen with help panel for Left Step Length.

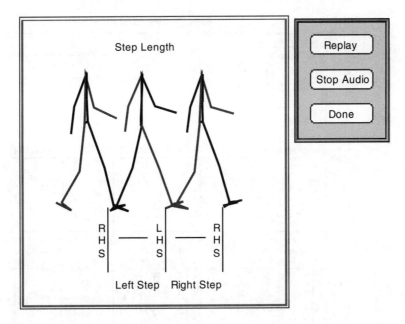

Figure 21-20. General definition "Help" picture displayed for Left Step Length.

Student A selects the sagittal plane joint angle graphs (Figure 21-21). Within seconds he notes that the right ankle flexion/extension graph looks abnormal, noting in particular that there is too much dorsiflexion at left heel-strike until weight release. He forms a hypothesis that the patient has a problem at the right ankle. He believes that more clues can be found by looking at the EMG data for specific muscles.

Student A opens the EMG data screen and decides to look at muscles around the ankles. Therefore, Student A selects tibialis anterior, gastrocnemius, and peroneal EMG data (Figure 21-9). Student A plays the case explanations for the left and right tibialis anterior and gastrocnemius. He thinks that the data for the left look slightly different from those for the right side, but the case explanation did not indicate that there was a great deviation. Student A is convinced that the right ankle's motion data were very abnormal, but that the muscle activity does not explain it. He is not quite sure what the cause is, but decides to try solving the case by selecting "Let me solve the case" from the I'm Done menu.

The system asks for the student's name. Student A enters "Student A" and clicks the OK button. Next, the system displays a window with a template of a gait report (Figure 21-11). This window functions as a text editor for the student to complete the report. There are four categories in the gait report: significant medical history information, primary pathological gait characteristics, gait characteristics that contribute to a lesser degree, and compensation mechanisms. Student A decides that there is nothing to report for the medical history, and that the primary pathology is the abnormal right ankle dorsiflexion. Student A is not sure about Question 3 (the lesser effects), and decides to ask for a hint by clicking the Give Me Some Hints button. The hint window opens (Figure 21-12) and Student A clicks on the third button. The following verbal message is heard: "One lesser effect is seen at the knee on the side opposite to that of the pathology where there is excessive knee flexion during weight acceptance. Take a look at the joint angle graphs for the sagittal plane and try to determine what is causing this excessive flexion."

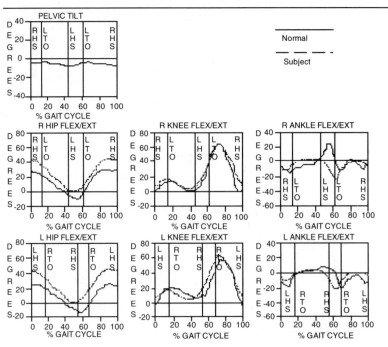

Figure 21-21. Sagittal plane joint angle graph data screen.

At this point, Student A follows the directions and views the sagittal plane joint angle graphs again (Figure 21-21), thus noting the excessive flexion at the left knee during weight acceptance. However, he cannot determine what is causing this deviation. For the last question regarding compensation mechanisms on the gait report, he remembers the abnormal posture from the stick figures and decides that if the primary problem is at the ankle, the postural change is surely a compensation. Student A's completed gait report is shown in Figure 21-22. Student A realizes that he has surely missed some important points here but is ready to save his report and hear the answers. Student A clicks the Finished–Save Report button, and a slide show begins (Figure 21-13). During the slide show, Student A hears that the primary disorder of insufficient gastrocnemius/soleus function on the right is seen in the excessive motion toward ankle dorsiflexion occurring late in single-limb stance and carried into weight release. Student A then reasons that the ankle motion deviation is a result of lack of gastrocnemius function, which was disguised by the EMG data that showed fairly normal gastrocnemius activity. The lesser effect is of interest, because Student A was unable to figure it out. The expert's explanation was, "The sudden collapse at the right ankle results in abnormal motion on the left side at the time the left leg catches the fall. An increased impact has to be absorbed by the left leg and is reflected in excessive left knee flexion during left weight acceptance. With the caving in of the right ankle the pelvis drops excessively on the right side during the same period, imposing a higher demand on the left gluteus medius muscle to stabilize the pelvis during that period." In listening to the expert's comments about compensation mechanisms, Student A realizes that he was able to correctly identify one of many compensations (the postural change). However he did not clearly state the reasons for the compensation. The expert's message about the postural change was, "The primary compensation mechanism used is a posture change to bring the center of mass further back, keeping the force line behind and close to the ankle for as long as possible, resulting in delayed and decreased ankle dorsiflexion during the first part of single limb stance. This posture change is seen in the pelvis and hip motion graphs and the stick figures. The pelvis is less tilted to the anterior, which shifts the hip pattern into more extension. The stick figures display an upright position to a slight backward lean of the trunk."

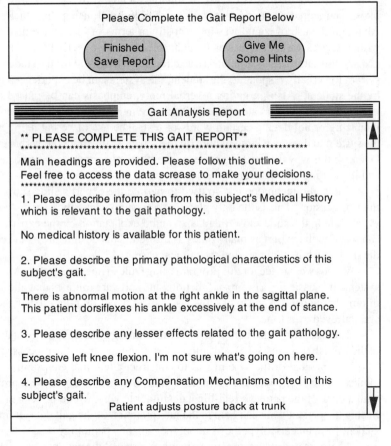

Figure 21-22. Student A's completed gait report.

Student A is satisfied with his first attempt at gait analysis and feels that he correctly identified some of the gait abnormalities of the patient, but decides that for the next tutoring session he will work on forming more thorough explanations for the anomalies identified. Student A decides he is done for the day and chooses the Quit option from the File menu.

Since Student A's gait report was saved to the computer's hard disk, his teacher will later read the report and discuss this case with him. The teacher will be able to know the areas where Student A needs the most help and will provide feedback and guidance in these areas.

21.3.3. Multimedia Design Concepts

As described above, the GAIT program utilized several multimedia design concepts: simple animation, still graphics, sound, and video [59–64]. These media were chosen with the intention of improving the student's learning by more closely simulating the solving of actual patient cases. Sound was used to help the student with definitions and explanations if the student asked for assistance during the session, making them less tedious. It was also used in slide show narrations at the end of the tutoring session to communicate the expert's opinions of the particular clinical case. Video was used as a means of data presentation.

First, we will discuss the use of sound. Sounds were recorded directly into the Macintosh and stored as sound resources on the hard disk using the MacRecorder software. Although the use of sound was more costly in terms of disk space than solely outputting written text explanations, it was thought to be a more effective teaching tool. One of the goals of this tutor was to simulate a true clinical environment for the student. In allowing the system to verbally respond to the student, the system can be experienced more as a teacher by the student. Also, in giving a verbal reply, emphasis can be placed on certain words to capture the student's attention. This may be more effective in teaching the student than italicizing or boldfacing certain words of text. The use of verbal help replies also allows the system to display a large picture on the screen to illustrate the verbal explanation being given. In this way the teaching system can effectively complete the two tasks of explaining and illustrating simultaneously.

The audio technique is also used to narrate the expert's slide show at the end of the tutoring session. This is the only place in the system where the expert's voice is heard. For every slide in the slide show, there is an audio explanation by the expert. Here the student can listen to the expert as many times as desired. This design allows the expert to speak to the student while summarizing the clinical case.

Videos were made for this program using QuickTime, a part of the Macintosh operating system. It is basically a group of functions and software routines that allow for the handling of time-based data. A video or movie is an example of time-based data that must be stored and retrieved over time.

There are two video components in this tutoring system: a movie of the patient walking in the gait lab (Figure 21-16) and animated stick figures from the processed gait data (Figure 21-17). One goal of the system was to construct a learning environment similar to a true clinical setting. The video is useful from this point of view, because it provides the student with a view of the patient's real-life gait similar to what would be seen in a clinical setting. Seeing the patient walk can help in the interpretation of the gait data. It might also help the student form an early hypothesis about the patient's pathology.

The animated stick figures are a reconstruction of the patient's gait. They are generated from the joint angle data from the Gait Lab and are printed on a page with the gait data. For the tutoring system, the stick figure data was animated in a format similar to the video.

21.3.4. Teaching Environment Design Concepts

One goal of the tutor that was mentioned previously is to build a system for learning that is similar to the actual clinical setting. For this reason, actual clinical data are used, allowing the student to learn from real patients. The use of true patient gait data forces the student to cope with data situations that occur in real lab data. For example, if, during a patient gait study, an EMG channel fails and muscle activity is not recorded for the patient for that muscle, the doctor must evaluate the available data and form a hypothesis without the EMG. Another example would be if motion data for a particular joint appear to follow a normal pattern, but are roughly 10 degrees above the normal curve for the entire gait cycle, the determination must be made whether the abnormality is with the patient's walking or possibly a deviation caused by the misplacement of the markers on the patient for the gait study. The main point is that real lab data are not sterile. There are occasional anomalies seen with the real lab data that the student should be aware of.

The tutoring system environment for viewing data was designed as a computerized patient gait chart. This makes the environment similar to the clinical situation in which the doctor receives the chart on the patient with the lab results, reads through the pages of data, and forms some conclusions about the patient's condition. In this tutoring system, after a clinical case has been loaded, the "medical chart" is ready for viewing. The student can pick and choose any available data to view. The data are listed in the pull-down menu in a typical viewing order. However, the student is free to access data in any order desired [65–72].

This free access to the data is very useful for the more advanced student who forms a hypothesis early on [73–80] and knows exactly which pieces of information are necessary for confirmation. This design provides an efficient way for the student to navigate through the data and make a diagnosis in a short amount of time. It avoids any frustration that a student might feel if access to and navigation through the data and tutoring session were more restrictive.

From a tutoring point of view, allowing the student to choose which data to view and which to ignore has merit. This information about the student's performance is useful for a teacher trying to diagnose what is causing a student's misconception or problem-solving difficulty.

At the gait lab, after a patient's lab results are complete, a medical report is written to interpret the results. Therefore, the tutoring system incorporates this report-writing aspect at the end of the tutoring session. When the student chooses the "Let me solve the case" option from the I'm Done menu, and is asked to complete the gait report shown on the screen, the tutoring system is trying to teach the student skills that will be encountered in the medical field: data interpretation and report writing. While completing the report, the student is able to access the patient's data freely, as would be possible in writing a real medical report. The skill of interpretive writing is possibly best learned by practice. The guidelines given in the report template are there to give the student instructions and directions for writing the report. These guidelines provide four categories on which the student should report. This focus is provided to keep the student on track with writing as well as to convey important categories of information that should be extracted from the data.

There are also hints for each category available to the student during the writing of the report. If a student is lost, it is hoped that, rather than giving up, she would choose to listen to a hint. The hints are meant to be helpful. They point the student to data screens that contain information relevant to the category.

Student Goals. Because the tutoring system was designed to allow maximum student freedom, the student has a great deal of control in determining the path of exploration. The system is exploratory and relies on curious and motivated students to seek the data and form hypotheses. However, suggested goals are built in and highlighted at the top of the time-distance data screen at the present time and will be added to all data screens in the future (Figure 21-18). These goals tell the student what important inferences should be derived from the particular page of data. With these goals, the system passively provides the student with a purpose while viewing each piece of data, as well as a focus on this particular clinical case. For example, on the time-distance data screen for clinical case number 1, there are two student goals stated as questions:

1. How much is this person's functional walking ability impaired?
2. Which leg or legs are likely to have the underlying pathology?

This tells the student that from the time-distance data on the screen, these two questions should be able to be answered. These questions do not include all relevant information to be derived from the data on the screen, but answering these questions should help the student with forming a correct hypothesis.

One goal for the tutoring system is for every data item on a screen to be a help button, thus allowing the student to execute a query by clicking the mouse on the data in question [65–72,81]. When a data item is clicked, a standard help panel appears in the upper right corner of the screen. For all help data, a verbal general definition with illustrative picture and a verbal case explanation are available by clicking the appropriate button (Figure 21-19).

If the student is a novice and needs a tremendous amount of help, it is always available. Every data screen and every piece of data was developed as a help button. Clicking on the information brings up the help menu, which provides the student with general or case-specific help. If a student wishes to work through the tutorial and gain access to the knowledge that it has to offer, this would be accomplished by viewing all data screens and listening to and reading through all on-line help.

Most likely the student would access this available help when specific information is needed. The categories, "general" and "case-specific," allow the student to choose only the information required, thus saving time.

21.3.5. Analysis of GAIT

Based on initial formative evaluations, we have found that GAIT provides a very effective means for giving practitioners access to patient data and associated explanations [7]. This experience with the use of GAIT as a tutoring system suggests that it would be an effective model for delivering patient data to the physicians and physical therapists who refer patients to gait labs.

21.4. INTEGRATING THE MODULES

QUAWDS and GAIT provide modules for automatic gait analysis and tutoring in a multi-media environment. The modules from each can be combined to support several functions. There are two main functions of the GAIT interpretation environment: (1) to make gait analysis reports easier to generate and understand, and (2) to provide support for tutoring.

21.4.1. Report Generation

In the context of report generation, QUAWDS has modules for automatically performing the subtasks of gait analysis, thus making analysis quicker and easier to do. However, QUAWDS generates a report that is essentially the same as the paper reports generated in a standard lab. As was outlined earlier, a multimedia report with explanation support would enable the report to be better understood. For example, a report that indicates an abnormality in the functioning of the gastroc soleus can better illustrate the problem by showing the relevant EMG data aligned with the motion graph. The GAIT instructional tool provides an interface that currently allows voice to be combined with other data. It can also provide general help on the terms of the report. This interface could be expanded with report generation tools that would tie into the expert system modules. For example, a physician using the system to generate a report could call on *Determine Findings*, which would result in a screen showing the abnormalities detected by QUAWDS. The physician could select any finding and ask the system why it determined that abnormality was present. The physician could also change the parameters affecting abnormality detection, such as decreasing the tolerance for range of motion from 10 degrees to 5 degrees from normal. Menus would be provided to allow the physician to add abnormalities not included by QUAWDS or to remove abnormalities from the list generated. When satisfied with the set of abnormalities, the physician would continue through the other subtasks of analysis, using the system to generate possibilities and then modifying these as necessary. At any point in report generation, the physician would be able to link parts of the report together, such as linking an abnormal finding to the data supporting its classification as abnormal.

21.4.2. Tutoring

As discussed earlier, the GAIT instructional tool provides an integrated environment for tutoring. However, each case in the system must have its solutions and case-sensitive explanations generated manually by an expert. This is because GAIT has no way to solve a case itself. Since QUAWDS provides modules for gait analysis, it could be used to generate solutions and justifications for new cases. The ability to enter new cases easily would provide a greater range of experience for students. In addition, a student could explore the domain of gait more thoroughly by generating cases herself to see how GAIT would solve them. For example, the student could start the system off with a set of abnormalities (or a single abnormality) and have GAIT generate the possible causes. Exploratory learning such as this has been shown to be an effective teaching tool [82].

21.4.3. Implementation Issues

To achieve the goal of a complete gait analysis system, several implementational issues must be considered. These include accessibility, integration of multiple sources, and report storage and delivery. First, the system must run on machines that are either already present at a lab or easy to obtain. Labs currently divide into two groups: those that have PC compatibles and those that have Macintosh computers. Therefore, it is desirable that GAIT run on either platform.

A second issue is the variety of information types and sources that must be accommodated. Information types include graphs, video, voice annotations, text, numbers, and combinations of these. The sources for this information are lab instruments, video cameras, computer programs, and actions taken by the person using the interface to the system. Clearly it is important to design GAIT to integrate easily all these data types as well as provide a convenient and efficient interface to the information. A well-implemented multimedia database based on our experiences with the instructional GAIT system should give us the functionality we need.

The function of a multimedia database is to collect and integrate information sources as well as provide convenient access to information. There are many database tools on the market, and more will be emerging in the near future. Care must be taken to choose a database that will provide the functionality necessary for the entire system. There are two database systems that currently exist in some form on both the PC and Macintosh platforms. These are (1) Authorware, which runs on both systems, and (2) a combination of Hypercard for the Macintosh and Toolbook for PCs. The scripting language in Authorware might not provide enough power to make as rich a user interface as we envision. Hypercard is not ideal either because it limits the amount of information on the screen at a time. On the horizon is ScriptX, which appears to have all the key elements but is not available yet. Another option is to program the system from scratch, as was done with the instructional GAIT system. The disadvantage to doing this is that it is more difficult to support multiple hardware platforms because of the large amount of recoding that must be done. Nevertheless, it is possible to build the envisioned system with tools and techniques that are available now.

Another issue is the method of storage and delivery of the report, which is dependent on the report's size and use. The gait analysis report that we envision will consist of text, images, movies, and sound. Table 21-2 shows the space requirements for various data types. The current gait analysis file used by the instructional tool takes 100 K to 3 Mb. Clearly these files can become quite large. For local storage, a hard disk or CD-ROM would be necessary to allow quick access to all the data.

TABLE 21-2 DATA TYPES AND SPACE REQUIREMENTS

Data Type	Space
Text (one page)	8 K
Image (one page)	300 K
Movies (one second)	50–200 K
Sound (one second)	15–100 K

There are two ways that a report might be used: (1) locally at the same lab that generated the report, or (2) remotely at the physician's office that requested the report. If the lab that uses the report is remote, there are two main ways to deliver the report: physically or electronically. Physically, a CD-ROM can be mailed to the requesting lab. The report would not be available for at least a day. Electronic connection between sites is becoming quite common and results in quick communication between the labs. The Internet provides one such electronic connection. It has existed for 20 years and currently has more than 9000 connections in 102 countries, connecting more than 10 million people. It uses wire and optic fiber and has a transfer rate of 45 Mb/s. In addition, there is an effort to improve the existing Internet system to use fiber optics and increase the availability of electronic connection within this country. Within the Internet system there are several methods of communicating data. Electronic mail provides communication between users on any connected network. File transfer protocol (FTP) allows transfer of files from one computer to another. Telnet allows users at one site to log in remotely and work on computers at another site. Gopher provides a client/server protocol that operates on multiple platforms to transfer files from one computer to another. World Wide Web (WWW) is a distributed hypermedia system created by CERN (European Laboratory for Particle Physics). It provides standards for hypermedia data and software that allows the data to be displayed on many platforms. Even if a lab is not on the Internet itself, it is possible for that lab to make a phone connection by modem to a site providing Internet service. This reduces the speed of the connection, but is still a reasonable method. Table 21-3 shows the electronic transfer speeds for some of the electronic protocols. In addition to providing a speedy method of report delivery, electronic connection also provides the potential for on-line consultation between labs. After receiving the report, the requesting lab could connect to the gait analysis lab to ask for more information or clarification of information in the report. Since both labs would have the report on-line, all the information for doing the consultation would be available.

TABLE 21-3 TRANSFER SPEED

Method	Speed
Modem	1.2K/s–14.4K/s
Ethernet	10 Mb/s max
FTP	60 K/s–500 K/s
FDDI (fiber distributed data interface)	50–100 Mb/s

21.5. SUMMARY

A multimedia gait analysis system provides support for many different aspects of the gait analysis task. The system affects the recording and maintaining of patient records by providing easy access to patient data from a visit and analysis of data across visits, and by maintaining the integration of patient data for clearer reports and better understanding. Research on gait analysis can be aided by the ability to analyze data across patients and visits and to analyze patterns of data. Patient information is augmented by the incorporation of voice, video, and interpretations as well as new ways to look at the data. Finally, the gait analysis system can be used for individualized training of orthopaedists, physical therapists, orthotists, prosthetists, students, residents, and physicians. This training can be basic or a refresher course on new treatment techniques, new kinds of data, or new ways to look at the data.

We believe that the envisioned gait analysis interpretation tool is feasible. Many tools exist for parts of the system. The instructional tool has proved useful in teaching gait analysis, and it serves as a solid basis for the entire system. Many of the multimedia issues have been explored while building GAIT. The artificial intelligence program is relatively accurate and will provide the building blocks for some data interpretation tools as well as explanations necessary for tutoring. Only time and careful design and implementation are necessary to realize our goals.

Acknowledgments

This work was supported, in part, by the U.S. Department of Education, National Institute on Disability and Rehabilitation Research grant H133E30009, the Hearst Foundation, and the United Cerebral Palsy Research and Education Foundation. The authors especially thank Mike Weintraub for his efforts on the QUAWDS system; Jean C. Nippa, M.S., M. G. Sriram, Ph.D., and Lawrence S. Stern, Ph.D., for their assistance on various aspects of this project; and the OSU Gait Lab staff for their time and patience.

References

[1] Schoenberg B, ed. *Advances in Neurology*, vol 19. New York, NY: Raven Press;1978.

[2] National Institutes of Health, Public Health Service, U.S. Department of Health and Human Services. *National Institute of Neurological and Communicative Disorders and Stroke Fact Book*;1981.

[3] Perry J. Normal and pathologic gait. In: Bunch, WH ed. *Atlas of Orthotics*, 2nd ed. St Louis, Mo: CV Mosby Company;1985.

[4] Weintraub MA, Bylander T, Simon SR. QUAWDS: A composite diagnostic system for gait analysis. *Computer Methods and Programs in Biomedicine*. 1990;32:91–106.

[5] Weintraub M, Bylander T. Combining different knowledge types in a diagnostic system. In: *Proceedings of the AAAI Spring Symposium on Artificial Intelligence in Medicine*, March 27–29, 1990, Stanford University.

[6] Weintraub MA. An explanation-based approach to assigning credit. Columbus, Ohio:The Ohio State University. 1991:PhD Thesis.

[7] Nippa J. *Development of a computer-based multi-media tutoring system for teaching gait analysis*. Columbus, Ohio: The Ohio State University, 1992:MS Thesis.

[8] Chandrasekaran B. Generic tasks in knowledge-based reasoning: High-level building blocks for expert system design. *IEEE Expert* 1986;1:23–30.

[9] Bylander T, Chandrasekaran B. Generic tasks for knowledge-based reasoning: The "right" level of abstraction for knowledge acquisition. *Int J Man-Machine Studies* 1987;26:231–243.

[10] Bylander T, Chandrasekaran B, Josephson JR. The generic task toolset. In: Salvendy G ed. *Cognitive Engineering in the Design of Human-Computer Interaction Proc Second Intl Conf on Human-Computer Interaction*. Amsterdam: Elsevier;1987:507–512.

[11] Bylander T, Smith JW, Svirbely JR. Qualitative representation of behavior in the medical domain, In: Salamon R, Blum B, Jorgensen M, eds. *MEDINFO 86: Proceedings of the Fifth Conference on Medical Informatics* New York, NY: North-Holland; 1986;5:7–11.

[12] Bylander T, Weintraub M. *Integrating Qualitative and Associational Models in Diagnosis in Complex Domains*. OSU CIS LAIR Technical Report. Columbus, Ohio: The Ohio State University; 1989.

[13] Bylander T, Mittal S. CSRL: A language for classificatory problem solving and uncertainty handling. *AI Magazine* 1986;7:66–77.

[14] Bylander T, Johnson TR, Goel A. Structured matching: A task-specific technique for making decisions, In: *Proceedings of the IEEE International Workshop on Tools for Artificial Intelligence*. Cambridge, Mass: IEEE Computer Society Press; 1989: 138–145.

[15] Josephson JR, Chandrasekaran B, Smith JW. Assembling the best explanation. In: *Proceedings of the IEEE Workshop on Principles of Knowledge-Based Systems*. Denver, Colo: IEEE Computer Society Press; 1984:185–190.

[16] Simon SR, Weintraub M, Bylander T. *A Study In Automated Human Pathologic Gait Interpretation*. Technical Report. Columbus, Ohio: The Ohio State University; 1992.

[17] Kumar D, Smith PJ, Helgeson S, White A. Advanced technologies for educational tools in science. In: Thomas D ed. *Scientific Visualization in Mathematics and Science Teaching*. Charlotte, Va: Association for the Advancement of Computers In Education; [in press].

[18] Anderson JR. *Cognitive Psychology and Its Implications*. 2nd ed. San Francisco, Calif: WH Freeman;1985.

[19] Ausubel DP. *Educational Psychology: A Cognitive View*. New York, NY: Holt Rinehart and Winston;1986.

[20] Bobbie E. *Survey Research Methods*. Belmont, Calif: Wadsworth Publishing Company;1990.

[21] Bogdan R, Taylor SJ. *Introduction to Research Methods*. New York, NY: John Wiley & Sons Inc;1975.

[22] Bork A. *Learning with Computers*. Bedford, Mass: Digital Press;1981.

[23] Bork A. Is Technology-based learning effective? *Contemporary Education*, 1991;63: 6-14.

[24] Box GE, Hunter WG, Hunter JS. *Statistics for Experimenters: An Introduction to Design, Data Analysis, and Model Building*. New York, NY: John Wiley & Sons Inc;1978.

[25] Butterfield EC, Nelson GD. Theory and Practice of Teaching for Transfer. *Educational Tech Res Dev* 1989;37(3):5–38.

[26] Cardiff RD. Teaching problem solving in pathology. *Arch Pathol Lab Med* 1986; 110:780–783.

[27] Collins A, Brown J, Newman S. Cognitive apprenticeship: Teaching students the craft of reading, writing and mathematics. In: Ressido L ed. *Knowing, Learning and Instruction: Essays in Honor of Robert Glazer*. Hillside, NJ: Erlbaum;1989.

[28] Dansereau DF, Collins KW, McDonald BA, Holley CD, Garland JC, Diekhoff GM, Evans SH. Development and evaluation of an effective learning strategy program. *J Educ Psych* 1979;71:64–73.

[29] Erickson F. Qualitative methods in research on teaching. In: Wittrock M ed. *Handbook of Research on Teaching*. New York, NY: Macmillan; 1986.

[30] Fienberg S, Tanur J. Combining cognitive and statistical approaches to survey design. *Science* 1989;243:1017–1022.

[31] Fleiss JL. *Statistical Methods for Rates and Properties*. New York, NY: John Wiley & Sons Inc;1973.

[32] Glaser R. The reemergence of learning theory within instructional research. *American Psychologist* 1990;45(1):29–39.

[33] Gagne R, Briggs L, Wager W. *Principles of Instructional Design*. 3rd ed. New York, NY: Holt Rinehart and Winston;1988.

[34] Hollander M, Wolfe D. *Nonparametric Statistical Methods*. New York: John Wiley & Sons Inc;1973.

[35] Jorgensen D. *Participant Observation: A Methodology for Human Studies*. Newbury Park, Calif: Sage Publications;1989.

[36] Kearsley G. Embedded training: The new look of computer based instruction. *Machine Mediated Learning* 1985;1(3):279–296.

[37] Kerlinger FN. Foundations of Behavioral Research. 3rd ed. New York, NY: Holt Rinehart and Winston;1986.

[38] King A. Effects of training in strategic questioning on children's problem-solving performance. *J Educ Psych* 1991;83:307–317.

[39] Kracjik JS, Simmons PE, Lunetta VN. Improving research on computers in science learning. *J Res Sci Teaching* 1986;23:465–470.

[40] Lynch W. Social aspects of human-computer interaction. *Educ Tech Res Dev* 1990;30: 26–31.

[41] Neter J, Wasserman W. *Applied Linear Statistical Models*. Homewood, Ill: Irwin; 1974.

[42] Schank R. *Dynamic Memory: A Theory of Learning in Computers and People*. Cambridge, England: Cambridge University Press; 1982.

[43] Sleeman D, Kelly A, Marlinak R, Ward R, Moore J. Studies of diagnosis and remediation with high-school algebra students. *Cognitive Science* 1989;13:551–568.

[44] Williams C, Brown S. A review of the research issues in the use of computer-related technologies for instruction: An agenda for research. *Education Media and Technology Yearbook* 1991;17:26–46.

[45] Winer BJ. *Statistical Principles in Experimental Design*. 2nd ed. New York, NY: McGraw-Hill Inc;1971.

[46] Zuboff S. *In the Age of Smart Machines*. New York, NY: Basic Books Inc;1988.

[47] Arand JU, Harding CG. An investigation into problem-solving in education: A problem-solving curricular framework. *J Allied Health* 1987;16:7–17.

[48] Babbott D, Halter WD. Clinical problem-solving skills of internists trained in the problem-oriented system. *J Med Educ* 1983;58:947–953.

[49] Barrows H. A Taxonomy of Problem-Based Learning. *Med Educ* 1988;61:481–486.

[50] Boring JR, Nutter DO. Analytical thinking: Educating students for the practice of modern medicine. *J Med Educ* 1984;59:875–880.

[51] Bransford J, Sherwood R, Vye N, Rieser J. Teaching thinking and problem solving: Research foundations. *American Psychologist* 1986;41:1078–1089.

[52] Burke MD, Connelly DP. Systematic Instruction in Laboratory Medicine. *Hum Pathol* 1981;12:134–144.

[53] Coles CR. Differences between conventional and problem-based curricula in their student's approaches to studying. *Med Educ* 1985;19:308–309.

[54] Irby DM. Clinical teaching and the clinical teacher. *J Med Educ* 1986;61:35–45.

[55] Kulik JA, Kulik CC, Cohen PA. Effectiveness of computer-based college teaching: A meta-analysis of findings. *Rev Educ Res* 1980;50:525–544.

[56] Michael JA, Rovick AA. Problem-solving in the pre-clinical curriculum: The uses of computer simulations. *Medical Teacher* 1986;8:19–25.

[57] Nehring WM, Durham JD, Macek MM. Effective teaching: A problem-solving paradigm. *Nurse Educator* 1986;II:23–26.

[58] Rocklin T, O'Donnell A, Dansereau DF, Lambiotte JG, Hythecker V, Larson C. Training learning strategies with computer-aided cooperative learning. *Education* 1985;9(1):67–71.

[59] Adelson B. Evocative agents and multi-media interface design. *Proceedings of Computer Human Interaction* 1992:351–356.

[60] Allen BS, Carter CD. Expert systems and interactive video tutorials: Separating strategies from subject matter. *J Computer Based Instruction* 1988;15(4):123–130.

[61] Elmore G. Integrated technologies: An approach to establishing multimedia applications for learning. *EDUCOM-Review* 1992;27:20–26.

[62] Jones L, Smith S. Can multimedia instruction meet our expectations? *EDUCOM-Review* 1992;27:39–43.

[63] Litchfield B. Science: Evaluation of inquiry-based science software and interactive multimedia programs. *Computing Teacher* 1992;19:41–43.

[64] Midoro V, Chioccariello A, Olimpo G, Persico D, Sarti L, Tavella M. Interactive video and artificial intelligence: A convenient marriage. *Programmed Learning and Educ Tech* 1988;25(4):299–309.

[65] Brown CM. Methodology for human-computer interface design. In: Pulat B, Alexander D. eds. *Industrial Ergonomics: Case Studies* New York, NY: McGraw-Hill Inc;1992:87–96.

[66] Conklin J. Hypertext: An introduction and survey. *IEEE Computer* 1987;26:17–41.

[67] Duchastel P. Examining cognitive processing in hypermedia usage. *Hypermedia* 1990;2:221–233.

[68] Frisse M. Searching for information in a hypertext medical handbook. *Communications of the ACM* 1988;31(7):880–886.

[69] Frisse M, Cousins S. Information retrieval from hypertext: Update on the dynamic medical handbook project. *Proc Hypertext* 1989:199–212.

[70] Glushko R. Design issues for multidocument hypertexts. *Proc Hypertext* 1989:51–60.

[71] Heller R. The role of hypermedia in education: A look at the research issues. *J Res on Computing in Ed* 1990;22:431–441.

[72] Neilsen J, Lyngbaek U. Two field studies of hypermedia usability. *Proc Hypertext* 1989;2:26–34.

[73] Barrows H, Feltovich PJ. The clinical reasoning process. *Medical Education* 1987;21:86–91.

[74] Connelly DP, Johnson PE. The medical problem-solving process. *Hum Pathol* 1980;11(5):412–419.

[75] Elstein AS, Shulman LS, Sprafka SA. *Medical Problem Solving: An Analysis of Clinical Reasoning*. Cambridge, Mass: Harvard University Press;1978.

[76] McGuire CH. Medical problem-solving: A critique of the literature. *J Med Educ* 1985;60:587–595.

[77] Norman GR, Tugwell P, Feightner JW, Muzzin LJ, Jacoby LL. Knowledge and clinical problem-solving. *Med Educ* 1985;19:344–356.

[78] Rubinstein MF. *Patterns of Problem-Solving*. Englewood Cliffs, NJ: Prentice-Hall Inc;1975.

[79] Smith PJ, Galdes D, Fraser JM, Miller TE, Smith JW, Svirbely JR, Blazina J, Kennedy M, Rudmann S, Thomas DL. Coping with the complexities of multiple solution problems: A case study. *Int J Man-Machine Studies* 1991;35:429–453.

[80] Wickelgren WA. *How to Solve Problems: Elements of a Theory of Problems and Problem-Solving*. San Francisco, Calif: WH Freeman;1974.

[81] Nielsen J. *Hypertext and Hypermedia*. New York, NY: Academic Press;1990.

[82] Schaube L, Glaser R, Raghavan K, Reiner M. Causal models and experimentation strategies in scientific reasoning. *J Learning Sciences* 1991;2.

Index